THE BIRDWATCHER'S YEARBOOK 2013

Designed and published by
Hilary Cromack

Edited by
David Cromack

BUCKINGHAM PRESS LTD

In association with

SWAROVSKI
OPTIK

Published in 2012 by
Buckingham Press Ltd
55 Thorpe Park Road, Peterborough
Cambridgeshire PE3 6LJ
United Kingdom

(Tel/Fax) 01733 561 739
e-mail: admin@buckinghampress.com
www.buckinghampress.co.uk

© Buckingham Press Ltd 2012

ISBN 978-0-9569876-3-1
ISSN 0144-364 X

Cover image: Ringed Plovers by John Threlfall.
John Thelfall can be reached at Saltflats Cottage, Rockcliffe, Dalbeattie, Kirkcudbrightshire DG5 4QQ; 01556 630 262; e-mail: john@johnthrelfall.co.uk
www.johnthrelfall.co.uk

Black and white images: by Steve Cale.
Steve Cale can be reached at 10 Fairview Drive, Colkirk, Norfolk NR21 7NT.
Tel: 01328 862 265; (M)07866 263 673; e-mail : steveshrike@aol.com
www.steve-cale-artist.co.uk

Printed and bound in Great Britain by
Information Press, Oxford UK.

CONTENTS

CONTENTS

Under each county heading you will find:
Bird atlases/avifaunas; bird recorders; bird reports; BTO
regional representatives; clubs and societies; ringing groups;
RSPB local groups; wildlife hospitals and county Wildlife Trusts.

PREFACE

THE SPIRITS of Britain's birdwatchers were undoubtedly at a low ebb during the nationwide deluge that blighted the spring and summer of 2012. The situation for the birds themselves was even grimmer as parents struggled to find enough insect food for their offspring and tried their hardest to protect chicks from cold and wet conditions.

And then came the Olympics and Paralympics! Sporting success was matched by spectacular organisational performance, but for many people the single most powerful element was the contribution made by the volunteer 'games makers' who welcomed visitors with such enthusiasm.

The media ensured that the Olympic Park volunteers had a sky-high profile, but I'd like to pay a tribute to the unsung heroes and heroines whose efforts allow conservation and ornithological bodies such as RSPB, British Trust for Ornithology and the Wildlife Trusts to carry out their important work.

Flick through the pages of the County Directory in this edition of the *Yearbook* and you will see scores of contact names, all carrying out roles for bird clubs, ringing groups, animal hospitals and as county recorders, all on a voluntary basis. According to the RSPB's own figures, they can call on 18,000 volunteers to assist paid staff each year, a massive cost-saving that means the Society's charitable funds are not drained from the prime task of conserving birds, wildlife and habitats.

All of us who regularly attend the British Birdwatching Fair at Rutland Water will be aware of the huge volunteer effort being carried out over the three days we are on site, but warden Tim Appleton, in his article on pages 8 to 11, points out that volunteers are helping to set up the site in advance and spending many days after the event picking up litter and restoring the site back into pristine condition.

Supporting wildlife charities with your membership fees remains vitally important, but could you be doing more in a volunteer capacity? I'm sure your local bird club would welcome people stepping up to help lead bird walks or edit the newsletter, so don't sit back and wait for someone else to take the initiative. Let's keep the volunteer spirit alive…. even if we can't match the Olympian razzamatazz.

David Cromack (EDITOR)

THANKS: We are greatly indebted to the hundreds of people who volunteer information to enable us to compile the contents of each *Birdwatcher's Yearbook*. We couldn't do it without you, so many thanks for your continuing support.

A MESSAGE FROM THE SPONSORS
OF THIS BOOK

WELCOME to the 33rd edition of *The Birdwatcher's Yearbook*, a publication that is still acknowledged as an invaluable source of information for anyone wanting the facts and figures relating to the birdwatching scene in Britain.

If you are buying the *Yearbook* for the first time, you will discover within its pages so many useful items it is hard to know where to look first. However, it is worth stressing that the book's greatest virtue is the fact that all the information it contains is checked and verified annually.

For instance, where else can you get up-to-date assessments of more than 400 nature reserves right across mainland Britain and the Scottish islands in one place? Need to make contact with your local RSPB group or bird club? Simply turn to the County Directory where you'll find a complete listing of clubs, alongside county recorders, BTO reps and animal hospitals.

While the internet is a fantastic potential source of information, it can be an extremely frustrating experience trawling through so many websites that don't deliver what you need. Gordon Hamlett's annual survey of interesting bird and wildlife-related websites is a great aid in picking out the wheat from the chaff. I think it is fair to say that the one-off features produced by guest writers address interesting and relevant topics of the day and taken together since 1981's first edition, provide a useful social history of the activity.

Swarovski Optik UK was first invited to sponsor the book in 2002 and it has been our pleasure to support the publication ever since, as we believe that Buckingham Press shares our own ethos of 'improving through innovation and attention to detail'. Put the *Birdwatcher's Yearbook* to the test and I'm sure you'll not find it wanting.

Let me end by wishing you much better weather and more successful birdwatching in 2013.

Peter Antoniou
Country Manager, UK & Republic of Ireland,
Swarovski Optik UK

SWAROVSKI
OPTIK

Features section: key contributors

TIM APPLETON has worked for the Leicestershire & Rutland Wildlife Trust at Rutland Water since its creation in 1975. As Reserve Manager he helped to instigate the British Birdwatching Fair and worked with Anglian Water in the site's Osprey introduction programme. In 2003 he was awarded an MBE for services to wildlife and conservation.

JACQUIE CLARK heads the Demography Team at the British Trust for Ornithology in Thetford and oversees the work done by the ringing dept and the Nest Record Scheme. A qualified ringer herself, Jacquie has a particular interest in the effects of weather on birds and migration and has contributed to many ornithological papers.

STEVE CALE is one of Britain's leading bird artists and produces a range of distinctive bookmarks, cards and prints as well as original paintings. He runs art courses in different parts of the UK and leads birding and wildlife art tours to places such as North Cyprus. Visit: www.steve-cale-artist.co.uk

RICHARD FACEY, who has a degree in zoology and works for the Countryside Council for Wales, is a keen birder and photographer in his spare time.

GORDON HAMLETT, a freelance writer based in Norfolk, is a regular contributor to *Bird Watching* magazine and is the author of the acclaimed book *Best Birdwatching Sites in the Scottish Highlands*.

FEATURES

David Cromack

Thanks to a successful introduction scheme, Osprey is now an established species at Rutland Water, home to the British Birdfair.

WHEN THE WORLD
COMES TO RUTLAND

In the past 24 years the British Birdwatching Fair, held on the banks of Rutland Water, has raised almost three million pounds to benefit bird conservation around the globe. Co-organiser Tim Appleton recalls how early successes have been built upon so that the event continues to grow, but without losing its original spirit.

LOOKING BACK over 24 years of Birdfair at Rutland Water there is no doubt that this international conservation event has been a mammoth success and positively touched the lives of tens of thousands of people (not to mention the wildlife) from every corner of the world. It has launched careers, businesses, saved countless hectares of wildlife-rich habitats and initiated a series of similar events, which in turn has helped to generate a healthy focus on wildlife to hundreds of thousands around the world.

When Martin Davies of the RSPB and I first developed the idea of a specialized event for birdwatchers to be held in some meadows in the heart of rural England, we could never have envisaged the impact that such an event would eventually have internationally.

I had regularly visited the Game Fair which always attracts huge numbers of visitors with a common interest and I was convinced there was scope to create our own fair for the growing numbers of birdwatchers and nature lovers in the UK. Up till then events of this nature had been small local affairs, never national, and Martin and I knew if we brought together all this local interest into one area we had the potential for a winning formula...

Martin, along with his colleague Steve Holliday (both then based in the East Midland's office of the RSPB) and myself (from the Leicestershire and Rutland Wildlife Trust) had already gained some experience from running a series of small scale, but successful, events at the Rutland Water nature reserves. We decided to build on this experience and so began a partnership which remains as strong and as full of enthusiasm as it was back in 1989.

From the outset we wanted to achieve three important goals;
  • Organise an event for birdwatchers and nature lovers to come together to meet old and new friends.
  • Create a shop window for the birdwatching and wildlife industry.
  • Raise as much money as possible for important conservation projects.

We felt strongly that the monies raised from the Birdfair should benefit international causes rather than home-based projects. We knew that for every pound sterling raised at Birdfair it would be worth twice, or even more, when spent in key areas of the world where biodiversity was under much greater threat.

So from here a formula developed whereby the Wildlife Trust working locally and the RSPB working nationally came together to raise funds for international conservation

8

WHEN THE WORLD COMES TO RUTLAND

projects. We have stuck to this simple idea over 24 years and the result has been a massive injection of funds, donated from the Birdfair to conservation projects, totalling almost three million pounds!

From the outset we had virtually no financial resources until Bruce Hanson from optics dealers inFocus stepped in and gave a helping hand by convincing a number of optical manufacturers that a golden opportunity was presenting itself – a chance to launch and publicise their products and businesses to an ever-increasing number of customers that Birdfair would attract to one venue over a weekend. Companies soon realised the potential of such an event and climbed aboard.

Britain's first Birdwatching Fair was held over the weekend of September 30 and

October 1, 1988 – it attracted 3,000 visitors and £3,000 was raised for the Stop the Massacre Campaign which was trying to combat illegal shooting on the island of Malta.

The following year we held the fair a month earlier to avoid the onset of winter weather and also extended the event by one day. It has remained a three day event ever since.

Initially Martin and I managed and co-ordinated the overseas projects ourselves, but we soon came to realise that the growth in

Birdfair's commercial importance means that the world's leading manufacturers of optics time the release of new products for the Rutland event. This scaffold tower is just one of the viewing opportunities on offer to visitors.

funds the Birdfair was raising warranted a 'bigger hitter' and so we approached BirdLife International. It now receives an annual cheque from Birdfair and guarantees that the money is spelt wisely on the projects we choose to support.

BirdLife International is also involved when it is decided which project Birdfair will support and help to finance. The day set aside to select the next project is always an exciting moment, though the weight of responsibility is huge, knowing that a massive injection of funding could be life-saving for some of the critically endangered species and habitats that will benefit.

In the early years we concentrated on European projects in Spain, Poland and Romania. Birdfair had rapidly become an important venue for specialist holiday companies promoting overseas trips and all of these countries host well-known areas that are visited by British birders who can see for themselves the value and results of Birdfair support.

9

However, we were coming under increasing pressure from BirdLife to look further afield and, with a little apprehension, in 1994 we agreed to strike out and support Halmahera in Indonesia and the unlikely named Wallace's Standard Wing, a strikingly unusual bird of paradise species. Fortunately the Birdfair community - visitors and exhibitors alike - got behind the 'quantum leap' and we raised more than £50,000 that year!

There was no turning back after this... Africa was next, followed by Asia and then onto the Mindo Forest in South America. 1998 saw a change to our choice and style of project when

we decided to fund the Globally Threatened Birds book. This became the 'Holy Grail' for advocacy and its publication on an international level no doubt helps to save even more habitats and birds by educating and drawing attention to all those species in danger.

Personally, my proudest moment came when we decided to become the sponsor of the Global Seabirds Programme: albatrosses and petrels were unnecessarily dying in their tens of thousands when caught up in long-line fishing. These long-lived

Birdfair is part commerce, part social interaction.... and most important of all it provides an opportinity for charitable giving on a grand scale. Donated items are auctioned each year to help raise funds for the selected BirdLife International good cause.

species were in very real danger of dying out across our oceans because their reproduction rate is very low and they were losing the battle to replace the victims of fishing.

At the time, in 2000, Birdfair was the sole funder in this project - this is all the more remarkable when you consider we were borne from England's smallest land-locked county. Now 13 years later there is promising and inspirational news that species such as the Black-browed Albatross is showing great signs of recovery.

As we entered the new century so the projects became potentially more controversial; pristine forests in Eastern Cuba and in Myanmar (formerly Burma) desperately needed protecting and when more than 5,000 pairs of Gurney's Pittas were discovered in Myanmar we knew we had made the right decision despite the controversy stirred up by the political situation in that country.

Before 2007 all the projects submitted for consideration by BirdLife International

WHEN THE WORLD COMES TO RUTLAND

were for a single annual funding, but by this stage Birdfair was raising approximately £200,000 each year and the projects were becoming increasing more complicated and multifarious. It was putting both the BirdLife International Cambridge office and the recipient country's BirdLife partner under considerable pressure to do justice to the funds and successfully 'complete' the project within a year to report back for the following year's Birdfair's audience.

So when BirdLife suggested the Preventing Extinctions Project that would run for three years from 2007 to 2009 we took the opportunity to support a project that needed longer term support and investment to get it up and running. This gamble paid off and from all over the world, individuals, companies and NGOs all came forward to become Species Champions and Species Guardians. Like the Seabird Programme this project will run on and on and demonstrates to the Birdfair visitors that with their support we can make a very real and positive difference to the world we live in.

Support for our Birdfair comes in many different guises, from so many companies and individuals. Our sponsors – many of whom have been associated with the fair from the outset – are invaluable, bringing financial security and support we couldn't move forward without.

Our legion of volunteers are crucial to setting up the event and help the three-day event run without a hitch. As the thousands of visitors and the 350 or so exhibitors vacate the site on the final day our volunteers still have several back-breaking days of clearing up and ensuring the site can recover and return to being a nature reserve and a Site of Special Scientific Interest.

The celebrities who return year after year also are a major factor to Birdfair's success, attracting a bigger audience to the Birdfair and guaranteeing our visitors are constantly entertained. In this world of celebrity and commercialism it is refreshing to see top names in the nature world waiving their fees and instead putting their name and efforts behind fantastic fundraising efforts.

The atmosphere at Birdfair is often described as unique – though commercially driven over the busy weekend with thousands of visitors spending tens of thousands of pounds, it has never lost its original aims. Competitors compete, but in a way rarely encountered in the business world. The 'Birdfair family' is driven by a large group all wanting to put something back into our shrinking environment.

As we head towards a quarter of a century of Birdfair in Rutland we are determined that our event will not lose sight of its roots, its goals and most of all, its friends.

Tim Appleton
British Birdwatching Fair

FOLLOW THAT BIRD

Researchers at the British Trust for Ornithology pioneered the gathering of information about birds through bird ringing, but Jacquie Clark (Head of the Ringing Team) says that new technologies have the power to unlock many of the remaining mysteries.

GATHERING INFORMATION about the lives of wild birds has been transformed in recent years by the availability of new technologies. When bird ringing began at the turn of the 19th Century it was all about finding out where birds went and a lot was learnt even in the very early days. However, metal ringing often only gives us a couple of snapshots of a bird's life – where and when it was ringed and then where and when it was subsequently found.

The traditional ringing of birds still plays an important role in understanding changes in survival and productivity and demonstrations like this, at Rutland Water, always excite a great deal of interest.

Though metal ringing continues to inform us about migration, as well as about changes in survival and productivity (which allow us to interpret population change), for a small number of birds we can now find out so much more.

Since the early 1960s we have been able to radio-track some of the larger species by putting a transmitter on their backs (fitted as a small backpack), and heading out with an antenna to check where the birds are. This system has its limitations because the range is generally quite short, making it difficult to follow birds on migration – this hasn't stopped some scientists heading off after their migrating birds by car or plane though!

For detailed information about the migratory journey the challenge was to develop more powerful devices light enough for birds to carry. In the last 10 years the bid to make electronic devices ever smaller and lighter has allowed very rapid development of a range of tags that can record where birds are. Indeed radio transmitters are now so small that they can be fitted to insects. More complex devices that collect a range of data can now be used on at least the larger bird species.

The size and type of tag and the method of attachment to the bird, ringed as part of the BTO Ringing Scheme, are very carefully controlled and monitored by a panel of experts and, of course, none of this would be possible without the skills and knowledge of ringers who are able to catch and mark birds safely.

Space surveillance

Satellite tags, which allow us to track birds accurately on long migrations, are still relatively heavy and expensive – both for the tags and the satellite time. Real-time information is transmitted by PTT (Platform Transmitter Terminal) satellite tags to the orbiting Argos satellites at regular intervals, giving locations for a bird to within about 150m.

PTTs, the smallest of which now weigh around 5g, have been used on the Cuckoos that BTO have been following over the last year (**Fig 1 - Cuckoo with tag attached**) with financial help from many sponsors (www.bto.org/cuckoos).

Fig 1

Before we had the results from these tags it was thought that Cuckoos breeding in Britain and Ireland headed off to Africa via Italy. Though three of the five birds tagged in 2011 did migrate through Italy, **Fig 2** shows that the bird named Lyster migrated via Iberia – but all five birds eventually ended up in and around the Congo rainforests during the winter months. Twelve more birds which were tagged during the spring of 2012 also chose to head south via Iberia.

GPS (Global Positioning System) are a regular GPS in miniature and are far more accurate than Argos PTTs, typically to 5-15m. There are two major types – ones which store data which can be downloaded on recapture, or those that transmit the data either by satellite or by

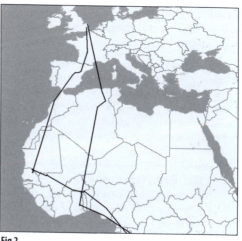

Fig 2

technologies such as Bluetooth to a nearby base station. Given their extra components and power requirements these are heavier but give much more accurate information.

Light regimes

PTT tags are now small enough to be used on medium and large sized species but for smaller birds we need lighter devices. Geolocators weigh as little as half a gram and can be used on

FOLLOW THAT BIRD

medium-sized birds (such as Nightingale and Swift) that weigh little more than 20g. They record light levels and times which can be used to calculate latitude and longitude to within about 200km, though this is a little tricky around the equator.

Geolocators are relatively cheap, but the data can only be downloaded from them once the bird has been recaught and the tag retrieved. This has proved to work well for birds that reliably return to the same place to breed, but can be quite frustrating if the individuals cannot be recaught. Geolocators have recently been used by the BTO to track Nightingales and Swifts.

The Swift project has generated some completley new information: all of the Swifts head west to a previously unknown stop-over site in Liberia where they fed up before rapidly heading back north.

'Dog tags'

PiT tags (Passive Integrated Transponders) can be used to understand the movements of birds on a smaller scale. You may well have experience of these tags, which are injected into dogs and cats to identify them. With wild birds PiT tags are added to a ring on their leg and are read when the bird is close to a reader, often at the nest or a feeding station, thus providing information about how much time they spend feeding and how often they return to the nest, as well as how far from the nest they go to find food.

Where next?

As technology advances and miniaturisation continues, we will be able to safely tag smaller and smaller birds, potentially answering many questions about the migration of birds and other animals – information that is vital for conservation.

Tags are still very expensive compared to metal rings and so are only added to a small number of birds, but combining information from the few tagged birds with that from metal-ringed birds, will really help us to understand what is happening. Getting detailed information about migration will allow us to understand the places that are vital sites to stop and increase fat, where they birds go and how long their migration takes. In addition, tracking local movements allows us to understand how they use their 'home' area, which individuals do well and why.

Bird ringing Opportunites

The incredible information we are now gaining by following a small number of birds with devices wouldn't be possible if we didn't already have a trained workforce of volunteer ringers who are able to catch and ring birds.

Metal ringing continues to help us to understand the movements of birds, but the focus of the modern Ringing Scheme is on demography. The data on recruitment and survival that we gather from ringing allows us to understand why populations are falling, thus allowing conservation action to be targeted at the appropriate part of the life cycle. For more information on the Ringing Scheme and the BTO, go to www.bto.org.

ORNITHOLOGICAL NEWS HEADLINES

Richard Facey presents a round-up of significant news stories about wild birds and habitats.

HELPING HAND FOR WORLD'S RAREST DUCK

WITH A population numbering just 22 in the wild, Madagascar Pochard (*Aythya innotata*) has the dubious accolade of being the world's rarest bird, and with only two or three ducklings surviving from one year to the next the future hasn't been looking bright.

However, the species has now successfully bred for the first time in captivity at specialist facilities in Antsohihy, Madagascar. The proud parents were originally collected as eggs in 2009 and hatched in captivity by experts from WWT and Durrell Wildlife Conservation Trust, and reached sexual maturity in time for the 2011/12 breeding season. Their unions resulted in 18 ducklings.

A captive breeding programme seems the best way to guarantee the survival of the world's rarest duck species, the Madagascar Pochard (an illustration by Steve Cale).

In the wild the entire population of the Madagascar Pochard is confined to Red Lake, a small lake in the north of the island. This very limited distribution makes the species highly vulnerable to extinction through disease or a pollution incident.

But the successful breeding in captivity provides much-needed hope for the species' survival and will enable birds to be released on to other lakes in due course to expand the range. But before this scientists need to determine why the species declined so much and so are studying the remaining wild birds.

MERCY FLIGHTS TO AID EMBATTLED SANDPIPERS

THE PLIGHT of the Spoon-billed Sandpiper (*Eurynorhynchus pygmeus*) never seems to be out of the ornithological limelight. With the remaining 100 or so pairs having incredibly low productivity and untold problems on their migration route, the species is in need of urgent help.

The heroes of the hour are definitely the staff at the Wildfowl & Wetlands Trust and their partner organisations which, in 2011, took the first steps in establishing a captive population. As we reported in last year's edition, 20 eggs were collected from the wild, hatched in Russia and the chicks flown to special facilities at WWT's Slimbridge headquarters.

ORNITHOLOGICAL NEWS HEADLINES

Having learnt a lot from last year's expedition, the team took a different tack in 2012, choosing to fly the eggs collected from the species' sub-Arctic tundra breeding grounds in the Russian Far East straight back to the UK to hatch them here. Sounds simple enough until you understand the sheer logistical feats involved!

Once the 20 eggs had been collected they had to survive a week-long journey of more than 7,000km (4,400 miles!) from the town of Anadyr to their new home in Gloucestershire, where staff eagerly awaited their hatching. Seventeen chicks hatched, which more than doubled the captive population in one go.

Meanwhile back in Russia a further nine Spoon-billed Sandpiper chicks took part in the project's head-start programme, which aims to hatch eggs in captivity before releasing the resultant chicks into the wild. It is hoped this will boost the number of fledgling produced, which without assistance is a worrying 0.6 chicks per pair! Removing these chicks from immediate dangers will also give the project its own head start in fine tuning field methods for future reintroductions.

This boost in the WWT's captive population is critical as flock size is important in triggering breeding in this diminutive wader. Spoon-billed Sandpipers become sexually mature at two years, so look out in 2013 for news of the first Spoon-billed Sandpiper to have been bred in captivity.

HOUSE SPARROWS GETTING CHIRPY AGAIN

THE RECENT steep decline in the UK's House Sparrow (*Passer domesticus*) population is well known but various surveys organised by the British Trust for Ornithology show that things are looking up for the little chirper.

Garden Birdwatch reports show that the numbers of House Sparrow using English gardens are approaching a six year high from a low point of 2006. However, this recovery is fragile and needs support. Gardeners can create a more hospitable environment for House Sparrows by cultivating thick vegetation, cleaning feeding stations regularly and by putting up nest boxes in close proximity as House Sparrows prefer communal breeding quarters. Other tips are provided in a BTO House Sparrow factsheet.

Reasons for the decline of House Sparrows are not fully understood, but it is great news that the species appears to be making a comeback, particularly in Wales.

16

ORNITHOLOGICAL NEWS HEADLINES

Across the border in Wales the House Sparrow has gone from strength to strength. The declines there and in Scotland have been much less of a problem; on average one in four of English gardens have lost their sparrows compared to fewer than one in ten for the Celtic nations. In fact the results of the BTO's 2011 Breeding Bird Survey showed that the Welsh House Sparrow population has more than doubled since 1994!

GIANT NEW WETLAND FOR SEVERN ESTUARY

A LOSING BATTLE to hold back coastal erosion is being turned into a massive plus for birdlife along the Severn estuary with the creation of the UK's largest new wetland.

The Severn estuary's population of Shelducks is significant and the species is bound to benefit from the creation of new saltmarsh habitat on the Steart Peninsula.

Almost 500 hectares of the Steart Peninsula, which juts out into the Bristol Channel near the mouth of the River Parret in Somerset, is to be turned into a mosaic of wetl and habitat which will include areas of saltmarsh and freshwater. The project involves breaching the man-made shingle sea defences which are no longer capable of holding back rising sea levels.

It is estimated that between 300-600 hectares of wetland habitat will need to be created over the next 20 years to compensate for the loss such habitat from the Severn Estuary as a result of sea-level rises and the construction of new coastal defences.

The Severn Estuary is internationally important for the wintering flocks of waders and waterfowl that it supports. The new wetland will bring benefit to beleaguered species such as Shelduck, Dunlin and Redshank. Though much of the site, which is owned by the Environment Agency but managed by the WWT, will remain agriculturally productive, the bulk of the area will evolve into saltmarsh that will absorb the impact of wave energy.

Work on the project began in the summer of 2012 and is estimated to take two years to complete. The River Parrett Trail will be re-aligned to give views over the estuary and the new freshwater areas. A car park south of Marsh Farm will have toilets and information boards for visitors

SINGING OWLS AND SOUTH AMERICAN 'FIRSTS'

PERU'S reputation as one of the most bird-rich countries in the world has been enhanced by the addition of a completely unknown new species. The Sira Barbet, a colourful near-passerine species, was originally discovered on an expedition to Peru in 2008 and was formally described in 2012 in the journal *Auk*.

The 2008 expedition to a little visited area of cloud forest included graduates from Cornell University in the USA, who honoured the director the Cornell Lab, John Fitzpatrick, by

17

ORNITHOLOGICAL NEWS HEADLINES

giving the new species the scientific name of *Captio fitzpatricki*. Fitzpatrick is known for his pioneering work in Peru, including discovering seven new species himself.

In August this year Auk published a paper about another new South American species, the Antioquia Wren (*Thryophilus sernai*). First seen in 2010, scientists photographed the new wren and recorded its vocalizations, from which they determined that the wren, found in dry forest in Colombia, was brand new to science.

Analysis of songs have led scientists to declare two new species of owl in the Phillipines. Announcing the discovery in *Forktail, the Journal of Asian Ornithology*, zoologist Pamela Rasmussen said: "When we first heard the songs of both owls, we were amazed because they were so distinctly different that we realized they were new species."

Pairs of one new species, the Camiguin Hawk Owl, often sing in duet while facing each other, with a distinct growling tone instead of the high-pitched melodious song usually associated with birds. The other new species is the Cebu Hawk Owl, of which there has been only one specimen sighted.

UNEXPECTED CELTIC CONNECTION FOR CHOUGHS
DESPITE a long absence, the Chough (*Pyrrhocorax pyrrhocorax*) is synonymous with Cornwall. The species went extinct there in 1947 and Cornwall would have to wait until 2001 for the species to once again grace its cliffs. It had been assumed that the Chough that recolonized Cornwall had originated from the nearest populations in Wales.

However, a recent genetic analysis of Cornwall's Choughs conducted by the University of Aberdeen has shown that the Celtic Connection to Cornwall is somewhat different. DNA taken from the feathers of Cornish Choughs matched more closely with that of birds from Ireland rather than Wales.

OSPREY'S WELSH HAT-TRICK
FOLLOWING an absence of several centuries, Osprey (*Pandion haliaetus*) bred in Wales for the first time in 2004, when one pair set up home in the Glaslyn Valley and another pair was located near Welshpool.

Since then only the Glaslyn pair has gone from strength to strength. Then in 2011 the Dyfi estuary played host to another pair; the first time in 400 years the species had bred there. 2012, however, heralded the news of a third active nest.

This third pair, also in the Glaslyn Valley, nested at a site managed by the Friends of the Osprey rather than the RSPB. Though all three nests were hit hard by wet weather, the adults managed to fledge four chicks between them.

HELPING THE NEXT GENERATION
CAN YOU remember the the difficulties you faced when beginning your birding career? For those without a birding mentor finding and identifying new birds could be a frustrating and off-putting experience, so a new global campaign to encourage fledgling birders is to be welcomed.

A non-profit organisation, Global Bird Initiative (GBI), has launched the Pledge to Fledge

Campaign to promote the growth and enjoyment of birding by forming a dynamic network of individuals and bird clubs to share their knowledge and enthusiasm with the general public.

The Pledge to Fledge Campaign, or P2F for short, is designed to encourage non-birders into becoming casual birders and, in the longer term, develop into someone concerned about bird conservation.

P2F was launched in August 2012 but you can still make your Pledge to help fledge others into birders at www.globalbirdinginitiative.org/pledge-2-fledge

WILDLIFE-FRIENDLY FARMING CAN BE PROFITABLE

MODERN FARMING, with its reliance on pesticides, herbicides and monoculture crops, has rightly been identified with the decline of many once-common bird species, but the Royal Society for the Protection of Birds has been determined to prove that protecting and increasing threatened species could go hand-in-hand with profitable farming.

Twelve years after buying a a farm of their own in Cambridgeshire, the RSPB has shown just that and summed up their experiences in the report "Hope Farm: farming for food, profit and wildlife".

Among the headline achievements of Hope Farm is the increase in an iconic farmland bird, the Skylark. In 2000 Hope Farm's Skylark population numbered just ten pairs, but since then the species has gone from strength to strength, and now numbers more than 40 territories. This staggering increase has largely come about through the development and use of Skylark plots; small areas of bare ground in crops where the birds can forage for insects when the rest of the crop becomes too dense.

It's just not Skylarks that have benefited. During the 12 years of the RSPB's tenure at Hope Farm, the national index for farmland birds (which comprises 19 species) has declined by 11%. Thanks to the implementation of wildlife friendly farming practices this same index on Hope Farm has increased by 300%. The number of Yellowhammer territories has more that doubled, while those that have Linnet have more than quadrupled. These increases have gone hand in hand with a profitable and thriving farming business.

Leaving patches of bare earth on the deges of cereal crops has allowed Skylarks to flourish at the RSPB's aptly-named Hope Farm.

Hope Farm: farming for food, profit and wildlife can be downloaded at www.rspb.org.uk/Images/hopefarmbooklet_tcm9-320935.pdf

BEST BIRD BOOKS OF THE YEAR

Completion of the epic *Handbook Of Birds of the World* project is the big publishing news of the year, but Gordon Hamlett finds many more titles he thinks our readers will enjoy owning.

THIS YEAR marks the end of a remarkable project. Volume 16 completes the main body of the monumental *Handbook of the Birds of the World (HBW)*, though we can expect to see the odd supplement and update in the next few years.

I can remember ordering the first volume with some trepidation, not knowing if it was going to be just another version of those multi-part magazine encyclopaedias, showing loads of stock photos of breeding plumaged males and not a lot else. I need not have worried.

Right from the beginning, the quality has been universally superb. Detailing every species of bird in the world, the photos were breath-taking, the articles and essays fascinating and the plates and references first class. The books were printed on high quality paper. Attention to detail was also apparent; one small example was the way that the covers were folded over top and bottom, reducing the chances of nicks and tears as you pulled the books off the shelf.

Anyone with the money to spend – a set will set you back about the same price as a top of the range telescope – and the shelf space to hold them will never regret their investment.

The last volume marks the end of an era for another reason too. I can't see there being any likelihood of another multi-volume reference work such as *HBW, Birds of the Western Palearctic* or *Birds of Africa*. There are two main reasons for this – increasing costs and the coming of the internet. I paid approximately twice as much for volume 16 as I did for volume 1. Unless there is going to be some major sponsorship (see below), large format books are going to price themselves out of the market.

There is an alternative though. Reference books work really well on the internet and I believe that we will see an increasing number of titles appearing this way. It is not just for large titles either. This year, the *Moray and Nairn Bird Report* appears online instead of in printed form. The advantages are many. Apart from issues of cost, the report contains many more photographs than previous reports. Errors and additions can be corrected easily and many more people are likely to look at the report online than buy the report. Hopefully this will result in many more records being submitted, leading to better reports in the future and so on.

That's fine for something small like a bird report but an online resource such as *HBW* will still cost a substantial amount of money to maintain, so what's the answer? Well, it is going to have to be a subscription service. My initial reaction is to baulk against this; I've got too used to my internet content being free, but I'm slowly coming round to the idea that we are going to have pay for our pleasure.

Let's look at the maths. No figure have been announced yet, but suppose we take an annual subscription of £40 per annum. For the price of a set of *HBW* books, that gives you about 50 years of membership. What's more, you also know that your information will be up to date, as new species get discovered, or taxonomists start lumping and splitting bird families. You will also have access to many more photos, video clips and sound recordings. Suddenly, the subscription seems pretty good value doesn't it? For more details, see http://www.lynxeds.com/catalog/hbw

If you remain devoted to the print and paper publications, here's my selection of the best titles released in the past 12 months:

ART & LITERATURE

Smaller publishing companies find it difficult to compete with the big boys when it comes to technical bird books. Where they can compete though is in the personal memoir sector, and this year, we have seen a good selection of such titles.

It speaks volumes about our society (no pun intended) that we still need people like Dave Dick, the former Senior Scottish Investigation Officer for the RSPB. His memoir, *Wildlife Crime* (**Dick, Whittles Publishing, pb, 196pp. £18.99, ISBN 978-1-84995-036-7**) is an engrossing read, and one guaranteed to make you angry.

On a similar theme, *The Ruffled Edge* (**Howard, Brambleby Books, pb, 104pp, £9.99, ISBN 978-1-908241-06-1**) is an evocative account of an RSPB warden working mainly in upland areas, monitoring Hen Harriers. I would willingly have dropped the colour plates and doubled the length of the book instead; I had finished it in an hour.

A good personal account should make you want to go out and visit the places and see the birds described. Author Stuart Rae claims that all encounters with Golden Eagles are memorable, a sentiment I agree with totally, so I was always going to enjoy *Eagle Days* (**Rae, Langford Press, pb 196pp. £18, ISBN 978-1-904078-44-9**), an account of his observations going back many years. Similarly, *A Patch Made in Heaven* (**Couzens, Hale, hb, 192pp, £12.99, ISBN 978-0-7090-9112-7**) covers a year in the life of a small area of southern Britain, looking at the reasons behind the birds' behaviour and movements. Great late night reading from the deservedly popular author Dominic Couzens.

BEST BIRD BOOKS OF THE YEAR

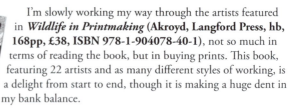

I'm slowly working my way through the artists featured in *Wildlife in Printmaking* (Akroyd, Langford Press, hb, 168pp, £38, ISBN 978-1-904078-40-1), not so much in terms of reading the book, but in buying prints. This book, featuring 22 artists and as many different styles of working, is a delight from start to end, though it is making a huge dent in my bank balance.

One of the artists featured is Robert Gillmor, and *Birds, Blocks and Stamps* (Gillmor, Two Rivers Press, pb 56pp, £12.50, ISBN 978-1-901677-79-9) details the process behind producing a series of lino cuts for a set of 24 postage stamps, a huge undertaking.

Sparrow (Todd, Reaktion Books, pb 192pp, £9.99, ISBN 978-1-86189-875-3) is the latest in a series devoted to the history and lore of individual species. Here, we have everything from Tobit in the Bible being blinded by sparrows' droppings to Mao Zedong's disastrous all-out war on the birds.

For something a little different, *Murmurations* (ed Royle, Two Ravens Press. Pb, 264pp, £9.99, ISBN 978-1906120597) is an 'anthology of uncanny stories about birds'. The best known story here is Daphne du Maurier's '*The Birds*', the source material for the Hitchcock film, with many of the other 29 short stories being brand new. All proceeds are going to the RSPB.

PRACTICAL ADVICE BOOKS

How to approach birds' songs and calls is a problem that has exercised many an author and editor; usually song is the poor relation in identification books. *Birdsong* (Elphick et al, Quadrille Publishing, hb, 256pp, £30 ISBN 978-1-84949-134-1) is a coffee-table book with one important addition. You can play the songs of 150 species as you read the text via an added electronic gizmo.

Birdwatching with your *Eyes Closed* by *Times* columnist Simon Barnes (Short Books, hb 276pp, £12,99 ISBN 978-1-907595-47-9) takes a more literary approach as he writes passionately about his love of birdsong, though with links to a website so that you can listen too.

Ultimately, both books fall a little short; the former because the book is just too unwieldy and limited in scope, and the latter because it is simply impossible to transcribe song into meaningful English phrases. Most birders listen online or download a birding app onto their smartphones.

BEST BIRD BOOKS OF THE YEAR

RSPB Birds: Their Hidden World (Holden, A&C Black, pb, 256pp, £14.99, ISBN 978-1-4081-4081-5262-1) is a gem of a book dealing with various aspects of bird behaviour such as roosting, migration and feeding. Aimed at beginners and improvers, this book by the former head of the Young Ornithologists Club provides an excellent introduction to its subject.

The heavyweight identification guide this year is *Cotingas and Manakins* (Kirwan and Green, Helm, hb, 624pp, £60, ISBN 978-0-7136-6025-8). Illustrated by 400 photos and 34 plates, the text fully describes the 130 species and looks at the latest taxonomic studies. It is likely to be the definitive guide for the foreseeable future.

When is a fieldguide not a fieldguide? When it is the large format version of the best field guide in the world, the second edition of the *Collins Bird Guide* (Mullarney et al, Collins, hb, 444pp, £50, ISBN 978-0-00-744902-6). The illustrations look even better at this scale, with the maps and print size also benefiting from the extra space.

A Photographic Guide to the Birds of Malta (Raine, Langford Press, pb, 200pp, £15, ISBN 978-1-904078-28-9) includes an overview to birding on the island, a complete checklist and many web references, many flagging up illegal hunting activities, as well as illustrating 130 of the commonest species.

Helm has a reputation second to none when it comes to the coverage of their fieldguides. The one that caught my eye this year was *Birds of Melanesia* (Dutson, Helm, pb, 448pp, £40, ISBN 978-0-7136-6540-6) which covers the Bismarcks, Solomons, Vanuatu and New Caledonia. What makes this book interesting is that of the 501 species depicted, over 40% are endemic birds.

WORKS OF REFERENCE

I was fascinated by *The Norfolk Cranes' Story* (Buxton and Durdin, Wren Publishing, hb 134pp, £30, ISBN 978-09542545-5-1) as it almost exactly mirrors my time as a birder. I can remember hearing vague rumours about there being Cranes 'somewhere in Norfolk', never dreaming that I would ever see anything as exotic. Starting with those early days, the book traces the slowly expanding population to the present day, with birds now breeding at Lakenheath RSPB and elsewhere.

Biggest bargain of the year is a mighty, full-colour avifauna *The Breeding Birds of North-East Scotland* (ed Francis and Cook, SOC, hb,

BEST BIRD BOOKS OF THE YEAR

518pp £25, ISBN 978-0-956-1126-3-7). Essential for anyone with an interest in Scottish birds, heavy sponsorship has kept the price at a ridiculously low level. Sponsorship support or publishing on the internet is the obvious way forward for books such as this.

If you are interested in the history of birds, two Poyser titles should appeal. *Extinct Birds* (**Hume and Walters, Poyser, hb 544pp, £50, ISBN 978-1-4081-5725-1**) offers up-to-date accounts of every species known to have become extinct in the last 700 years. It includes hypothetical birds and those with insufficient data to prove the case one way or another.

Moving further back in time is *Avian Survivors* (**Finlayson, Poyser, hb 304pp, £50, ISBN 978-0-7136-8865-8**). Subtitled *'The History and Biogeography of Palearctic Birds'*, this highly academic work re-evaluates the timing of bird speciation (moving to a time well before the asteroid that wiped out the dinosaurs) and suggest new classification possibilities.

If you've got eyes like a hawk, just how good is your eyesight? There has been surprisingly little research done into how birds use their senses, but *Bird Sense* (**Birkhead, Bloomsbury, hb, 266pp, £16.99, ISBN 978-1-4088-2013-1**) looks not just at the traditional sight, sound, taste, touch and smell, but also birds' emotions and their ability to detect changes in the Earth's magnetic field.

I loved the author's previous title, *The Wisdom of Birds*, and this was easily the most interesting book I read this year. Definitely an author to watch.

It wouldn't be a review of the year without a monograph from Poyser and this year's self-recommending title concerns the world's commonest gull – *The Kittiwake* (**Coulson, Poyser, hb, 304pp, £50, ISBN 978-1-4081-0966-3**). Particular study has been made of the colony at North Shields.

My final choice is almost a case of reverse engineering. Rather than looking at the birds themselves, *Bird Habitats in Ireland* (**ed Nairn and O'Halloran, The Collins Press, hb 306pp, £31.99, ISBN 978-1-84889-138-8**) (takes a look at various habitats and why they support the birds they do. With 25 contributing authors, this full colour book covers everything from towns to bogs.

BEST BOOK NOMINATIONS

My favourite books, with one pick from each category, are:-
Wildlife in Printmaking
Cotingas and Manakins
Bird Sense

YOUR GUIDE TO BIRDING WEBSITES WORTH VIEWING

Sorting wheat from the internet chaff can be a time-consuming and frustrating experience, but website enthusiast Gordon Hamlett tackles the job on your behalf and comes up with 50 sites well worth exploring.

WHEN I WANTED to check out a restaurant's menu the other day, I automatically did a quick search on the internet. But there was nothing there. Yes, there were a few mentions in trade directories and the odd user review but the restaurant didn't have its own website.

Amid emotions ranging from anger to bewilderment, it struck me as how unusual this was. After all, surely every business has a website these days. Then I started to think about this a bit more and I wondered if we weren't falling out of love with the net just a little. Not the end user, the thirst for knowledge is seemingly unquenchable, but rather those who provide the information in the first place.

Two examples struck me particularly. I sign up for all sorts of online birding e-mail groups; as a writer, it is a useful way of keeping up to date with what's happening. A few years ago, these were buzzing, with like-minded birders happy to send in details of their own sightings and comment on those from other members. Information could be put out immediately, reaching the maximum number of interested parties.

This year, the number of people contributing to such groups seems to be right down. A few counties such as Hampshire have e-mail groups that maintain a high level of interest but the overriding feeling is that people can't be bothered any more. The novelty has worn off.

Instead, we are seeing a fragmentation of information as birders resort to blogs, Twitter and Facebook. The information is still out there, but dispersed further and wider. It is almost as if we are reverting to times past, but in a high-tech environment. Whereas we would just phone a few friends, we now keep in touch with those friends online, and without telling the rest of the world.

My other gripe comes from those people who actually maintain the websites. I have no problems with the information that's out there but where many of these sites fall down is in providing a human interface with the website.

I had hoped to be able to select my books of the year (see pages 21 to 26) from a much wider selection, or choose from a larger range of reserves in the county directories to pick just two pertinent areas of complaint. So what went wrong? Too many contact e-mail address were dead, wrong, or referred to people no longer working for a given organisation. If your e-mail got through, there was no guarantee that anyone would ever answer it.

Nobody escapes the blame here: publishing companies, press and publicity officers, wildlife organisations big and small, bird clubs… These may sound like the misanthropic ramblings of a grumpy old man, but I'm hearing the same complaints over and over again.

The internet is a truly wonderful thing, but 'with great power comes great responsibility' as they say in the Spiderman comics. Your website is more often than not, the first port of call for anyone wanting to find out about you. If your information is wrong, or out of date, then people will go elsewhere.

TOP TEN ESSENTIAL WEBSITES

An alphabetical order, this is my list of the top ten websites that every British birder should have bookmarked.

http://www.birdforum.net/
With more than 100,000 members discussing anything and everything bird-related, this is the number one social media site for birders.

http://www.birdguides.com/
The place to come for the latest rare bird news, photos etc. There is a basic free service, with extra content if you want to subscribe.

http://www.bto.org/
The British Trust for Ornithology's site includes the fabulous Birdtrack, for online migration recording as well as lots of other survey work.

http://www.fatbirder.com/
Whatever you are searching for, look here first; there are links to thousands of other birding websites.

http://ibc.lynxeds.com/
If you want to know what a bird looks like, this is the best place to start. At the time of writing, there were video clips of 75% of the world's species, photos of 85% and sound clips of 45%.

http://www.rspb.org.uk/
The RSPB is the number one birding charity and its site has details of British species (including sounds), reserves and conservation projects.

http://www.the-soc.org.uk/
The Scottish Ornithologists' Club covers all matter of Scottish birding including site guides and recent sightings.

http://www.surfbirds.com/
The pick of the online magazines, Surfbirds has recent rarity photos, hundreds of blogs, trip reports, discussions etc.

http://www.wildlifetrusts.org/
An umbrella site, giving access to the 47 individual trusts as well as general information on the work of the trusts.

http://www.wwt.org.uk/
Details of all the Wildfowl and Wetland Trust's reserves can be found here, together with details of latest sightings and news etc.

OTHER WEBSITES WORTH EXPLORING

ART AND MUSIC

http://www.newa-uk.com
The National Exhibition of Wildlife Art showcases works by upcoming as well as familiar artists. You can view and buy the many exhibits online though viewing is not helped by the superimposition of the letters 'NEWA' across each picture. I know that this is for copyright purposes but there has to be a

better way. There is an excellent selection of links to artists' individual websites.

http://www.operaunlimited.org.uk/theconferenceofbirds.html
The Conference of Birds is a group of musicians looking to combine music with bird song, as well as performing music by other composers, from Vivaldi to Messiaen, who were also inspired by the sounds of the natural world.

YOUR GUIDE TO BIRDING WEBSITES WORTH VIEWING

ATLASES AND POPULATIONS

http://jncc.defra.gov.uk/page-3176
These are the figures the government uses when it comes to monitoring the populations of 25 species of seabird. For each species, you can download accounts that list and map all the major colonies. Sadly most of data refers to the time around 2000, and many populations have crashed considerably since then.

http://www.sovon.nl/ebcc/eoa/
This Dutch site is a breeding atlas of European birds. You can search for a species by English or scientific name and get fully zoomable maps. The only problem is that I can't find any information on the methodology used or how up-to-date the information is. It might be on the parent site, but my Dutch isn't up to it.

BIRD REPORTS

http://www.britishbirds.co.uk/
If you have any gaps in your collection of *British Birds* magazine, worry not. The first 100 years of magazines have been put online. Simply register – it's free – and you can search away to your heart's content. A magnificent resource.

http://www.the-soc.org.uk/sbr.php
The Scottish Ornithologists' Club is putting all its old bird reports online. You can search for a particular species in any particular recording area, for any given year, up to and including 2007. This is a brilliant idea. It's just a pity that there isn't a corresponding body that could do the same with English and Welsh reports.

BLOGS

http://hughharropwildlifephotography. blogspot.co.uk/
Here's a stunning range of photos taken mostly on Shetland, or on Hugh's guided tours to Scandinavia. Subjects include cetaceans and the Northern Lights as well as a mouth-watering selection of scarce birds.

http://markavery.info/
Mark Avery was a former Conservation Director

for the RSPB. He is not afraid to speak his mind as posts on this blog will testify. There are certainly no punches pulled here. You can also sign up for a free monthly newsletter.

http://onlyfoolsandbirders.wordpress.com/
Only Fools and Birders is a blog from several leading Norfolk birders, taking a wry look at the current birding scene. There are details of recent sightings, trip reports, equipment reviews and site guides etc. to counteract the humorous stuff.

BRITISH BIRDING

http://www.birdsinmorayandnairn.org/
Is this the way forward for county bird reports? The recorder for Moray and Nairn has decided that it is no longer economical to publish written bird reports, so everything is going online instead. And for free too. The website already includes recent sightings and articles. Future plans include a site guide.

www.caithness-sea-watching.co.uk
Though a cetacean rather than a birding site, this Caithness website does have details on the best places to go seawatching and it's a safe bet that if an area is good for whales and dolphins, it will be good for seabird passage too.

http://www.cumbriabirdclub.org.uk/
A very clean looking website from the Cumbria Bird Club. There is the usual mix of latest sightings, photos, a county checklist and site guide. Past newsletters are available online, though the most recent ones are available to club members only.

http://www.guernseybirds.org.gg/
http://www.jerseybirds.co.uk/
These two websites cover the two largest Channel Islands, Jersey and Guernsey. As well as all the expected features, such as photos and recent sightings, you can also download (from the Jersey site) the latest checklist covering all the Channel Islands.

http://shropshirebirder.co.uk/index.html
Shropshire has the unenviable reputation of being one of the worst birding counties in Britain, so it is great to see someone trumpeting its attractions. As well as the blog itself, birder and photographer Jim Almond has written about the best birding sites,

YOUR GUIDE TO BIRDING WEBSITES WORTH VIEWING

profusely illustrated the website and included a section on Shropshire's dragonflies.

www.stjohnspool-birds.co.uk
It's about as far north as you can go without getting your feet wet and once there, the hide isn't easy to find. So why bother? Just look at the geographical location. As well as a fantastic breeding colony of Arctic Terns, St John's Loch in Caithness has an unbelievable list of rarities including Oriental Turtle Dove, Caspian Tern, Black-headed Bunting and several Lesser Scaup...

CONSERVATION

http://www.bto.org/about-birds/birdtrends
Bird Trends from the BTO presents up-to-date information on the populations of our commonest birds. Each species is summarised on its own page, and you can expand key sections if you want more details. There is an excellent collection of references at the end of each account.

www.earthtimes.org/
The Earth Times is a green magazine website, covering a full range of environmental stories. A nature section includes plenty of in-depth articles, the latest bird-related topic being a paper on the soaring habits of Golden Eagles. You can subscribe to a free newsletter and there are plenty of blogs too. There is a lot of content here.

www.swift-conservation.org
Dedicated to reversing the decline in Swift populations, by preserving and augmenting websites in both the UK and the EC, this extensive site provides ample detail of how to maintain and set up nest places for Swifts. It also has a directory of local experts who can assist with nest box projects, links to advice available in several European countries, details of nestboxes (both DIY and commercially produced), and downloadable advice leaflets.

www.youtube.com/watch?v=5pZ4My_ ZUeU&feature=relmfu
This award-winning documentary comes in four parts. It looks at an attempt to re-establish the Waldrapp or Northern Bald Ibis back into Austria, where archaeological remains show that the birds can be dated back

to the Stone Age. A group of imprinted birds are trained to follow a microlight, teaching them migration routes over the Alps.

www.youtube.com/watch?v=7GprXFdC2FQ& feature=related
This video clip is an abridged version of a presentation by Dr John Edwards, a biologist working for the Hawk and Owl Trust. His theme is raptor conservation, as seen from a biologist's perspective. It is such a calm, measured presentation of the facts, covering the subject in seven minutes, you wonder how anyone could possibly argue against them.

FIELDCRAFT

http://birding.about.com/od/birdingbasics/a/ Pishing.htm
I don't know whether British birders are too shy, or British birds are more intelligent that their trans-Atlantic counterparts, but for some reason, 'pishing' doesn't seem to work very well over here. Perhaps this article on how to attract small birds by making funny noises will show us just where we are going wrong.

FOREIGN BIRDING

http://www.stateofcanadasbirds.org/
We're used to seeing regular updates of our own birds, but what about elsewhere in the world? Here we have an overview of the current state of Canada's bird life, its first ever report of this nature. Currently, about 15% of its species are threatened, either through environmental problems in the country itself or from problems migratory species are experiencing elsewhere.

HUMOUR

http://www.bannedinhollywood.com/30-pictures-of-birds-attacking-people/
http://www.youtube.com/ watch?v=wySFpiXzpkc
We shouldn't laugh, but you can't help yourself. Here are two collections of video clips and photographs of birds attacking people. That most of the people are Americans and fully deserve their punishments is merely the cherry on top of a very large cake.

YOUR GUIDE TO BIRDING WEBSITES WORTH VIEWING

http://www.youtube.com/
watch?v=b07b7VLNbSA
I'm not sure whether this should be filed
under humour or behaviour. Two Russian
Hooded Crows manage to induce two cats to
start fighting each other via a persistent series
of tail-pulling manoeuvres. I've seen this
tail-tweaking before though, while watching
Hoodies attack a White-tailed Eagle, so
perhaps it is a behavioural trait.

IDENTIFICATION ARTICLES

www.manchesterbirding.com/
flavawagtailsarticle.htm
Separating the different races of Yellow
Wagtail is difficult at the best of times and
matters aren't helped by all the various
intergrades. This article looks at Channel
Wagtails, a cross between 'our' Yellow Wagtail
and the continental Blue-headed Wagtail.
Another article in the same identification
section of this website looks at further
intergrades.

http://www.uk400clubonline.co.uk/?cat=75
Here's a really impressive series of papers
from Lee Evans, dealing with such tricky
ID problems as separating Greenland and
Northern Wheatears, Lesser and Mealy
Redpolls, Arctic Redpolls, Pied and White
Wagtails etc.

MIGRATION

www.youtube.com/watch?v=r0IZ-
Hb86wg&feature=relmfu
Originally released in the cinema, *Winged
Migration* is one of the classic wildlife films,
covering birds on all seven continents. Filmed
over a three year period, the film is presented
here in eight parts so you will need to follow
the links to the next clip.

SATELLITE TRACKING

http://www.bto.org/science/migration/
tracking-studies/cuckoo-tracking
The British Trust for Ornithology attached
transmitters to five Norfolk Cuckoos in 2011
and you can follow their progress here. The
2012 project follows some Scottish birds
because the populations north of the border

seem to be faring a lot better than their
English counterparts.

http://ringwoodcock.net/
Anyone interested in Woodcocks should check
out this site which features studies into
Woodcock migration via traditional ringing
methods.

www.woodcockwatch.com/
Sponsored by the Game and Wildlife
Conservation Trust, this project is attempting
to discover more about the little-known
movements of Woodcocks. A Woodcock moon
— a full moon in November — brings many
thousands of birds to Britain, but where do
they come from?

SPECIES

http://gull-research.org/index.html
This is an excellent resource for gull lovers,
complete with articles, photos, a discussion
forum and a good selection of links to various
blogs and other gull-related websites. Design
and navigation leave a lot to be desired, but
substance wins over style every time.

http://tech.groups.yahoo.com/group/
Swallows-Martins-Swifts-Worldwide/
This discussion group, as the name suggests,
covers everything to do with swallows, martins
and swifts across the world. Traffic is high for
a group like this with, for example, nearly 400
messages posted in May 2012 covering topics
such as the seeming crash in numbers in the
UK following the dreadful spring.

http://www.thegreatcraneproject.org.uk/
Hoping to build on the small population of
birds in East Anglia, the Great Crane Project
is a scheme to establish a breeding population
in Somerset, with chicks being raised at WWT
Slimbridge before being released into the
wild.

www.youtube.com/twiterecoveryproject
This ten minute video looks at Twite in
Yorkshire where they are known locally as
'Pennine Finches'. Habitat requirements are
discussed, showing how the birds move from
one seed crop to the next as the seasons
progress. There is also an identification guide
with practical tips on separating Twite from
confusion species.

VIDEOS

http://birdcinema.com
This North American site hosts thousands of bird-related video clips from all over the world, though there is obviously a huge trans-Atlantic bias. You can upload your own recordings too.

http://vimeo.com/album/1767069/video/28944508
This eight minute film shows edited highlights of a Peregrine nest in the Pentland Hills near Edinburgh during the 2011 breeding season. The nest is prone to disturbance by egg collectors so it is an added bonus to see the chicks fledging successfully.

http://www.youtube.com/watch?v=Jlyd04dwn7g&feature=player_embedded
If you have ever wanted to get close up to a Capercaillie, then watch this Russian video. It shows perfectly well why certain rogue Capers in Scotland have to be relocated for their own protection. Warning: contains scenes that some viewers might find disturbing.

http://www.youtube.com/watch?v=AffGN5OYCFY
The most successful birds are those that can adapt to whatever opportunities present themselves. This clip shows a Herring Gull feasting on young bats emerging from their roost in the eaves of a house.

ID Insights Pocket Cards

British Birds
113 common but tricky-to-identify species. Illustrated by Dave Nurney with ID tips from top writer Dominic Couzens. Ten cards.

British Dragonflies
Expert illustrator Dan Powell covers 51 species of dragonflies and damselflies, together with details of habitats, distribution and main flight times, on 13 cards.

British Garden Birds
Perfect for beginners, children and casual birdwatchers. Covers 65 species on 11 cards and feature artwork and ID advice from Dan and Rosie Powell.

Butterflies of Great Britain
Life-size artwork of 58 species on 12 cards. Rosie Powell illustrates male and female, plus wing patterns for each species. Also habitats, distribution and main flight times.

Handy and hard-wearing A6 Pocket Cards mean you can forget about lugging around hefty fieldguides. Join the thousands of customers who have discovered the practical benefits of always having ID information whenever it is needed.

Contact Buckingham Press on 01733 561 739 or visit our website at:
www.buckinghampress.co.uk

£5.95 per set or £15 for three sets

DIARY 2013

David Cromack

Once-common species such as Lapwing have declined because of habitat loss, so the World Wetlands Day in February has important work to do in raising awareness.

EVENTS DIARY 2013

While every effort has been made to check the accuracy of these entries, the publishers advise making contact with the event organisers to ensure there are no late changes. TBA = To Be Announced (for those dates not settled before the Yearbook went to press).

JANUARY

14-28: Big Schools Birdwatch
UK-wide event to get children interested in wild birds.
Contact: www.rspb.org./schoolswatch for events in your area.

26-27: Big Garden Birdwatch
UK-wide survey of garden birds, aimed at members of the public.
Contact: www.rspb.org.uk/birdwatch

FEBRUARY

2: World Wetlands Day
Various 'Wetlands and Water Management' events around the globe celebrating the International Year of Water Co-operation.
Contact: www.ramsar.org

20-24: Pacific Seabird Group AGM
Portland Hilton, Portland, Oregon.
Contact: www.pacificseabirdgroup.orgnmnh.si.edu

MARCH

16: SOC/BTO Scottish Birdwatchers' Conference
Event at Our Dynamic Earth in Edinburgh hosts the launch of BirdAtlas 2007-11.
Contact: www.the-soc.org.uk

26-28: BOU annual spring conference:
From populations to policy impact: avian demography in a changing world.
University of Leicester.
Contact: www.bou.org.uk

APRIL

6: African Bird Club joint meeting with British Ornithologists' Club and Natural History Museum.
ABC AGM, plus full programme of talks on research and conservation work in Africa. £5 donation invited from non-members of ABC

and BOC. Natural History Museum, London SW7.
Contact: info@africanbirdclub.org or www.africanbirdclub.org

12-14: RSPB Members' Weekend
University of York
Contact: www.rspb.org.uk

19-21: BTO bird survey techniques residential course. Also bird ID course.
Malham Tarn Field Studies Centre, Yorkshire
Contact: info@bto.org

20-21: Deepdale Outdoor & Wildlife Festival
Dalegate Market, Burnham Deepdale, north Norfolk.
Contact: Deepdale Farms; 01485 210 036; e-mail: jason@deepdalefarm.co.uk www.deepdaleoutdoorfestival.co.uk

26-28: BTO bird ID residential course
Juniper Hall Field Studies Centre, Surrey
Contact: info@bto.org

MAY

2: One-day BTO bird ID course
Minsmere RSPB reserve, Suffolk
Contact: info@bto.org

3: One-day BTO bird ID course
Minsmere RSPB reserve, Suffolk
Contact: info@bto.org

3-5: BTO bird survey techniques residential course
How Hill Trust, Ludham, Norfolk
Contact: info@bto.org

10-12: BTO bird survey techniques residential course
Juniper Hall Field Studies Centre, Surrey
Contact: info@bto.org

11-12: Scottish Birdfair
Hopetoun House, Edinburgh
Contact: stacey.maden@rspb.org.uk or visit www.scottishbirdfair.org.uk

EVENTS DIARY 2013

24-26: BTO bird survey techniques residential course
Kingcombe Centre, Dorchester, Dorset
Contact: info@bto.org

26: Neotropical Bird Club general meeting
AGM, plus talks, quizzes and book sales at
Cley Village Hall, Norfolk. Starts 10.30am.
Contact: d.j.fisher@ntlworld.com or
secretary@neotropicalbirdclub.org.uk

31-June 2: BTO bird survey techniques residential course
Rhyd-y-Creuau Field Studies Centre, Betws-y-Coed
Contact: info@bto.org

JUNE

1-9: Make Your Nature Count
UK-wide scheme run by RSPB to survey
summer wildlife
Contact: www.rspb.org.uk/naturecount

JULY

6: AGM of OSME (Ornithological Society of the Middle East, Caucasus and Central Asia).
Doors open 10am.
Non-members welcome for five talks on the
region's birds.
The Nunnery, Thetford, Norfolk.
Contact: secretary@osme.org or 01545 571
022.

21-25: 26th International Congress for Conservation Biology
Baltimore, Maryland.

AUGUST

16-18: British Birdwatching Fair
Egleton Nature Reserve, Rutland Water,
Rutland
Contact: etate@birdfair.org.uk or visit www.
birdfair.org.uk

28-31: European Ornithologists Union 9th Conference
University of East Anglia, Norwich.
Contact: www.norwich.eounion.org

SEPTEMBER

TBA: Bakewell Festival of Bird Art
National championships of British Decoy
Wildfowl Carvers Association, plus supporting
bird artists and crafts people. Agricultural
Business Centre, Bakewell DE45 1AH.
Contact: www.bdwca.org

16-18: BTO bird ID residential course
How Hill Trust, Ludham, Norfolk
Contact: info@bto.org

24-29: Waterbird Society's 37th annual meeting
Wilhelmshaven, Germany.
Contact: www.waterbirds.org

OCTOBER

4-6 & 26-28: BTO bird ID residential course
Kingcombe Centre, Dorchester, Dorset
Contact: info@bto.org

12: RSPB Members' Day and AGM
Westminster, London
Visit www.rspb.org.uk

31-Nov 10: 'The Natural Eye' — Society of Wildlife Artists annual exhibition.
Receiving Days 8,9th September.
Mall Galleries, Pall Mall, London.
Contact: www.swla.co.ukExhib runs Thurs
31st Oct – Sun 10 Nov 2013

NOVEMBER

2: Welsh Ornithological Society Annual Conference
Venue in Gwent to mark the 50th anniverssary
of Gwent ornithological society.
Contact: www.birdsinwales.org.uk

DECEMBER

6-8: BTO Annual Conference
Hayes Conference Centre, Swanwick,
Derbyshire
Contact: info@bto.org

DIARY – JANUARY 2013

1	Tue	New Year holiday
2	Wed	Holiday (Scotland)
3	Thu	
4	Fri	
5	Sat	
6	Sun	
7	Mon	
8	Tue	
9	Wed	
10	Thu	
11	Fri	
12	Sat	
13	Sun	
14	Mon	
15	Tue	
16	Wed	
17	Thu	
18	Fri	
19	Sat	
20	Sun	
21	Mon	
22	Tue	
23	Wed	
24	Thu	
25	Fri	
26	Sat	
27	Sun	
28	Mon	
29	Tue	
30	Wed	
31	Thu	

1	Fri	
2	Sat	
3	Sun	
4	Mon	
5	Tue	
6	Wed	
7	Thu	
8	Fri	
9	Sat	
10	Sun	
11	Mon	
12	Tue	
13	Wed	
14	Thu	
15	Fri	
16	Sat	
17	Sun	
18	Mon	
19	Tue	
20	Wed	
21	Thu	
22	Fri	
23	Sat	
24	Sun	
25	Mon	
26	Tue	
27	Wed	
28	Thu	

DIARY – MARCH 2013

1	Fri	
2	Sat	
3	Sun	
4	Mon	
5	Tue	
6	Wed	
7	Thu	
8	Fri	
9	Sat	
10	Sun	Mothering Sunday
11	Mon	
12	Tue	
13	Wed	
14	Thu	
15	Fri	
16	Sat	
17	Sun	St Patrick's Day
18	Mon	
19	Tue	
20	Wed	
21	Thu	
22	Fri	
23	Sat	
24	Sun	
25	Mon	
26	Tue	
27	Wed	
28	Thu	
29	Fri	Good Friday
30	Sat	
31	Sun	British Summertime begins – Easter Day

38

1	Mon	Easter Monday
2	Tue	
3	Wed	
4	Thu	
5	Fri	
6	Sat	
7	Sun	
8	Mon	
9	Tue	
10	Wed	
11	Thu	
12	Fri	
13	Sat	
14	Sun	
15	Mon	
16	Tue	
17	Wed	
18	Thu	
19	Fri	
20	Sat	
21	Sun	
22	Mon	
23	Tue	
24	Wed	
25	Thu	
26	Fri	
27	Sat	
28	Sun	
29	Mon	
30	Tues	

DIARY – MAY 2013

1	Wed	
2	Thu	
3	Fri	
4	Sat	
5	Sun	
6	Mon	May Day
7	Tue	
8	Wed	
9	Thu	
10	Fri	
11	Sat	
12	Sun	
13	Mon	
14	Tue	
15	Wed	
16	Thu	
17	Fri	
18	Sat	
19	Sun	
20	Mon	
21	Tue	
22	Wed	
23	Thu	
24	Fri	
25	Sat	
26	Sun	
27	Mon	Spring Bank Holiday
28	Tue	
29	Wed	
30	Thu	
31	Fri	

DIARY – JUNE 2013

1	Sat	
2	Sun	
3	Mon	
4	Tue	
5	Wed	
6	Thu	
7	Fri	
8	Sat	
9	Sun	
10	Mon	
11	Tue	
12	Wed	
13	Thu	
14	Fri	
15	Sat	
16	Sun	
17	Mon	
18	Tue	
19	Wed	
20	Thu	
21	Fri	
22	Sat	
23	Sun	
24	Mon	
25	Tue	
26	Wed	
27	Thu	
28	Fri	
29	Sat	
30	Sun	

DIARY – JULY 2013

1	Mon	
2	Tue	
3	Wed	
4	Thu	
5	Fri	
6	Sat	
7	Sun	
8	Mon	
9	Tue	
10	Wed	
11	Thu	
12	Fri	
13	Sat	
14	Sun	
15	Mon	
16	Tue	
17	Wed	
18	Thu	
19	Fri	
20	Sat	
21	Sun	
22	Mon	
23	Tue	
24	Wed	
25	Thu	
26	Fri	
27	Sat	
28	Sun	
29	Mon	
30	Tue	
31	Wed	

DIARY – AUGUST 2013

1	Thu	
2	Fri	
3	Sat	
4	Sun	
5	Mon	
6	Tue	
7	Wed	
8	Thu	
9	Fri	
10	Sat	
11	Sun	
12	Mon	
13	Tue	
14	Wed	
15	Thu	
16	Fri	
17	Sat	
18	Sun	
19	Mon	
20	Tue	
21	Wed	
22	Thu	
23	Fri	
24	Sat	
25	Sun	
26	Mon	Summer Bank Holiday
27	Tue	
28	Wed	
29	Thu	
30	Fri	
31	Sat	

DIARY – SEPTEMBER 2013

1	Sun	
2	Mon	
3	Tue	
4	Wed	
5	Thu	
6	Fri	
7	Sat	
8	Sun	
9	Mon	
10	Tue	
11	Wed	
12	Thu	
13	Fri	
14	Sat	
15	Sun	
16	Mon	
17	Tue	
18	Wed	
19	Thu	
20	Fri	
21	Sat	
22	Sun	
23	Mon	
24	Tue	
25	Wed	
26	Thu	
27	Fri	
28	Sat	
29	Sun	
30	Mon	

DIARY – OCTOBER 2013

1	Tue	
2	Wed	
3	Thu	
4	Fri	
5	Sat	
6	Sun	
7	Mon	
8	Tue	
9	Wed	
10	Thu	
11	Fri	
12	Sat	
13	Sun	
14	Mon	
15	Tue	
16	Wed	
17	Thu	
18	Fri	
19	Sat	
20	Sun	
21	Mon	
22	Tue	
23	Wed	
24	Thu	
25	Fri	
26	Sat	
27	Sun	British Summertime ends
28	Mon	
29	Tue	
30	Wed	
31	Thu	

DIARY – NOVEMBER 2013

1	Fri	
2	Sat	
3	Sun	
4	Mon	
5	Tue	
6	Wed	
7	Thu	
8	Fri	
9	Sat	
10	Sun	Remembrance Sunday
11	Mon	
12	Tue	
13	Wed	
14	Thu	
15	Fri	
16	Sat	
17	Sun	
18	Mon	
19	Tue	
20	Wed	
21	Thu	
22	Fri	
23	Sat	
24	Sun	
25	Mon	
26	Tue	
27	Wed	
28	Thu	
29	Fri	
30	Sat	

54

1	Sun	
2	Mon	
3	Tue	
4	Wed	
5	Thu	
6	Fri	
7	Sat	
8	Sun	
9	Mon	
10	Tue	
11	Wed	
12	Thu	
13	Fri	
14	Sat	
15	Sun	
16	Mon	
17	Tue	
18	Wed	
19	Thu	
20	Fri	
21	Sat	
22	Sun	
23	Mon	
24	Tue	
25	Wed	Christmas Day
26	Thu	Boxing Day
27	Fri	
28	Sat	
29	Sun	
30	Mon	
31	Tues	

YEAR PLANNER 2014

January	
February	
March	
April	
May	
June	
July	
August	
September	
October	
November	
December	

LOG CHARTS

David Cromack

Little Egrets are now firmly established in many places in the UK, so it's likely you'll be recording it on the Checklist for 2013.

A CHECKLIST OF BIRDS
Based on the British List formulated by the British Ornithologists' Union

MANY READERS have asked why our Checklist of Birds keeps changing from year to year. It is based on the official British List maintained by The British Ornithologists' Union (BOU) which sits in judgement on which birds you can count on your lists, and which you can't. They do this in two ways:

1): If someone claims to have seen a species never recorded in Britain, a panel of experts (the BOU Rarities Committee) assesses the record, making sure that the identification of the bird was proved beyond all possible doubt. Then the bird's credentials are also assessed, to determine whether it was a genuine vagrant, rather than one that had just hopped over the fence from the nearest zoo or aviary.

Only if the bird passes every single strenuous test does it get accepted onto the list....a process that may take many years. Similarly, historical records are reassessed in the light of advances in identification skills.

2): The BOU also takes advice from taxonomists on the need to split or lump together sub-species. The current trend towards splitting is usually driven by DNA evidence suggesting that a particular sub-species is sufficiently different to warrant full species status.

Since the publication of the last *Birdwatcher's Yearbook*, there are four new additions to the British list: Madeiran Storm Petrel, Hudsonian Whimbrel, Cabot's Tern and Siberian Stonechat. The petrel is a newly-seen species, whereas the other three result from splitting existing species. Cabot's Tern is the North American form of Sandwich Tern, previously known as Cayenne Tern.

As a result of these changes, the official British list now stands at 596 species, made up of 578 species in Category A, nine in Category B and nine in Category C. See below for a full description of what the different categories mean.

In addition, there have been a few minor tweaks to the order of some species. For a full discussion of these changes, go to the BOU's website, **www.bou.org.uk**. In this edition, species in Category C (introduced species) have been sub-divided into six separate categories (see below).

SPECIES, CATEGORIES, CODES – YOUR GUIDE TO GET THE BEST USE FROM THE CHECKLIST

Species categories (column 1)

The following categories are those assigned by the British Ornithologists' Union.

A - Species recorded in an apparently natural state at least once since January 1, 1950.

B - Species recorded in an apparently natural state at least once between January 1, 1800 and December 31,1949, but not subsequently.

C - Species that, though introduced, now derive from the resulting self-sustaining populations: C1 (*Naturalized introduced species)* Species that have occurred only as a result of introduction, e.g. Egyptian Goose; C2 (*Naturalized established species)* – Species resulting from introduction by Man, but which also occur in an apparently natural state, e.g. Greylag Goose; C3 (*Naturalized re-established species*) Species successfully re-established by Man in areas of former occurrence, e.g. Red Kite; C4 (*Naturalized feral species)* Domesticated species established in the wild, e.g. Rock Pigeon (Dove)/Feral Pigeon; C5 (*Vagrant naturalized species)* Species from established naturalized populations abroad. There are currently no species in category C5; C6 (*Former naturalized species)* Species formerly in C1

whose naturalized populations are either no longer self-sustaining or are considered extinct, e.g. Lady Amherst's Pheasant.

D - Species where there is reasonable doubt that they have ever occurred in a natural state. Species placed solely in Category D form no part of the British List, and are not included in the species totals.

E - Species that have been recorded as introductions, human-assisted transportees or escapees from captivity, and whose breeding populations (if any) are thought not to be self-sustaining. Species in Category E that have bred in the wild in Britain are designated as E*. Category E species form no part of the British List (unless already included within Categories A, B or C).

A species is usually placed in only one category, but some are placed in multiple categories, for example, those species occurring in Category A which now have naturalised populations (e.g. Red Kite).

The British List comprises only those species in Categories A, B and C.

LOG CHARTS

Species list (column 2)

The *Yearbook* Checklist includes all species from categories A, B and C on the British List, based on the latest BOU listing. Selected species included in categories D and E are listed separately at the end of the log chart.

Vagrants which are not on the British List, but which may have occurred in other parts of the British Isles, are not included. Readers who wish to record such species may use the extra rows provided on the last page. In this connection it should be noted that separate lists exist for Northern Ireland (kept by the Northern Ireland Birdwatchers' Association) and the Isle of Man (kept by the Manx Ornithological Society), and that Irish records are assessed by the Irish Rare Birds Committee.

The commoner species in the log charts are indicated by the * symbol to help make record-keeping easier.

The species names are those most widely used in the current fieldguides and each is followed by its scientific name, printed in italics.

Life list (column 3)

Ticks made in the 'Life List' column suffice for keeping a running personal total of species. However, added benefit can be obtained by replacing ticks with a note of the year of first occurrence. To take an example: one's first-ever Marsh Sandpiper, seen on April 14, 2013, would be logged with '13' in the Life List and '14' in the April column (as well as a tick in the 2013 column). As Life List entries are carried forward annually, in years to come it would be a simple matter to relocate this record.

First and last dates of migrants

Arrivals of migrants can be recorded by inserting dates instead of ticks in the relevant month columns. For example, a Common Sandpiper on March 11 would be recorded by inserting '11' against Common Sandpiper in the March column. The same applies to departures, though dates of last sightings can only be entered at the end of the year after checking one's field notebook.

Unheaded columns

The three unheaded columns on the right of the December column of each chart are for special (personal) use. This may be, for example, to cater for a second holiday, a particular county or a 'local patch'. Another use could be to indicate species on, for example, the Northern Ireland List or the Isle of Man List.

BTO species codes (column 23)

British Trust for Ornithology two-letter species codes are shown in brackets in the fourth column from the right. Readers should refer to the BTO if more codes are needed.

Rare breeding birds (column 24)

Species monitored by the Rare Breeding Birds Panel (see National Directory) comprise all those on Schedule 1 of the Wildlife and Countryside Act 1981 (see Quick Reference) together with all escaped or introduced species breeding in small numbers. The following annotations in the charts (third column from the right) reflect the **RBBP's** categories:

A) Rare Breeding Birds in UK (Regular Breeders); B) Rare Breeding Birds in UK (Occasional Breeders); C) Rare Breeding Birds in UK (Potential Breeders); D) Rare Non-native Breeding Birds in UK (Regular Breeders); E) Rare Non-native Breeding Birds in UK (Occasional Breeders); F) Rare Non-native Breeding Birds in UK (Potential Breeders).

Rarities (column 25)

Rarities are indicated by a capital letter 'R' in the column headed BBRC (British Birds Rarities Committee).

EURING species numbers (column 26)

EURING databanks collect copies of recovery records from ringing schemes throughout Europe and the official species numbers are given in the last column. As they are taken from the full Holarctic bird list there are many apparent gaps. It is important that these are not filled arbitrarily by observers wishing to record species not listed in the charts, as this would compromise the integrity of the scheme.

Similarly, the addition of a further digit to indicate sub-species is to be avoided, since EURING has already assigned numbers for this purpose. The numbering follows the Voous order of species so some species are now out of sequence following the re-ordering of the British List. For full details, visit: www.euring.org

BOU	SWANS, GEESE, DUCKS		Life list	2013 list	24 hr	Garden	Holiday	Jan	Feb	Mar	Apr	May	Jun	Jul	Aug	Sep	Oct	Nov	Dec			BTO	RBBP	BBRC	EU No
*AC2	Mute Swan	Cygnus olor																				MS			0152
*A	Bewick's Swan	C. columbianus																				BS	C		0153
*A	Whooper Swan	C. cygnus																				WS	A		0154
*A	Bean Goose	Anser fabalis																				BE	E		0157
*A	Pink-footed Goose	A. brachyrhynchus																				PG	E		0158
*A	White-fronted Goose	A. albifrons																				WG	E		0159
*A	Lesser White-fronted Goose	A. erythropus																				LC	F	R	0160
AC2C4E	Greylag Goose	A. anser																				GJ			0161
*A	Snow Goose	A. Caerulescens																				SJ	D		0163
AC2E	Canada Goose	Branta canadensis																				CG			0166
AC2E	Barnacle Goose	B. leucopsis																				BY	D		0167
*A	Brent Goose	B. bernicla																				BG			0168
A	Red-breasted Goose	B. ruficollis																				EB	E	R	0169
C1E	Egyptian Goose	Alopochen aegyptiaca																				EG	D		0170
BDE	Ruddy Shelduck	Tadorna ferruginea																				UD	D		0171
*A	Shelduck	T. tadorna																				SU			0173
C1E	Mandarin Duck	Aix galericulata																				MN			0178
*A	Wigeon	Anas penelope																				WN	A		0179
A	American Wigeon	A. americana																				AW			0180
*AC2	Gadwall	A. strepera																				GA			0182
*AE	Baikal Teal	A. formosa																						R	1830
*A	Teal	A. crecca																				T			0184
A	Green-winged Teal	A. carolinensis																					C		1842
AC2C4E	Mallard	A. platyrhynchos																				MA			0186
	Sub total																								

DUCKS Cont

BOU	Species	Scientific name	Life list	2013 list	24 hr	Garden	Holiday	Jan	Feb	Mar	Apr	May	Jun	Jul	Aug	Sep	Oct	Nov	Dec	BTO	RBBP	BBRC	EU No
A	Black Duck	A. rubripes																		BD	B	R	0187
*A	Pintail	A. acuta																		PT	A		0189
*A	Garganey	A. querquedula																		GY	A		0191
A	Blue-winged Teal	A. discors																		TB	E	R	0192
*A	Shoveler	A. clypeata																		SV	A		0194
AC2E	Red-crested Pochard	Netta rufina																		RQ	D		0196
A	Canvasback	Aythya valisineria																				R	0197
*A	Pochard	A. ferina																		PO	A		0198
A	Redhead	A. americana																		AZ		R	0199
A	Ring-necked Duck	A. collaris																		NG	B		0200
A	Ferruginous Duck	A. nyroca																		FD	B		0202
*A	Tufted Duck	A. fuligula																		TU			0203
*A	Scaup	A. marila																		SP	B		0204
*A	Lesser Scaup	A. affinis																		AY		R	0205
*A	Eider	Somateria mollissima																		E			0206
*A	King Eider	S. spectabilis																		KE	C	R	0207
A	Steller's Eider	Polysticta stelleri																		ES		R	0209
A	Harlequin Duck	Histrionicus histrionicus																		HQ		R	0211
*A	Long-tailed Duck	Clangula hyemalis																		LN	C		0212
*A	Common Scoter	Melanitta nigra																		CX	A		0213
A	Black Scoter	M. americana																				R	2132
*A	Surf Scoter	M. perspicillata																		FS			0214
A	Velvet Scoter	M. fusca																		VS	C		0215
A	Bufflehead	Bucephala albeola																		VH		R	0216
	Sub total																						

DUCKS, GAMEBIRDS, DIVERS, ALBATROSS

BOU	Species	Scientific	Life list	2013 list	24 hr	Garden	Holiday	Jan	Feb	Mar	Apr	May	Jun	Jul	Aug	Sep	Oct	Nov	Dec	BTO	RBBP	BBRC	EU No
A	Barrow's Goldeneye	B. islandica																				R	0217
*A	Goldeneye	B. clangula																		GN	A		0218
A	Hooded Merganser	Lophodytes cucullatus																				R	2190
*A	Smew	Mergellus albellus																		SY	C		0220
*A	Red-breasted Merganser	Mergus serrator																		RM			0221
*A	Goosander	M. merganser																		GD			0223
C1E	Ruddy Duck	Oxyura jamaicensis																		BY	D		0225
*A	Red Grouse	Lagopus lagopus																		RG			0329
*A	Ptarmigan	Lagopus muta																		PM			0330
*A	Black Grouse	Tetrao tetrix																		BK			0332
*BC3	Capercaillie	T. urogallus																		CP	A		0335
C1E	Red-legged Partridge	Alectoris rufa																		RL			0358
*AC2E	Grey Partridge	Perdix perdix																		P			0367
*A	Quail	Coturnix coturnix																		Q	A		0370
C1E	Pheasant	Phasianus colchicus																		PH			0394
C1E	Golden Pheasant	Chrysolophus pictus																		GF	D		0396
C6E	Lady Amherst's Pheasant	C. amherstiae																		LM	D		0397
*A	Red-throated Diver	Gavia stellata																		RH	A		0002
*A	Black-throated Diver	G. arctica																		BV	A		0003
A	Pacific Diver	G. pacifica																				R	0033
*A	Great Northern Diver	G. immer																		ND	C		0004
A	White-billed Diver	G. adamsii																		IW	C		0005
A	Black-browed Albatross	Thalassarche melanophris																		AA	C	R	0014
A	Yellow-nosed Albatross	T. chlororhynchos																				R	0150
	Sub total																						

64

FULMAR, PETRELS, SHEARWATERS, CORMORANTS, FRIGATEBIRDS, BITTERNS

BOU	Name	Scientific	Life list	2013 list	24 hr	Garden	Holiday	Jan	Feb	Mar	Apr	May	Jun	Jul	Aug	Sep	Oct	Nov	Dec			BTO	RBBP	BBRC	EU No
*A	Fulmar	Fulmarus glacialis																				F			0020
A	Fea's Petrel	Pterodroma feae																						R	0026
A	Capped Petrel	Pt. hasitata																						R	0029
A	Cory's Shearwater	Calonectris diomedea																				CQ			0036
*A	Great Shearwater	Puffinus gravis																				GQ			0040
*A	Sooty Shearwater	P. griseus																				OT			0043
A	Manx Shearwater	P. puffinus																				MX			0046
A	Balearic Shearwater	P. mauretanicus																							0046
A	Macaronesian Shearwater	P. baroli																					C	R	0048
*A	Wilson's Petrel	Oceanites oceanicus																							0050
B	White-faced Petrel	Pelagodroma marina																						R	0051
*A	Storm Petrel	Hydrobates pelagicus																				TM			0052
A	Madeiran Storm Petrel	Oceanodroma castro																						R	0580
*A	Leach's Petrel	O leucorhoa																				TL			0055
A	Swinhoe's Petrel	O. monorhis																						R	0056
A	Red-billed Tropicbird	Phaethon aethereus																						R	0064
*A	Gannet	Morus bassanus																				GX			0071
*A	Cormorant	Phalacrocorax carbo																				CA			0072
A	Double-crested Cormorant	P. auritus																						R	0078
*A	Shag	P. aristotelis																				SA			0080
*A	Magnificent Frigatebird	Fregata magnificens																						R	0093
A	Ascension Frigatebird	F. aquila																						R	
*A	Bittern	Botaurus stellaris																				BI	A		0095
A	American Bittern	B. lentiginosus																				AM		R	0096
	Sub total																								

65

BOU	BITTERNS, HERONS, STORKS, SPOON-BILL, GREBES, RAPTORS		Life list	2013 list	24 hr	Garden	Holiday	Jan	Feb	Mar	Apr	May	Jun	Jul	Aug	Sep	Oct	Nov	Dec			BTO	RBBP	BBRC	EU No
A	Little Bittern	Ixobrychus minutus																				LL	B	R	0098
A	Night Heron	Nycticorax nycticorax																				NT	E		0104
A	Green Heron	Butorides virescens																				HR		R	0107
A	Squacco Heron	Ardeola ralloides																				QH		R	0108
A	Cattle Egret	Bubulcus ibis																				EC	B		0111
A	Snowy Egret	Egretta thula																						R	0115
*A	Little Egret	E. garzetta																				ET	A		0119
A	Great Egret	Ardea alba																				HW	C		0121
A	Grey Heron	A. cinerea																				H			0122
A	Great Blue Heron	A. herodias																						R	1230
A	Purple Heron	A. purpurea																				UR	B		0124
A	Black Stork	Ciconia nigra																				OS		R	0131
A	White Stork	C. ciconia																				OR	C		0134
A	Glossy Ibis	Plegadis falcinellus																				IB		R	0136
*A	Spoonbill	Platalea leucorodia																				NB	A		0144
A	Pied-billed Grebe	Podilymbus podiceps																				PJ	B	R	0006
*A	Little Grebe	Tachybaptus ruficollis																				LG			0007
*A	Great Crested Grebe	Podiceps cristatus																				GG			0009
*A	Red-necked Grebe	P. grisegena																				RX	B		0010
*A	Slavonian Grebe	P. auritus																				SZ	A		0011
*A	Black-necked Grebe	P. nigricollis																				BN	A		0012
*A	Honey-buzzard	Pernis apivorus																				HZ	A		0231
A	Black Kite	Milvus migrans																				KB	B		0238
*AC3	Red Kite	M. milvus																				KT	A		0239
	Sub total																								

BOU	RAPTORS Cont		Life list	2013 list	24 hr	Garden	Holiday	Jan	Feb	Mar	Apr	May	Jun	Jul	Aug	Sep	Oct	Nov	Dec	BTO	RBBP	BBRC	EU No
*AC3E	White-tailed Eagle	Haliaeetus albicilla																		WE	A		0243
B	Egyptian Vulture	Neophron percnopterus																				R	0247
A	Short-toed Eagle	Circaetus gallicus																				R	0256
*A	Marsh Harrier	Circus aeruginosus																		MR	A		0260
*A	Hen Harrier	C. cyaneus																		HH	A		0261
A	Pallid Harrier	C. macrourus																			C	R	0262
*A	Montagu's Harrier	C. pygargus																		MO	A		0263
AC3E	Goshawk	Accipiter gentilis																		GI	A		0267
*A	Sparrowhawk	A. nisus																		SH			0269
*A	Buzzard	Buteo buteo																		BZ			0287
*A	Rough-legged Buzzard	B. lagopus																		RF	C		0290
B	Greater Spotted Eagle	Aquila clanga																				R	0293
*A	Golden Eagle	A. chrysaetos																		EA	A		0296
*A	Osprey	Pandion haliaetus																		OP	A		0301
A	Lesser Kestrel	Falco naumanni																				R	0303
*A	Kestrel	F. tinnunculus																		K			0304
A	American Kestrel	F. sparverius																				R	0305
*A	Red-footed Falcon	F. vespertinus																		FV			0307
A	Amur Falcon	F. amurensis																				R	3080
*A	Merlin	F. columbarius																		ML	A		0309
*A	Hobby	F. subbuteo																		HY	A		0310
A	Eleonora's Falcon	F. eleonorae																					0311
*A	Gyrfalcon	F. rusticolus																		YF	C	R	0318
*A	Peregrine	F. peregrinus																		PE	A	R	0320
	Sub total																						

67

CRAKES, GALLINULES, CRANES, BUSTARDS AND WADERS

BOU	Species	Scientific name	Life list	2013 list	24 hr	Garden	Holiday	Jan	Feb	Mar	Apr	May	Jun	Jul	Aug	Sep	Oct	Nov	Dec	BTO	RBBP	BBRC	EU No
*A	Water Rail	Rallus aquaticus																		WA	A		0407
*A	Spotted Crake	Porzana porzana																		AK	A		0408
A	Sora	P. carolina																				R	0409
A	Little Crake	P. parva																		JC		R	0410
A	Baillon's Crake	P. pusilla																		VC	C	R	0411
*A	Corncrake	Crex crex																		CE	A		0421
*A	Moorhen	Gallinula chloropus																		MH			0424
A	Allen's Gallinule	Porphyrio alleni																				R	0425
A	Purple Gallinule	P. martinica																				R	0426
*A	Coot	Fulica atra																		CO			0429
A	American Coot	F. americana																				R	0430
*A	Crane	Grus grus																		AN	A		0433
A	Sandhill Crane	G. canadensis																				R	0436
A	Little Bustard	Tetrax tetrax																				R	0442
A	Macqueen's Bustard	Chlamydotis macqueenii																				R	0444
A	Great Bustard	Otis tarda																		US	B	R	0446
*A	Oystercatcher	Haematopus ostralegus																		OC			0450
*A	Black-winged Stilt	Himantopus himantopus																		IT	B	R	0455
*A	Avocet	Recurvirostra avosetta																		AV	A		0456
*A	Stone-curlew	Burhinus oedicnemus																		TN	A		0459
A	Cream-coloured Courser	Cursorius cursor																				R	0464
A	Collared Pratincole	Glareola pratincola																				R	0465
A	Oriental Pratincole	G. maldivarum																		GM		R	0466
A	Black-winged Pratincole	G. nordmanni																		KW		R	0467
	Sub total																						

LOG CHARTS

BOU	WADERS Cont		Life list	2013 list	24 hr	Garden	Holiday	Jan	Feb	Mar	Apr	May	Jun	Jul	Aug	Sep	Oct	Nov	Dec	BTO	RBBP	BBRC	EU No
*A	Little Ringed Plover	Charadrius dubius																		LP	A		0469
*A	Ringed Plover	C. hiaticula																		RP	A		0470
A	Semipalmated Plover	C. semipalmatus																		TV		R	0471
A	Killdeer	C. vociferus																		KL	C	R	0474
A	Kentish Plover	C. alexandrinus																		KP	B		0477
A	Lesser Sand Plover	C. mongolus																				R	0478
A	Greater Sand Plover	C. leschenaultii																				R	0479
A	Caspian Plover	C. asiaticus																				R	0480
*A	Dotterel	C. morinellus																		DO	A		0482
A	American Golden Plover	Pluvialis dominica																		ID			0484
A	Pacific Golden Plover	P. fulva																		IF		R	0484
*A	Golden Plover	P. apricaria																		GP			0485
*A	Grey Plover	P. squatarola																		GV			0486
A	Sociable Lapwing	Vanellus gregarius																		IP		R	0491
A	White-tailed Lapwing	V. leucurus																				R	0492
*A	Lapwing	V. vanellus																		L			0493
A	Great Knot	Calidris tenuirostris																		KO		R	0495
*A	Knot	C. canutus																		KN			0496
*A	Sanderling	C. alba																		SS	C		0497
A	Semipalmated Sandpiper	C. pusilla																		PZ		R	0498
A	Western Sandpiper	C. mauri																		ER		R	0499
A	Red-necked Stint	C. ruficollis																				R	0500
*A	Little Stint	C. minuta																		LX			0501
*A	Temminck's Stint	C. temminckii																		TK	B		0502
	Sub total																						

69

BOU	WADERS Cont		Life list	2013 list	24 hr	Garden	Holiday	Jan	Feb	Mar	Apr	May	Jun	Jul	Aug	Sep	Oct	Nov	Dec		BTO	RBBP	BBRC	EU No
A	Long-toed Stint	C. subminuta																					R	0503
A	Least Sandpiper	C. minutilla																			EP		R	0504
A	White-rumped Sandpiper	C. fuscicollis																			WU			0505
A	Baird's Sandpiper	C. bairdii																			BP		R	0506
A	Pectoral Sandpiper	C. melanotos																			PP	C		0507
A	Sharp-tailed Sandpiper	C. acuminata																			VV		R	0508
*A	Curlew Sandpiper	C. ferruginea																			CV			0509
A	Stilt Sandpiper	C. himantopus																					R	5150
*A	Purple Sandpiper	C. maritima																			PS	A		0510
*A	Dunlin	C. alpina																			DN			0512
A	Broad-billed Sandpiper	Limicola falcinellus																			OA	C	R	0514
A	Buff-breasted Sandpiper	Tryngites subruficollis																			BQ	C		0516
*A	Ruff	Philomachus pugnax																			RU	A		0517
*A	Jack Snipe	Lymnocryptes minimus																			JS	C		0518
*A	Snipe	Gallinago gallinago																			SN			0519
A	Wilson's Snipe	G. delicata																					R	5192
A	Great Snipe	G. media																			DS	C	R	0520
A	Short-billed Dowitcher	Limnodromus griseus																					R	0526
A	Long-billed Dowitcher	L. scolopaceus																			LD		R	0527
*A	Woodcock	Scolopax rusticola																			WK			0529
*A	Black-tailed Godwit	Limosa limosa																			BW	A		0532
A	Hudsonian Godwit	L. haemastica																			HU		R	0533
*A	Bar-tailed Godwit	L. lapponica																			BA	C		0534
A	Little Whimbrel	Numenius minutus																					R	0536
	Sub total																							

BOU	WADERS Cont, PHALAROPES AND SKUAS		Life list	2013 list	24 hr	Garden	Holiday	Jan	Feb	Mar	Apr	May	Jun	Jul	Aug	Sep	Oct	Nov	Dec	BTO	RBBP	BBRC	EU No
B	Eskimo Curlew	N. borealis																				R	0537
A	Hudsonian Whimbrel	N. hudsonicus																				R	
*A	Whimbrel	N. phaeopus																		WM	A		0538
A	Slender-billed Curlew	N. tenuirostris																				R	0540
*A	Curlew	N. arquata																		CU			0541
A	Upland Sandpiper	Bartramia longicauda																		UP		R	0544
A	Terek Sandpiper	Xenus cinereus																		TR		R	0555
*A	Common Sandpiper	Actitis hypoleucos																		CS			0556
A	Spotted Sandpiper	A. macularius																		PQ	B	R	0557
*A	Green Sandpiper	Tringa ochropus																		GE	A		0553
A	Solitary Sandpiper	T. solitaria																		I		R	0552
A	Grey-tailed Tattler	T. brevipes																		YT		R	0558
*A	Spotted Redshank	T. erythropus																		DR		R	0545
A	Greater Yellowlegs	T. melanoleuca																		LZ		R	0550
*A	Greenshank	T. nebularia																		GK	A		0548
A	Lesser Yellowlegs	T. flavipes																		LY		R	0551
*A	Marsh Sandpiper	T. stagnatilis																		MD		R	0547
*A	Wood Sandpiper	T. glareola																		OD	A		0554
*A	Redshank	T. totanus																		RK			0546
*A	Turnstone	Arenaria interpres																		TT	C		0561
A	Wilson's Phalarope	Phalaropus tricolor																		WF		R	0563
*A	Red-necked Phalarope	P. lobatus																		NK	A		0564
*A	Grey Phalarope	Phalaropus fulicarius																		PL			0565
*A	Pomarine Skua	Stercorarius pomarinus																		PK			0566
	Sub total																						

71

SKUAS cont. GULLS

BOU	Species	Scientific name	Life list	2013 list	24 hr	Garden	Holiday	Jan	Feb	Mar	Apr	May	Jun	Jul	Aug	Sep	Oct	Nov	Dec	BTO	RBBP	BBRC	EU No
*A	Arctic Skua	S. parasiticus																		AC	A		0567
*A	Long-tailed Skua	S. longicaudus																		OG			0568
*A	Great Skua	S. skua																		NX			0569
A	Ivory Gull	Pagophila eburnea																		IV		R	0604
*A	Sabine's Gull	Xema sabini																		AB			0579
*A	Kittiwake	Rissa tridactyla																		KI			0602
A	Slender-billed Gull	Chroicocephalus genei																		EI	C	R	0585
A	Bonaparte's Gull	C. philadelphia																		ON		R	0581
*A	Black-headed Gull	C. ridibundus																		BH			0582
*A	Little Gull	Hydrocoloeus minutus																		LU	B		0578
A	Ross's Gull	Rhodostethia rosea																		QG		R	0601
*A	Laughing Gull	Larus atricilla																		LF		R	0576
A	Franklin's Gull	L. pipixcan																		FG		R	0577
*A	Mediterranean Gull	L. melanocephalus																		MU	A		0575
A	Audouin's Gull	L. audouinii																				R	0589
B	Great Black-headed Gull	L. ichthyaetus																				R	0573
*A	Common Gull	L. canus																		CM			0590
*A	Ring-billed Gull	L. delawarensis																		IN	B		0588
*A	Lesser Black-backed Gull	L. fuscus																		LB			0591
*A	Herring Gull	L. argentatus																		HG			0592
A	Yellow-legged Gull	L. michahellis																			A		5927
A	Caspian Gull	L. cachinnans																					5927
A	American Herring Gull	L. smithsonianus																				R	26632
*A	Iceland Gull	L. glaucoides																		IG			0598
	Sub total																						

BOU	GULLS Cont, TERNS, AND AUKS		Life list	2013 list	24 hr	Garden	Holiday	Jan	Feb	Mar	Apr	May	Jun	Jul	Aug	Sep	Oct	Nov	Dec				BTO	RBBP	BBRC	EU No
A	Glaucous-winged Gull	L. glaucescens																							R	5960
*A	Glaucous Gull	L. hyperboreus																					GZ	B		0599
*A	Great Black-backed Gull	L. marinus																					GB			0600
A	Aleutian Tern	Onychoprion aleutica																							R	0617
A	Sooty Tern	O. fuscata																							R	0623
A	Bridled Tern	O. anaethetus																							R	0622
*A	Little Tern	Sternula albifrons																					AF	A		0624
A	Gull-billed Tern	Gelochelidon nilotica																					TG	B	R	0605
A	Caspian Tern	Hydroprogne caspia																					CJ		R	0606
*A	Whiskered Tern	Chlidonias hybrida																					WD		R	0626
*A	Black Tern	C. niger																					BJ	C		0627
*A	White-winged Black Tern	C. leucopterus																					WJ			0628
A	Cabot's Tern	Sterna acuflavida																							R	
*A	Sandwich Tern	S. sandvicensis																					TE			0611
A	Royal Tern	S. maxima																					QT		R	0607
A	Lesser Crested Tern	S. bengalensis																					TF	B	R	0609
A	Forster's Tern	S. forsteri																					FO		R	0618
*A	Common Tern	S. hirundo																					CN			0615
*A	Roseate Tern	S. dougallii																					RS	A		0614
*A	Arctic Tern	S. paradisaea																					AE			0616
*A	Guillemot	Uria aalge																					GU			0634
A	Brünnich's Guillemot	U. lomvia																					TZ		R	0635
*A	Razorbill	Alca torda																					RA			0636
B	Great Auk 1 (extinct)	Pinguinus impennis																								
	Sub total																									

BOU	AUKS, DOVES, CUCKOOS AND OWLS		Life list	2013 list	24 hr	Garden	Holiday	Jan	Feb	Mar	Apr	May	Jun	Jul	Aug	Sep	Oct	Nov	Dec		BTO	RBBP	BBRC	EU No
*A	Black Guillemot	Cepphus grylle																			TY			0638
A	Long-billed Murrelet	Brachyramphus perdix																					R	6412
A	Ancient Murrelet	Synthliboramphus antiquus																					R	0645
*A	Little Auk	Alle alle																			LK			0647
*A	Puffin	Fratercula arctica																			PU			0654
A	Tufted Puffin	F. cirrhata																					R	
A	Pallas's Sandgrouse	Syrrhaptes paradoxus																					R	0663
AC4E	Rock Dove / Feral Pigeon	Columba livia																			DV			0665
*A	Stock Dove	C. oenas																			SD			0668
*A	Woodpigeon	C. palumbus																			WP			0670
*A	Collared Dove	Streptopelia decaocto																			CD			0684
*A	Turtle Dove	S. turtur																			TD			0687
A	Rufous Turtle Dove	S. orientalis																					R	0689
A	Mourning Dove	Zenaida macroura																					R	0695
C1E	Ring-necked Parakeet	Psittacula krameri																			RI			0712
A	Great Spotted Cuckoo	Clamator glandarius																			UK		R	0716
*A	Cuckoo	Cuculus canorus																			CK			0724
A	Black-billed Cuckoo	Coccyzus erythrophthalmus																					R	0727
A	Yellow-billed Cuckoo	C. americanus																					R	0728
*A	Barn Owl	Tyto alba																			BO			0735
A	Scops Owl	Otus scops																				C	R	0739
*A	Snowy Owl	Bubo scandiacus																			SO	B	R	0749
A	Hawk Owl	Surnia ulula																					R	0750
*C1	Little Owl	Athene noctua																			LO			0757
	Sub total																							

BOU	OWLS cont. NIGHTJARS, SWIFTS, KINGFISHERS, BEE-EATERS AND WOODPECKERS		Life list	2013 list	24 hr	Garden	Holiday	Jan	Feb	Mar	Apr	May	Jun	Jul	Aug	Sep	Oct	Nov	Dec				BTO	RBBP	BBRC	EU No
*A	Tawny Owl	Strix aluco																					TO			0761
*A	Long-eared Owl	Asio otus																					LE	A		0767
*A	Short-eared Owl	A. flammeus																					SE	A		0768
A	Tengmalm's Owl	Aegolius funereus																							R	0770
*A	Nightjar	Caprimulgus europaeus																					NJ			0778
B	Red-necked Nightjar	C. ruficollis																							R	0779
A	Egyptian Nightjar	C. aegyptius																							R	0781
A	Common Nighthawk	Chordeiles minor																							R	0786
A	Chimney Swift	Chaetura pelagica																							R	0790
A	Needle-tailed Swift	Hirundapus caudacutus																					NI		R	0792
*A	Swift	Apus apus																					SI			0795
A	Pallid Swift	A. pallidus																						C	R	0796
A	Pacific Swift	A. pacificus																							R	0797
A	Alpine Swift	A. melba																					AI			0798
A	Little Swift	A. affinis																							R	0800
*A	Kingfisher	Alcedo atthis																					KF			0831
A	Belted Kingfisher	Megaceryle alcyon																							R	0834
A	Blue-cheeked Bee-eater	Merops persicus																							R	0839
*A	Bee-eater	M. apiaster																					MZ	B		0840
A	Roller	Coracias garrulus																								0841
*A	Hoopoe	Upupa epops																					HP	B		0846
*A	Wryneck	Jynx torquilla																					WY	A		0848
*A	Green Woodpecker	Picus viridis																					G			0856
A	Yellow-bellied Sapsucker	Sphyrapicus varius																							R	0872
	Sub total																									

VIREOS, SHRIKES AND CORVIDS

BOU		Species	Scientific name	Life list	2013 list	24 hr	Garden	Holiday	Jan	Feb	Mar	Apr	May	Jun	Jul	Aug	Sep	Oct	Nov	Dec			BTO	RBBP	BBRC	EU NO
*A	Great Spotted Woodpecker		Dendrocopos major																				GS			0876
*A	Lesser Spotted Woodpecker		D. minor																				LS	A		0887
A	Eastern Phoebe		Sayornis phoebe																						R	0909
A	Yellow-throated Vireo		Vireo flavifrons																						R	1628
A	Philadelphia Vireo		V. philadelphicus																				EV		R	1631
A	Red-eyed Vireo		V. olivaceus																						R	1633
*A	Golden Oriole		Oriolus oriolus																				OL	A		1508
A	Brown Shrike		Lanius cristatus																						R	1513
A	Isabelline Shrike		L. isabellinus																				IL		R	1514
*A	Red-backed Shrike		L. collurio																				ED	A		1515
A	Long-tailed Shrike		L. schach																						R	1517
*A	Lesser Grey Shrike		L. minor																						R	1519
*A	Great Grey Shrike		L. excubitor																				SR	C		1520
A	Southern Grey Shrike		L. meridionalis																						R	1520
A	Woodchat Shrike		L. senator																				OO			1523
A	Masked Shrike		L. nubicus																						R	1524
*A	Chough		Pyrrhocorax pyrrhocorax																				CF	A		1559
*A	Magpie		Pica pica																				MG			1549
*A	Jay		Garrulus glandarius																				J			1539
A	Nutcracker		Nucifraga caryocatactes																				NC		R	1557
*A	Jackdaw		Corvus monedula																				JD			1560
*A	Rook		C. frugilegus																				RO			1563
*A	Carrion Crow		C. corone																				C			1567
*A	Hooded Crow		C. cornix																							1567
	Sub total																									

'CRESTS', TITS, LARKS, MARTINS AND SWALLOWS

BOU	Name	Scientific	Life list	2013 list	24 hr	Garden	Holiday	Jan	Feb	Mar	Apr	May	Jun	Jul	Aug	Sep	Oct	Nov	Dec		BTO	RBBP	BBRC	EU No
*A	Raven	C. corax																			RN			1572
*A	Goldcrest	Regulus regulus																			GC			1314
*A	Firecrest	R. ignicapilla																			FC	A		1315
A	Penduline Tit	Remiz pendulinus																			DT	C	R	1490
*A	Blue Tit	Cyanistes caeruleus																			BT			1462
*A	Great Tit	Parus major																			GT			1464
*A	Crested Tit	Lophophanes cristatus																			CI			1454
*A	Coal Tit	Periparus ater																			CT			1461
*A	Willow Tit	Poecile montana																			WT	A		1442
*A	Marsh Tit	P. palustris																			MT			1440
*A	Bearded Tit	Panurus biarmicus																			BR	A		1364
A	Calandra Lark	Melanocorypha calandra																					R	0961
A	Bimaculated Lark	M. bimaculata																					R	0962
A	White-winged Lark	M. leucoptera																					R	0965
A	Black Lark	M. yeltoniensis																					R	0966
A	Short-toed Lark	Calandrella brachydactyla																			VL			0968
A	Lesser Short-toed Lark	C. rufescens																					R	0970
A	Crested Lark	Galerida cristata																					R	0972
*A	Woodlark	Lullula arborea																			WL	A		0974
*A	Skylark	Alauda arvensis																			S			0976
*A	Shore Lark	Eremophila alpestris																			SX	B		0978
*A	Sand Martin	Riparia riparia																			SM			0981
A	Tree Swallow	Tachycineta bicolor																					R	0983
A	Purple Martin	Progne subis																					R	0989
	Sub total																							

BOU	SWALLOWS Cont, WARBLERS		Life list	2013 list	24 hr	Garden	Holiday	Jan	Feb	Mar	Apr	May	Jun	Jul	Aug	Sep	Oct	Nov	Dec	BTO	RBBP	BBRC	EU NO
A	Crag Martin	Ptyonoprogne rupestris																				R	0991
*A	Swallow	Hirundo rustica																		SL			0992
*A	House Martin	Delichon urbicum																		HM			1001
A	Red-rumped Swallow	Cecropis daurica																		VR	C		0995
A	Cliff Swallow	Petrochelidon pyrrhonota																				R	0998
*A	Cetti's Warbler	Cettia cetti																		CW	A		1220
*A	Long-tailed Tit	Aegithalos caudatus																		LT			1437
A	Eastern Crowned Warbler	Phylloscopus coronatus																				R	12860
A	Green Warbler	P. nitidus																				R	12910
A	Greenish Warbler	P. trochiloides																		NP	C		1293
A	Arctic Warbler	P. borealis																		AP		R	1295
A	Pallas's Warbler	P. proregulus																		PA			1298
*A	Yellow-browed Warbler	P. inornatus																		YB		R	1300
A	Hume's Warbler	P. humei																				R	1300
A	Radde's Warbler	P. schwarzi																					1301
A	Dusky Warbler	P. fuscatus																		UY			1303
A	Western Bonelli's Warbler	P. bonelli																		IW		R	1307
A	Eastern Bonelli's Warbler	P. orientalis																				R	1307
*A	Wood Warbler	P. sibilatrix																		WO			1308
*A	Chiffchaff	P. collybita																		CC			1311
A	Iberian Chiffchaff	P. ibericus																			C	R	1311
*A	Willow Warbler	P. trochilus																		WW			1312
*A	Blackcap	Sylvia atricapilla																		BC			1277
*A	Garden Warbler	S. borin																		GW			1276
	Sub total																						

BOU	WARBLERS Cont		Life list	2013 list	24 hr	Garden	Holiday	Jan	Feb	Mar	Apr	May	Jun	Jul	Aug	Sep	Oct	Nov	Dec		BTO	RBBP	BBRC	EU No
A	Barred Warbler	S. nisoria																			RR			1273
*A	Lesser Whitethroat	S. curruca																			LW			1274
A	Orphean Warbler	S. hortensis																					R	1272
A	Desert Warbler	S. nana																				C	R	1270
*A	Whitethroat	S. communis																			WH			1275
A	Spectacled Warbler	S. conspicillata																				C	R	1264
*A	Dartford Warbler	S. undata																			DW	A		1262
A	Marmora's Warbler	S. sarda																			MM	C	R	1261
A	Rüppell's Warbler	S. rueppelli																					R	1269
A	Subalpine Warbler	S. cantillans																				C		1265
A	Sardinian Warbler	S. melanocephala																				C	R	1267
A	Pallas's Grasshopper Warbler	Locustella certhiola																					R	1233
A	Lanceolated Warbler	L. lanceolata																					R	1235
*A	Grasshopper Warbler	L. naevia																			GH			1236
A	River Warbler	L. fluviatilis																			VW	C	R	1237
A	Savi's Warbler	L. luscinioides																			VI	A	R	1238
A	Thick-billed Warbler	Iduna aedon																					R	1254
A	Booted Warbler	I. caligata																				C	R	1256
A	Sykes's Warbler	I. rama																					R	12562
A	Eastern Olivaceous Warbler	I. pallida																					R	1255
A	Olive-tree Warbler	Hippolais olivetorum																					R	12580
*A	Icterine Warbler	H. icterina																			IC	B		1259
*A	Melodious Warbler	H. polyglotta																			ME	C		1260
A	Aquatic Warbler	Acrocephalus paludicola																			AQ			1242
	Sub total																							

79

BOU	WARBLERS Cont, WAXWNGS, NUTHATCHES, TREECREEPERS AND THRUSHES		Life list	2013 list	24 hr	Garden	Holiday	Jan	Feb	Mar	Apr	May	Jun	Jul	Aug	Sep	Oct	Nov	Dec		BTO	RBBP	BBRC	EU No
*A	Sedge Warbler	A. schoenobaenus																			SW			1243
A	Paddyfield Warbler	A. agricola																			PY		R	1247
A	Blyth's Reed Warbler	A. dumetorum																				C	R	1248
*A	Marsh Warbler	A. palustris																			MW	A		1250
*A	Reed Warbler	A. scirpaceus																			RW			1251
A	Great Reed Warbler	A. arundinaceus																			QW	C	R	1253
A	Fan-tailed Warbler	Cisticola juncidis																					R	1226
A	Cedar Waxwing	Bombycilla cedrorum																					R	1046
*A	Waxwing	B. garrulus																			WX	C		1048
A	Wallcreeper	Tichodroma muraria																					R	1482
A	Red-breasted Nuthatch	Sitta canadensis																					R	1472
*A	Nuthatch	S. europaea																			NH			1479
*A	Treecreeper	Certhia familiaris																			TC			1486
A	Short-toed Treecreeper	C. brachydactyla																			TH	C	R	1487
*A	Wren	Troglodytes troglodytes																			WR			1066
A	Northern Mockingbird	Mimus polyglottos																					R	1067
A	Brown Thrasher	Toxostoma rufum																					R	1069
A	Grey Catbird	Dumetella carolinensis																					R	1080
*A	Starling	Sturnus vulgaris																			SG			1582
A	Rose-coloured Starling	S. roseus																			OE			1594
*A	Dipper	Cinclus cinclus																			DI			1050
A	White's Thrush	Zoothera dauma																					R	1170
A	Varied Thrush	Ixoreus naevius																			VT		R	1172
A	Wood Thrush	Hylocichla mustelina																					R	1175
	Sub total																							

BOU	THRUSHES Cont, CHATS		Life list	2013 list	24 hr	Garden	Holiday	Jan	Feb	Mar	Apr	May	Jun	Jul	Aug	Sep	Oct	Nov	Dec	BTO	RBBP	BBRC	EU No
A	Hermit Thrush	Catharus guttatus																				R	1176
A	Swainson's Thrush	C. ustulatus																				R	1177
A	Grey-cheeked Thrush	C. minimus																				R	1178
A	Veery	C. fuscescens																				R	1179
A	Siberian Thrush	Geokichla sibirica																		RZ		R	1171
*A	Ring Ouzel	Turdus torquatus																		B			1186
*A	Blackbird	T. merula																					1187
A	Eyebrowed Thrush	T. obscurus																				R	1195
A	Dusky Thrush	T. eunomus																				R	1196
A	Naumann's Thrush	T. naumanni																				R	11960
A	Black-throated Thrush	T. atrogularis																				R	1197
A	Red-throated Thrush	T. ruficollis																				R	11970
*A	Fieldfare	T. pilaris																		FF	A		1198
*A	Song Thrush	T. philomelos																		ST			1200
*A	Redwing	T. iliacus																		RE	A		1201
*A	Mistle Thrush	T. viscivorus																		M			1202
A	American Robin	T. migratorius																		AR		R	1203
A	Rufous Bush Chat	Cercotrichas galactotes																				R	1095
A	Brown Flycatcher	Muscicapa dauurica																				R	
*A	Spotted Flycatcher	M. striata																					1335
*A	Robin	Erithacus rubecula																		R			1099
A	Siberian Blue Robin	Larvivora cyane																				R	1112
A	Rufous-tailed Robin	Luscinia sibilans																				R	1102
A	Siberian Rubythroat	L. calliope																				R	1105
	Sub total																						

81

CHATS, FLYCATCHERS AND WHEATEARS

BOU	Name	Scientific	Life list	2013 list	24 hr	Garden	Holiday	Jan	Feb	Mar	Apr	May	Jun	Jul	Aug	Sep	Oct	Nov	Dec				BTO	RBBP	BBRC	EU No
A	White-throated Robin	*Irania gutturalis*																							R	1117
A	Red-flanked Bluetail	*Tarsiger cyanurus*																							R	1113
A	Thrush Nightingale	*L. luscinia*																					FN	C	R	1103
*A	Nightingale	*L. megarhynchos*																					N			1104
A	Bluethroat	*L. svecica*																					BU	B		1106
*A	Red-breasted Flycatcher	*Ficedula parva*																					FY			1343
A	Taiga Flycatcher	*F. albicilla*																							R	1343
A	Collared Flycatcher	*F. albicollis*																							R	1348
*A	Pied Flycatcher	*F. hypoleuca*																					PF			1349
*A	Black Redstart	*Phoenicurus ochruros*																					BX	A		1121
*A	Redstart	*P. phoenicurus*																					RT			1122
A	Moussier's Redstart	*P. moussieri*																							R	1127
A	Rock Thrush	*Monticola saxatilis*																					OH		R	1162
A	Blue Rock Thrush	*M. solitarius*																							R	1166
*A	Whinchat	*Saxicola rubetra*																					WC			1137
A	Siberian Stonechat	*S. maurus*																							R	
*A	Stonechat	*S. torquatus*																					SC			1139
A	Isabelline Wheatear	*Oenanthe isabellina*																							R	1144
*A	Wheatear	*O. oenanthe*																					W			1146
*A	Pied Wheatear	*O. pleschanka*																					PI		R	1147
A	Black-eared Wheatear	*O. hispanica*																							R	1148
A	Desert Wheatear	*O. deserti*																							R	1149
A	White-crowned Black Wheatear	*O. leucopyga*																							R	1157
*A	Dunnock	*Prunella modularis*																					D			1084
	Sub total																									

BOU	SPARROWS, WAGTAILS, PIPITS AND FINCHES		Life list	2013 list	24 hr	Garden	Holiday	Jan	Feb	Mar	Apr	May	Jun	Jul	Aug	Sep	Oct	Nov	Dec				BTO	RBBP	BBRC	EU No
A	**Alpine Accentor**	*P. collaris*																							R	1094
*A	**House Sparrow**	*Passer domesticus*																					HS			1591
A	**Spanish Sparrow**	*P. hispaniolensis*																							R	1592
*A	**Tree Sparrow**	*P. montanus*																					TS			1598
A	**Rock Sparrow**	*Petronia petronia*																							R	1604
*A	**Yellow Wagtail**	*Motacilla flava*																					YW			1017
A	**Citrine Wagtail**	*M. citreola*																						C	R	1018
*A	**Grey Wagtail**	*M. cinerea*																					GL			1019
*A	**Pied White Wagtail**	*M. alba*																					PW			1020
A	**Richard's Pipit**	*Anthus richardi*																					PR			1002
A	**Blyth's Pipit**	*A. godlewskii*																							R	1004
A	**Tawny Pipit**	*A. campestris*																					TI			1005
A	**Olive-backed Pipit**	*A. hodgsoni*																					OV		R	1008
*A	**Tree Pipit**	*A. trivialis*																					TP			1009
A	**Pechora Pipit**	*A. gustavi*																							R	1010
*A	**Meadow Pipit**	*A. pratensis*																					MP			1011
A	**Red-throated Pipit**	*A. cervinus*																					VP			1012
*A	**Rock Pipit**	*A. petrosus*																					RC			1014
*A	**Water Pipit**	*A. spinoletta*																					WI			1014
A	**Buff-bellied Pipit**	*A. rubescens*																							R	1014
*A	**Chaffinch**	*Fringilla coelebs*																					CH			1636
*A	**Brambling**	*F. montifringilla*																					BL	B		1638
*A	**Serin**	*Serinus serinus*																					NS	B		1640
*A	**Greenfinch**	*Carduelis chloris*																					GR			1649
	Sub total																									

FINCHES AND NEW WORLD BUNTINGS

BOU	Name	Scientific	Life list	2013 list	24 hr	Garden	Holiday	Jan	Feb	Mar	Apr	May	Jun	Jul	Aug	Sep	Oct	Nov	Dec			BTO	RBBP	BBRC	EU No
A	Citril Finch	C. citrinella																						R	1653
*A	Goldfinch	C. carduelis																				GO			1654
*A	Siskin	C. spinus																				SK			1660
*A	Linnet	C. cannabina																				LI			1662
*A	Twite	C. flavirostris																				TW			1663
*A	Lesser Redpoll	C. cabaret																				LR			1663
*A	Mealy Redpoll	C. flammea																					A		1663
A	Arctic Redpoll	C. hornemanni																				AL			1664
*A	Two-barred Crossbill	Loxia leucoptera																				PD		R	1665
*A	Common Crossbill	L. curvirostra																				CR			1666
*A	Scottish Crossbill	L. scotica																				CY			1667
*A	Parrot Crossbill	L. pytyopsittacus																				PC	A		1668
A	Trumpeter Finch	Bucanetes githagineus																						R	1676
*A	Common Rosefinch	Carpodacus erythrinus																				SQ	B		1679
A	Pine Grosbeak	Pinicola enucleator																						R	1699
*A	Bullfinch	Pyrrhula pyrrhula																				BF			1710
*A	Hawfinch	Coccothraustes coccothraustes																				HF	A		1717
A	Evening Grosbeak	Hesperiphona vespertina																						R	1718
*A	Snow Bunting	Plectrophenax nivalis																				SB	A		1850
A	Lapland Bunting	Calcarius lapponicus																				LA	B		1847
A	Summer Tanager	Piranga rubra																						R	1786
A	Scarlet Tanager	P. olivacea																						R	1788
A	Rose-breasted Grosbeak	Pheucticus ludovicianus																						R	1887
A	Indigo Bunting	Passerina cyanea																						R	1892
	Sub total																								

BOU	NEW WORLD SPARROWS AND BUNTINGS		Life list	2013 list	24 hr	Garden	Holiday	Jan	Feb	Mar	Apr	May	Jun	Jul	Aug	Sep	Oct	Nov	Dec		BTO	RBBP	BBRC	EU No
A	Eastern Towhee	Pipilo erythrophthalmus																					R	1798
A	Lark Sparrow	Chondestes grammacus																					R	1824
A	Savannah Sparrow	Passerculus sandwichensis																					R	1826
A	Song Sparrow	Melospiza melodia																					R	1835
A	White-crowned Sparrow	Zonotrichia leucophrys																					R	1839
A	White-throated Sparrow	Z. albicollis																					R	1840
A	Dark-eyed Junco	Junco hyemalis																			JU		R	1842
A	Black-faced Bunting	Emberiza spodocephala																					R	1853
A	Pine Bunting	E. leucocephalos																			EL		R	1856
*A	Yellowhammer	E. citrinella																			Y			1857
*A	Cirl Bunting	E. cirlus																			CL	A		1958
A	Rock Bunting	E. cia																					R	1860
A	Ortolan Bunting	E. hortulana																			OB			1866
A	Cretzschmar's Bunting	E. caesia																					R	1868
A	Yellow-browed Bunting	E. chrysophrys																					R	1871
A	Rustic Bunting	E. rustica																						1873
A	Chestnut-eared Bunting	E. fucata																					R	1869
A	Little Bunting	E. pusilla																			LJ			1874
A	Yellow-breasted Bunting	E. aureola																				C	R	1876
*A	Reed Bunting	E. schoeniclus																			RB			1877
A	Pallas's Reed Bunting	E. pallasi																					R	1878
A	Black-headed Bunting	E. melanocephala																					R	1881
*A	Corn Bunting	E. calandra																			CB			1882
A	Bobolink	Dolichonyx oryzivorus																					R	1897
	Sub total																							

NEW WORLD WARBLERS

BOU	NEW WORLD WARBLERS		Life list	2013 list	24 hr	Garden	Holiday	Jan	Feb	Mar	Apr	May	Jun	Jul	Aug	Sep	Oct	Nov	Dec			BTO	RBBP	BBRC	EU No
A	Brown-headed Cowbird	Molothrus ater																						R	1899
A	Baltimore Oriole	Icterus galbula																						R	1918
A	Black-and-white Warbler	Mniotilta varia																						R	1720
A	Golden-winged Warbler	Vermivora chrysoptera																						R	1722
A	Tennessee Warbler	V. peregrina																						R	1724
A	Northern Parula	Parula americana																						R	1732
A	Yellow Warbler	Dendroica petechia																						R	1733
A	Chestnut-sided Warbler	D. pensylvanica																						R	1734
A	Blackburnian Warbler	D. fusca																						R	1747
A	Cape May Warbler	D. tigrina																						R	1749
A	Magnolia Warbler	D. magnolia																						R	1750
A	Yellow-rumped Warbler	D. coronata																						R	1751
A	Blackpoll Warbler	D. striata																						R	1753
A	Bay-breasted Warbler	D. castanea																						R	1754
A	American Redstart	Setophaga ruticilla																					AD		R	1755
A	Ovenbird	Seiurus aurocapilla																						R	1756
A	Northern Waterthrush	S. noveboracensis																						R	1757
A	Common Yellowthroat	Geothlypis trichas																						R	1762
A	Hooded Warbler	Wilsonia citrina																						R	1771
A	Wilson's Warbler	W. pusilla																						R	1772
	Sub total																								

BOU	CATEGORY D & E SPECIES, PLUS SELECTED EUROPEAN SPECIES		Life list	2013 list	24 hr	Garden	Holiday	Jan	Feb	Mar	Apr	May	Jun	Jul	Aug	Sep	Oct	Nov	Dec				BTO	RBBP	BBRC	EU No
D	Ross's Goose	*Anser rossii*																								0181
D	Falcated Duck	*A. falcata*																					FT		R	0183
D	Baikal Teal	*A. formosa*																					IK		R	0195
D	Marbled Duck	*Marmaronetta angustirostris*																							R	0226
EU	White-headed Duck	*Oxyura leucocephala*																					WQ			0357
EU	Rock Partridge	*Alectoris graeca*																								0359
EU	Barbary Partridge	*A. barbara*																								0082
EU	Pygmy Cormorant	*P. pygmeus*																								0088
D	Great White Pelican	*Pelecanus onocrotalus*																					YP		R	0089
EU	Dalmatian Pelican	*P. crispus*																								0147
D	Greater Flamingo	*Phoenicopterus roseus*																					FL		R	0235
EU	Black-winged Kite	*Elanus caeruleus*																								0244
D	Bald Eagle	*H. leucocephalus*																							R	0246
EU	Lammergeier	*Gypaetus barbatus*																								0255
D	Black (Monk) Vulture	*Aegypius monachus*																							R	0273
EU	Levant Sparrowhawk	*A. brevipes*																								0288
EU	Long-legged Buzzard	*B. rufinus*																								0292
EU	Lesser Spotted Eagle	*Aquila pomarina*																								0295
EU	Imperial Eagle	*A. heliaca*																								0298
EU	Booted Eagle	*Hieraaetus pennatus*																								0299
EU	Bonelli's Eagle	*H. fasciatus*																								0314
EU	Lanner Falcon	*Falco biarmicus*																					FB			0316
D	Saker Falcon	*F. cherrug*																					JF		R	0400
EU	Andalusian Hemipode	*Turnix sylvatica*																								
	Sub total																									

BOU	CATEGORY D & E SPECIES, PLUS SELECTED EUROPEAN SPECIES		Life list	2013 list	24 hr	Garden	Holiday	Jan	Feb	Mar	Apr	May	Jun	Jul	Aug	Sep	Oct	Nov	Dec				BTO	RBBP	BBRC	EU No
EU	Purple Gallinule	*Porphyrio porphyrio*																								0427
EL	Crested Coot	*F. cristata*																								0431
EU	Spur-winged Plover	*Hoplopterus spinosus*																					UW			0487
EU	Black-bellied Sandgrouse	*Pterocles orientalis*																								0661
EU	Pin-tailed Sandgrouse	*P. alchata*																								0662
EU	Eagle Owl	*Bubo bubo*																					EO			0744
EU	Pygmy Owl	*Glaucidium passerinum*																						bD		0751
EU	Ural Owl	*S. uralensis*																								0765
EU	Great Grey Owl	*S. nebulosa*																								0766
EL	White-rumped Swift	*Apus caffer*																								0799
EU	Grey-headed Woodpecker	*Picus canus*																								0855
EU	Black Woodpecker	*Dryocopus martius*																								0863
EU	Syrian Woodpecker	*D. syriacus*																								0878
EU	Middle Spotted Woodpecker	*D. medius*																								0883
EU	White-backed Woodpecker	*D. leucotos*																								0884
EU	Three-toed Woodpecker	*Picoides tridactylus*																								0898
EU	Dupont's Lark	*Chersophilus duponti*																								0959
EU	Thekla Lark	*G. theklae*																								0973
EU	Black Wheatear	*Oenanthe leucura*																							R	1158
EU	Cyprus Warbler	*S. melanothorax*																								1268
D	Mugimaki Flycatcher	*F. mugimaki*																							R	1344
EU	Semi-collared Flycatcher	*F. semitorquata*																								1347
EU	Sombre Tit	*P. lugubris*																								1441
EU	Siberian Tit	*P. cinctus*																								1448
	Sub total																									

BOU	CATEGORY D & E SPECIES, PLUS SELECTED EUROPEAN SPECIES		Life list	2013 list	24 hr	Garden	Holiday	Jan	Feb	Mar	Apr	May	Jun	Jul	Aug	Sep	Oct	Nov	Dec							BTO	RBBP	BBRC	EU No
EU	Krüper's Nuthatch	Sitta krueperi																											1469
EU	Corsican Nuthatch	S. whiteheadi																											1470
EU	Rock Nuthatch	S. neumayer																											1481
EU	Siberian Jay	Perisoreus infaustus																											1543
EU	Azure-winged Magpie	Cyanopica cyana																											1547
EU	Alpine Chough	Pyrrhocorax graculus																											1558
D	Daurian Starling	Sturnus sturninus																										R	1579
EU	Spotless Starling	S. unicolor																											1583
D	(White-winged) Snow Finch	Montifringilla nivalis																										R	1611
D	Palm Warbler	D. palmarum																										R	1752
D	Yellow-headed Blackbird	Xanthocephalus xanthocephalus																											1911
EU	Cinereous Bunting	E. cineracea																											1865
D	Chestnut Bunting	E. rutila																										R	1875
D	Red-headed Bunting	E. bruniceps																											1880
D	Blue Grosbeak	Guiraca caerulea																										R	1891
	Sub total																											

BRITISH DRAGONFLY LIST

SPECIES	2013 list	Life list
DAMSELFLIES		
Calopterygidae (Demoiselles)		
Banded Demoiselle		
Beautiful Demoiselle		
Coenagrionidae (Blue, blue-tailed & red damselflies)		
Small Red Damselfly		
Northern Damselfly		
Irish Damselfly		
Southern Damselfly		
Azure Damselfly		
Variable Damselfly		
Dainty Damselfly		
Common Blue Damselfly		
Red-eyed Damselfly		
Small Red-eyed Damselfly		
Blue-tailed Damselfly		
Scarce Blue-tailed Damselfly		
Large Red Damselfly		
Lestidae (Emerald damselflies)		
Southern Emerald Damselfly		
Scarce Emerald Damselfly		
Emerald Damselfly		
Willow Emerald Damselfly		
Winter Damselfly		
Platycnemididae (White-legged damselflies)		
White-legged Damselfly		
DRAGONFLIES		
Aeshnidae (Hawkers and Emperors)		
Southern Migrant Hawker		
Azure Hawker		
Southern Hawker		
Brown Hawker		
Norfolk Hawker		

SPECIES	2013 list	Life list
Common Hawker		
Migrant Hawker		
Vagrant Emperor		
Emperor Dragonfly		
Lesser Emperor		
Hairy Dragonfly		
Cordulegastridae (Golden-ringed Dragonflies)		
Golden-ringed Dragonfly		
Corduliidae (Emerald dragonflies)		
Downy Emerald		
Northern Emerald		
Brilliant Emerald		
Gomphidae (Club-tailed Dragonflies)		
Common Club-tail		
Libellulidae (Chasers, Skimmers and Darters)		
Scarlet Darter		
White-faced Darter		
Broad-bodied Chaser		
Scarce Chaser		
Four-spotted Chaser		
Black-tailed Skimmer		
Keeled Skimmer		
Wandering Glider		
Black Darter		
Vagrant Darter		
Yellow-winged Darter		
Red-veined Darter		
Banded Darter		
Ruddy Darter		
Common Darter		
TOTAL		

90

COMMON BRITISH BUTTERFLIES LIST

SPECIES	2013 list	Life list
Hesperiidae - Skippers		
Chequered Skipper		
Lulworth Skipper		
Essex Skipper		
Small Skipper		
Silver-spotted Skipper		
Large Skipper		
Grizzled Skipper		
Dingy Skipper		
Papilionidae		
Swallowtail		
Pieridae - The Whites		
Wood White		
Clouded Yellow		
Brimstone		
Large White		
Small White		
Green-veined White		
Orange Tip		
Lycaenidae - Hairstreaks, Coppers and Blues		
Green Hairstreak		
Brown Hairstreak		
Purple Hairstreak		
White-letter Hairstreak		
Black Hairstreak		
Large Copper		
Small Copper		
Small Blue		
Silver-studded Blue		
Northern Brown Argus		
Brown Argus		
Common Blue		
Chalkhill Blue		
Adonis Blue		
Holly Blue		

SPECIES	2013 list	Life list
Large Blue		
Riodinidae - Metalmarks		
Duke of Burgundy		
Nymphalidae - Vanessids, Emperors and Fritillaries		
White Admiral		
Purple Emperor		
Painted Lady		
Small Tortoiseshell		
Red Admiral		
Peacock		
Comma		
Small Pearl-bordered Fritillary		
Pearl-bordered Fritillary		
High Brown Fritillary		
Dark Green Fritillary		
Silver-washed Fritillary		
Marsh Fritillary		
Glanville Fritillary		
Heath Fritillary		
Satyridae - The Browns		
Speckled Wood		
Wall		
Scotch Argus		
Mountain Ringlet		
Gate Keeper		
Marbled White		
Grayling		
Meadow Brown		
Ringlet		
Small Heath		
Large Heath		
TOTAL		

LOG CHARTS

91

Best Birdwatching Sites

The trusted name for accurate, accessible site information

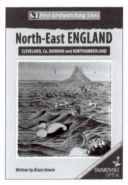

Best Birdwatching Sites: North-East England
by Brian Unwin.
Features 17 birding sites in Cleveland; 37 sites in Co Durham and 42 sites in Northumberland. 308 pp. **Price £17.95**

Best Birdwatching Sites: Dorset by Neil Gartshore.
Features 65 reserves and birding areas, including a full range of habitats from heathland to coastal sites.
248 pp. **Price £17.95**

Best Birdwatching Sites: The Solway
by John Miles.
Features 76 birding sites in Cumbria and 84 in Dumfries & Galloway. 260 pp. **Price £17.50**

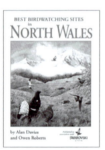

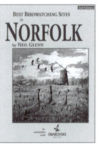

Best Birdwatching Sites in Cornwall & Scilly
by Sara McMahon and Nigel Hudson. Features 52 mainland sites, plus seven routes around the key islands of Scilly. 208pp. **Price: £17.50 15.00**

Best Birdwatching Sites in North Wales
by Alan Davies and Owen Roberts. Features 58 major sites in Gwynedd and Clwyd, plus 11 smaller birding spots around Wrexham. 192pp. **Price: £15.95**

Best Birdwatching Sites in Norfolk
(2nd Edition) by Neil Glenn. Contains 83 sites (ten more than 1st Edition) – all information updated. 256pp.
Price: £16.95.

Best Birdwatching Sites in the Scottish Highlands
by Gordon Hamlett. Features 22 birding routes from John O'Groats to Pitlochry. 164 maps, 240pp.
Price: £15.95

For details of latest special offers on our books please contact Buckingham Press, 55 Thorpe Park Road, Peterborough PE3 6LJ. 01733 561 739; or visit www.buckinghampress.co.uk (see entry on page 109).

DIRECTORY OF ARTISTS, PHOTOGRAPHERS AND LECTURERS

David Cromack

The colourful birds of North America, such as this Green-winged Towhee, feature in several of the talks on offer from speakers in the Directory of Lecturers.

ART/PHOTOGRAPHY/LECTURERS

DIRECTORY OF WILDLIFE ART GALLERIES

BIRDSCAPES GALLERY
Offers top quality bird art all year round, plus landscapes and other wildlife originals, sculptures, prints, wildlife art books and cards. More than 50 regular artists, including SWLA members, are represented, with new exhibitions each month.
Opening times: Mon-Sat, (10am-5pm), Sunday, (10am-4pm). The gallery may be closed for part of the day before a new exhibition.
Address: The BIRDscapes Gallery, Manor Farm Barns, Glandford, Holt, Norfolk. NR25 7JP. 01263 741 742; e-mail: art@birdscapes.co.uk
www.birdscapesgallery.co.uk

NATURE IN ART
The world's first museum dedicated exclusively to art inspired by nature. The collection spans 1,500 years, covers 60 countries and includes work by Tunnicliffe, Harrison, Thorburn, Scott and other bird artists. See work being created by artists in residence (see website for dates), plus a vibrant exhibitions programme. Sculpture garden, coffee shop, gift shop and children's activity areas.
Opening times: 10am-5pm (Tuesday to Sunday and bank holidays). Admission £5.25 (adults), £15 (family), under-8s free.
Address: Wallsworth Hall, Twigworth, Gloucester GL2 9PA (two miles N of city on A38). 01452 731 422. e-mail: enquiries@nature-in-art.org.uk
www.nature-in-art.org.uk

THE WILDLIFE ART GALLERY
Opened in 1988 as a specialist in 20th Century and contemporary wildlife art. It exhibits work by many of the leading European wildlife artists, both painters and sculptors, and has published several wildlife books.
Opening times: Mon-Sat (10am-4.30pm) and Sun (2pm-4.30pm).
Address: 98/99 High Street, Lavenham, Suffolk CO10 9PZ; 01787 248 562; (Fax) 01787 247 356.
E-mail: info@wildlifeartgallery.com
www.wildlifeartgallery.com

DIRECTORY OF WILDLIFE ARTISTS

ALLEN, Richard
Watercolour paintings, sketches and illustrations of birds, wildlife, flowers and landscapes, mainly based on extensive field sketching. Book work includes: *Sunbirds* (Helm) and *Guide to Birds of SE Asia* (New Holland). Also stamp designs for The Solomons, Ascencion Island and Kiribati and in RSPB *Birds* magazine.
Artwork for sale: Watercolour paintings, limited edition prints, original cover paintings from *Birding World* and header illustrations from *British Birds*. See website for details.
Address: 34 Parkwood Avenue, Wivenhoe, Essex, CO7 9AN; 01206 826 753.
E-mail: richard@richardallen31.wanadoo.co.uk
www.richardallenillustrator.com

DAVIS, John
Paintings and illustrations of many wildlife subjects and landscapes. Published work includes a new book from Langford Press: *Beyond the Plough*, illustrations for the new Buckingham Press title: *Best Birdwatching Sites: Dorset*, regular illustrations for RSPB's *Birdlife Magazine*. Member of SWLA since 1987 and exhibits at their annual exhibition at the Mall Galleries.
Formats: Paints in oils, acrylics and watercolour.
Exhibitions for 2013: Wildfowl and Wetlands centre at Slimbridge in Sept.
Artwork for sale: Commissions accepted.
Address: 6 Redmoor, Birdham, West Sussex PO20 7HS; 01243 512 351;
e-mail: johndavis.wildlife@tiscali.co.uk

DEMAIN, Michael
Started painting in 1992, turning professional in 1998. In his spare time he helps the RSPB, monitoring breeding raptors in the Bowland Fells.
Artwork for sale: A selection of Acrylic and Oil paintings and limited edition prints
Exhibitions for 2013: CLA Game Fair, Bird Fair, Rutland Water, NEWA,
Address: 175 Richmond Road, Accrington, Lancs BB5 0JB; 01254 237 378;
e-mail: mdemainwildart@aol.com
www.michaeldemainwildlifeart.co.uk

GARNER FRSA, Jackie
Professional wildlife artist specialising in original paintings based on field sketches. Current projects: *The Wildlife Artist's Handbook*, illustrations for research project on Egyptian wildlife. *Bird Art & Photography* contributor, Aigas Field Centre tutor.
Formats: Acrylics, watercolours, sketches, illustrations.
Exhibitions for 2013: Group exhibitions (SWLA,

NEWA etc) & book launches. See website for details
Artwork for sale: Originals, limited edition prints, cards, puzzles. See website for latest availability. Commissions accepted.
Address: The Old Cider House Studio, Humphries End, Randwick, Stroud, Glos GL6 6EW; 01453 847 420; (M)07800 804 847.
e-mail: artist@jackiegarner.co.uk
www.jackiegarner.co.uk

GRIFFITHS, Ian
Birds and their habitat is the main subject matter for Griff's paintings. Having lived throughout the UK and travelled widely around the world, he has a wealth of field experience to draw upon. In 2011 he was a winner in the *BBC Wildlife* artist of the year competition and runner-up in 2012.
Subjects: Mainly birds in various mediums.
Exhibitions for 2013: Lost Gardens of Heligan. His own studio/gallery.
Artwork for sale: Commissions considered and through his website.
Address: Griff's wildlife studio, Creftow, 6 Church Street, Helston, Cornwall TR13 8TG; 07971 678 464.
e-mail: mail@artbygriff.com www.artbygriff.com

LEAHY, Ernest
Original watercolours and drawings of Western Palearctic birds, wildlife and country scenes. Also paints British mammals and butterflies. Illustrations for many publications including Poysers. Commissions accepted and enquiries welcome. See website for available artwork.
Formats: Wide range of framed and unframed originals available. E-mail for details of current work available and for quotations on commissioned work.
Artwork for sale: See www.flickr.com/photos/ernsbirdart for latest work.
Address: 32 Ben Austins, Redbourn, Herts, AL3 7DR; 01582 793 144; e-mail: ernest.leahy@ntlworld.com
www.flickr.com/photos/ernsbirdart

MILLER, David
Based in West Wales, David is best known for his underwater paintings of game, sea and coarse fish and he has provided images for the UK rod licence over the past few years. He also specialises in sea-birds and waders and regularly exhibits at both the Birdfair and BIRDscapes Gallery, Glandford, Norfolk.
Subjects: British fish, coastal birds and wildlife mostly in oils. Some mixed media.
Exhibitions for 2013: Wildlife & Sporting Art Exhibition at The Jerram Gallery, Sherbourne, Dorset (March 2-20). Visit David's website for events and exhibitions later in the year.
Artwork for sale: A selection of original oils and prints of British wildlife, fish and birds are available to buy on the website. Commissions available.
Address: Nyth-Gwdi-Hw, New Mill, St Clears, Carmarthenshire SA33 4HY; 01994 453 545; (M)07900 825 404; e-mail: david@davidmillerart.co.uk
www.davidmillerart.co.uk

POMROY, Jonathan
Lives and works on the edge of the North York Moors. Paintings of birds and landscapes in watercolour and oils, always from field sketches, made on trips across the British Isles. Work always on show at BIRDscapes nr Cley, Norfolk and at Gallery Beyond, Nunnington, North Yorkshire.
Subjects: Wildlife and landscapes.
Exhibitions for 2013: WWT Slimbridge, January 14-February 25; Helmsley Arts Centre, March 12 -April 12; Annual Summer Exhibition at The West Barn, Bradford on Avon June 29-30, CLA Gamefair July 19th - 21, BIRDscapes, Norfolk autumn 2012. See website for more details about these and other exhibitions.
Artwork for sale: Original watercolours and oils at one man exhibitions and from website.
Address: Swift House, Back Lane, Ampleforth, North Yorkshire YO62 4DE; 01439 788 014.
e-mail: jonathan@pomroy.plus.com
www.jonathanpomroy.co.uk

ROSE, Chris
Originals in oils and acrylics of birds and animals in landscapes. Particular interest in painting water and its myriad effects. Limited edition reproductions available. Art book, *In a Natural Light - the Wildlife Art of Chris Rose* published 2005. Illustrated many books including *Grebes of the World* (publ.2002) and *Handbook to the Birds of the World*.
Artwork for sale: Original drawings and paintings, linocuts, illustrations, limited edition reproductions, postcards.
Address: 6 Whitelee Cottages, Newtown St Boswells, Melrose, Scotland TD6 0SH; (Tel/Fax)01835 822 547.
e-mail: chris@chrisrose-artist.co.uk
www.chrisrose-artist.co.uk

SCOTT, Dafila
Trained as a zoologist then studied art under Robin Child at the Lydgate Art Research Centre UK. Has exhibited widely in the UK. Recent work includes both figurative and abstract paintings of wildlife, people and landscape.
Artwork for sale: Media: Oil, acrylics and pastels
Exhibitions for 2013: WWT, Welney, March 2013, SWLA, Mall Galleries 2013
Address: White Roses, The Hythe, Reach, Cambridgeshire, CB5 0JQ; www.dafilascott.co.uk
e-mail: dafilascott@yahoo.co.uk

THRELFALL, John
Member of the Society of Wildlife Artists. Swarovski/ *Birdwatch* Bird Artist of the Year 2007. Award-winner at the NEWA 2001, 2004, 2006 exhibitions. BIRDscapes Gallery award 2007.
Formats: Paintings in acrylic or pastel.
Artwork for sale: Contact artist.
Address: Saltflats Cottage, Rockcliffe, Dalbeattie, Kirkcudbrightshire DG5 4QQ; 01556 630 262.
e-mail: john@johnthrelfall.co.uk
www.johnthrelfall.co.uk

ART/PHOTOGRAPHY/LECTURERS

WARREN, Michael
Member of Society of Wildlife Artists (treasurer). President of Nottinghamshire Birdwatchers. His latest book *American Birding Sketchbook* was published by Langford Press in 2012.
Exhibitions for 2013: Will exhibit at Rutland Birdfair in August, and Society of Wildlife Artists in October - See website for more information during year.

Artwork for sale: Original watercolour paintings of birds, all based on field observations. Books, calendars, cards and commissions welcomed.
Address: The Laurels, The Green, Winthorpe, Nottinghamshire, NG24 2NR; 01636 673 554.
e-mail: mike.warren@tiscali.co.uk
www.mikewarren.co.uk

DIRECTORY OF WILDLIFE PHOTOGRAPHERS

ALMOND, Jim
Bird Photographer with additional interest in butterflies and odonata.
Subjects: All UK birds, special interest in wild Peregrines. See website for main interests, gallery and portfolio.
Products and services: Images for publication, lectures and workshops / individual tuition available. Vast library of images. Available for commissions, lectures / tours. Competitive terms for larger projects.
Address: 5 Coolock Close, St Peters Park, Shrewsbury SY3 9QD; 07940 678 719;
e-mail: almond.jim@virgin.net
http://shropshirebirder.co.uk/

BASTON, Bill
Photographer, lecturer.
Subjects: East Anglian rarities and common birds, Mediterranean birds and landscapes, UK wildlife and landscapes, Northern Greece & Western Turkey, Spain, Goa, general wildlife photography, The Gambia, Northern India (birds and tigers), Costa Rica, North East India and the Himalayan foothills.
Products and services: Prints, slides, digital, mounted/unmounted.
Address: 86 George Street, Hadleigh, Ipswich, IP7 5BU; 01473 827 062; www.billbaston.com
e-mail: billbaston@btinternet.com

BEJARANO, Santiago
An Ecuadorean naturalist and wildlife photographer who worked in the Galapagos for almost two decades, with a great depth of knowledge and unique insight into these remarkable islands and their wildlife.
Subjects: Flora and fauna of Galapagos Islands and birds of Ecuador.
Products and services: Prints and posters of the wildlife of the Galapagos Islands and birds of Ecuador. Introductory classes to wildlife photography, including digital and basic Photoshop® techniques.
Address: 25 Trinity Lane, Beverley, East Yorkshire HU17 0DY; 01482 872 716; www.thinkgalapagos.com
e-mail: info@thinkgalapagos.com

BELL, Graham
Professional ornithologist, photographer, author, cruise lecturer worldwide.
Subjects: Birds, animals, flowers, landscapes, all seven continents, from Arctic to Antarctic.....
Products and services: Original slides for sale, £2 each. Lecture: 'Taking Better Photos'.
Address: Ros View, South Yearle, Wooler, Northumberland, NE71 6RB; 01668 281310.
e-mail: seabirdsdgb@hotmail.com

BROADBENT, David
Professional photographer.
Subjects: UK birds and wild places.
Products and services: All-new website features a fully searchable picture library of UK wildlife and landscapes to the editorial market; lectures and photo training days; print sales and gallery art prints.
Address: Based in the Forest of Dean. 07771 664 973.
e-mail: info@davidbroadbent.com
www.davidbroadbent.com

BROOKS, Richard
Guided birding and wildlife photographer.
Subjects: Owls (Barn especially), raptors, Kingfisher and a variety of European birds (Lesvos especially) and landscapes. Limited edition calendars available.
Products and services: Mounted and unmounted computer prints (6x4 to A3+ size), framed pictures, A5 greetings cards, surplus slides for sale. Norfolk bird calendar available (see website).
Address: 24 Croxton Hamlet, Fulmodeston, Fakenham, Norfolk, NR21 0NP; 01328 878 632.
e-mail: email@richard-brooks.co.uk
www.richard-brooks.co.uk

BUCKINGHAM, John
Worldwide bird and wildlife photographer.
Subjects: Huge range of birds, botany and wildlife in UK and Europe, plus great coverage from Africa, Americas, Australia and worldwide.
Products and services: Original slides for lectures and personal use.
Address: 3 Cardinal Close, Tonbridge, Kent, TN9 2EN; (Tel/fax) 01732 354 970.
e-mail: john.birdtalk@btinternet.com

DIRECTORY OF WILDLIFE PHOTOGRAPHERS

COSTER, Bill
Professional wildlife photographer, writer and photographic tour leader, author of the books *'Creative Bird Photography'* and *'Creative Nature Photography'*, published by New Holland.
Subjects: Wildlife and landscape from around the world.
Products and services: Images for publication, prints for sale. See my website for details. Stunning new digital shows (see Directory of Lecturers).
Address: 15-17 Elm Road, South Woodham Ferrers, Chelmsford, Essex CM3 5QB; 01245 320 066.
e-mail: billcoster@hotmail.com www.billcoster.com

DUGGAN, Glenn
Specialist in tropical birding.
Subjects: Tropical birds, Trogons, Tanagers, Birds of Paradise.
Address: 25 Hampton Grove, Fareham, Hampshire, PO15 5NL; 01329 845 976, (M)07771 605 320.
e-mail: glenn.m.duggan@ntlworld.com
www.birdlectures.com

GALVIN, Chris
A birding photographer with passion for birds for more than 30 years.
Subjects: Birds.
Products and services: Images for publication, prints, mounted prints, commissions considered.
Address: 17 Henley Road, Allerton, Liverpool, Merseyside L18 2DN; 07802 428 385 or 0151 729 0123.
e-mail: chris@chrisgalvinphoto.com
www.chrisgalvinphoto.com

LANE, Mike
Wildlife photographer and lecturer.
Subjects: Birds and wildlife from around the world, also landscapes and the environment.
Products and services: Website with instantly downloadable online pictures. Talks and workshops.
Address: 36 Berkeley Road, Shirley, Solihull, West Midlands B90 2HS; 0121 744 7988; (M)07766 418 013;
e-mail: mikelane@nature-photography.co.uk
www.nature-photography.co.uk

LENTON, Graham
PhD Ornithology/Ecology. Former lecturer at Oxford University and Oxford Brookes University. Lifetime photographer of wildlife — publications of articles and photographs of birds and wildlife.
Subjects: Worldwide birds, mammals of Africa, wildlife, worldwide travel.
Products and services: Photos available for sale or reproduction.
Address: The Old School, 25A Standlake Road, Ducklington, Witney, Oxon OX29 7UR; 01993 899 033.
e-mail: grahamlenton@btopenworld.com
www.gml-art.co.uk

LINGARD, David
Wildlife photographer, retired from RAF, now UK delegate to LIPU (BirdLife in Italy).
Subjects: Birds and views of places visited around the world.

Products and services: 35mm transparencies (last Century) but now, exclusively digital images.
Address: Fernwood, Doddington Road, Whisby, Lincs LN6 9BX; 01522 689 030; e-mail: mail@lipu-uk.org
www.lipu-uk.org

MAGENNIS, Steve
Steve Magennis Wildlife Photography, wildlife photographer, lecturer and workshop leader, *British Wildlife* Photography Awards 2012 Highly Commended image.
Subjects: British wildlife, bird life and landscapes.
Products and services: Commisioned photography, image library, framed and mounted prints, mounted prints (various sizes), greetings cards (cards can be personalised with personal or company details) and photo keyrings. Photographic workshops, (half-day, full-day and holidays).
Address: 3 Chepstow Close, St James, Northampton, Northants, NN5 7EB; 01604 467 848; (M)07803 619 272; e-mail: photos@stevemagennis.co.uk
www.stevemagennis.co.uk

MARTIN, Nick
A keen naturalist with a passion for photography.
Subjects: Wildlife, landscapes plus people and wildlife and environmental themes.
Products and services: Digital images, presentations, written articles and interpretation.
Address: 57 Newton Road, Solihull, West Midlands, B93 9HN; 07810 863 177
e-mail: nick@martinimages.co.uk
www.martinimages.co.uk

NASON, Rebecca
East Anglia-based bird and wildlife photographer.
Subjects: Wildlife photography. Specializing in birds, common and rare, from Suffolk to the Shetland Islands and beyond.
Products and services: Large image stock library. Professionally printed images available, various sizes, mounts and frames from 6 x 4 to A1+. Acrylics, aluminium and canvases, greetings card range.
Address: 8 Angel Lane, Woodbridge, Suffolk IP12 4NG; 01394 385 030; (M)07919 256 386.
e-mail: rebecca@rebeccanason.com
www.rebeccanason.com

NEWTON, Ian
Photographer (ARPS) and lecturer, Chairman York Ornithological Club.
Subjects: Mainly birds and other wildlife of North, Central and South America, Europe and UK.
Products and services: Prints, canvas & board-mounted images etc.
Address: 5 Fairfields Drive, Skelton, York YO30 1YP; 01904 471 446; (M)07976 849 832;
e-mail: iannewton@acsemail.co.uk
www.iannewtonphotography.com

OFFORD, Keith
Photographer, writer, tour leader, conservationist.
Subjects: Raptors, UK wildlife and scenery, birds and other wildlife of USA, Africa, Spain, Australia, India.

ART/PHOTOGRAPHY/LECTURERS

97

DIRECTORY OF LECTURERS

Products and services: Conventional prints, greetings cards, framed pictures.
Address: Yew Tree Farmhouse, Craignant, Selattyn, Nr Oswestry, Shropshire, SY10 7NP; 01691 718 740.
e-mail: keith.offord@virgin.net
www.keithofford.co.uk

PARKER, Susan and Allan ARPS
Professional photographers (ASPphoto - Images of Nature) lecturers and tutors.
Subjects: Birds, plus other flora and fauna from the UK, Spain, Lesvos, Cyprus, Florida and Texas.
Products and services: 35mm and digital images, mounted digital images, greetings cards and digital images on CD/DVD for reproduction (high quality scans up to A3+).
Address: Windhover Barn, 51b Kiveton Lane, Todwick, Sheffield, South Yorkshire, S26 1HJ; 01909 770 238; e-mail: aspphoto@btinternet.com

READ, Mike
Photographer (wildlife and landscapes), tour leader, writer.
Subjects: Birds, mammals, plants, landscapes, and some insects. UK, France, USA, Ecuador (including Galapagos) plus many more. Behaviour, action, portraits, artistic pictures available for publication. More than 100,000 images in stock.
Products and services: Extensive stock photo library. Canvas and giclee prints, greetings cards, books.
Address: Claremont, Redwood Close, Ringwood, Hampshire, BH24 1PR; 01425 475 008.
e-mail: mike@mikeread.co.uk
www.mikeread.co.uk

SMART, Oliver
Photographer, lecturer and ornithologist.
Subjects: All wildlife subjects, UK based, also Alaska, Canada, Cuba, Ethiopia, Europe, Madagascar and the Seychelles.

Products and services: Bean bags, canvas prints, desk calendars, digital stock library, digital slideshow lectures, greeting cards, mounted prints (to A2 size) and photographic workshops.
Address: 78 Aspen Park Road, Weston-Super-Mare, Somerset BS22 8ER; (M)07802 417 810.
e-mail: oliver@smartimages.co.uk
www.smartimages.co.uk

TYLER, John
Subjects: Plants, fungi, insects and other invertebrates.
Products and services: Images for sale.
Address: 5 Woodfield, Lacey Green, Buckinghamshire, HP27 0QQ; 07814 392 335.
e-mail: johnclarketyler@gmail.com
www.johntyler.co.uk

WARD, Chris
Lecturer, N Bucks RSPB Local Group Leader.
Subjects: Primarily birds (and some other wildlife) and landscapes from UK and worldwide (Spain, Mallorca, Romania, Cyprus, Oman, Americas, Africa).
Products and services: Digital images and prints on request.
Address: 41 William Smith Close, Woolstone, Milton Keynes, MK15 0AN; 01908 669 448.
e-mail: cwphotography@hotmail.com
www.cwardphotography.co.uk

WILLIAMS, Nick
Photographer, lecturer, author.
Subjects: W.Palearctic also Cape Verde Islands and Falkland Islands.
Products and services: Glossy photographs and beautiful wildlife calendars for sale.
Address: Owl Cottage, Station Street, Rippingale, Lincs, PE10 0TA; (Tel/Fax) 01778 440 500.
e-mail: birdmanandbird@hotmail.com
www.nickwilliams.eu

DIRECTORY OF LECTURERS

ALMOND, Jim
Photographer and very active birder. Experienced lecturer.
Subjects: See website for full descriptive details and titles. Wild Peregrines; Birding in Shropshire/ Venus Pool; Out and About in the UK (year listing); North Norfolk; Bird and Nature Photography; Bird identification plus other wildlife including Butterflies and Dragonflies. All talks are digitally presented in an entertaining style with audio-visual finale. I can cater for all levels of interest.
Fees: £75 for standard lecture plus fuel at 30p per mile. **Limits:** None. **Time limitations:** None.
Address: 5 Coolock Close, St Peters Park, Shrewsbury SY3 9QD; 07940 678 719;
e-mail: almond.jim@virgin.net
http://shropshirebirder.co.uk/

BAINES, Richard
Director for Yorkshire Coast Nature. Professional Ecologist and Birder, Conservation Officer for Flamborough Bird Observatory.
Subjects: Flamborough Headland; Rarities on the Great White Cape; Birds and Environmental Stewardship on Flamborough Headland.
Fees: Flexible. **Limits:** None.
Time limitations: None.
Address: 01262 851 999;
e-mail: richard.baines@yorkshirecoastnature.co.uk
www.yorkshirecoastnature.co.uk

BASTON, Bill
Photographer, lecturer.
Subjects: East Anglian rarities and common birds; Mediterranean birds and landscapes; UK wildlife and

landscapes; Northern Greece & Western Turkey; Spain; Goa; General wildlife photography; The Gambia, Northern India (birds and tigers), Costa Rica, North East India and the Himalayan foothills.
Fees: Negotiable.
Limits: Preferably within East Anglia.
Address: 86 George Street, Hadleigh, Ipswich, IP7 5BU; 01473 827 062; www.billbaston.com
e-mail: billbaston@btinternet.com

BEJARANO, Santiago
An Ecuadorean naturalist and wildlife photographer who worked in the Galapagos for over a decade, with a great depth of knowledge and unique insight into these remarkable islands and their wildlife.
Subjects: 'Galapagos Islands', 'Birds of Galapagos', 'Ecuador Land of Mega Diversity', 'Hummingbirds'.
Fees: £40. **Limits:** None. **Time limitations:** None.
Address: 25 Trinity Lane, Beverley, East Yorkshire HU17 0DY; 01482 872 716; www.thinkgalapagos.com
e-mail: info@thinkgalapagos.com

BELL, Graham
Cruise lecturer worldwide, photographer, author, former BBRC member.
Subjects: Arctic, Antarctic, Siberia, Australia, Iceland, Seychelles. UK – identification, behaviour, seabirds, garden birds, entertaining bird sound imitations, birds in myth and fact, bird names, taking better photos, etc.
Fees: £20 plus travel and B&B if required. **Limits:** None. **Time limitations:** None.
Address: Ros View, South Yearle, Wooler, Northumberland, NE71 6RB; 01668 281310.
e-mail: seabirdsdgb@hotmail.com

BOND, Terry
Ex-Company Chairman, International consultant, Bank director. Conference speaker worldwide, photographer, group field leader, lecturer on birds for more than thirty years.
Subjects: Six talks – including Scilly Isles, Southern Europe, North America, Scandinavia, 'Birdwatching Identification - a New Approach' (an audience participation evening).
Fees: By arrangement (usually only expenses). **Limits:** Most of UK. **Time limitations:** Evenings.
Address: 3 Lapwing Crescent, Chippenham, Wiltshire, SN14 6YF; 01249 462 674.
e-mail: terryebond@btopenworld.com

BOWDEN, Paul
Birdwatcher and nature photographer for 30+ years (serious amateur). Founder member and current Chairman of Glamorgan Wildlife Photographic Club. Lectures to local clubs and nature groups.
Subjects: Birds, Butterflies and Dragonflies of Europe (Bulgaria, Estonia, Finland, Germany, Greece, Hungary, Italy, Portugal, Spain, Sweden & UK), Libya, Oman, USA (8 states), Canada, Panama, Hong Kong, Japan or Australia (Video, HDV and/or Powerpoint).
Fees: £50 plus reasonable travelling expenses. **Limits:** None, but longer trips may require overnight stay.

Time limitations: Evenings and weekends only.
Address: 4 Patmore Close, Gwaelod-y-Garth, Cardiff, CF15 9SU; 029 2081 3044.
e-mail: bowden_pe@hotmail.com
www.glamorganwildlifephotoclub.org.uk

BROADBENT, David
Photographer.
Subjects: UK birds and wild places; In praise of natural places.
Fees: £45 locally. **Limits:** 50mls without travel costs, anywhere otherwise. **Time limitations:** None.
Address: Based in the Forest of Dean. 07771 664 973.
e-mail: info@davidbroadbent.com
www.davidbroadbent.com

BROOKS, Richard
Wildlife photographer, writer, lecturer, birding guide.
Subjects: 12 talks (including Lemnos, Lesvos, Evros Delta, Kerkini, Spain, Israel, Canaries, E.Anglia, Scotland and Western Isles, Wales, Oman).
Fees: £80 plus petrol. **Limits:** None if accom provided.
Time limitations: None.
Address: 24 Croxton Hamlet, Fulmodeston, Fakenham, Norfolk, NR21 0NP; 01328 878 632.
e-mail: email@richard-brooks.co.uk
www.richard-brooks.co.uk

BUCKINGHAM, John
Long-standing and popular lecturer, photographer, tour leader.
Subjects: 60+ titles covering birds, wildlife, botany, ecology and habitats in UK, Europe, Africa, Australia, Indian sub-continent, North-South and Central America incuding favourites such as 'How Birds Work', 'The Natural History of Birds' and 'Wonders of Bird Migration'.
Fees: £85 plus expenses. **Limits:** None. **Time limitations:** None.
Address: 3 Cardinal Close, Tonbridge, Kent, TN9 2EN; (Tel/fax) 01732 354 970.
e-mail: john.birdtalk@btinternet.com

CARRIER, Michael
Lifelong interest in natural history.
Subjects: 1) Birds in Cumbria, 2) The Solway and its Birds and 3) The Isle of May, 4) A look at Bird Migration, 5) A Lifetime of Birds, 6) Some Remarkable Islands.
Fees: £20. **Limits:** None but rail connection helpful.
Time limitations: Sept-March inclusive, afternoons or evenings.
Address: Lismore Cottage, 1 Front Street, Armathwaite, Carlisle, Cumbria, CA4 9PB; 01697 472 218; e-mail: m.carrier131@btinternet.com

CARTY, Peter
National Trust's Countryside, Parkland and Garden Manager in South Shropshire. A warden for 26 years, from the Sefton Coast in Merseyside to the Seychelles. A keen birder and enthusiastic observer of plants, reptiles, amphibians, dragonflies, butterflies and mammals. He has led tours to Bulgaria.

ART/PHOTOGRAPHY/LECTURERS

DIRECTORY OF LECTURERS

Subjects: Various talks on birds, natural history and conservation in Bulgaria.
Fees: £50 (negotiable) plus travel expenses. **Limits:** Two hours from Bishop's Castle in Shropshire, eg North and South Wales, Manchester, Liverpool, Birmingham and Bristol areas. **Time limitations:** None.
Address: Sefton, Harley Jenkins Street, Bishop's Castle, Shropshire SY9 5AH;01588 638 664.
e-mail: peter@carty.org.uk

CLEAVE, Andrew MBE
Wildlife photographer, author, lecturer and tour leader.
Subjects: More than 30 talks (including India, Galapagos; Iceland; Mediterranean birds and wildlife; Lundy; Shetland; Ancient Woodlands; Dormice and Seashore. Full list available.
Fees: £65 plus petrol. **Limits:** Approx. 60 mls without o.n accom. **Time limitations:** Afternoons and evenings, not school holidays.
Address: 31 Petersfield Close, Chineham, Basingstoke, Hampshire, RG24 8WP; 01256 320 050.
e-mail: andrew@bramleyfrith.co.uk

COLLINS, Chris
Wildwings tour leader, Neotropical Bird Club council member & treasurer and semi-professional wildlife photographer.
Subjects: In search of the Spoon-billed Sandpiper/Birds of the Russian Far East; A Pacific Odyssey: Birding from New Zealand to Japan; Birds of Antarctica and the Southern Ocean Islands; South America: The Bird Continent; Amazing Birds.
Fees: £100 + travel expenses. **Limits:** Three hours from Surrey/London. **Time limitations:** None - lecture dates/times by prior agreement.
Address: 9 Pound Close, Long Ditton, Surbiton, Surrey KT6 5JW; 020 8398 1742;
E-mail: chris@birdsandwildlife.com

COSTER, Bill
Professional wildlife photographer, author and photographic tour leader.
Subjects: Stunning new digital shows provide a unique look at subjects around the world, including: Pacific Northwest USA, Antarctica, Shetland, Norway & Finland, Hungary and Spain, Florida, Britain and more. See my website for full details.
Fees: £85, plus 35p per mile. **Limits:** None. **Time limitations:** None.
Address: 15-17 Elm Road, South Woodham Ferrers, Chelmsford, Essex CM3 5QB; 01245 320 066.
e-mail: billcoster@hotmail.com
www.billcoster.com

COUZENS, Dominic
Full-time birdwatcher, tour leader (UK and overseas); writer and lecturer.
Subjects: The Secret Lives of Garden Birds', 'Birds Behaving Badly - the trials and tribulations of birds through the year', 'Have Wings Will Travel' -the marvel of bird migration, 'Vive la Difference' - a comparison of British birds with those across the Channel, 'My Family and 50 Other Animals' - a year spent trying to show 2 young children 50 species of mammals in Britain, 'Birding a Local Patch'.
Fees: £80 plus travel. **Limits:** London and south. **Time limitations:** None.
Address: 3 Clifton Gardens, Ferndown, Dorset, BH22 9BE; (Tel/fax) 01202 874 330. www.birdwords.co.uk
e-mail: dominic.couzens@btinternet.com

CROMACK, David
Editor of *Bird Art & Photography* magazine, president of Peterborough Bird Club.
Subjects: Subjects: 1) Bird Magazines and the Art of Bird Photography; 2) Wild West Birding (Arizona and California); 3) World Class Bird Images (International Wildbird Photographer competitions); 4) More World Class Bird Images; 5) Asia's Teardrop - Birding in Sri Lanka; 6) Bird Artists of the Modern Era. Leaflet available on request.
Fees: £75 plus travel expenses (30p per mile). **Limits:** 150 miles from Peterborough. **Times:** All requests considered.
Address: 55 Thorpe Park Road, Peterborough PE3 6LJ. 01733 566 815; (Fax) 01733 561 739;
e-mail: editor@buckinghampress.com

CROUCHER, Roy
Lecturer, Former RSPB staff member, former local authority ecologist.
Subjects: 'The wildlife of northern France', 'Managing the countryside for wildlife'.
Fees: £60, plus the cost of petrol from Leicester (return) at £15 per 100 miles. **Limits:** Anywhere in mainland Britain. **Time limitations:** November and December.
Address: Place de L'Eglise, 53700, Averton, France; 0033 243 00 6969; e-mail: nfwt@online.fr
www.northernfrancewildlifetours.com

DAVIES, Alan & MILLER, Ruth
Alan and Ruth both worked for RSPB before setting new birding world record for the most bird species recorded in a single year: 4341 species. They now run The Biggest Twitch, their own birdwatching tour and talks company, which runs tours throughout the UK and beyond.
Subjects: The Biggest Twitch, Around the World in 4000 birds — the entertaining warts-and-all story of their big birding year. Illustrated talks covering birding in the UK, Europe, South America, North America, Ethiopia, Southern Africa, Australia, and India. New talks are regularly added to the range.**Fees:** £60 plus the cost of fuel used on the return journey. **Limits:** None, though overnight accommodation needed for talks too far from North Wales.
Time limitations: Please e-mail to check availability.
Address: 12 Ormeside Court, 19 Church Walks, Llandudno Ll30 2HG; 01492 872 407;
e-mail: info@thebiggesttwitch.com
www.thebiggesttwitch.com

DIRECTORY OF LECTURERS

DUGGAN, Glenn
Ex-Commander Royal Navy, tour leader, researcher.
Subjects: Ten talks including, the rare and extinct birds of the world, birds of paradise and bower birds, Trogons and Tanagers, history of bird art (caveman to present day), modern day bird art, famous Victorian bird artists (John Gould, the Birdman and John James Audubon), scientific voyages of discovery. For something different how about two different talks (each of 45 minutes duration) in one evening to provide variety to your members?
Fees: £70 plus reasonable expenses. **Limits:** none with o.n accom. **Time limitations:** None.
Address: 25 Hampton Grove, Fareham, Hampshire, PO15 5NL; 01329 845 976, (M)07771 605 320.
e-mail: glenn.m.duggan@ntlworld.com
www.birdlectures.com

EYRE, John
Author, photographer, conservationist and ex-chairman Hampshire Ornithological Society.
Subjects: Many talks covering birding around the world (Europe, Africa, Asia, Australasia and the Americas), plus special Hampshire subjects. Examples include: 'New Zealand - Seabird Feast, Land Bird Famine'; California Birds — Sea, Sage and Spotted Owls'; 'Gilbert White's Birds'; and 'The Changing Fortunes of Hampshire Birds'. Several others so please call or e-mail to discuss options.
Fees: £70 plus travel. **Limits:** Any location negotiable. **Time limitations:** None.
Address: 3 Dunmow Hill, Fleet, Hampshire, GU51 3AN; 01252 677 850; e-mail: John.Eyre@ntlworld.com

GALLOP, Brian
Speaker, photographer, tour leader.
Subjects: 35 talks covering UK, Africa, India, Galapagos, South America and Europe — All natural history subjects. Made-to-measure talks available on request. 24hr emergency service.
Fees: £50 plus travel expenses. **Limits:** None - o.n acc. if over 100 mls. **Time limitations:** None.
Address: 13 Orchard Drive, Tonbridge, Kent, TN10 4LT; 01732 361 892;
e-mail: brian_gallop@hotmail.co.uk

GALVIN, Chris
A birding photographer with passion for birds for more than 30 years.
Subjects: Northwest Year', 'Package Holiday Birding', 'Bee-eaters & Kingfishers: An Introduction to the Birds of Goa', 'Birding by Camera'.
Fees: £70-£125 depending on distance travelled. **Limits:** 125 miles.
Address: 17 Henley Road, Allerton, Liverpool, Merseyside L18 2DN; 07802 428 385 or 0151 729 0123.
e-mail: chris@chrisgalvinphoto.com
www.chrisgalvinphoto.com

GARNER FRSA, Jackie
Professional wildlife artist, author & illustrator of *The Wildlife Artist's Handbook.*

Subjects: Birds/Nature in Art; Focus on the Falklands; Wildlife of Ancient Egypt; Wildlife Artist's World; The Making of a Wildlife Art Book.
Fees: £100 + expenses. **Distance limits:** None.
Time limits: None.
Address: The Old Cider House Studio, Humphries End, Randwick, Stroud, Glos GL6 6EW; 01453 847 420; (M)07800 804 847; www.jackiegarner.co.uk
e-mail: artist@jackiegarner.co.uk

GARNER, David
Wildlife photographer.
Subjects: 20 live talks and audio-visual shows on all aspects of wildlife in UK and some parts of Europe - list available.
Fees: £40 plus 25p per ml. **Limits:** None.
Time limitations: None.
Address: 73 Needingworth Road, St Ives, Cambridgeshire, PE27 5JY; (H)01480 463194; (W)01480 463194; e-mail: david@hushwings.co.uk
www.hushwings.co.uk

GARTSHORE, Neil
23-years working in nature conservation (National Trust, South Africa, RSPB) now a freelance contractor, writer, lecturer, tour guide and book seller.
Subjects: Various talks including South Africa; Sub-Antarctic Prince Edward Islands; Japan; Farne Islands; Heathlands; Poole Harbour.
Fees: Negotiable. **Limits:** Anything considered. **Time limitations:** Flexible.
Address: Moor Edge, 2 Bere Road, Wareham, Dorset BH20 4DD; 01929 552 560.
e-mail: neil@onaga54.freeserve.co.uk

GLENN, Neil
Author of *Best Birdwatching Sites in Norfolk*; regular contributor to *Bird Watching* magazine; bird tour leader for Avian Adventures.
Subjects: Wildlife of the Lower Rio Grande Valley, Texas; Birding the Arctic Circle; Moroccan Spice: From The Sahara to The Atlas Mountains. More to follow!
Fees: Negotiable. **Limits:** None.
Time limitations: Any day.
Address: 13 Gladstone Avenue, Gotham, Nottingham NG11 0HN; 0115 983 0946;
e-mail: n.glenn@ntlworld.com

GROVE, Ashley
Professional photographer, providing photo workshops, wildlife photography tour leader for Focus4nature and lecturer with growing subject matter. References on request if required.
Subjects: 1)'Shetland to Scilly; Birds of the British Isles', 2) 'Jewels of the Gambia, Kingfishers, Bee-eaters & Rollers', 3) 'Great British Birds', 4) Wildlife of Southern France (Available Winter 2013). More talks under construction.
Fees: £80 plus 25p per mile expenses (this may be negotiable if you are able to recommend a nearby group to speak to on an adjacent evening).
Limits: Willing to travel widely — within reason.

Time limitations: None.
Address: 16, Lint Meadow, Wythall, Worcestershire B47 5PH; 07704 189 835;
e-mail: birdergrove@gmail.com
www.ashleygrovewildimages.co.uk

GUNTON, Trevor
Ex.RSPB Staff, recruitment advisor, lecturer and consultant.
Subjects: Wide range of talks suitable for wildlife groups, bird clubs, U3A etc - (write or phone for full list). Key lecture areas include 'Birds and Pits', 'I Know an Island (UK)', 'Spitsbergen and The Norwegian Coastal Cruise', 'Polar Bears, Penguins and The White Continent', 'Viking/Norse history, Shetland', 'Look again at Garden Birds', 'Yorkshire' etc.
Fees: Variable (basic £70 plus petrol). Limits: None, up to end of 2013, then within 2hrs driving of Little Paxton. Time limitations: Anytime, anywhere.
Address: 15 St James Road, Little Paxton, St Neots, Cambs, PE19 6QW; 01480 473 562.

HASSELL, David
Birdwatcher and photographer.
Subjects: Six talks (including British Seabirds, Shetland Birds, British Birds, USA Birds, including Texas, California, Florida).
Fees: £50 plus petrol. Limits: None.
Time limitations: None.
Address: 15 Grafton Road, Enfield, Middlesex, EN2 7EY; 020 8367 0308; e-mail: dave@davehassell.com
www.davehassell.com

LANE, Mike
Wildlife photographer and lecturer.
Subjects: Many talks from the UK and abroad.
Fees: Negotiable. Limits: None.
Time limitations: None.
Address: 36 Berkeley Road, Shirley, Solihull, West Midlands B90 2HS; 0121 744 7988; (M)07766 418 013;
e-mail: mikelane@nature-photography.co.uk
www.nature-photography.co.uk

LENTON, Graham
PhD Ornithology/Ecology. Former lecturer at Oxford University and Oxford Brookes University. Lifetime photographer of wildlife - publications of articles and photographs of birds and wildlife.
Subjects: Barn Owls of Malaysia and Rat Control; Birds of the Seychelles; Wildlife and Birds of Antarctica; Birds of New Zealand; Birds of Namibia; Two Islands (Handa & The Farnes); An Arctic Journey; Gorilla in my midst - a Ugandan Odyssey; Barn Owls - Past, Present and their Future.
Fees: £65. Limits: Preferably within 60mls.
Time limitations: 60 to 90 minute talks.
Address: The Old School, 25A Standlake Road, Ducklington, Witney, Oxon OX29 7UR; 01993 899 033.
e-mail: grahamlenton@btopenworld.com
www.gml-art.co.uk

LINGARD, David
Photographer, retired from RAF, now UK delegate to LIPU (BirdLife in Italy).
Subjects: Choice of talks on birding but primarily on Birdwatching in Italy and the work of LIPU.
Fees: Donation to LIPU, plus petrol costs.
Limits: None. Time limitations: None.
Address: Fernwood, Doddington Road, Whisby, Lincs LN6 9BX; 01522 689 030; e-mail: mail@lipu-uk.org
www.lipu-uk.org

LOVELL, Stephen
Naturalist, RSPB lecturer, photographer, adult education teacher.
Subjects: 30+ topics including the natural history of several European destinations including Costa Rica, Trinidad and Tobago, Lesvos, Mallorca, Extremadura, Britain. Other talks available on New Zealand, Australia, St Lucia, Tanzania, Nepal, Sri Lanka and Southern India.
Fees: £45 to £90 plus travel. Limits: None.
Time limitations: None.
Address: 6 Abingdon Close, Doddington Park, Lincoln LN6 3UH; 01522 689 456; (M)07957 618 684.
e-mail: stephenlovell58@btinternet.com
www.stevelovellgreenspaces.co.uk

MAGENNIS, Steve
Steve Magennis Wildlife Photography, wildlife photographer, lecturer and workshop leader, *British Wildlife* Photography Awards 2012 Highly Commended image.
Subjects: All talks are audio visual and subjects include wildlife photography, bird life and related subjects (see website for full details).
Fees: £95 plus travel @ 40p per mile. Limits: Up to 150 miles. Time limitations: Available all year round, day or evening.
Address: 3 Chepstow Close, St James, Northampton, Northants NN5 7EB; 01604 467 848; (M)07803 619 272; e-mail: photos@stevemagennis.co.uk
www.stevemagennis.co.uk

MARTIN, Nick
RSPB Senior Site Manager, wildlife photographer and tour leader
Subjects: Secret Wildlife of the Cairngorms; Discovering Scotland's Western Isles; Furry Fables... the Stories of Our British Mammals; A Photographer's Wild Britain. Secrets of Wildlife Photography.
Fees: £60 plus 25p/mile from Solihull. Limits: A couple of hours from the Midlands.
Time limitations: Flexible.
Address: 57 Newton Road, Solihull, West Midlands, B93 9HN; 07810 863 177.
e-mail: nick@martinimages.co.uk
www.martinimages.co.uk

MATHER, BEM, Dr John Robert
Ornithologist, writer, tour guide, lecturer.
Subjects: Birds and other wildlife of: Kenya,

DIRECTORY OF LECTURERS

Tanzania, Uganda, Ethiopia, Namibia, South Africa, Costa Rica, India, Nepal; 'Algonquin to Niagara - a tour around the Great Lakes'; 'Landscapes, Flowers and Wildlife of the American West'; 'Bird on the Bench' - a fascinating account of bird biology; 'Wildlife and Scenery of Coastal Alaska, and the Canadian Rockies'; 'From the mountains of Bulgaria and Romania to the Black Sea and the Danube Delta'; Flora and Fauna of the Algarve, Spain and Majorca'. **Fees:** £75 plus 30p per mile. Overnight accommodation or £30 if over 75 miles. **Limits:** Approx. 100 mls. **Time limitations:** None. **Address:** Eagle Lodge, 44 Aspin Lane, Knaresborough, North Yorkshire, HG5 8EP; 01423 862 775.

MAYER, Edward
Founder of "London's Swifts" and "Swift Conservation".
Subjects: Swifts and their Conservation; Biodiversity in the Built Environment. Presentations and training for the general public, Town Planners, Biodiversity Officers, and Architects.
Fees: £50 upwards, depending on type of talk, or collection/donation, plus travel expenses.
Limits: UK/EC (further by special arrangement).
Address: 28 Yale Court, Honeybourne Road, London NW6 1JG; 020 7794 2098.
e-mail: mail@swift-conservation.org
www.swift-conservation.org

MEREDITH, Stuart
Former RSPB and WWT employee who is now a tour guide and proprietor of Ribble Bird Tours.
Subjects: Currently offers around a dozen different talks covering birding destinations in the UK and abroad, as well as general interest areas.
Fees: £40 plus travel expenses. **Limits:** Mainly North West England, within 100 miles of Fylde Coast, but will consider further afield. **Time limitations:** Anytime of day.
Contact: 01253 312 043; www.ribblebirdtours.co.uk
e-mail: smrbt@blueyonder.co.uk

MILES, John
Former warden for RSPB Geltsdale in Cumbria, tour guide, consultant and author of *Best Birdwatching Sites: The Solway, Hadrian's Birds, Exploring lakeland Wildlife, Pharoah's Birds, Hadrian's Wildlife* and magazine articles. Series of children's books with first out in November 2012.
Subjects: 1) 'The Solway' covers birding throughout the whole of Cumbria and Dumfries & Galloway; 2) 'Hadrian's Wildlife' examines the habitats along Hadrian's Wall from Cumbria to Tyne & Wear and the history of birds back to Roman times.
Fees: Prices on request. **Limits:** Anywhere in UK w/o overnight accommodation.
Time limitations: Evenings best.
Address: Jockey Shield, Castle Carrock, Carlisle, Cumbria CA4 9NF; 01228 670 205;
e-mail: jmiles3@toucansurf.com

NASON, Rebecca
UK, East Anglia-based bird and wildlife photographer.
Subjects: A Fair Isle Season'. Working, birding and photography at Britain's premier birding hotspot.
Fees: Please e-mail for fee details. There is a set fee plus travel expenses depending on location. **Limits:** Within 2 hours drive of Woodbridge, Suffolk.
Time limitations: Flexible. Talks last from 1-2 hours.
Address: 8 Angel Lane, Woodbridge, Suffolk IP12 4NG; 01394 385 030; (M)07919 256 386.
e-mail: rebecca@rebeccanason.com
www.rebeccanason.com

NEWTON, Ian
Photographer (ARPS) and lecturer, Chairman York Ornithological Club.
Subjects: 14 talks, all digital, mainly birds and other wildlife of North, Central and South America, Europe and UK.
Fees: £60 plus petrol. **Limits:** None.
Time limitations: None.
Address: 5 Fairfields Drive, Skelton, York YO30 1YP; 01904 471 446; (M)07976 849 832;
e-mail: iannewton@acsemail.co.uk
www.iannewtonphotography.com

OFFORD, Keith
Photographer, writer, tour leader, conservationist.
Subjects: 16 talks covering raptors, flight, uplands, gardens, migration, woodland wildlife, Australia, Southern USA, Tanzania, Gambia, Spain, Costa Rica, Namibia, Western Cape.
Fees: £100 plus travel. **Limits:** None.
Time limitations: Sept to April.
Address: Yew Tree Farmhouse, Craignant, Selattyn, Nr Oswestry, Shropshire, SY10 7NP; 01691 718 740.
e-mail: keith.offord@virgin.net
www.keithofford.co.uk

PARKER, Susan and Allan ARPS
Professional photographers, (ASPphoto - Images of Nature), lecturers and tutors.
Subjects: 16 plus slide and digital talks on birds and natural history, natural history photography - countries include UK, USA (Texas, Florida), Spain, Greece, Cyprus.
Fees: On application. **Limits:** Any distance with o.n accom or up to 120 mls without.
Time limitations: None.
Address: Windhover Barn, 51b Kiveton Lane, Todwick, Sheffield, South Yorkshire, S26 1HJ; 01909 770 238; e-mail: aspphoto@btinternet.com

PEARSON, Mark
Tour Leader Yorkshire Coast Nature. Professional Ornithologist, Birder.
Subjects: The joys of patch birding - from urban London to an east coast observatory; Greyhounds and Bluebirds — backpacker-birding the USA.
Fees: Flexible. **Limits:** None.
Time limitations: None.

Address: 01262 851 999;
e-mail: mark.pearson@yorkshirecoastnature.co.uk
www.yorkshirecoastnature.co.uk

PETTIT, Brian
Wildlife consultant and photographer.
Subjects: Wide range of talks on wildlife from UK
and worldwide, incorporating plants, invertebrates,
reptiles, mammals, birds and wildlife photography.
Full list on website or on application.
Fees: From £60 (4:3) and £100 (16:9 widescreen) for
single club meetings, to £250 for major fundraising
events. We have all our own equipment including
screens and sound system. **Limits:** Anwhere
worldwide. **Time limitations:** Talk season from Oct 1
to March 31.
Address: 18 Okeford Road, Broadstone, Poole, Dorset
BH18 8PA; 07979 056 144.
e-mail: wildlifepics@ntlworld.com
www.naturepicturesworldwide.com

PICKERING, Pollyanna
Wildlife artist, conservationist.
Subjects: 12 talks available on a variety of subjects,
from running a wildlife sanctuary in Derbyshire to
travelling into remote areas to paint endangered
species in their natural habitat. Details of individual
talks on request.
Fees: £125 plus travelling expenses. **Limits:** None.
Time limitations: Evening talks only.
Address: Brookvale House, Oaker, Matlock,
Derbyshire DE4 2JJ; 01629 55 851.
e-mail: annalouise@talktalk.net
www.pollyannapickering.co.uk

RACE, Steve
Professional wildlife photographer, birder, website
manager for Scarborough Birders.
Subjects: Life on the Ledge-Seabirds of Bempton
Cliffs; Yorkshire Coast Nature—Wildlife Photography
from the Yorkshire Coast; Digi-scoping Tanzania.
Fees: Flexible. **Limits:** None.
Time limitations: None.
Address: 01262 851 999;
e-mail: steve.race@yorkshirecoastnature.co.uk
www.yorkshirecoastnature.co.uk

READ, Mike
Photographer, tour leader, writer.
Subjects: 12 talks featuring British and foreign
subjects (list available on receipt of sae or see
website).
Fees: £70 plus travel. **Limits:** 100 mls from
Ringwood. **Time limitations:** Talks available Sept 1 to
March 31 each winter.
Address: Claremont, Redwood Close, Ringwood,
Hampshire, BH24 1PR; 01425 475 008.
e-mail: mike@mikeread.co.uk
www.mikeread.co.uk

REDMAN, Nigel
Tour leader, publisher and author.
Subjects: Mostly birds, including Morocco, Russia
(and former Soviet Union), the Caucasus, Kenya,
Ethiopia, and the Horn of Africa.
Fees: Negotiable. **Limits:** None (but overnight
accommodation may be required).
Time limitations: None.
Address: Moons Hill Cottage, Moons Hill, Ninfield,
East Sussex TN33 9LH; 01424 893 023; 07734 88 6515.
e-mail: nredman@acblack.com

SMART, Oliver
Photographer, lecturer and ornithologist.
Subjects: 1)'Birds of Lesvos'; 2) 'Grizzly Bears of
Alaska'; 3) 'Wildlife on Handa Island, NW Scotland';
4) 'Cameras and Creatures, from Cumbria to
Canada'; 5) 'Cuba: A Flicker of Interest'; 6) 'RAW
Nature: Images Uncovered'; 7) 'From 60 Degrees
North', 8) 'Butterfly Britain' (available spring 2013);
9) 'Exploring Ethiopia' (available autumn 2013).
Fees: £80 plus 25p per mile plus £10 per hour above
two hours total travel time. **Limits:** None and can
also provide own accommodation.
Time limitations: None.
Address: 78 Aspen Park Road, Weston-Super-Mare,
Somerset BS22 8ER; (M)07802 417 810.
e-mail: oliver@smartimages.co.uk
www.smartimages.co.uk

TODD, Ralph
Lecturer & photographer, former tour leader and
course tutor.
Subjects: 10 talks incl. 'Galapagos Wildlife'; 'On the
Trail of the Crane – parts 1 and 2'; 'Polar Odyssey';
'Operation Osprey'; 'Natural Wonders and Wildlife
of Iceland; 'Man & Birds-Travels Through Time'; 'A
Summer in Northern Landscapes'; 'Where Yeehaa
meets Ole'; Birds in the Land of Disney; Antarctic
Adventure; Wildlife of Pyrenees and Lesvos.
Fees: £75 plus expenses. **Limits:** None. **Time
limitations:** Anytime - also short notice.
Address: 9 Horsham Road, Bexleyheath, Kent, DA6
7HU; (Tel/fax) 01322 528 335.
e-mail: rbtodd@btinternet.com

TYLER, John
Wildlife walks and talks.
Subjects: Life in a Nutshell (The world of small
things); The Island of Crabs; Volcanoes and Dragons;
Changing Wildlife of the Chilterns; The Ridgeway;
The Glow-worm; The World of Fungi; Making Space
for Wildlife.
Fees: £60 plus 50p per mile. **Limits:** 25 mile radius
from Princes Risborough, Bucks.
Time limitations: None.
Address: 5 Woodfield, Lacey Green,
Buckinghamshire, HP27 0QQ; 07814 392 335; www.
johntyler.co.uk
e-mail: johnclarketyler@gmail.com

DIRECTORY OF LECTURERS

WARD, Chris
Photographer, N Bucks RSPB Local Group Leader. **Subjects:** 20+ talks on UK and worldwide topics (Spain, Mallorca, Romania, Cyprus, Oman, Americas, Africa) — primarily birds, some other wildlife. **Fees:** £50 plus petrol @30p/mile. **Limits:** 120 miles. **Time limitations:** Evenings. **Address:** 41 William Smith Close, Woolstone, Milton Keynes, MK15 0AN; 01908 669 448. e-mail: cwphotography@hotmail.com www.cwardphotography.co.uk

WILLIAMS, Nick
Photographer, lecturer, author. **Subjects:** Several audio-visual shows (including Morocco, Mongolia, Spain, N.Germany, Camargue, Turkey, N.Norway, Cape Verde Islands, Falklands and Birds of Prey). **Fee:** £110 - £140 depending on group size and distance. Travel costs included in the fee.

Limits: None. **Time limitations:** None. **Address:** Owl Cottage, Station Street, Rippingale, Lincs, PE10 0TA; (Tel/Fax)01778 440 500. e-mail: birdmanandbird@hotmail.com www.nickwilliams.eu

WREN, Graham J. ARPS
Wildlife photographer, lecturer, tour guide. **Subjects:** 25 talks on UK birds, including 'Breeding Birds of Southern Britain' and 'Northern Britain', including habitats. Also Scandinavia. Nest-boxes (new), the environment, wildlife - Kenya. Detailed information package supplied on request. **Fees:** £50-80 plus petrol. **Limits:** None. **Time limitations:** None. **Address:** The Kiln House, Great Doward, Whitchurch, Ross-on-Wye, Herefordshire, HR9 6DU; 01600 890 488. e-mail: grahamjwren@aol.com or susanjhampshire@aol.com

BTO SPEAKERS

This directory has been compiled to help Bird Clubs and similar organisations in finding speakers for their indoor meetings. Each entry consists of an individual speaker, a list of talks/ lectures available, details of fees and expenses required and travel distance limitations. If you are interested in any of the speakers, please contact Ieuan Evans (ieuan.evans@bto.org) or Ellen Walford (ellen.walford@bto.org) directly. Alternatively, contact BTO: 01842 750 050. Members of the BTO/ Bird Clubs Partnership have a 25% discount.

Appleton, Graham (Director of Communications)
Subjects: Atlas 2007 – 11; Flyway to Iceland; Time to Fly – Bird Migration; Tracking African Migrants **Fees:** £40 Negotiable. **Distance:** Dependent on expenses.

Austin, Dr Graham (Senior Research Ecologist, Wetland & Marine Research)
Subjects: Wetland Bird Survey. **Fees:** £40. **Distance:** Travel by agreement.

Baille, Dr Stephen (Science Director Modelling & Demography)
Subjects: BirdTrack; Population Monitoring. **Fees:** £40. **Distance:** Travel By agreement.

Baker, Jeff (Head of Marketing)
Subjects: Little Brown Jobs - Warblers & How to Identify Them; The Work of the BTO; Garden Birds & Feeding. **Fees:** £40. **Distance:** Dependent on expenses.

Balmer, Dawn (Atlas Co-ordinator)
Subjects: Atlas 2007 - 11. **Fees:** £40. **Distance:** 100 mile radius of Thetford.

Barimore, Carl (Nest Records Organiser)
Subjects: Nest Records Scheme; Barn Owl Monitoring Programme. **Fees:** £40. **Distance:** By agreement.

Blackburn, Jez (Licensing and Sales Manager)
Subjects: Demography Team Bird Moult (suitable for ringers); Ringing for Conservation; Sule Skerry Seabirds. **Fees:** £40 (£70 for private talks). **Distance:** East Anglia.

Bray, James (Fieldwork & Training Coordinator BTO Scotland)
Subjects:; The Work of BTO Scotland; BTO Atlas 2007-11; BBS, Birdtrack & other BTO surveys in Scotland; Garden BirdWatch. **Fees:** £40. **Distance:** By agreement.

Clark, Jacquie (Head of Demography Team & Head of Ringing Scheme)
Subjects: Waders & Severe Weather; Ringing for Conservation; Why Ring Birds? **Fees:** £40. **Distance:** 100 mile radius of Thetford.

DIRECTORY OF LECTURERS

Clark, Dr Nigel (Head of Projects Development Department)
Subjects: Waders, Man & Estuaries; What hope for the Spoon-billed Sandpiper?
Fees: £40. Distance: 100 mile radius of Thetford.

Conway, Greg (Research Ecologist, Land-use Research)
Subjects: Nightjars; Woodlarks; Dartford Warblers; Wintering Warblers in the UK; Firecrests.
Fees: £40. Distance: 100 mile radius of Thetford.

Dadam, Dr Daria (Reseach Ecologist Demography)
Subjects: Bird Disease.
Fees: Negotiable. Distance: By agreement.

Fuller, Prof Rob (Director of Science)
Subjects: Changing Times for Woodland Birds.
Fees: £40. Distance: Anywhere.

Gillings, Dr Simon (Senior Research Ecologist Land Use Research)
Subjects: Atlas 2007 - 11; Winter Golden Plovers & Lapwings; Waders; Knot Migration; Winter Farmland Birds. Fees: £40. Distance: Negotiable.

Gough, Su (Editor, BTO News & Training Officer)
Subjects: The Work of the BTO; Urban Birds. Private talks: Wildlife of Canada; Wildlife of Southwestern USA; Wildlife of European Mountains; Wildlife of Texas; Wildlife of the Middle East.
Fees: £40. Distance: Negotiable.

Harrison, Dr Tim (GBW Development Officer)
Subjects: Are Gardens Good for Birds or Birdwatchers?
Fees: £40. Distance: 50 mile radius of Thetford.

Henderson, Dr Ian (Senior Research Ecologist International Research)
Subjects: Arable Farming and Birds.
Fees: £40. Distance: By agreement.

Johnson, Dr Alison (Ecological Statistician, Population Ecology & Modelling)
Subjects: Climate Change and Birds.
Fees: £40. Distance: East Anglia

Lack, Dr Peter (Information Services Manager)
Private talks: Palearctic Migrants in Africa; On Foot in Rwanda and Zambia; Ecology in East African Savannahs; General Natural History of Eastern Africa.
Fees: Negotiable. Distance: 60 miles of Bury St Edmunds.

Marchant, John (Projects Co-ordinator Monitoring)
Subjects: Monitoring Heronries: Nine Decades of Monitoring; Waterways Bird & Breeding Bird Surveys.
Fees: £40. Distance: By agreement.

Moran, Nick (BirdTrack Organiser)
Subjects: Mapping migration with BirdTrack; Hard weather effects on birds; Birds and birding in Arabia (private talk).
Fees: £40. Distance: By agreement.

Musgrove, Dr Andy (Head of Monitoring)
Subjects: The Wetland Bird Survey; Little Egrets in the UK. Fees: £40. Distance: By agreement.

Newson, Dr Stuart (Senior Research Ecologist' Population Ecology & Modelling)
Subjects: Tree Nesting Cormorants.
Fees: £40. Distance: By agreement.

Noble, Dr David (Principal Ecologist, Monitoring)
Subjects: Developing Bird Indicators; Population Trends. Fees: £40. Distance: By agreement.

Pearce-Higgins, Dr James (Principal Ecologist, Climate Change)
Subjects: Birds and climate change; Upland birds; A year in the life of a Golden Plover.
Fees: £40. Distance: By agreement.

Risely, Kate (Breeding Bird Survey National Organiser)
Subjects: BTO/JNCC/RSPB Breeding Birds Survey.
Fees: £40. Distance: By agreement.

Robinson, Dr Rob (Principal Ecologist, Modelling & Demography)
Subjects: Farming & Birds; Conservation Value of Ringing. Fees: £40. Distance: By agreement.

Siriwardena, Dr Gavin (Head of Land-Use Research)
Subjects: Research Farmland Birds (General); Marsh & Willow Tits; Quantifying Migratory Strategies; Winter Feeding of Farmland Birds.
Fees: £40. Distance: Negotiable.

Stancliffe, Paul (Press Officer)
Subjects: Atlas 2007-11; Homes to Let – Nestboxes; Birds, Birders and the Work of the BTO; Tracking African Migrants
Fees: £40. Distance: Negotiable.

Toms, Mike (Head of Garden Ecology Team)
Subjects: Are Gardens Good for Birds or Birdwatchers?
Fees: £40. Distance: 50 mile radius of Thetford.

Wernham, Dr Chris (Senior Research Ecologist BTO Scotland)
Subjects: The Work of BTO Scotland; Breeding Bird Survey in Scotland; BirdTrack in Scotland.
Fees: £40. Distance: Travel Scotland and NE England.

Wright, Dr Lucy (Research Ecologist, Wetland and Marine Research)
Subjects: Non-native Waterbirds in Eurasia & Africa.
Fees: £40. Distance: By agreement.

TRADE DIRECTORY

Hilary Cromack

Spectacular scenery like this view of Oxbow Bend, in the Grand Teton National Park, Wyoming, adds to the magic of a birding holiday overseas and a number of tour companies offer trips to exciting destinations like this.

TRADE DIRECTORY

ARK WILDLIFE LTD

Company ethos: Everything for garden wildlife. Friendly, knowledgeable staff, great service, next day delivery, on-line and full colour mail order catalogue.

Key product lines: Carefully selected natural bird and wildlife food, habitats, accessories and garden wildlife-related gifts, wildflower seeds.

Other services: Mail order company, 24-hour shopping on-line, with free next day delivery. Phone for a free catalogue.

Opening times: Mon - Fri (9am-5.30pm). Out of hours answer phone service.

Address: Dog Kennel Farm, Charlton Road, Hitchin, Hertfordshire SG5 2AB. 0800 085 4865; (fax) 01462 420 022; e-mail: office@arkwildlife.co.uk
www.arkwildlife.co.uk

BAMFORDS TOP FLIGHT

Company ethos: Family owned manufacturing company providing good quality bird foods via a network of UK stockists or mail order. B.T.O. Business Ally.

Key product lines: A range of wild bird mixtures containing the unique 'Pro-tec Health Aid', developed by Bamfords, to protect and promote the welfare of wild birds. Vast array of other foods and seeds for birds.

Other services: Trade suppliers of bulk and pre-packed bird and petfoods. Custom packing/own label if required.

New for 2013: New, fully recyclable packaging for all Wild Bird Foods.

Opening times: Mon - Fri 8am-5.30pm; Sat 8am-12 noon; (Sunday 10am-12 noon, Mill Shop only).

Address: Globe Mill, Midge Hall, Leyland, Lancashire PR26 6TN:01772 456 300; (fax) 01772 456 302. e-mail: sales@bamfords.co.uk www.bamfords.co.uk

CJ WILDBIRD FOODS LTD

Company ethos: CJ Wildlife aims to make significant, recognisable contributions to the protection and welfare of wild birds and other wildlife. Our ornithologists and wildlife advisors undertake research projects to ensure we are continually producing not only high quality products, but products designed specifically for the wildlife they are intended.

Key product lines: CJ Wildlife bird feeders, bird food, nest boxes, wildlife-friendly plants, bird tables and accessories, along with a broad range of wildlife care products. Products are available via website or by mail order from our free catalogue.

Other services: Free Handbook of Garden Wildlife catalogue with advice, tips and products. CJ Wildlife products are also stocked in selected supermarkets, garden centres and pet shops.

New for 2013: We are continuously adding new products to the range. Visit the website, or follow us on Twitter and Facebook for the latest news and offers.

Opening times: Call centre (Freephone 0800 731 2820) Monday to Friday (9am-5pm), Saturday (9am-12pm). Online ordering 24hrs.

Address: The Rea, Upton Magna, Shrewsbury, Shropshire SY4 4UR; 0800 731 2820; (fax) 01743 709 504; e-mail: sales@birdfood.co.uk
www.birdfood.co.uk

ERNEST CHARLES

Company ethos: Caring for Britain's wildlife since 1844, Ernest Charles offers an extensive range of quality wild bird feeds and seed blends developed following research carried out by our partners at The British Trust for Ornithology.

Key product lines: Nutritious range of Wild Bird Blends, Seed Straights and Suet products, bird feeders and accessories, nest boxes and bird tables, BTO recommended products including bird feed, gifts, optics and outdoor clothing, humane pest deterrents, plus a great range of products to help encourage garden wildlife.

Other services: Request a free catalogue or visit us at www.ernest-charles.com for our full range of products and services including advice on how to care for garden wildlife.

New for 2013: Join the NEW Ernest Charles Community at www.ernest-charles.com for the latest information from our experts and the BTO. To receive the latest offers, subscribe to our FREE e-newsletter and follow us on Facebook, Twitter and our blog. Check the evolving product line on our website.

Opening times: Call our friendly and knowledgeable team on FREEPHONE 0800 731 6770, Monday – Friday 8.30am – 5pm or order from www.ernest-charles. com 24/7.

Address: Ernest Charles Ltd, High Street, Moulton, Spalding, Lincolnshire PE12 6QD; FREEPHONE 0800 731 6770; e-mail: enquiries@ernest-charles.com
www.ernest-charles.com

BIRD MAGAZINES AND BOOK PUBLISHERS

VINE HOUSE FARM BIRD FOODS

Company ethos: Growing and selling wild bird food on their family run farm. A full range of high quality bird foods and accessories direct to the customer through our mail order service and farm shop.

Key product lines: A full range of bird food including home grown black sunflowers and a range of specialist mixes and feeder accessories.

Other services: A number of farm walks and open days in early summer for people to view our conservation award winning farm. We also have a range of products available for wholesale customers.

New for 2013: The Wildlife Trusts have been recommending our bird seed to their members and 5% of every sale goes to the county wildlife trusts.

Opening times: Mon to Fri (8am-5pm), Sat (8am-4pm), Sun (10am-4pm).

Contact: Nicholas Watts, Vine House Farm, Deeping St Nicholas, Spalding PE11 3DG; 01775 630 208; (fax) 01775 630 244; www.vinehousefarm.co.uk
e-mail:birdseed@vinehousefarm.co.uk

BIRD MAGAZINES

BIRDING WORLD

Type of publication: The cutting edge monthly journal for keen birders, lavishly illustrated with colour photographs throughout. Emphasis is on rare and scarce British and European bird news and advances in identification and taxonomy, as well as overseas birding. Monthly, available only on subscription.

Other services: Own on-line bird and wildlife bookshop Books for Birders www.birdingworld.co.uk has huge stocks and offers very prompt, friendly and helpful service.

Editor: Steve Gantlett.

Contact: Birding World, Sea Lawn, Coast Road, Cley-next-the-Sea, Norfolk NR25 7RZ; 01263 741 139; e-mail: steve@birdingworld.co.uk
www.birdingworld.co.uk

BIRDWATCH

Type of publication: A monthly magazine available either by subscription, in newsagents, WH Smith, and selected supermarkets, plus also available as a digital magazine via the *Birdwatch* app on iTunes or Android. Containing informative features each month on birding ID, the latest reports, optics reviews, birding around the world and more, this is the UK's number one monthly magazine for expert birders.

Other services: The Birdwatch Bookshop, free e-newsletter, reader holidays and more can be found at www.birdwatch.co.uk

Editor: Dominic Mitchell.

Contact: Birdwatch Magazine, Warners Group Publications, The Chocolate Factory, 5 Clarendon Road, London N22 6XJ; 020 8881 0550.
e-mail: editorial@birdwatch.co.uk
www.birdwatch.co.uk

BIRD WATCHING (BAUER MEDIA)

Type of publication: A4 magazine (116 to 124pp) published 13 times a year. Available on subscription and at newstand. Contents include latest bird sightings, news, reviews, site guides and ID advice for birdwatchers of all abilities.

Other services: Website, Facebook and Twitter pages, Bookshop (run through WildSounds (www.wildsounds.com), regular Readers' Holidays through Heatherlea, Avian Adventures and The Grant Arms.

Editor: Matt Merritt (acting editor).

Contact: Bird Watching (editorial or advertising), Media House, Lynch Wood, Peterborough PE2 6EA; 01733 468 536; www.birdwatching.co.uk
e-mail: birdwatching@bauermedia.co.uk

BRITISH BIRDS

Company ethos: *British Birds* is the birdwatchers' journal of record, publishing ground-breaking articles on (e.g.) identification, distribution, migration, conservation and taxonomy. *British Birds* is published by BB 2000 Ltd, which is wholly owned by a charitable trust; all profits generated by the journal support worthwhile conservation and research projects.

Type of publication: Subscription-only monthly journal. Annually also publishes the reports of the British Birds Rarities Committee and the UK Rare Breeding Birds Panel.

Other services: *British Birds'* 100+ year archive can be accessed free of charge on www.britishbirds.co.uk, with the most recent material available exclusively to subscribers.

Editor: Roger Riddington.

Contact: British Birds, 4 Harlequin Gardens, St Leonards-on-Sea, East Sussex TN37 7PF; 01424 755 155; e-mail: subscriptions@britishbirds.co.uk
www.britishbirds.co.uk

BOOK PUBLISHERS

BUCKINGHAM PRESS LTD

Imprints: Single imprint company — publishers of *The Birdwatcher's Yearbook* since 1981, *Who's Who in Ornithology* (1997), *Best Birdwatching Sites* series covering North-East England, Norfolk, Sussex, Highlands of Scotland, Solway (Cumbria and Dumfries & Galloway), North Wales, Cornwall & Scilly. Plus sets of identification cards for British birds, garden birds, dragonflies and butterflies.

New for 2013: *Best Birdwatching Sites: Norfolk*, 3rd edition.

Address: 55 Thorpe Park Road, Peterborough, PE3 6LJ, 01733 561 739.
e-mail: admin@buckinghampress.com
www.buckinghampress.co.uk

BOOK PUBLISHERS

CHRISTOPHER HELM PUBLISHERS

Special offers on new subscriptions appear on the *British Birds* website from time to time.
Imprints: *Christopher Helm*: the leading publisher of ornithology books in the world; includes many field guides, identification guides, family guides, county and country avifaunas, and a Where to Watch Birds series.
T & AD Poyser: an acclaimed series of respected ornithology monographs.
Birds of Africa: the standard series of handbooks on African birds.
A & C Black: publisher of definitive natural history books.
New for 2013: *The Birds of Africa Volume VIII: The Malagasy Region* by Roger Safford and Frank Hawkins; *Mammals of Africa: Volumes I-VI* edited by Jonathan Kingdon et al.; *Harrap's Wild Flowers* by Simon Harrap; *RSPB Handbook of the Seashore* by Maya Plass; *Field Guide to Invasive Plants and Animals* by Olaf Booy, Max Wade and Helen Roy; *Kenya: A Natural History* by Stephen Spawls and Glenn Mathews; *The Great British Wildlife Hunt* by Anne Harrap; *The Nature Tracker's Handbook* by Nick Baker; *A History of Birdwatching in 100 Objects* by David Callahan and Dominic Mitchell; *Ghosts of Gone Birds* edited by Ceri Levy. Also, e-books are now available for most titles and the entire Poyser monograph series is now back in print.
Address: 50 Bedford Square, London, WC1B 3DP; 020 7631 5600; (fax) 020 7631 5800;.
e-mail: nigel.redman@bloomsbury.com
www.bloomsbury.com/naturalhistory

HARPER COLLINS PUBLISHERS

Imprints: *Collins Natural History*: — the leading publisher of field guides to the natural world.
Collins New Naturalist Series: the encyclopaedic reference for all areas of British natural history.
HarperCollins: — publisher of the best illustrated books.
New for 2013: *Wonders of Life*; New Naturalists - *Vegetation, Terns and Bird Populations*; Collins Pocket Guides. (*British Bird Guide, British Tree Guide, British Butterfly Guide, British Wild Flower Guide, British Wild Places*), *Collecting the New Naturalists, Springwatch Unsprung - All Your Wildlife Questions Answered, Collins Fungi Guide* (paperback), *The Salmon: The Extraordinary Life of the King of Fish*.
Address: 77-85 Fulham Palace Rd, Hammersmith, London, W6 8JB; 020 8741 7070;
e-mail: Myles.Archibald@harpercollins.co.uk
www.harpercollins.co.uk www.newnaturalists.com

THE LANGFORD PRESS

Imprints: Wildlife Art Series (WAS) — *American Birding Sketchbook* by Mike Warren, *Jewels beyond the Plough* (grasslands) by R.Jefferson and John Davis and *Troubled Waters* (Albatrosses) by Bruce Pearson the latest in a series of lavishly illustrated books. First two volumes in myweebooks range aimed at children are available as both hardbacks and paperbacks.
New for 2013: Wildlife & People series to continue with volumes on Red Kites, Harriers, Honey Buzzards, Short-eared Owls and a book by Derek Ratcliffe. New WAS titles will include a book by John Threlfall showing his coastal paintings. New titles in the myweebooks range.
Address: 10 New Road, Langtoft, Peterborough PE6 9LE; e-mail: sales@langford-press.co.uk
www.langford-press.co.uk

NEW HOLLAND PUBLISHERS (UK) LTD

Imprints: Imprints include New Holland UK, New Holland Australia, New Holland New Zealand and Struik. Specializes in field guides, photographic guides, garden wildlife books and other illustrated titles on birds and general wildlife, plus personality-led natural history. Bestsellers include *Advanced Bird ID Guide, Atlas of Rare Birds, Bill Oddie's Birds of Britain and Ireland, Birds' Magic Moments, Birds of the Indian Ocean Islands, Creative Bird Photography, Field Guide to the Birds of Borneo, Field Guide to the Birds of South-East Asia, New Holland Concise Bird Guide, Sasol Birds of Southern Africa, Slater Field Guide to Australian Birds, Tales of a Tabloid Twitcher* and *The Urban Birder*.
Address: Garfield House, 86-88 Edgware Road, London W2 2EA; 020 7724 7773; (fax) 020 7258 1293; e-mail: simon.papps@nhpub.co.uk
www.newhollandpublishers.com

PRINCETON/WILDGUIDES LTD

Imprints: *WILDGuides*: natural history fieldguides covering Britain's wildlife: butterflies, dragonflies, reptiles and amphibians, orchids, arable plants and plant galls.
OCEANGuides: identification guides to marine wildlife covering Antarctic, Atlantic and Pacific oceans.
Destination Guides: Lavishly illustrated visitor guides to some of the world's most diverse wildlife locations.
Recently published: *Britain's Sea Mammals; Animals of the Masai Mara; Birds of the Masai Mara; Field Guide to the Wildlife of South Georgia; Petrels,*

BOOK SELLERS

Albatrosses, and Storm-Petrels of North America; Birdscapes.
New for 2013: *The World's Rarest Birds; Britain's Hoverflies; Britain's Day-flying Moths; The Unfeathered Bird.* Please visit our website for latest information.
Ordering Address: Princeton University Press, c/o John Wiley & Sons Ltd, New Era Estate, Oldlands Way, Bognor Regis, West Sussex, PO22 9NQ.
Sales office: 0800 243407
Order e-mail: cs-books@wiley.com
www.press.princeton.edu/wildguides

THE SOUND APPROACH

Company ethos: An independent publishing company committed to turning bird-watchers into bird-listeners. We publish high quality books by talented authors and aim to change people's perception of the world of birdsong. We hope our books provide readers with the tools for understanding the birds heard in the field and encourage them to start recording for themselves.
Imprints: Founder Mark Constantine launched the company with *The Sound Approach To Birding* and followed with *Petrels Night And Day* by Magnus Robb and *Birding From The Hip* by Anthony McGeehan.
New for 2013: Latest publication *Catching the Bug* by Mark Constantine and Nick Hopper available from 2012. All titles come with two CDs packed with exclusive high quality recordings of bird songs and call, colour photographs and illustrations by renowned artist Killian Mullarney.
Address: 12 Market Street, Poole, Dorset BH15 1NF; 01202 641 004; e-mail: info@soundapproach.co.uk
www.soundapproach.co.uk

BOOK SELLERS

BOOKS FOR BIRDERS

Company ethos: Offering a fast, friendly and helpful service to customers requiring books, DVDs, CDs and CD-ROMS covering birds and all other natural history subjects.
Key subjects: Comprehensive range of bird titles covering Britain, Europe and the world, plus a variety of other natural history subjects.
Other services: Fully searchable stock list on website. Free postage and packing in Britain.
Opening times: 9am-5pm for office, 24hr orderline on website.
Address: Books For Birders, Stone Runner, Coast Road, Cley-next-the-Sea, Norfolk NR25 7RZ: 01263 741 139; (fax) 01263 741 173;
www.birdingworld.co.uk
e-mail sales@birdingworld.co.uk

CALLUNA BOOKS

Company ethos: We specialise in buying and selling out of print natural history titles, with an emphasis on quality stock at competitive prices.
Key subjects: Birds, mammals, flora, invertebrates

in the UK and worldwide, including the Poyser and New Naturalist series, and general natural history, conservation and countryside titles including some reports and journals. Stock of 2000+ titles maintained.
Other services: Catalogues issued (usually 3 p.a). We exhibit at some bird fairs including Rutland Water. Wants lists welcomed – no obligation to buy.
Opening times: Mail order but viewing by appointment possible.
Address: Moor Edge, 2 Bere Road, Wareham, Dorset BH20 4DD; 01929 552 560.
e-mail: enquiries@callunabooks.co.uk
www.callunabooks.co.uk

NHBS - everything for wildlife, science & environment

Company ethos: A unique natural history, conservation and environmental supplier offering the world's largest range of wildlife books and field equipment.
Key subjects: Natural history, birding, conservation, environmental science, zoology, habitats, botany, marine biology, bat detecting, entomology, GPS.
Other services: Search and browse our full online catalogue of more than 110,000 titles (www.nhbs. com). Rapidly growing range of field equipment and essential travel kit for safari and expeditions.
Opening times: Mon-Fri (9am-5pm), for mail-order service. Browse or order anytime at www.nhbs.com
Address: 2-3 Wills Road, Totnes, Devon TQ9 5XN; 01803 865 913;
e-mail: customer.services@nhbs.co.uk
www.nhbs.com

PICTURE BOOK

Company ethos: Picture Book is a general bookshop specialising in bird books and local history.
Key subjects: Birdwatching, natural history, local history. Churnet Valley publish local history and Arnold Bennett titles in paperback and hardback with introductions by the Arnold Bennett Society.
Other services: Amazon mail order, new and secondhand books.
Opening times: The shop is open to the public Tuesday to Saturday 9.30am - 4.30pm (Thursday - 2.30pm). Best to phone to check if travelling any distance.
Address: Picture Book, 6 Stanley Street, Leek ST13 5HG; 01538 399 033 & 384 337; (fax) 01538 399 696.
e-mail: info@leekbooks.co.uk www.leekbooks.co.uk
or www.picturebookleek.co.uk

TRADE DIRECTORY

111

CLOTHING AND EQUIPMENT SUPPLIERS

SECOND NATURE

Company ethos: Buying and selling out-of-print/secondhand/antiquarian books on natural history, topography and travel.

Key subjects: Birds, mammals, flowers and all other aspects of natural history.

Other services; Exhibits at bird/wildlife fairs.

New for 2013: A comprehensive website - www.secondnaturebooks.com

Opening times: Mail order only.

Address: Knapton Book Barn, Back Lane, Knapton, York YO26 6QJ; 01904 795 489.

e-mail: SecondnatureYork@aol.com
www.secondnaturebooks.com

SUBBUTEO NATURAL HISTORY BOOKS

Company ethos: Specialisation and careful selection has enhanced our reputation for supplying and publishing natural history books, DVDs, travel and fieldguides for those who enjoy birdwatching and the natural world, while providing a fast, knowledgeable and efficient service.

Key subjects: Ornithology; UK, Europe & worldwide, mammals, reptiles & amphibians, aquatic fauna, butterflies & moths, plants & fungi, natural history, ecology & environmental science, wildlife art & photography.

Other services: Comprehensive online bookstore, gift wrap service, booklist service, worldwide book sourcing. Online ordering, with free delivery on orders over £50 (in-print titles & UK titles only), free catalogue, updates and monthly e-newsletter. Subbuteo Natural History Books is a division of CJ WildBird Foods Ltd.

New for 2013: Continuously adding new titles to our extensive range - call for a catalogue, visit the website or visit us in Shropshire. You can now find us on Twitter and Facebook for the latest news and offers.

Opening times: Call 01743 709 420 Monday to Friday (9am-5pm). Saturday (9am-12pm). Online ordering 24 hrs.

Address: The Rea, Upton Magna, Shrewsbury, Shropshire SY4 4UR; 01743 709 420; (fax) 01743 709 504; e-mail: info@wildlifebooks.com
www.wildlifebooks.com

WILDSOUNDS

Company ethos: Species Champion for the endangered Spoonbill Sandpiper. Donates a significant portion of profit to bird conservation, committed to sound environmental practices, official bookseller to African Bird Club. Operates the *Bird Watching* magazine bookshop.

Key product lines: Bird and other wildlife books, including wildlife art and photography, at discounted prices. Publisher of *Birding in Eastern Europe* by Gerard Gorman. Attends all major Bird Fairs and many local events.

New for 2013: Expanded range on offer - see the enhanced and improved website.

Opening times: Weekdays (9.30am-5pm).

Address: Cross Street, Salthouse, Norfolk NR25 7XH; 01263 741 836; e-mail: sales@wildsounds.com
www.wildsounds.com

CLOTHING SUPPLIERS

COUNTRY INNOVATION

Company ethos: Specialists in high performance clothing, footwear and accessories specifically for the birdwatching market. Friendly advice by well trained staff. Total customer satisfaction.

Key product lines: Full range of outdoor wear: jackets, fleeces, trousers, travel clothing, Ventile garments, Brasher footwear, Tilley hats, bags and accessories. Ladies fit available.

Other services: Retail shop, mail order sales and online sales at www.countryinnovation.co.uk. Check website for appearances at shows and events.

New for 2013: Traveller range – Traveller Jacket, a unique multi-pocketed waterproof jacket, Traveller Waistcoat, Shirts and Trousers all made from a lightweight, highly breathable fabric, perfect for travel and summer birding.

Opening times; Tues-Fri (9am-5pm), Sat (10am-2pm).

Address: 1 Broad Street, Congresbury, North Somerset BS49 5DG; 01934 877 333.

e-mail: sales@countryinnovation.com
www.countryinnovation.com

PARÁMO DIRECTIONAL CLOTHING SYSTEMS

Company ethos: Innovators of technical mountain, birding and travel clothing using revolutionary and long-lasting Nikwax fabrics and functional design to provide quiet performance and comfort for all outdoor enthusiasts, professionals & fieldworkers. Ethical manufacture.

Key product lines: Waterproof jackets and trousers, technical baselayers, insulating overlayers & ultra-cooling travel wear. Of especial note: Halcon & Pájaro birdwatching jackets & Pájaro waterproof trousers, new Halcon Waistcoat with 14 pockets, plus Andy Rouse Limited Edition Aspira Smock, Cascada Trousers, Grid Baselayer and Katmai Shirt.

Other services: Repair, service & recycling of Páramo garments; online sales at www.naturallyparamo.co.uk

HOLIDAY COMPANIES

New for 2013: Páramo Recycling scheme launched. Páramo garments can be returned for refurbishment or recycling and will earn their owners a reward. Info at paramo.co.uk/recycle.
Opening times; For independent retailers, consult our website or ring 01892 786 444 for stockist list and catalogue pack. Páramo London Store, 29 Henrietta Street, WC2E 8NA open 10.30am – 7pm Mon – Sat, 11am- 4pm on Sunday.
Address: Unit F, Durgates Industrial Estates, Wadhurst, East Sussex TN5 6DF, UK; 01892 786 444. e-mail: info@paramo.co.uk www.paramo.co.uk

EQUIPMENT SUPPLIERS

ALWYCH BOOKS
Company ethos: The Bird Watcher's All-Weather Flexible Pocket Note Book.
Key product lines: Alwych Notebooks with all-weather flexible covers.
Opening times: Order online 24 hours a day.
Address: 84 Stewarton Street, Wishaw, Lanarkshire ML2 8AG. Sales: 0845 270 2828; Admin: 01698 357 223; www.alwych.co.uk

BIRD IMAGES
Company ethos: High quality products at affordable prices.
Key product lines: Bird DVDs. A range of titles including identification guides and innovative guides to birdwatching places.
New for 2013: Birdwatching In Wales DVD (219 species covered in 2 hours 11 minutes). Price £13.95.
Opening times: Telephone first.
Address: 28 Carousel Walk, Sherburn in Elmet, North Yorkshire LS25 6LP; 01977 684 666.
e-mail: paul@birdvideodvd.com
www.birdvideodvd.com

BIRDGUIDES LTD
Company ethos: Better birding through technology. The number one birder's website.
Key product lines: Software and video guides to birds and insects. Rare bird news services via web, apps, email and sms. An expanding range of natural history products for mobile phones.
New for 2013: New apps, search for BirdGuides on the iTunes store.
Address: BirdGuides Ltd, 3 Warple Mews, Warple Way, London W3 0RF; 020 8141 3272; order line (freephone) 0800 919 391; www.birdguides.com
e-mail: contact@birdguides.com

BLUEBIRD TECHNOLOGY

Company ethos: Bluebird Technology focuses on creating quality wildlife recording software products for all birders to enjoy. All of our software is really easy to use; you don't have to be a computer or database geek to use it.
Key product lines: Bird Journal for the Desktop, Bird Journal for the iPhone.
Opening times: Lines are open 9am-5pm (UK time), Monday to Friday, except national holidays. Calls charged at local rate.
Address: Bluebird Technology, 1 Turnbridge Court, Cambridge, CB24 4GH; 0845 094 6012.
e-mail: mail@bluebirdtechnology.com
www.bluebirdtechnology.com
Follow us on Twitter: http://twitter.com/Bluebird_Tech/; FaceBook: http://www.facebook.com/BluebirdTechnology/

WILDLIFE WATCHING SUPPLIES
Company ethos: To bring together a comprehensive range of materials, clothing and equipment to make it easier and more comfortable for you to blend in with the environment. Quick and friendly service.
Key product lines: Hides, camouflage, bean bags, lens and camera covers, clothing etc.
New for 2013: Some new designs and more outdoor products.
Opening times: Mon to Fri (9am-5pm), mail order. Visitors by appointment.
Address: Wildlife Watching Supplies, Tiverton Way, Tiverton Business Park, Tiverton, Devon EX16 6TG; +44 (0)1884 254 191; Fax: +44 (0)1884 250 460.
e-mail: enquiries@wildlifewatchingsupplies.co.uk
www.wildlifewatchingsupplies.co.uk

WILDSOUNDS
Company ethos: Species Champion for the highly-endangered Spoonbill Sandpiper. Donates a significant portion of profit to bird conservation, committed to sound environmental practices. Operates the Bird Watching magazine shop, selling books and DVDs.
Key product lines: Mail order wildlife CDs, DVDs and multi-media guides at discounted prices. Distributor of many best-selling DVDs i.e. British Butterflies, North Norfolk Coast - Birder's Guide, plus DVDs produced by Dave Gosney (easybirder). Field recording equipment stockist. Attends all major Bird Fairs and many local events.
New for 2013: See enhanced and improved website.
Opening times: Weekdays (9.30am-5pm).
Address: Cross Street, Salthouse, Norfolk NR25 7XH; 01263 741 836; e-mail: sales@wildsounds.com
www.wildsounds.com

TRADE DIRECTORY

113

HOLIDAY COMPANIES

AVIAN ADVENTURES

Company ethos: First class value-for-money tours, escorted by friendly, experienced leaders at a fairly relaxed pace. Financial protection - ATOL 3367.
Types of tours: Birdwatching, birds and wildlife photography and wildlife safaris, all suitable for both the first-time and the more experienced traveller.
Destinations: 50 tours worldwide.
New for 2013: Bhutan; Trinidad & St. Lucia; Spain (for Iberian lynx); Mongolia; Sweden (Birds & Butterflies); Spain photographic tour.
Brochure from: 49 Sandy Road, Norton, Stourbridge, DY8 3AJ; 01384 372 013; (Fax)01384 441 340. e-mail: avianadventures@btinternet.com
www.avianadventures.co.uk

BIRDFINDERS

Company ethos: Top-value birding tours to see all specialities/endemics of a country/area, using leading UK and local guides. ATOL 5406.
Types of tours: Birdwatching holidays for all abilities.
Destinations: Nearly 80 tours in UK, Europe, Africa, Asia, Australasia, North, Central and South America and Antarctica.
New for 2013: Cape Verde Islands, Japan winter, Netherlands winter, Ohio & Michigan (Magee Marsh) and Portugal.
Brochure from: Vaughan Ashby, Westbank, Cheselbourne, Dorset DT2 7NW. 01258 839 066. Our office is open seven days a week (8am-8pm). e-mail: info@birdfinders.co.uk
www.birdfinders.co.uk

BIRDWATCHING BREAKS

Company ethos: Overseas breaks and Black Isle Birding: watching birds in their natural habitat and putting money into the local economy.
Types of tours: Birding tours for all abilities to little-known destinations, plus more traditional areas, using local guides in addition to our own. No more than 8 clients per tour, to give the best views of birds and wildlife. We also specialise in Northern Scotland including the Highlands and Islands under the Black Isle Birding banner. Many of our tours are suitable for photography.
Destinations: Australia, Belarus, Canada, Cambodia & Vietnam, Chile, Cyprus, Ethiopia, France, Ghana, Hungary, India, Israel, Jamaica, Japan, Lesser Antilles, Malaysia, Russia, Senegal, Seychelles, Uganda, USA and numerous in Scotland. Some tours are regularly featured, while others are old favourites re-introduced for this year.
New for 2013: Bolivia, British Columbia, Myanmar, Slovenia & Croatia.
Brochure from: Birdwatchinig Breaks, Cygnus House, Gordon's Mill, Balblair, Ross-shire IV7 8LQ; 01381 610 495; e-mail: enquiries@birdwatchingbreaks.com or markfin55@btinternet.com
www.birdwatchingbreaks.com

BIRD WATCHING & WILDLIFE CLUB

Company ethos: To provide birdwatchers with high quality, reasonably priced accommodation, enabling them to experience the abundance of wildlife in the area.
Types of tours: Based at the 3-star, 50-bedroom Grant Arms Hotel, the BWWC provides information and advice on wildlife sites nearby (guided trips can also be arranged), helping guests to make the most of their holiday whilst remaining free to create their own itinerary.
Destinations: Cairngorms, Speyside and North East Scotland.
Opening times: 7am -10.30pm, seven days a week.
Brochure from: Grant Arms Hotel, 25 The Square, Grantown-on-Spey, Highlands PH26 3HF; 01479 872 526; e-mail: bookings@bwwc.co.uk
www.bwwc.co.uk

BRITISH-BULGARIAN SOCIETY

Company ethos: To introduce people to the beauty of Bulgarian wildlife at exceptional value prices with expert leaders. ATOL 4465.
Types of tours: Birdwatching tours in winter, spring and autumn, also early summer and midsummer butterfly tours. Group size 12-14 persons.
Destinations: Specialists to Bulgaria, over 35 years experience.
New for 2013: Spring birdwatching; Spring natural history in Eastern Rhodope Mountains; Bulgarian mountains and Greek wetlands; Autumn migration on the Via Pontica.
Free society membership for 2013 with all B-BS tour bookings.
Brochure from: Balkania Travel Ltd, Avanta Harrow, 79 College Road, Harrow, Middlesex, HA1 1BD. (Tel) 020 7536 9400; e-mail: ognian@balkaniatravel.com or annie.kay@btinternet.com www.bbfs.org.uk

CLASSIC JOURNEYS

Company ethos: Professional and friendly company, providing well organised and enjoyable walking, wildlife and photography holidays.

Types of tours: Walking holidays, plus wildlife and photography holidays.
Destinations: Antarctica, The Arctic, Brazil, Bhutan, Borneo, Canada, Ecuador & Galapagos, India, Morocco, Myanmar (Burma), Nepal, Peru, Sri Lanka, Tanzania and Tibet.
New for 2013: Myanmar - The Land of Golden Pagodas.
Opening times: Mon-Fri (9:30am - 4pm).
Further Information: www.classicjourneys.co.uk 01773 873 497; e-mail: info@classicjourneys.co.uk

DORSET BIRDING
Company ethos: To provide a local knowledge and an expertise of Dorset's birds and wildlife catering for all levels of experience and tailor-made to your requirements.
Types of tours: A guiding service for individuals and groups aimed at providing an experience of Dorset's birds, wildlife and landscapes. Although there is a particular emphasis on birds, all species groups are covered. Half-day, full day, weekends or longer breaks are available.
Destinations: Dorset.
Brochure from: Moor Edge, 2 Bere Road, Wareham, Dorset BH20 4DD;01929 552 560.
e-mail: enquiries@dorsetbirdingandwildlife.co.uk
www.dorsetbirdingandwildlife.co.uk

GLENLOY WILDLIFE
Company ethos: We offer guided exploration of the stunning West Coast of Scotland, based from beautiful Glen Loy near Fort William in a former hunting lodge with views over the
Nevis Range. The glen contains Red Deer, Eagles, Otter and Chequered Skippers with Pine Martens visiting the Lodge each evening.
Types of tours: We visit a variety of habitats by minibus and by foot. Suitable for anyone who can walk 3-4 miles.
Destinations: We explore the region of Lochaber, including the Great Glen, Ardnamurchan peninsula and the Small Isles.
Further information from: Jon Mercer, Glenloy Lodge Guest House, Banavie, Nr Fort William PH33 7PD; 01397 712 700 or 07817 443 370.
e-mail: info@glenloylodge.co.uk
www.glenloylodge.co.uk
www.glenloy-wildlife.org.uk

HEATHERLEA
Company ethos: Exciting holidays to see all the birds of Scotland and selected overseas destinations. Experienced guides and comfortable award winning hotel offering great customer service.
Types of tours: Birdwatching and other wildlife watching tours.
Destinations: Scottish Highlands, including holidays

from our base in Nethybridge, plus Outer Hebrides, Orkney, Shetlands and more. Selected overseas destinations include the Pyrenees, Lesvos, Kenya and Trinidad.
New for 2013: Scotland - Heatherlea have five stars from visitScotland, rating our Wildlife Experience as 'Exceptional'. We are the only operator in Scotland with this, the highest possible grading. New holidays this year include Highlands and Mull, Highlands and Skye, Scottish Specials including 'The Burma Bank', Orkney Island Adventure and many more. Overseas - new destinations include Turkey, Azores, Faroes, Asturias, Andaman Islands and Skyros.
Brochure from: The Mountview Hotel, Nethybridge, Inverness-shire PH25 3EB; 01479 821 248; (Fax)01479 821 515; e-mail: info@heatherlea.co.uk
www.heatherlea.co.uk - twitter@heatherleabirds

IBERIAN WILDLIFE TOURS
Company ethos: Highly experienced bilingual guides offer top quality, low impact small group tours to help visitors observe and appreciate Spain's enormous wealth of wildlife.
Types of tours: Tailor-made and fixed itinerary trips, from half and full-day local trips up to 15 days for longer excursions. For individuals, couples and groups (max. 14 clients with two guides). Birds, wildflowers, mammals, butterflies, dragonflies, reptiles and amphibians.
Destinations: Throughout Spain, but principally Madrid and surrounds, Extremadura & Gredos, Picos de Europa, Pyrenees and Andújar (Iberian lynx +).
Information from: John Muddeman, Teresa Farino and Mike Lockwood, Calle Alcocer 1 1-C, Fresnedillas de la Oliva, 28214 Madrid, Spain; (0034) 649 608 747.
e-mail: john@iberianwildlife.com
www.iberianwildlife.com

JULIAN SYKES WILDLIFE HOLIDAYS
Company ethos: Smaller groups – bigger experiences.
Types of tours: From the beginner to the keenest watcher, our tailor-made tours, holidays and short breaks feature all types of wildlife with an emphasis on various species. We keep it interesting, informative and fun!
Destinations: Spain (Extremadura, Pyrenees, Picos de Europa, Iberian Lynx, Cantabrian Bear, Iberian Wolf and Wild Cat), plus India (Tigers & Taj Mahal), Southern Morocco, Jordan (Petra & Wildlife), Finland - (Owls & Woodpeckers), Southern Turkey and Estonia (Mammals).
Information from: Julian Sykes or Jane Lees, Avinguda Font d'en Carros 16,Oliva 46780, Valencia, Spain (0034 687 567 286 or 630 603 753).
e-mail: info@juliansykeswildlife.com
www.juliansykeswildlife.com

115

HOLIDAY COMPANIES

NATURETREK

Company ethos: Friendly, gentle-paced, birdwatching holidays with broad-brush approach. Sympathetic to other wildlife interests, history and local culture. Also operate faster-paced bargain birdwatching selection. ATOL no 2692.

Types of tours: Escorted birdwatching, botanical and natural history holidays worldwide.

Destinations: Worldwide - see brochure.

New for 2013: 30+ exciting new European tours, plus several new long-haul destinations.

Brochure from: Cheriton Mill, Cheriton, Alresford, Hampshire SO24 0NG; 01962 733 051; (Fax)01962 736 426; e-mail: info@naturetrek.co.uk
www.naturetrek.co.uk

NORTHERN FRANCE WILDLIFE TOURS

Company ethos: Friendly personal attention, including meals by a qualified chef(Shirley). Normally a maximum of 5 per group, but other arrangements can be made. Totally flexible approach.

Types of tours: Beginners to experienced birders. Local birds include Black Woodpecker, Bluethroat, Melodious Warbler.

Destinations: Brittany, Normandy, and Pays de la Loire.

Brocure from: Roy and Shirley Croucher, Place de l'église, 53700, Averton,France.
00 33 243 00 6969; e-mail: nfwt@online.fr.
www.northernfrancewildlifetours.com

NORTH WEST BIRDS

Company ethos: Friendly, relaxed and unhurried but targetted to scarce local birds.

Types of tours: Very small groups (up to four) based on large family home in South Lakes with good home cooking. Short breaks with birding in local area. Butterflies in season.

Destinations: Local to Northwest England. Lancashire, Morecambe Bay and Lake District.

Brochure from: Mike Robinson, Barn Close, Beetham, Cumbria LA7 7AL; (Tel/fax)015395 63191. e-mail: mike@nwbirds.co.uk www.nwbirds.co.uk

ORIOLE BIRDING

Company ethos: Enhancing your ID skills and enjoyment of birding with small group tours.

Types of tours: Norfolk and South Wales birding tours year-round, covering all the best sites and species, plus a selection of Britain's best destinations. Also a comprehensive range of international holidays and pelagics. ATOL protected 6839.

Destinations: Norfolk, South Wales, Solway, Speyside, Cornwall, Isles of Scilly, pelagics, North-east England, Fair Isle, County Wexford, Mull and Iona, Extremadura, Romania, South Africa, The Gambia, Israel, Finland, Madeira, India, Lesvos, Turkey, Morocco, Poland, Holland.

New for 2013: Somerset Levels & Forest of Dean, Southern Ireland, Shetland, Finland Summer Wildlife, Snowdonia in Winter, Sicily.

Brochure from: Oriole Birding, 8 Newcastle Hill, Bridgend CF31 4EY; 01656 711 152.
e-mail: info@oriolebirding.com
www.oriolebirding.com

ORNITHOLIDAYS

Company ethos: Oldest bird tour company in the world (established 1965). Friendly and fun holidays led by full-time tour leaders. ATOL no 0743.

Types of tours: Escorted birdwatching, photographic and natural history tours.

Destinations: Worldwide including Trinidad and Tobago, Chile, Cuba, Bhutan, Taiwan, Sri Lanka, South Africa, Iceland, Spitsbergen and Antarctica.

New for 2013: Jordan, Australia, St Lucia, Guyana, Morocco, USA (Texas) and Iceland.

Brochure from: 29 Straight Mile, Romsey, Hampshire SO51 9BB; 01794 519 445; (fax) 01794 523 544.
e-mail: info@ornitholidays.co.uk
www.ornitholidays.co.uk

ROMNEY MARSH BIRDWATCHING BREAKS

Company ethos: To pass on an appreciation of the wildlife of Romney Marsh in a family-friendly atmosphere.

Types of tours: Fully inclusive 3 or 5 day Birdwatching Breaks based at our cottage in Lydd-on-Sea. Also, one day birdwatching and historical tours around Romney Marsh.

Destinations: Romney Marsh, including Dungeness and Rye Harbour, and elsewhere across Kent and Sussex.

New for 2013: Day trips to northern France.

Brochure from: Paul Trodd, Plovers, 1 Toby Road, Lydd-on-Sea, Romney Marsh, Kent TN29 9PG; 01797 366 935 & 07920 197 535; www. plovers.co.uk
e-mail: troddy@plovers.co.uk

SPAINBIRDS NATURE TOURS

Company ethos: A registered travel agent legally able to offer ground packages with a small team of highly experienced, resident, long-standing bilingual guides to ensure high quality, low-impact, small-group experiences.

Types of tours: Mainly birdwatching and photography tours. Tailor-made and more fixed itinerary trips, from half-day local trips up to 15 days for longer excursions. For individuals, couples or groups of all knowledge levels; max. 14 clients with 2 guides. Birds, mammals, butterflies, dragonflies, etc.

Destinations: Throughout Spain; principally Madrid, La Mancha, Andújar (Iberian lynx+), Strait of Gibraltar, Doñana, Extremadura & Gredos, Picos de Europa & Pyrenees.

Brochure from: Santi Villa C/Nogal, 7 - 1°B,

Guadalix de la Sierra, 28794 Madrid, Spain;
(+34) 687 83 77 19; e-mail: info@spainbirds.com
www.spainbirds.com

SPEYSIDE WILDLIFE

Company ethos: Fun-filled wildlife experiences with expert guides, where you are always treated as an individual, not one of a crowd.

Types of tours: Fully inclusive bird and mammal watching holidays in Scotland and Overseas (ATOL no 4259). Also tailor-made trips, day guiding and dusk watches.

Destinations: Speyside in the Cairngorms National Park and around Scotland, Europe; Scandinavia and the Arctic; North, Central and South America; Africa, Asia.

New for 2013: Botswana, Mongolia, New Mexico (USA), Pantanal (Brazil).

Brochure from: Wester Camerorie, Ballieward, Grantown-on-Spey, Cairngorms National Park, Highlands PH26 3PR:
(Tel/fax) +44 (0) 1479 812 498 ;
e-mail: enquiries@speysidewildlife.co.uk
www.speysidewildlife.co.uk, Twitter:@SpeyWildlife
www.facebook.com/speysidewildlife

SPEYSIDE WILDLIFE *international.*

SUNBIRD

Company ethos: Enjoyable birdwatching tours led by full-time professional leaders. ATOL no 3003.

Types of tours: Birdwatching, Birds & Music, Birds & History.

Destinations: Worldwide.

New for 2013: A variety of exciting new tours can be found on the Sunbird website

Brochure from: 26B The Market Square, Potton, Sandy, Bedfordshire SG19 2NP; 01767 262 522; (fax) 01767 262 916; e-mail: sunbird@sunbirdtours.co.uk
www.sunbirdtours.co.uk check new destinations.

THE TRAVELLING NATURALIST

Company ethos: Friendly, easy-going, expertly-led birdwatching and wildlife tours. ATOL no.3435. AITO 1124.

Types of tours: Birds and Butterflies, Butterflies and Flowers, Tigers, Whales, also Wild Ambitions – wildlife holidays for independent travellers.

Destinations: Worldwide.

New for 2013: Moths in Dordogne, Orcas & Auroras in Iceland, Spanish Lynx Quest.

Brochure from: PO Box 3141, Dorchester, Dorset DT1 2XD; 01305 267994; (fax) 01305 265 506.
e-mail: info@naturalist.co.uk
www.naturalist.co.uk www.wildambitions.co.uk

THINKGALAPAGOS

Company ethos: Specialists in the Galapagos Islands, great value, expert guides and personal attention to ensure a once-in-a-lifetime adventure

travel experience.

Types of tours: Friendly and relaxed holidays that are educationally orientated for people with a keen interest in wildlife and photography. Suitable for both the first-time and more experienced traveller.

Destinations: Galapagos and mainland Ecuador.

Brochure from: Rachel Dex, 25 Trinity Lane, Beverley, East Yorkshire HU17 0DY; 01482 872 716.
info@thinkgalapagos.com www.thinkgalapagos.com

WILD INSIGHTS

Company ethos: Friendly, no-rush tours designed to savour, understand and enjoy birds and wildlife fully, rather than simply build large tick lists. Emphasis on quality. ATOL no 5429 (in association with Wildwings).

Types of tours: Skills-building UK courses, UK workshops plus a range of overseas tours.

Destinations: Various UK locations, plus selected destinations throughout USA, Central America, Africa, Northern India and Europe.

New for 2013: South Africa:Kruger & Drakensberg, Hungary in Autumn.

Calender brochure from: Yew Tree Farmhouse, Craignant, Selattyn, Oswestry, Salop SY10 7NP; (Tel/fax) 01691 718 740; e-mail: keith.offord@virgin.net
www.wildinsights.co.uk

WILDWINGS

Company ethos: Superb value voyages and holidays led by expert guides.

Types of tours: Birdwatching holidays, whale and dolphin-watching holidays, mammal tours and wildlife cruises worldwide.

Destinations: Europe, Arctic, Asia, The Americas, Antarctica, Africa, Australasia and the Pacific.

New for 2013: Chile, Ecuador, Ethiopia, Guyana, Norway, Peru, S W Pacific Cruises.

Brochure from: Davis House, Lodge Causeway, Fishponds, Bristol BS16 3JB. 0117 9658 333
e-mail: wildlife@wildwings.co.uk
www.wildwings.co.uk

YORKSHIRE COAST NATURE

Company ethos: Yorkshire Coast Nature is dedicated to providing unforgettable wildlife experiences in one of England's most beautiful, inspiring regions. At YCN we make it a policy to help the wildlife and places which give us so much enjoyment. We allocate significant company resources to local and national conservation projects.

Types of tours: Nature Tours from Snakes and Badgers to Honey Buzzards and rare bird finding on the glorious east coast of Yorkshire

Destinations: Yorkshire Coast and beyond.

New for 2013: North Yorkshire nature safaris in forest and moorland, Seabird Spectacular on Flamborough Headland, Migration Discovery Days at Spurn NNR.

TRADE DIRECTORY

OPTICAL DEALERS

Address: 5 Coastguard Cottages, Lighthouse Road, Flamborough, YO15 1AW. 01262 851 999; e-mail: info@yorkshirecoastnature.co.uk www.yorkshirecoastnature.co.uk

OPTICAL DEALERS

CLIFTON CAMERAS
Company ethos: Optical specialists for binoculars and spotting scopes based near Slimbridge Wetland Centre in Gloucestershire. Main sponsors of the Dursley birdwatching society.
Optical stock: All top brands stocked. Nikon Premier Dealer, Swarovski Premier Dealer, Zeiss Centre Partner and Leica Premier Dealer.
Non-optical stock: Professional camera supplier, Canon, Nikon, Pentax, Sigma and Gitzo Tripods to name a few.
New products to try: Zeiss Conquest and Victory HT binoculars, Swarovski ATX modular spotting scopes and Leica M cameras.
Opening times: Mon-Sat (9am-5.30pm).
Address: 28 Parsonage Street, Dursley, Gloucestershire GL11 4AA;01453 548 128.
e-mail: sales@cliftoncameras.co.uk
www.cliftoncameras.co.uk

cliftoncameras.co.uk

FOCALPOINT
Company ethos: Friendly advice by well-trained staff, competitive prices, no "grey imports".
Viewing facilities: Fantastic open countryside for superb viewing from the shop, plenty of wildlife. Parking for up to 20 cars.
Optical stock: All leading brands of binoculars and telescopes from stock, plus many pre-owned binoculars and telescopes available.
Non-optical stock: Bird books, outdoor clothing, boots, tripods plus full range of Skua products etc. available from stock.
Opening times: Mon-Fri (9:30am-5pm); Sat (10.00am-4.00pm)
Address: Marbury House Farm, Bentleys Farm Lane, Higher Whitley, Warrington, Cheshire WA4 4QW; 01925 730 399; e-mail: focalpoint@dial.pipex.com
www.fpoint.co.uk

FOCUS OPTICS
Company ethos: Friendly, expert service. Top quality instruments. No 'grey imports'.
Viewing facilities: Our own pool and nature reserve with feeding stations.
Optical stock: Full range of leading makes of binoculars and telescopes.
Non-optical stock: Waterproof clothing, fleeces, walking boots and shoes, bird food and feeders. Books, videos, walking poles.
Opening times: Mon-Sat (9am-5pm). Some Bank-holidays.

Address: Church Lane, Corley, Coventry, CV7 8BA; 01676 540 501/542 476; (Fax) 01676 540 930. e mail: enquiries@focusoptics.eu
www.focusoptics.eu

IN-FOCUS
Company ethos: The binocular and telescope specialists, offering customers informed advice at birdwatching venues throughout the country. Leading sponsor of the British Birdwatchng Fair.
Viewing facilities: Available at all shops (contact your local outlet), or at field events (10am-4pm) at bird reserves (see *Bird Watching* magazine or website www.at-infocus.co.uk for calendar)
Optical stock: Many leading makes of binoculars and telescopes, plus own-brand Delta range of binoculars and tripods.
Non-optical stock: Wide range of tripods, clamps and other accessories. Repair service available.
Opening times: These can vary, so please contact local shop or website before travelling.

BRANCHES:
Gloucestershire: The Wildfowl and Wetlands Trust, Slimbridge, Gloucestershire GL2 7BT.
Tel: 01453 890 978.

Hertfordshire: Willows Farm Village, Coursers Road, London Colney, Hertfordshire AL2 1BB.
Tel: 01727 827 799.

Lancashire: The Wildfowl and Wetlands Trust, Martin Mere, Burscough, Ormskirk, Lancashire L40 0TA.
Tel: 01704 897 020.

London, South West: The Wildfowl and Wetlands Trust, London Wetland Centre, Queen Elizabeth's Walk, Barnes, London SW13 9WT.
Tel: 020 8409 4433.

Norfolk: Main Street, Titchwell, Nr. Kings Lynn, Norfolk PE31 8BB
Tel: 01485 210 101.

Rutland: Anglian Water Birdwatching Centre, Egleton Reserve, Rutland Water, Rutland LE15 8BT
Tel: 01572 770 656.

Yorkshire: Westleigh House Office Estate, Wakefield Road, Denby Dale, West Yorkshire HD8 8QJ
Tel: 01484 864 729.

LONDON CAMERA EXCHANGE
Company ethos: To supply good quality optical equipment at a competitive price, helped by knowlegeable staff.
Viewing facilities: In shop and at local shows. Contact local branch for details of local events.
Optical stock: All leading makes of binoculars and scopes.
Non-optical stock: All main brands of photo, digital and video equipment.
Opening times: Most branches open 9am to 5.30pm.

BRANCHES
Bath: 13 Cheap Street, Bath, Avon, BA1 1NB; 01225 462 234.

OPTICAL IMPORTERS AND MANUFACTURERS

Bristol: 53 The Horsefair, Bristol BS1 3JP; 01179 276 185.

Chester: 9 Bridge Street Row, CH1 1NW; 01244 326 531.

Chesterfield: 1A South Street, Chesterfield, Derbyshire, S40 1QZ; 01246 211 891.

Colchester: 12 Led Lane, Colchester, Essex CO1 1LS; 01206 573 444.

Derby: 17 Sadler Gate, Derby, Derbyshire, DE1 3NH; 01332 348 644.

Exeter: 174 Fore Street, Exeter, Devon, EX4 3AX; 01392 279 024/438 167.

Fareham: 135 West Street, Fareham, Hampshire, PO16 0DU; 01329 236 441.

Guildford: 8/9 Tunsgate, Guildford, Surrey, GU1 2DH; 01483 504 040.

Lincoln: 6 Silver Street, Lincoln, LN2 1DY; 01522 514 131.

London, Strand: 98 The Strand, London, WC2R 0AG; 020 7379 0200.

Manchester: 37 Parker Street, Picadilly, M1 4AJ; 0161 236 5819.

Norwich: 12 Timber Hill, Norwich, Norfolk NR1 3LB; 01603 612 537.

Nottingham: 7 Pelham Street, Nottingham, NG1 2EH; 0115 941 7486.

Paignton: 71 Hyde Road, Paington, Devon, TQ4 5BP; 01803 553 077.

Plymouth: 10 Frankfort Gate, Plymouth, Devon, PL1 1QD; 01752 668 894.

Portsmouth: 40 Kingswell Path, Cascados, Portsmouth, PO1 4RR; 023 9283 9933.

Reading: 7 Station Road, Reading, Berkshire, RG1 1LG; 0118 959 2149.

Salisbury: 6 Queen Street, Salisbury, Wiltshire, SP1 1EY; 01722 335 436.

Southampton: 10 High Street, Southampton, Hampshire, SO14 2DH; 023 8022 1597.

Taunton: 6 North Street, Taunton, Somerset, TA1 1LH; 01823 259 955.

Winchester: 15 The Square, Winchester, Hampshire, SO23 9ES; 01962 866 203.

WILKINSON CAMERAS

Company ethos: The widest range of photographic and birdwatching equipment available at competitive prices at all times.
Viewing facilities: Optical field days at selected nature reserves in northern England. See website for details of photographic courses and other events.
Optical stock: Binoculars from Canon, Celestron, Hawke, Leica, Nikon, Swarovski. Spotting scopes from Celestron, Hawke, Leica, Nikon, Swarovski.
Non-optical stock: Wide range of bags, tripods, digital cameras, lenses and video equipment.

Opening times: Branches open 9am to 5:30pm Monday to Saturday. Sunday 11am to 4pm (Preston, Carlisle & Warrington only);
e-mail: sales@wilkinson.co.uk www.wilkinson.co.uk

Wilkinson Cameras
www.wilkinson.co.uk

BRANCHES

Blackburn: 42 Northgate, Blackburn, Lancs BB2 1JL: 01254 581 272; (Fax) 01254 695 867; e-mail: preston@wilkinson.co.uk

Burnley: 95 James Street, Burnley, Lancs BB11 1PY; 01282 424 524; (Fax) 01282 831 722; e-mail: preston@wilkinson.co.uk

Bury: 61 The Rock, Bury, Greater Manchester BL9 0NB; 01617 643 402; (Fax) 01617 615 086; e-mail: preston@wilkinson.co.uk

Carlisle: 13 Grapes Lane, Carlisle, Cumbria CA3 8NQ; 01228 538 583; (Fax) 01228 514 699. e-mail: preston@wilkinson.co.uk

Kendal: 19A The Westmorland Centre, Kendal, Cumbria LA9 4AB; 01539 735 055; (Fax) 01539 734 929; e-mail: preston@wilkinson.co.uk

Lancaster: 6 James Street, Lancaster, Lancs LA1 1UP; 01524 380 510; (Fax) 01524 380 512. e-mail: preston@wilkinson.co.uk

Preston: 27 Friargate, Preston, Lancs PR1 2NQ; 01772 556 250; (Fax) 01772 259 435; e-mail: preston@wilkinson.co.uk

Southport: 38 Eastbank Street, Southport, Merseyside, PR8 1ET. 01704 534 534; (Fax) 01704 501 546; e-mail: southport@wilkinson.co.uk

Warrington: 10 The Mall, The Golden Square, Warrington WA1 1QE. 01925 638 290; e-mail: warrington@wilkinson.co.uk

OPTICAL IMPORTERS AND MANUFACTURERS

CARL ZEISS LTD
Company ethos: World renowned, high quality performance and innovative optical products.
Product lines: Victory FL, Conquest, Stabilised, Victory and Classic compacts and Diascope FL telescopes.
Address: PO Box 78, Woodfield Road, Welwyn Garden City, Hertfordshire AL7 1LU; 01707 871 350; e-mail: binos@zeiss.co.uk
www.zeiss.co.uk/sportsoptics

DEBEN GROUP INDUSTRIES
Company ethos: We design Hawke Sport Optics as a quality range of binoculars and spotting scopes, which in turn offer excellent value for money. We have various market leaders within the range and

TRADE DIRECTORY

119

OPTICAL IMPORTERS AND MANUFACTURERS

will continue to create a simple but very popular range.
Product lines: Hawke Sport Optics consists of the following families: New Panorama ED, New Sapphire ED, Frontier ED, Endurance PC and the much-loved Nature-Trek range. The full range offers compacts, mid-size and full size binoculars from £50 - £600, plus spotting scopes (from £100 - £1300) which also includes models with double ED glass. A range of trap cameras for filming wildlife now has an 8M HD model with colour screen.
New for 2013: New flagship spotting scope called Panorama Double ED in a 82mm and new lightweight Endurance ED spotting scopes in both a 68mm and 85mm. New compact binoculars available in the Endurance PC and our first flat field view binocular will be launched in the Panorama range by the Spring.
Address: Avocet House, Wilford Bridge Road, Melton, Woodbridge,Suffolk IP12 1RB; 01394 387 762.
e-mail: salesl@deben.com www.hawkeoptics.com

INTRO 2020 LTD
Company ethos: Experienced importer of photo and optical products.
Product lines: Steiner binoculars, Tamron lenses, Crumpler bags, Tamrac bags, Velbon tripods, Slik tripods, Hoya and Cokin filters, Optech straps. Plus many other photographic accessories.

New for 2013: Phottix photographic accessories, Integral Memory.
Address: Unit 1, Priors Way, Maidenhead, Berkshire SL6 2HP; 01628 674 411; (fax) 01628 771 055.
e-mail: sales@intro2020.co.uk
www.intro2020.co.uk, www.bags4gear.co.uk, www.cokin.co.uk, www.lensbaby.co.uk, www.lenspens.co.uk, www.optechusa.co.uk, www.phottix.co.uk, www.sliktripod.co.uk, www.steiner-binoculars.co.uk, www.tamrac.co.uk, www.tamron.co.uk, www.velbon.co.uk

NEWPRO UK LTD
Company ethos: Vortex, a very well-established and respected brand name with new company technology and attitude.
Product lines: Vortex binoculars, scopes and monoculars - all with an unlimited lifetime warranty. ROR (Residual Oil Remover) optics cleaner.
New for 2013: Vortex Viper HD binoculars and Viper HD scopes.
Opening times: Mon-Fri (8.30am-5pm) plus many outdoor events.
Address: Old Sawmills Road, Faringdon, Oxon SN7 7DS;01367 242 411; (fax) 01367 241 124.
e-mail: sales@newprouk.co.uk
www.newprouk.co.uk

OPTICRON
Company ethos: To continuously develop high quality binoculars, telescopes and accessories that are useful, ergonomically sound and exceptional value for money.
Product lines: Opticron binoculars, monoculars, telescopes, tripods, telephotography/digi-scoping equipment and accessories.
Address: Unit 21, Titan Court, Laporte Way, Luton LU4 8EF; 01582 726 522; (fax) 01582 273 559.
e-mail: sales@opticron.co.uk www.opticron.co.uk

SWAROVSKI OPTIK
Company ethos: Swarovski Optik is committed to supporting international conservation projects to ensure the survival of some of the world's most endangered species and also supports the Society of Wildlife Artists' annual competition. Our wish is to reveal the beauty of the world 'with the eyes of a hawk and to constantly improve what is good with innovative products.
Product lines: EL 42 and 50 Swarovision, CL Companion 8 and 10 x 30 and SLC 42 HD binoculars, and a choice of tripods.
New for 2013: The innovative ATX/STX series of modular telescopes features a choice of angled or straight ocular elements to use with various objective modules (ATX 25-60X with 65mm and 85mm and ATX 30-70X with 95mm objective lens, plus excellent photo accessories and the ATS/STS observation telescope with 25-50XW and 20-60X eye piece).
Address: Perrywood Business Park, Salfords, Surrey RH1 5JQ; 01737 856 812; (fax) 01737 856 885.
e-mail: info@swarovski.com

OPTICAL REPAIRS AND SERVICING

OPTREP OPTICAL REPAIRS
Company ethos: To give a speedy, economical and effective repair service.
Key services: Servicing and repair of binoculars, telescopes etc. Conversant with the special needs of birdwatchers.
Opening times: Mon-Thu (9am-5pm), Fri (9am-3pm)
Address: 16 Wheatfield Road, Selsey, West Sussex PO20 0NY; 01243 601 365.
e-mail: info@opticalrepairs.com
www.opticalrepairs.com

BIRD RESERVES AND OBSERVATORIES

David Cromack

The RSPB has built an impressive visitor centre at its Newport Wetlands reserve in Gwent — it is one of 37 Welsh sites in the Bird Reserves section of *The Yearbook*.

ALL ENTRIES in the Reserves Directory are listed on a regional basis. This has been the standard practice for Scotland and Wales in recent editions, whereas the English counties have been listed alphabetically, but it is felt that grouping counties into regions will be more helpful to our readers.

We hope this proves helpful but welcome reader feedback on any way we can improve this section of the *Yearbook*.

Please e-mail your comments to the Editor David Cromack at: editor@buckinghampress.com

Central England

Derbyshire, Gloucestershire, Leicestershire & Rutland, Lincolnshire, Northamptonshire, Nottinghamshire, Oxfordshire, Shropshire, Staffordshire, Warwickshire, West Midlands, Worcestershire

Derbyshire

LAKES and gravel pits such as Carsington Water, Willington, Ogston Reservoir and Foremark Reservoir attract huge gull roosts in winter, with a corresponding number of dedicated larophiles searching for scarce species and unusual plumages. Valleys, such as those in the Peak District, attract Redstarts, Pied Flycatchers and Wood Warblers.

1. CARR VALE NATURE RESERVE

Derbyshire Wildlife Trust.
Location: SK 45 70. 1km W of Bolsover on A632 to Chesterfield. Turn L at roundabout (follow brown tourist signs) into Riverside Way. Car park at end of road. Follow footpath (waymarked) around Peter Fidler reserve.
Access: Open all year.
Facilities: Car park, coach parking on approach road, good disabled access, paths, viewing platforms.
Public transport: Various Stagecoach services from Chesterfield (Stephenson Place) all pass close to the reserve: Mon to Sat - 83 serves Villas Road, 81, 82, 82A and 83 serve the roundabout on the A632. Sun - 81A, 82A serve the roundabout on the A632.
Habitat: Lakes, wader flashes, reedbed, sewage farm, scrub, arable fields.
Key birds: Up to 150 species seen annually at this productive site. *Winter*: Large numbers of wildfowl including flocks of Wigeon and Teal, also wintering flocks of finches and buntings, Water Rail. Large skeins of geese fly over in early and late winter. *Spring/autumn*: Birds on migration including Swallows, pipits and thrushes. In September Swallows gather in the marsh, in a gigantic roost of between 10-12,000 birds. They usually attract Hobbies. *Early summer*: Breeding birds, including Reed and Sedge Warblers, Whitethroat, Yellowhammer, Moorhen and Gadwall, plus Skylark. Long list of rarities.
Other notable fauna: Dragonflies, mammals (hare, water vole, harvest mouse, water shrew).
Contact: Derbyshire Wildlife Trust, 01773 881 188; e-mail: enquiries@derbyshirewt.co.uk
www.derbyshirewildlifetrust.org.uk

2. CARSINGTON WATER

Severn Trent Water.
Location: SK 24 51 (for visitor centre and main facilities). Off B5035 Ashbourne to Cromford road.
Access: Open all year except Christmas Day. The car parks are open from 7am to sunset (Apr - end Oct) and 7.30am to sunset in winter. There are various access points. New lower track opened in spring 09 to improve access.
Facilities: Visitor centre with exhibition, restaurant, four shops (inc RSPB), play area and toilets. RSPB 'Aren't Birds Brilliant' project operates here twice a week. Four bird hides and three car parks (two chargeable, one free).
Public transport: TM Travel operates service 411 from Matlock and Ashbourne. The nearest train station is at Cromford. Call TM on 01142 633 890.
Habitat: Open water, islands, mixed woodland, scrub and grasslands, small reedbed.
Key birds: *Winter*: Wildfowl and a large gull roost plus possibility of divers and rare grebes. *Spring*: Good spring passage including Yellow and White Wagtails, Whimbrel, Black and Arctic Terns. *Summer*: Warblers and breeding waders. *All year*: Tree Sparrows and Willow Tits.
Other notable flora and fauna: Species-rich hay meadows, ancient woodlands with bluebells, three species of orchid, five species of bat, 21 species of butterfly and water vole.
Contact: Carsington Water Visitor Centre, 01629 540 696; e-mail: customer.relations@severntrent.co.uk
www.moretoexperience.co.uk and www.carsingtonbirdclub.co.uk

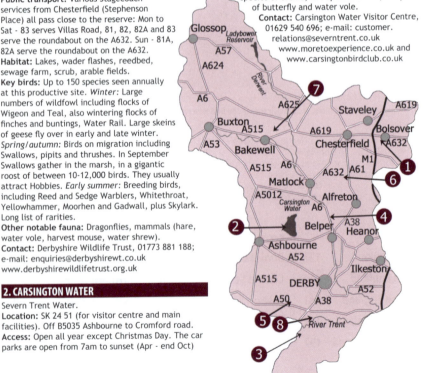

NATURE RESERVES - CENTRAL ENGLAND

3. DRAKELOW NATURE RESERVE

E-ON, leased to Derbyshire Wildlife Trust.
Location: SK 223 204 (OS Landranger 128, Explorer 245). Drakelow Power Station, one mile NE of Walton-on-Trent, off A38, S of Burton-on-Trent.
Access: Dawn to dusk for permit-holders only (plus up to two guests). Annual permit can be obtained from Derbyshire Wildlife Trust.
Facilities: Five hides, no other facilities.
Public transport: None.
Habitat: Disused flooded gravel pits with wooded islands and reedbeds.
Key birds: *Summer:* Breeding Reed and Sedge Warblers. Water Rail, Hobby. *Winter:* Wildfowl (Goldeneye, Gadwall, Smew), Merlin, Peregrine. Recent rarities include Great White and Little Egrets, Bittern, Spotted Crake, Ring-necked Duck and American Wigeon.
Other notable flora and fauna: Good for common species of dragonflies and butterflies.
Contact: Trust HQ, 01773 881 188.
e-mail: enquiries@derbyshirewt.co.uk

4. EREWASH MEADOWS

Derbyshire & Notts Wildlife Trusts
Location: SK 441 517 (OS Landranger 129, Explorer 260). In three parts: Aldercar Flash, Brinsley Meadows and part of Cromford Canal. Ripley is nearest town.
Access: Open all year — please keep to paths.
Facilities: None.
Public transport: Local bus services.
Habitat: The sites are now part of the largest floodplain grassland and wetlands in Erewash Valley.
Key birds: *Spring/summer:* Breeding Lapwing, Snipe, Reed Bunting and warblers. Raptors, waders and wildfowl seen on passage. *Winter:* Wildfowl species.
Other notable flora and fauna: Grass snake, amphibians, dragonflies, butterflies.
Contact: Trust HQ, 01773 881 188.
e-mail: enquiries@derbyshirewt.co.uk
www.derbyshirewildlifetrust.org.uk

5. HILTON GRAVEL PITS

Derbyshire Wildlife Trust.
Location: SK 249 315 (OS Landranger 128, Explorer 259). From Derby, take A516 from Mickleover W past Etwall onto A50 junction at Hilton. Turn R at first island onto Willowpit Lane (DE65 5FN). Turn L next to a large white house and park next to the gate. Follow track along S side of the pools.
Access: Open all year. Main path and viewing screen suitable for wheelchair users.
Facilities: Tracks, boardwalks, viewing screens, bench.
Public transport: Local Trent Barton Villager V1 & V2 bus services from Derby to Burton-on-Trent and Arriva X50 bus service from Derby to Stoke-on-Trent.
Habitat: Ponds, scrub, wood, fen.
Key birds: *Spring/summer:* Great Crested Grebe, Common Tern, warblers. *Winter:* Wildfowl, Siskin,

Goldcrest. *All year:* All three woodpeckers, Kingfisher, tits inc possible Willow Tit, Tawny Owl, Bullfinch.
Other notable flora and fauna: Dragonflies (15 species inc emperor, ruddy darter and red-eyed damselfly), great crested newt, orchids, black poplar, fungi.
Contact: Trust HQ, 01773 881 188.
e-mail: enquiries@derbyshirewt.co.uk

6. OGSTON RESERVOIR

Severn Trent Water Plc.
Location: SK 37 60 (Landranger map 119). From Matlock, take A615 E to B6014, just after Tansley. From Chesterfield take A61 S of Clay Cross onto B6014, towards Tansley. Cross railway, the reservoir is on L after the hill.
Access: View from roads, car parks or hides. Suitable for coaches. Heronry in nearby Ogston Carr Wood (Derbyshire Wildlife Trust) viewable from road, W of reservoir.
Facilities: Three car parks (no charges), with toilets at N and W locations. Ogston BC members-only hide and public hide both wheelchair-accessible. Information pack on request.
Public transport: Hulleys 63 bus service (Chesterfield to Clay Cross) and 64 service (Clay Cross to Matlock) both serves N end of reservoir (not Sundays).
Habitat: Open water, pasture, mixed woodland.
Key birds: All three woodpeckers, Little and Tawny Owls, Kingfisher, Grey Wagtail, warblers. Passage raptors (inc. Osprey), terns and waders. *Winter:* Gull roost attracts thousands of birds, inc regular Glaucous and Iceland Gulls. Top inland site for Bonaparte's Gull and also attracts Caspian / Herring Gull complex. Good numbers of wildfowl, tit and finch flocks.
Contact: Malcolm Hill, Treasurer, Ogston Bird Club, c/o 2 Sycamore Avenue, Glapwell, Chesterfield, S44 5LH. 01623 812 159; www.ogstonbirdclub.co.uk

7. PADLEY GORGE

The National Trust (East Midlands).
Location: From Sheffield, take A625. After eight miles, turn L on B6521 to Nether Padley. Grindleford Station is just off B6521 (NW of Nether Padley) and one mile NE of Grindleford village.
Access: All year. Not suitable for disabled people or those unused to steep climbs. Some of the paths are rocky. No dogs allowed.
Facilities: Café and toilets at Longshaw lodge.
Public transport: Bus: from Sheffield to Bakewell stops at Grindleford/Nether Padley. Tel: 01709 566 000. Train: from Sheffield to Manchester Piccadilly stops at Grindleford Station. Tel: 0161 228 2141.
Habitat: Steep-sided valley containing largest area of sessile oak woodland in south Pennines.
Key birds: *Summer:* Pied Flycatcher, Spotted Flycatcher, Redstart, Wheatear, Whinchat, Wood Warbler, Tree Pipit.
Contact: National Trust, High Peak Estate Office, 01433 670 368; www.nationaltrust.org.uk

8. WILLINGTON GRAVEL PITS

Derbyshire Wildlife Trust
Location: SK 285 274. DE65 6BX (Repton Road).
From A50 'Toyota Island' head towards Willington
and Repton. Go through village towards Repton. Just
before bridge over River Trent, turn R onto un-made
track (Meadow Lane). Park here and walk along lane.
Access: Access along Meadow Lane to viewing
platforms all year. No access on site.
Facilities: Viewing platforms and benches. Limited
parking in lane.
Public transport: Local trains stop at Willington,
local Trent Barton Villager V3 bus service from Derby

to Burton-on-Trent.
Habitat: Open water, reedbed, shingle island,
grassland.
Key birds: *Summer:* Breeding Lapwing, other waders,
Common Tern, raptors, including Peregrine, Kestrel,
Hobby and Sparrowhawk, Sand Martin, wildfowl.
Winter: Waders and large flocks of wildfowl including
Wigeon, Teal, Pochard and Shoveler. *Passage:* Large
numbers of Curlew in spring, up to 20 species of
waders in spring/autumn.
Other notable flora and fauna: Short-leaved water
starwort. Several species of dragonfly, plus occasional
otter signs, fox and other mammals.
Contact: Trust HQ, 01773 881 188.

Gloucestershire

THE FOREST OF DEAN is one of the best places
in Britain to see good numbers of Goshawks,
especially when they are displaying in February and
March. Symonds Yat has a well-known Peregrine
watchpoint. WWT Slimbridge is renowned for its
wintering wildfowl, including Bewick's Swans.
Conservation projects there currently involve
Cranes and Spoon-billed Sandpipers.

1. ASHLEWORTH HAM NATURE RESERVE

Gloucestershire Wildlife Trust.
Location: SO 830 265. Leave Gloucester N on
A417; R at Hartpury and follow minor road through
Ashleworth towards Hasfield.
Access: Access prohibited at all times but birds may
be viewed from new hide in Meerend Thicket.
Facilities: Bird viewing hide and screen,
interpretation panels.
Habitat: Low-lying grassland flood plain.
Key birds: *Winter:* Wildfowl (inc. 4,000 Wigeon,
1,500 Teal, Pintail, Goldeneye, Bewick's Swan),
passage waders, Peregrine. *Summer:* Hobby.
Contact: Trust HQ, 01452 383 333.
e-mail: info@gloucestershirewildlifetrust.co.uk
www.gloucestershirewildlifetrust.co.uk

2. COTSWOLD WATER PARK

Cotswold Water Park Society.
Location: The CWP comprises 163 lakes in the Upper
Thames Valley, between Cirencester and Swindon.
Many lakes are accessible via public rights of way.
Start from Cotswold Water Park Gateway Visitor
Centre (SU 072 971), immediately on L after A419.
For Millennium Visitor Centre at Keynes Country Park
(SU 026 957) from A419, take B4696 towards Ashton
Keynes. At staggered crossroads, go straight over,
heading towards Somerford Keynes. Take next R turn
to Cirencester. Entrance to Keynes Country Park is
second entrance on R.
Access: Cotswold Water Park is open all year round.
The visitor centres are open every day except
Christmas Day.
Facilities: Paths are flat but with stiles and
footbridges. Many are wheelchair accessible. Toilets,

refreshments, car parking and information available
from the visitor centres. Hides available at Cleveland
Lakes/Waterhay (lakes 68a and 68c), Shorncote
Reedbed (lakes 84/85), Cokes Pit (Lake 34) and
Whelford Pools (Lake 111). Free copies of the CWP
Leisure Guide are available from the visitor centres,
also the guidebook *Wildlife in the Cotswold Water
Park: Where to go and what to see.*
Public transport: Bus: from Kemble, Cheltenham,
Cirencester and Swindon. 08457 090 899. Train:
nearest station is four miles away at Kemble. 08457
484 950.
Habitat: Gravel extraction has created more than
1,000ha of standing open water, plus other associated
wetland habitats, creating one of the largest man-
made wetlands in Europe.
Key birds: *Winter:* Common wildfowl, Smew,
Red-crested Pochard, Merlin, Peregrine. *Summer:*
Breeding ducks, warblers, Nightingale, Hobby,
Common Tern, Black-headed Gull colony, Reed
Bunting, hirundines.
Contact: Cotswold Water Park Soc., 01793 752 413.
e-mail: info@waterpark.org www.waterpark.org

3. HIGHNAM WOODS

RSPB (South West England Office).
Location: SO 778 190. Signed on A40 three miles W
of Gloucester.
Access: Open at all times, no permit required.
The nature trails can be very muddy. Some limited
wheelchair access. Dogs allowed on leads.
Facilities: One nature trail (approx 1.5 miles).
Public transport: Contact Traveline (public transport
information) on 0871 2002 233 between 7am-10pm
each day.
Habitat: Ancient woodland in the Severn Vale with
areas of coppice and scrub.
Key birds: *Spring/summer:* The reserve has about 12
pairs of breeding Nightingales. Resident birds include
all three woodpeckers, Buzzard and Sparrowhawk.
Ravens are frequently seen. *Winter:* Feeding site near
car park good for woodland birds.
Other notable flora and fauna: Tintern spurge in late
June-early July. White-letter hairstreak and white
admiral butterflies seen annually.
Contact: The Site Manager, 01594 562 852. e-mail:
highnam.woods@rspb.org.uk www.rspb.org.uk

NATURE RESERVES - CENTRAL ENGLAND

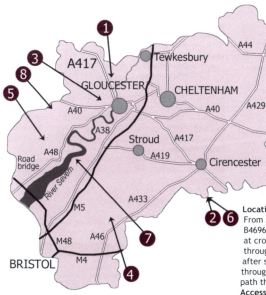

of the reserve is a mixture of open areas and conifer/mixed woodland. **Key birds:** *Spring:* Pied Flycatcher, Wood Warbler, Redstart, warblers. *Summer:* Nightjar. *Winter:* Siskin, Crossbill in some years. *All year:* Buzzard, Raven, Hawfinch, all three woodpeckers.
Other notable fauna: Golden-ringed dragonfly seen annually. Silver-washed and small pearl-bordered fritillaries and white admiral butterflies present.
Contact: The Site Manager, 01594 562 852. e-mail: highnam.woods@rspb.org.uk

6. SHORNCOTE REEDBED (LAKES 84/85)

Cotswold Water Park Society.
Location: Lakes 84 and 85, Cotswold Water Park. From A419 Cirencester to Swindon road, take B4696 towards Cotswold Water Park West. Turn R at crossroads towards South Cerney. Follow road through village and park in playing fields car park after sharp R bend (SU 044 970). Take footpath through playing fields, cross road and continue on path through reedbeds to small lakes and hides.
Access: Open at all times, most paths firm and flat so suitable for wheelchairs.
Facilities: Toilets, refreshments, car parking and information available from nearby Keynes Country Park adjacent. Two hides.
Public transport: Bus: from Kemble, Cheltenham, Cirencester and Swindon. 08457 090 899. Train: Kemble station four miles. 08457 484 950.
Habitat: Lakes with reedbed, marsh, ditches, islands and loafing areas.
Key birds: *Winter:* Common wildfowl, Smew, Peregrine, Merlin, Bittern, Stonechat. *Summer:* Breeding ducks, warblers, Hobby, Sand Martin, Reed Bunting.
Other notable flora and fauna: Several species of dragonfly and damselfly.
Contact: Cotswold Water Park Soc., 01793 752 413.

4. LOWER WOODS NATURE RESERVE

Gloucestershire Wildlife Trust.
Location: ST 749 885. Reserve is about one mile E of Wickwar. Main parking is at Lower Woods Lodge, via a track off the Wickwar-Hawkesbury road. Public footpaths and bridleways cross the reserve.
Access: Open all year.
Facilities: Well-marked footpaths and bridleways. Walk leaflet available.
Habitat: Mixed woodland, mildly acidic or slightly calcareous clay, grassland, river, springs.
Key birds: *Spring/summer:* Nightingale. *All year:* Usual woodland species including Tawny Owl, Jay, Nuthatch and Sparrowhawk. Kingfisher on river.
Other notable flora and fauna: 71 species of ancient woodland plants.
Contact: Trust HQ. 01452 383 333, e-mail: info@gloucestershirewildlifetrust.co.uk

5. NAGSHEAD

RSPB (South West England Office).
Location: SO 097 085. In Forest of Dean, N of Lydney. Signed immediately W of Parkend village on the road to Coleford.
Access: Open at all times, no permit required. The reserve is hilly but there is limited wheelchair access. Dogs must be kept on leads during bird nesting season and under close control at all other times.
Facilities: Two nature trails (one mile and 2.25 miles). Information centre, with toilet facilities (including disabled), open at weekends mid-Apr to end Aug. Schools education programme available.
Public transport: Contact Traveline (0871 2002 233).
Habitat: Much of the reserve is 200-year-old oak plantations, grazed in some areas by sheep. The rest

7. SLIMBRIDGE

The Wildfowl & Wetlands Trust.
Location: SO 723 048. On banks of River Severn, S of Gloucester. Signposted from M5 (exit 13 or 14).
Access: Open daily (9am-5.30pm or 5pm in winter) except Dec 25. Last entry 30 mins before closing. Wheelchair hire (book beforehand) — all paths wheelchair accessible. Free parking. Admission charges for non-WWT members.
Facilities: Restaurant, gift shop, gallery, cinema, discovery centre. Outdoor facilities inc 15 hides, tropical house, worldwide collection of wildfowl species, observatory and observation tower. Plenty of family attactions including a pond zone, wader aviary, commentated swan feeds in the winter, Land Rover safaris and a canoe safari trail.
Public transport: Request bus service - contact www. stroud.gov.uk. Nearest train station at Cam and Dursley (4 miles).

Habitat: Reedbed, saltmarsh, freshwater pools, mudflats and wet grassland.
Key birds: *Winter:* Between 30,000 to 40,000 wildfowl esp. Bewick's Swan, White-fronted Goose, Wigeon, Teal, Pintail. Waders inc Lapwing, Golden Plover, Spotted Redshank and Little Stint. Often there are large roosts of Starlings and gulls. *Breeding:* Kingfisher, Lapwing, Redshank, Oystercatcher, Common Tern, Reed Bunting and a good range of warblers. *Passage:* Waders, terns and gulls, inc Mediterranean and Yellow-legged Gulls. Yellow Wagtail and large passerine movements. Hobbies now reach double figures and good list of rarities.
Other notable flora and fauna: Brown hare, otter, polecat and water vole. Scarce chaser and hairy dragonfly among 22 recorded species.
Contact: Marketing Manager, WWT, Slimbridge, 01453 891 900; e-mail: info.slimbridge@wwt.org.uk

8. SYMOND'S YAT

RSPB/Forestry Commission England.
Location: SO 563 160. Hill-top site on the edge of Forest of Dean, three miles N of Coleford on B4432, signposted from Forest Enterprise car park. Also signposted from A40, S of Ross-on-Wye.
Access: Open at all times. RSPB Information Officer on site daily, April to August.
Facilities: Car park, toilets with adapted facilities for disabled visitors, picnic area, drinks and light snacks. Environmental education programmes available.
Public transport: Very limited.
Habitat: Cliff above the River Wye and woodland.
Key birds: *Summer:* Peregrine, Buzzard, Goshawk, Raven and woodland species. Telescope is set up daily to watch the Peregrines on the nest.
Contact: RSPB, 01594 562 852.

Leicestershire and Rutland

THE MANY birders who visit Rutland Water to see breeding Ospreys, huge numbers of wildfowl, and good selection of passage waders may not be aware that the county wildlife trust manages another 31 sites, including Cossington Meadows, a good wildfowl site near Leicester. Back in Rutland, Eyebrook Reservoir is excellent for Smew, huge Golden Plover flocks and roosting gulls in winter.

1. BEACON HILL COUNTRY PARK

Leicestershire County Council.
Location: SK 522 149. From Loughborough, take A512 SW for 2.5 miles. Turn L onto Woodhouse Lane and follow it for 2.5 miles through Nanpantan. The Lower car park is on R. For Upper car park, continue past Lower car park, turn R onto Beacon Road, car park is on R at the top of hill.
Access: Open all year from 7am. Closing times are clearly displayed at the park. A permissive path from Deans Lane to Woodhouse Lane is occasionally closed during the year. Please check first.
Facilities: Two pay-on-entry car parks, waymarked tracks and woodland paths. Several climbs to hill tops. Rocky outcrops slippery after rain. Information boards. Toilets at lower & upper car parks. Park paths have Wheelchair access but no access to summit. Refreshments at Bull's Head, Woodhouse Eaves.
Public transport: Bus: Nos 54, 121 and 123 from Loughborough calls at Woodhouse Eaves. Tel: 0870 608 2608.
Habitat: Forest, one of the oldest geological outcrops in England.
Key birds: *All year:* Treecreeper, Nuthatch, Lesser Spotted, Greater Spotted and Green Woodpeckers, Great and Coal Tits, Little Owl, wagtails. *Summer:* Pied Flycatcher, Whitethroat, Blackcap, Whinchat, Garden Warbler, Stonechat, Tree Pipit.
Contact: Beacon Hill Country Park, 0116 305 8790.

2. EYEBROOK RESERVOIR

Corby & District Water Co.
Location: SP 853 964. Reservoir built 1940. S of Uppingham, from unclassified road W of A6003 at Stoke Dry.
Access: Access to 150 acres private grounds granted to members of Leics and Rutland OS and Rutland NHS. All visitors should sign in at fishing lodge. Organised groups should contact Andy Miller on 01536 772 930.
Facilities: SSSI since 1956. Three bird hides. Fishing season March - Nov. Toilets and visitor centre at fishing lodge.
Public transport: None.
Habitat: Open water, plantations and pasture.
Key birds: *Summer:* Good populations of breeding birds, sightings of Ospreys and Red Kite. Passage waders and Black Tern. *Winter:* Wildfowl (inc. Goldeneye, Goosander, Smew) and waders. Tree Sparrow and Yellowhammer at feeding station also Barn and Short-eared Owl can be seen hunting at dusk near Great Easton village (close to recycling centre).
Other notable flora and fauna: Otter, muntjac deer, red darter, demoiselles and blue damselfly.
Contact: Andy Miller, Fishery Estate Manager, 01536 772 930; www.eyebrook.com

3. NARBOROUGH BOG

Leics and Rutland Wildlife Trust.
Location: SP 549 979. Reserve lies between River Soar and M1, 8km S of Leicester. From city, turn L off B4114 just before going under motorway, follow track to sports club. Park near club house and walk across recreation ground to reserve entrance.
Access: Open at all times, please keep to paths. Not suitable for wheelchairs. Dogs on short leads only.
Facilities: None. Small bus/coach could park in sports field car park.
Public transport: Narborough train station. Buses X5, 140 to Narborough then 1km walk. Contact Traveline for more information on 0871 200 22 33.

Habitat: Peat bog SSSI (the only substantial deposit in Leicestershire), wet woodland, reedbed, dense scrub and fen meadow.

Key birds: More than 130 species of birds recorded including all three species of woodpeckers, six species of tit, Tawny Owl, Sparrowhawk and Kingfisher.

Other notable flora and fauna: Good range of butterflies including common blue, meadow brown, large and small skippers, small heath and gatekeeper. Banded demoiselles, also good for moths and beetles. Harvest mice and water voles recorded, also breeding grass snakes. In the meadow area, meadow saxifrage, common meadow-rue and marsh thistle.

Contact: Trust HQ, 0116 272 0444; e-mail: info@lrwt.org.uk

4. RUTLAND WATER

Location: Two nature reserves — 1: Egleton Reserve SK 878 075: from Egleton village off A6003 or A606 S of Oakham. Hosts British Birdwatching Fair every August. 2: Lyndon Reserve SK 894 058: south shore E of Manton village off A6003 S of Oakham. Follow 'nature reserve' signs to car park.

Access: 1. Open daily 9am-5pm, (4pm Nov to Jan). 2. Open winter (Sat, Sun 10am-4pm), Summer daily (9am-5pm). Day permits available for both. Reduced admission for disabled and carers. Closed Dec 25 and 26. Badger-watching hide can be booked from mid-April to July.

Facilities: 1: Birdwatching Centre has toilets and disabled access, mobility scooter to hire, conference facilities. Disabled access possible to 20 hides, incl three on newly-created lagoon 4. Nine new lagoons planned. 2: Interpretive centre toilets, including disabled, paths, use of a mobility scooter. Seven hides, four accessible to wheelchairs. Trail leaflet.

Public transport: None.

Habitat: Ramsar designated reservoir, lagoons, scrapes, woods, meadows, plantations, reedbeds.

Key birds: *Spring/autumn:* Outstanding wader passage, with up to 28 species recorded. Also wide range of harriers, owls, passerine flocks, terns

(Black, Arctic, breeding Common, occasional Little and Sandwich). *Winter:* Up to 28 species of wildfowl (inc international important numbers of Gadwall and Shoveler). Also Goldeneye, Smew, Goosander, rare grebes, all divers, Ruff. *Summer:* Ospreys among 70 breeding species.

Other notable flora and fauna: Otter, badger, fox, weasel, stoat. Up to 20 species of dragon and damselflies and 24 butterfly species.

Contact: Tim Appleton, 01572 770 651; www.rutlandwater.org.uk www.ospreys.org.uk

5. SENCE VALLEY FOREST PARK

Forestry Commission

Location: SK 400 115. Within The National Forest. 10 NW of Leicester and two miles SW of Coalville, between Ibstock and Ravenstone. The car park is signed from A447 N of Ibstock.

Access: Open all year. Car park open 8.30am-dusk (precise times on noticeboard). Lower car park (2.2m height barrier) gives easy access to wheelchair-friendly surfaced paths. Week's notice required for coach or minibuses visits.

Facilities: Two car parks, toilets (including disabled and baby-changing facilities), information and recent sightings boards, hide, surfaced trails.

Public transport: None.

Habitat: New forest (native broadleaf, mixed and pine), rough grassland, wildflower meadow, pools, wader scrape, river.

Key birds: *Spring/summer:* Artificial Sand Martin nesting wall, Wheatear, Whinchat, Redstart, Common and Green Sandpiper, Ringed and Little Ringed Plovers, Redshank. Dunlin and Greenshank frequent, possible Wood Sandpiper. Reed Bunting, Meadow Pipit, Skylark, Linnet, Yellow Wagtail. Possible Quail. Kestrel and Barn Owl seen occasionally. *Winter:* Stonechat, Redpoll, Short-eared Owl, Goosander and Wigeon possible.

Contact: Forestry Commission, 01889 586 593. e-mail:info_nationalforest@forestry.gsi.org.uk www.forestry.gov.uk

Lincolnshire

GIBRALTAR POINT is a famous bird observatory but the coastal RSPB reserves at Frampton and Freiston are also worth exploring. The county includes the northern section of the Wash, complete with huge numbers of Brent Geese, waders, raptors and owls in winter. Peregrines breed on Lincoln Cathedral and are spreading to other man-made edifices in the county.

1. DONNA NOOK

Lincolnshire Wildlife Trust.

Location: TF 422 998. Several access points off the main A1031 coastal road with parking facilities at Stonebridge (TF 422 998), Howden's Pullover (TF 449 952), Sea Lane, Saltfleet (TF 456 944) and Saltfleet

Haven (TF 4679 35).

Access: Donna Nook beach is closed on weekdays as this is an active bombing range, but dunes remain open. Dogs on leads. Some disabled access.

Facilities: No toilets or visitor centre.

Habitat: Dunes, slacks and intertidal areas, seashore, mudflats, sandflats.

Key birds: *Summer:* Little Tern, Ringed Plover, Oystercatcher. *Winter:* Brent Goose, Shelduck, Twite, Lapland Bunting, Shore Lark, Linnet.

Other notable flora and fauna: The reserve has one of the largest and most accessible breeding colonies of grey seals in the UK. Other mammals include fox, badger, stoat and weasel and three species of shrew have been identified. Common lizard.

Contact: Lincolnshire Wildlife Trust, 01507 526 667. e-mail: info@lincstrust.co.uk www.lincstrust.org.uk

2. EPWORTH TURBARY

Lincolnshire Wildlife Trust.
Location: SE 758 036. SW of Scunthorpe. Take A18 W from Scunthorpe then A161 S to Epworth. Turn R on High Street, and head towards Wroot. The entrance is near bridge over Skyer's Drain. Parking available through gate, which should be kept closed, or on verge adjoining reserve. Park well away from corner.
Access: Open at all times. Keep to waymarked paths and use hides when viewing open area. In order to avoid disturbing birds on the ponds, please do not climb on the banks.
Facilities: Car park, way-marked trail, two hides.
Habitat: One of the few relics of raised bog in Lincolnshire. Although extensively dug for peat in the past, areas of active sphagnum bog still exist. Areas of reed swamp and mixed fen vegetation, also fen and wet heath conditions and a considerable area of birch woodland of varying ages.
Key birds: Breeding birds include Tree Pipit, warblers, finches, Green and Great Spotted Woodpeckers and Woodcock. Greenshank, Green Sandpiper and Little Grebe are attracted to the wet area. Around Steve's Pond, occasional Hobby and Marsh Harrier, plus Teal, Little Grebe, Tree Pipit, Sparrowhawk and Buzzard. Willow Tit, Long-tailed Tit, Reed Bunting and Willow Warbler in the woodland areas. Occasionally Corn Buntings on the adjoining farmland. *Autumn/winter:* Large flocks of Rooks, Crows and Jackdaws fly into the reserve to roost. At Pantry's Pond in winter occasional Hen Harrier. Other birds include Yellowhammer, Linnet, Jay and Magpie. Sometimes in winter Long-eared Owls can be observed roosting close to the path.
Other notable flora and fauna: 11 species of breeding dragonflies and damselflies recorded. Wood tiger moth is well established. Plants include sneezewort, yellow and purple-loosestrife, meadow-rue, and devil's-bit scabious.
Contact: Lincolnshire Wildlife Trust, 01507 526 667. e-mail: info@lincstrust.co.uk ww.lincstrust.org.uk

3. FRAMPTON MARSH

RSPB (Eastern England Office).
Location: TF 356 392. Four miles SE of Boston. From A16 follow signs to Frampton then Frampton Marsh.
Access: Visitor Centre open 10am-4pm each day (Oct-Mar) except Dec 25, 10am-4pm weekdays, 10am-5pm weekends (Apr-Sept). Footpaths and hides open at all times, free. Visitor Centre (including toilets), footpaths and hides all suitable for wheelchairs.
Facilities: Visitor Centre with hot drinks and snacks, three hides, footpaths, benches, viewpoints, 50-space car park (three for disabled visitors), binocular hire, bicycle rack, free information leaflets and events programmes. Children's activities.
Public transport: The nearest bus stop is in Kirton village, approx three miles from reserve. The 113 Brylaine bus and the 58 Kimes bus run from Boston through Kirton weekdays and Saturdays. No buses on Sundays. Train: Boston is about four miles.
Habitat: Saltmarsh, wet grassland, freshwater scrapes and developing reedbed.
Key birds: *Summer:* Breeding Redshank, Avocet, Lapwing, Skylark, Little Ringed Plover, Ringed Plover, Sand Martin and several species of ducks plus passage waders (inc Greenshank, Curlew Sandpiper, Wood Sandpiper, Little and Temminck's Stints, Ruff and Black-tailed Godwit), Marsh Harrier and Hobby. *Winter:* Hen Harrier, Short-eared Owl, Merlin, dark-bellied Brent Goose, Twite, Golden Plover, Lapland Bunting.
Other notable flora and fauna: Water vole, muntjac and roe deer, stoat. Dragonflies inc emperor, hawkers, chasers and darters. Common butterflies plus wall brown, painted lady and speckled wood. Scarce pug, star wort and crescent striped moths on saltmarsh. Important brackish water flora and fauna includes nationally scarce spiral tassleweed and several rare beetles.
Contact: Reserve Manager, 01205 724 678; e-mail: lincolnshirewashreserves@rspb.org.uk www.rspb.org.uk

4. FREISTON SHORE

RSPB (Eastern England Office).
Location: TF 398 425. Four miles E of Boston. From A52 at Haltoft End follow signs to Freiston Shore.
Access: Open at all times, free.
Facilities: Footpaths, two car parks, bird hide, wetland trail. Free information leaflets on site, guided walks programme. Bicycle rack, benches, viewpoints, seawatching shelter, reservoir viewing screen, wet grassland viewing platform.
Public transport: None.
Habitat: Saltmarsh, saline lagoon, mudflats, wet grassland.
Key birds: *Summer:* Breeding waders including Avocet, Ringed Plover and Oystercatcher, Common Tern, Corn Bunting and Tree Sparrow. *Winter:* Twite, dark-bellied Brent Goose, wildfowl, waders, Short-eared Owl and Hen Harrier. *Passage:* Waders, including Greenshank, Curlew Sandpiper and Little Stint. *Autumn:* Occasional seabirds including Arctic and Great Skuas.
Other notable flora and fauna: Water vole, muntjac and roe deer, stoat. Dragonflies inc emperor, hawkers, chasers and darters. Common butterflies plus wall brown, painted lady and speckled wood. Scarce pug, star wort and crescent striped moths on saltmarsh. Important lagoon invertebrates and plants.
Contact: As Frampton Marsh

5. GIBRALTAR POINT NNR & BIRD OBSERVATORY

Lincolnshire Wildlife Trust.
Location: TF 556 580. Three miles S of Skegness on the N edge of The Wash. Signposted from Skegness town centre.
Access: Reserve open dawn-dusk all year. Charges for car parking. Free admission to reserve, visitor centre and toilets. Some access restrictions to sensitive sites at S end, open access to N. Dogs on leads at all

times — no dogs on beach during summer. Visitor centre and toilets suitable for wheelchairs, as well as network of surfaced foot paths. Bird observatory and four hides suitable for wheelchairs. Day visit groups must be booked in advance. Access for coaches. Contact The Wash Study Centre for residential or day visits.
Facilities: Visitor centre and café open (10am -4pm) Apr-end Oct, (11am-3pm) weekdays, (11am -4pm) weekends Nov-end Mar. Site also location of Wash Study Centre and Bird Observatory. Field centre is an ideal base for birdwatching/natural history groups in spring, summer and autumn. Toilets open daily. Footpaths bisect all major habitats. Public hides overlook freshwater and brackish lagoons. Wash viewpoint overlooks saltmarsh and mudflats.
Public transport: Bus service from Skegness runs occasionally but summer service only. Otherwise taxi/car from Skegness. Cycle route from Skegness.
Habitat: Sand dune grassland and scrub, saltmarshes and mudflats, freshwater marsh and lagoons.
Key birds: Large scale visible migration during spring and autumn passage. Internationally important populations of non-breeding waders between Jul-Mar (peak Sep/Oct). Winter flocks of Brent Geese, Shelduck and Wigeon on flats and marshes with Hen Harrier, Merlin and Short-eared Owl often present. Red-throated Divers offshore, (peak Feb). A colony of Little Tern and Ringed Plover in summer. More than 100 species can be seen in a day during May and Sept. Good passage of autumn seabirds in northerly winds.
Other notable flora and fauna: Patches of pyramidal orchids. Grey and common seal colonies, with porpoises offshore in most months. Butterflies include brown argus and green hairstreak.
Contact: Reserve and wildlife: Kev Wilson. Visit bookings: Jill Hardy, Sykes Farm, Gibraltar Point Nature Reserve, Gibraltar Road, Skegness, Lincs PE24 4SU. 01754 898 057; e-mail: kwilson@linwtrust.co.uk or gibadmin@lincstrust.co.uk www.lincstrust.org.uk and GibraltarPointBIrdObservatory.blogspot.com

6. KILLINGHOLME HAVEN PITS

Lincolnshire Wildlife Trust.
Location: TA 165 199 NW of Grimsby. Take A180 W, turn R on A1173 towards Immingham. Turn L at roundabout and continue to A160. Turn L then R onto Eastfield road. Turn R onto Chase Hill road then L onto Haven road. The reserve is situated to the S of Haven Road on the approach to North Killingholme Haven. Park carefully on the road.
Access: No general access to the reserve, but adequate viewing points are available from the public road and bank-top footpath.
Facilities: None. **Habitat:** Marsh/wetland.
Key birds: A good site for water birds. Diving ducks, such as Pochard, Tufted Duck and, occasionally, Scaup. Breeding species include Little Grebe, and Reed, Sedge, Willow and Grasshopper Warblers. Ruddy Duck has also been known to breed here. The two large shallow pits are of the greatest importance for birds, particularly for migrant waders

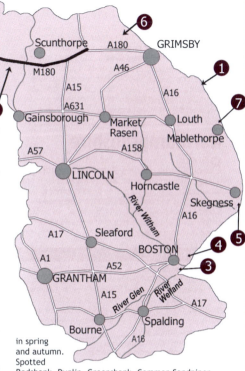

in spring and autumn. Spotted Redshank, Dunlin, Greenshank, Common Sandpiper, Little Ringed Plover, Ruff and Black-tailed Godwit, the latter often in large numbers, are regular visitors. Long list of scarce and rare species, including Spoonbill, Avocet, Little Egret, Little and Temminck's Stints, Red-necked Phalarope, and Curlew, Pectoral, Baird's and White-rumped Sandpipers.
Contact: Lincolnshire Wildlife Trust, 01507 526 667. e-mail: info@lincstrust.co.uk www.lincstrust.org.uk

7. SALTFLEETBY-THEDDLETHORPE DUNES NNR

Natural England.
Location: TF 465 924 - TF 490 883. Approx two miles N of Mablethorpe. All following car parks may be accessed from the A1031: Crook Bank, Brickyard Lane, Churchill Lane, Rimac, Sea View.
Access: Open all year at all times. Keep dogs under close control or on a lead, owners should clean up after dogs and place bags in bins provided. Easy access trail, 850m, starts by Rimac car park.
Facilities: Apr - end Oct events programme. Easy access trail at Rimac with two panorama viewing platforms that have wheel chair access and overlook the saltmarsh and sand dunes.
Public transport: Grayscroft coaches (01507 473 236) and Lincolnshire Roadcar (01522 532 424) run services past Rimac entrance (Louth to Mablethorpe service). Lincs Roadcar can connect with trains at Lincoln. Applebys Coaches (01507 357 900) Grimsby

to Saltfleet bus connects with Grimsby train service.
Habitat: 13th Century dunes, freshwater marsh,
new dune ridge with large areas of sea buckthorn,
saltmarsh, remnants of a shingle ridge and foreshore.
Key birds: *Summer:* Breeding birds in scrub
include Grasshopper Warbler, Whitethroat, Lesser
Whitethroat. *Winter:* Large flocks of Brent Goose,
Shelduck, Teal and Wigeon. Wintering Short-eared
Owl, Hen Harrier. Can be good for autumn/ spring

passage particularly thrushes, warblers and passerines.
Other notable flora and fauna: Impressive show of
sea lavender on saltmarsh in late summer, orchids in
marsh and dunes including pyramidal, southern marsh
and bee. 16 species of dragonfly including emperor.
Water vole, roe and muntjac deer, foxes and badgers
may be seen occasionally.
Contact: Peter Roworth, Natural England Workshops,
01507 338 611.

Northamptonshire

RED KITES were re-introduced in the area north-
east of Corby and they, along with Buzzards, are
thriving and spreading out. Blatherwycke Lake is good
for Mandarins, while Thrapston and Ditchford gravel
pits, Pitsford and Hollowell reservoirs are good for
a range of wildfowl, especially in winter. Harrington
airfield can hold good numbers of wintering Short-
eared Owls and other raptors.

1. DITCHFORD LAKES

Beds, Cambs, Northants & Peterborough Wildlife Trust.
Location: SP 931 678. From Wellingborough, take
A45 towards Rushden and Higham Ferrers. Take exit
marked A5001 to Rushden. Turn L at roundabout onto
Ditchford Road towards Irthlingborough/Ditchford.
500 m on R is small car park with height restriction.
Entrance is off car park.
Access: Rough grass paths, flat overall. Some areas
soft and muddy especially in winter. Grazing animals
at certain times of the year.
Facilities: None.
Public transport: Northampton/Wellingborough-
Irthlingborough bus, then walk 1.5 miles.
Habitat: Part of the upper Nene valley floodplain
– a complex of old gravel pits, grassland, lakes
surrounded by mature scrub.
Key birds: *Winter:* Common Sandpiper, Snipe, Teal,
Wigeon, Gadwall, Tufted Duck. *Spring:* Redshank,
Oystercatcher, Cetti's Warbler, Little Grebe, Grey
Heron. *Summer:* Reed Warbler, Sedge Warbler, Swift,
House Martin. *Autumn:* Snipe, Great Crested Grebe,
Moorhen, Coot, Grey Heron.
Other notable flora and fauna: Hairy dragonfly,
grass snake, otter. Plants include marsh woundwort,
dropwort, great burnet.
Contact: Trust HQ. 01954 713 500;
e-mail: northamptonshire@wildlifebcn.org
www.wildlifebcnp.org

2. OLD SULEHAY

Beds, Cambs, Northants & Peterborough Wildlife Trust.
Location: TL 094 9805. Stamford seven miles. From
A1 take exit to Wansford. In Wansford take minor
road past church towards Fotheringhay, Nassington
and Yarwell. After one mile turn R at crossroads in
Yarwell onto Sulehay Road. From here access can be
gained to nature reserve by various public rights of
way. Limited parking in lay-bys along Sulehay Road.
Access: Main ride is surfaced in woodland although

other paths can get muddy. Quarry has uneven paths
and steep slopes. Grazing animals at certain times of
the year.
Facilities: Ring Haw section has surfaced track and
grassed paths.
Public transport: Bus Oundle to Peterborough stops
at Yarwell (Stagecoach).
Habitat: Mosaic of limestone quarries, grassland,
woodland and wetland.
Key birds: *Winter:* Snipe, Woodcock. *Spring:*
Nuthatch, migrant warblers. *Summer:* Buzzard, Red
Kite. *Autumn:* Fieldfare, Redwing. *All year:* Green
Woodpecker, Jay, Bullfinch.
Other notable flora and fauna: Butterflies, green
tiger beetle, long horn beetle. Common lizard, grass
snake. Badger, fox. Plants include stinking hellebore,
spurge laurel, toothwort, ramsons, nettle-leaved
bellflower, ploughman's spikenard, yellow-wort,
clustered bellflower, common spotted-orchid,
woodland and limestone grassland fungi.
Contact: Trust HQ. 01954 713 500; e-mail:
northamptonshire@wildlifebcn.org

3. PITSFORD WATER

Anglian Water, managed by Beds, Cambs, Northants &
Peterborough Wildlife Trust.
Location: SP 787 702. Five miles N of Northampton.
On A43 take turn to Holcot and Brixworth. On A508
take turn to Brixworth and Holcot.
Access: Permit required in advance. Reserve open all
year to permit holders. Lodge open mid-Mar to mid-
Nov from 8am-dusk. Winter opening times variable,
check in advance. No dogs. Disabled access from
Lodge to first hide.
Facilities: Toilets available in Lodge, 15 miles of
paths, nine bird hides, car parking.
Habitat: Open water (up to 120 ha), marginal
vegetation and reed grasses, wet woodland, grassland
and mixed woodland (40 ha).
Key birds: Typically 165-170 species per year with a
total list of 253 species. *Summer:* Breeding warblers,
terns, grebes, herons. *Autumn:* Waders if water
levels suitable. *Winter:* Up to 10,000 wildfowl,
feeding station with Tree Sparrow and occasional
Corn Bunting.
Other notable flora and fauna: 32 butterfly species,
392 macro moths, 21 dragonfly species (including
damselflies), 377 species of flora and 105 bryophytes,
404 fungi species.
Contact: Dave Francis, Pitsford Water Lodge,
Brixworth Road, Holcot, Northampton, NN6 9SJ.
01604 780 148; e-mail: dave.francis@wildlifebcnp.org

4. STORTON'S PITS LNR

Beds, Cambs, Northants & Peterborough Wildlife Trust.
Location: SP 732 600. In Northampton. From junction of A45 with A43 west of town centre take A45 N to first roundabout and turn R. At next roundabout turn R and immediately L into Fisherman's car park. The two sites are either side of the track.
Access: Flat overall. Section of surfaced path to viewing platform, other paths soft and uneven in places with many steps on peninsula. The two reserves are adjoining.
Facilities: Viewing platform, paths, some surfaced.
Public transport: Train to Northampton then walk 1 mile or bus to St Giles and get off at Sixfields roundabout.
Habitat: One of a number of old gravel pits along the Nene valley.
Key birds: *Winter*: Water Rail, Snipe, Teal, Tufted Duck, Starling. *Spring*: Cuckoo, Green Woodpecker, Reed Bunting, Bullfinch, tits. *Summer*: Whitethroat, Blackcap, Reed Warbler, Sedge Warbler, Common Tern, Swift, House Martin. *Autumn*: Snipe, Great Crested Grebe, Moorhen, Coot, Grey Heron.
Other notable flora and fauna: Holly blue and green-veined white butterflies, water beetles. Grass snake. Bats. Cuckoo flower, reed sweet-grass, marsh woundwort, purple loosestrife, water mint.
Contact: Trust HQ. 01954 713 500; e-mail: cambridgeshire@wildlifebcnp.org

5. SUMMER LEYS LNR

Northamptonshire County Council.
Location: SP 886 634. Three miles from Wellingborough, accessible from A45 and A509, situated on Great Doddington to Wollaston Road.
Access: Open 24 hours a day, 365 days a year, no permits required. Dogs welcome but must be kept on leads at all times. 40 space car park, small tarmaced circular route suitable for wheelchairs.
Facilities: Three hides, one feeding station. No toilets, nearest are at Irchester Country Park on A509 towards Wellingborough.
Public transport: Nearest main station is Wellingborough. No direct bus service, though buses run regularly to Great Doddington and Wollaston, both about a mile away. Tel: 01604 670 060 (24 hrs) for copies of timetables.
Habitat: Scrape, two ponds, lake, scrub, grassland, hedgerow.
Key birds: Hobby, Lapwing, Golden Plover, Ruff, Gadwall, Garganey, Pintail, Shelduck, Shoveler, Little Ringed Plover, Tree Sparrow, Redshank, Green Sandpiper, Oystercatcher, Black-headed Gull colony, terns.
Contact: Chris Haines, Countryside Service, Northamptonshire Council, 01604 237 227.
e-mail: countryside@northamptonshire.gov.uk

6. THRAPSTON GRAVEL PITS & TITCHMARSH LNR

Beds, Cambs, Northants & Peterborough Wildlife Trust/Natural England.
Location: TL 008 804. Seven miles E of Kettering. From A14 take A605 N. For Titchmarsh turn L at Thorpe Waterville, continue towards Aldwincle. Take first L after church and continue to small car park on L. Take footpath to reserve.
Access: As well as the Aldwincle access point, there is a public footpath from layby on A605 N of Thrapston.
Facilities: Six hides.
Public transport: Bus service to Thrapston.
Habitat: Alder/birch/willow wood; old duck decoy, series of water-filled gravel pits.
Key birds: *Summer*: Breeding Grey Heron (no access to heronry), Common Tern, Little Ringed Plover; warblers. Migrants, inc. Red-necked and Slavonian Grebes, Bittern and Marsh Harrier recorded. *Winter*: Good range of wildfowl inc Goosander and gulls.
Contact: Northants Wildlife Trust, 01604 405 285; e-mail: northamptonshire@wildlifebcnp.org
www.wildlifebcnp.org

7. TOP LODGE FINESHADE WOOD

Location: SP 978 983. Off the A43 between Stamford and Corby. Follow brown tourist signs to Top Lodge Fineshade Woods.
Access: Fully accessible visitor centre (10am – 5pm summer: closes 4pm winter), open daily except Christmas Day. Caravan Club site open Mar-Nov (please see CC website for details). Smelter's Walk is an all-ability trail leading to the hide.
Facilities: Two pay-and-display car parks. Visitor centre with live footage of Red Kite nests in season, toilets, Top Lodge Café, guided

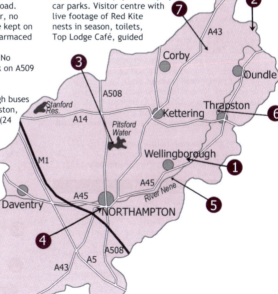

walks and events throughout the year. Wildlife hide in wood. Three waymarked walking trails (one is for all abilities, two are surfaced), 1 horse trail, 1 family cycle trail, dedicated coach and horse box parking.
Public transport: None.
Habitat: Ancient woodland, coniferous woodland, beech woodland, open areas, small pond.
Key birds: Centre of Northants' Red Kite reintroduction scheme. A wide range of birds of mixed woodlands. *All year:* Red Kite, Great Spotted Woodpecker, Goshawk, Nuthatch, Crossbill, Marsh

Tit, Willow Tit. *Summer:* Turtle Dove, warblers. *Winter:* Hawfinch.
Other notable flora and fauna: Adder, grass snake, slow worm, common lizard. Fallow deer, badger. Orchids including greater butterfly, early purple and common spotted, other flora of ancient woodland.
Contact: Forestry Commission, Top Lodge, Fineshade, Nr. Corby, Northamptonshire NN17 3BB. 01780 444 920; e-mail: northants@forestry.gsi.gov.uk
www.forestry.gov.uk/toplodge

Nottinghamshire

GRAVEL PITS are the dominant birding habitat in Nottinghamshire. The most recently developed of these is the Idle Valley NR (formerly known as Lound). Colwick, Netherfield and Holme Pierrepont are close enough together to be worked in a day. The raptor watchpoint at Welbeck can produce Honey Buzzard, Goshawk and Osprey and you can try for Hawfinches winter in Clumber Park.

1. ATTENBOROUGH NATURE RESERVE

Nottingham alongside River Trent. Signposted from main road.
Access: Open at all times. Dogs on leads (guide dogs only in visitor centre). Paths suitable for disabled access. Coaches welcome by prior appointment.
Facilities: Education and visitor centre with café and shop, all accessible to wheelchair users. Nature trail (leaflet from Notts WT), one hide.
Public transport: Railway station at Attenborough – reserve is five mins walk away, visitor centre a further 10 minutes. Rainbow 5 bus service between Nottingham Broadmarsh and Derby bus station runs regularly throughout day. Alight at Chilwell Retail Park and walk 500m along Barton Lane.
Habitat: Disused, flooded gravel workings with associated marginal and wetland vegetation.
Key birds: *Spring/summer:* Breeding Common Tern (40-plus pairs), Reed Warbler, Black Tern regular (bred once). *Winter:* Wildfowl (including Bittern), Grey Heron colony, adjacent Cormorant roost.
Other notable flora and fauna: Smooth newt, dragonflies including four-spotted chaser and migrant hawker.
Contact: Attenborough Nature Centre, 01159 721 777. www.attenboroughnaturecentre.co.uk
e-mail: enquiries@attenboroughnaturecentre.co.uk

2. BESTHORPE NATURE RESERVE

Nottinghamshire Wildlife Trust.
Location: SK 817 640 and SK813 646 (access points). Take A1133 N of Newark. Turn into Trent Lane S of Besthorpe village, reserve entrances second turn on L and R turn at end of lane (nr River Trent).
Access: Open access to a hide, several screens (one with disabled access from car park at present). No access to SSSI meadows. Limited access to areas grazed with sheep. Dogs on leads.

Facilities: No toilets (pubs etc in Besthorpe village), one hide, paths, nature trail (northern part), several screens.
Public transport: Buses (numbers 22, 67, 68, 6, S7L) run by Marshalls, Lincs, Road Car and Travel Wright along A1133 to Besthorpe village (0.75 mile away). Tel: 0115 924 0000 or 01777 710 550 for information.
Habitat: Gravel pit with islands, SSSI neutral grasslands, hedges, reedbed, etc.
Key birds: *Spring/summer:* Breeding Grey Heron, Cormorant, Little Ringed Plover, Kingfisher, Grasshopper Warbler. *Winter:* Large numbers of ducks (Pochard, Tufted Duck, Pintail, Wigeon) and Peregrine. Recent re-profiling of water margins has increased the numbers of visiting waders.
Contact: Notts Wildlife Trust, 01159 588 242; e-mail: info@nottswt.co.uk
www.wildlifetrust.org.uk/nottinghamshire

3. BUNNY OLD WOOD WEST

Nottinghamshire Wildlife Trust.
Location: Lies SW of Keyworth on either side of A60. Limited parking off the A60 at SK 579 283. Please do not obstruct access. Further footpath access is at SK 584 293 off Wysall Lane.
Access: Open all year. No coach parking available.
Facilities: None. **Public transport:** None.
Habitat: Mixed woodland.
Key birds: *All year*: Usual woodland species, all three woodpeckers, Tawny and Little Owls and Hawfinch. *Spring/summer*: Usual visitors, including Blackcap. Possible Brambling.
Other notable flora and fauna: Bluebells, plus good selection of common woodland plants. Butterflies including white-letter hairstreak.
Contact: Notts Wildlife Trust, 01159 588 242; e-mail: info@nottswt.co.uk
www.wildlifetrust.org.uk/nottinghamshire

4. COLWICK COUNTRY PARK

Nottingham City Council.
Location: SK 610 395. Off A612 three miles E of Nottingham city centre.
Access: Open at all times, but no vehicle access after dusk or before 7am.
Facilities: Nature trails. Sightings log book in Fishing Lodge.
Public transport: Call park office for advice.
Habitat: Lakes, pools, woodlands, grasslands, new plantations, River Trent.
Key birds: *Summer*: Warblers, Hobby, Common Tern (15+ pairs). *Winter*: Wildfowl and gulls. Passage migrants.
Other notable flora and fauna: Purple and white letter hairstreak butterflies.
Contact: Head Ranger, The Fishing Lodge, Colwick, Country Park, River Road, Colwick, Nottingham NG4 2DW. 01159 870 785; www.nottinghamcity.gov.uk

5. IDLE VALLEY (SUTTON & LOUND GRAVEL PITS)

Nottinghamshire Wildlife Trust/Tarmac/Private.
Location: SK 690 856. S end of reserve is 0.5 mile N of Retford off A638 to Barnby Moor, via entrance to Tarmac. Learning Centre is on R. N end of reserve near Lound village. Park at Blue Bell Inn, not on verges or Town Street, then walk R from pub car park, then R along Neatholme Road (Lane). Reserve occupies both sides of bridleway after Linghurst Lakes on L. For central area, head E along Chainbridge Lane from village crossroads and park sensibly along lane.
Access: Open all year. Keep to walkways and public rights of way only, no access on private areas. Parking for reserve is in first parking bay (large car park is for Learning Centre only). Footpath at S end is wheelchair accessible.
Facilities: Learning Centre reception and toilets open (10am- 4pm) all year. Refreshments (vending machine) available Mon-Sun (10am- 4pm). Idle Valley Café open weekends (11.30am-2.00pm). Six viewing screens, two off Chainbridge Lane (overlooking Chainbridge NR Scrape), two at Neatholme Scrape and single screens at Neatholme Fen and Neatholme Pit. Two hides in Chainbridge Wood.
Public transport: Buses from Doncaster, Gainsborough and Worksop to Retford (Bus station) then on local Stagecoach service 27 via Lound Village crossroads (Chainbridge Lane).
Habitat: Former sand and gravel quarries, restored gravel workings, conservation grazed areas, woodland, reedbed, river valley, farmland, scrub, willow plantations, open water.
Key birds: 251 species recorded. *Summer*: Gulls, terns, wildfowl and waders. Passage waders, terns, passerines and raptors. *Winter*: Wildfowl, gulls, raptors. Recent rarities have included Broad-billed Sandpiper, Great White Egret, Baird's Sandpiper and Steppe Grey Shrike. Past rarities have included Ring-billed Gull, Caspian, White-winged Black, Gull-billed and Whiskered Terns, Manx Shearwater, Lesser Scaup, Ring-necked Duck, Green-winged and Blue-winged Teal, Richard's Pipit, Pectoral and Buff-breasted Sandpipers, Long-billed Dowitcher, Killdeer, Spoonbill, Bluethroat, Snow Bunting, Shore Lark, Great Skua, Cattle Egret.
Contact: Lound Bird Club, Gary Hobson (Secretary), 01924 384 419; e-mail: loundbirdclub@btinternet.com www.loundbirdclub.com
Nottinghamshire Wildlife Trust, James Simpson (Reserve Officer), Idle Valley Rural Learning Centre, Great North Road, Retford. DN22 8RQ. e-mail: jsimpson@nottswt.co.uk

6. WOLLATON PARK

Wollaton Hall.
Location: Situated N of A52, Derby road, approx three miles W of Nottingham City Centre.
Access: Open all year from dawn-dusk.
Facilities: Pay/display car parks. Some restricted access (deer), leaflets.
Public transport: Trent Buses: No (2) and Nottingham City Transport: No 30 to entrance, 35 and 36 along Derby Road running approx every 15 mins.
Habitat: Lake, small reedbed, woodland.
Key birds: *All year*: Main woodland species present, with good numbers of Nuthatch, Treecreeper and all three woodpeckers. *Summer*: Commoner warblers, incl Reed Warbler, hirundine species, Spotted Flycatcher. *Winter*: Pochard, Gadwall, Wigeon, Goosander, occasional Smew and Goldeneye. Flocks of Siskin and Redpoll, often feeding by the lake, Redwing and occasional Fieldfare.
Contact: Wollaton Hall & Park, Wollaton,, Nottingham, NG8 2AE. 01159 153 900; e-mail: wollaton@ncmg.org.uk
www.wollatonhall.org.uk

Oxfordshire

THE LARGE RSPB reserve at Otmoor offers a mix of wet meadows and reedbed, with displaying waders such as Redshank, Snipe and Lapwing in spring and Hobbies in summer. Wildfowl numbers increase in winter and Hen Harriers, Merlins, Peregrines and Short-eared Owls hunt. Red Kites are easy to see over the Chilterns but for rarities the large concrete reservoirs at Farmoor have an enviable record.

1. ASTON ROWANT NNR

Natural England.
Location: SU 731 966. From the M40 Lewknor interchange at J6, travel NE for a short distance and turn R onto A40. After 1.5 miles at the top of hill, turn R and R again into a narrow, metalled lane. Drive to car park, which is signposted from the A40.
Access: Open all year. Some wheelchair access, please contact Reserve Manager for more information.
Facilities: On-site parking, easy access path to viewpoint, seats, interpretation panels.
Public transport: Regular coach services (Oxford Tube) from Oxford and London, alight at Lewknor or local bus from High Wycome stops at Aston Hill.
Habitat: Chalk grassland, chalk scrub, beech woodland.
Key birds: *Spring/summer:* Blackcap, other warblers, Turtle Dove. Passage birds inc Ring Ouzel, Wheatear and Stonechat. *Winter:* Brambling, Siskin, winter thrushes. *All year:* Red Kite, Buzzard,

Sparrowhawk, Woodcock, Tawny Owl, Green and Great Spotted Woodpeckers, Skylark, Meadow Pipit, Marsh Tit.
Other notable flora and fauna: Rich chalk grassland flora, including Chiltern gentian clustered bellflower, frog, bee, pyramidal and fragrant orchids. Good range of less common butterflies, inc silver-spotted, dingy and grizzled skippers, chalkhill blue, adonis blue, green hairstreak and green fritillary.
Contact: Natural England, Aston Rowant NNR, 01844 351 833; email: enquiries@naturalengland.org.uk
www.naturalengland.org.uk

2. FOXHOLES RESERVE

Berks, Bucks & Oxon Wildlife Trust.
Location: SP 254 206. Head N out of Burford on the A424 towards Stow-on-the-Wold. Take third turning on R. Head NE on unclassified road to Bruern for 3.5km. Just before reaching Bruern, turn L along track following Cocksmoor Copse. After 750m, park in car park on R just before some farm buildings.
Access: Open all year. Please keep to the paths.
Facilities: Car park, footpaths. Can be very muddy in winter.
Public transport: None.
Habitat: Broad-leaved Woodland, and grassland.
Key birds: *Spring/summer:* Spotted Flycatcher, Marsh Tit and warblers. *Winter:* Redwing, Fieldfare, Woodcock. *All year:* Raven, little Owl, all three woodpeckers.
Other notable flora and fauna: Fantastic show of bluebells in May. Autumn fungi. Silver-washed fritillary butterfly.
Contact: Berks, Bucks & Oxon Wildlife Trust, 01865 77 5476; e-mail: wendytobbitt@bbowt.org.uk
www.bbowt.org.uk/reserves/Foxholes

3. OTMOOR NATURE RESERVE

RSPB (Central England Office).
Location: SP 570 126. Car park seven miles NE of Oxford city centre. From J8 of M40, take A40 W to Wheatley, then B4027. Take turn to Horton-cum-Studley, then first L to Beckley. After 0.67 miles at the bottom of a short hill turn R (before the Abingdon Arms public house). After 200 yards, turn L into Otmoor Lane. Reserve car park is at the end of the lane (approx one mile).
Access: Open dawn-dusk. No permits or fees. No dogs allowed on the reserve visitor trail (except public rights of way). In wet conditions, the visitor route can be muddy and wellingtons are essential.
Facilities: Limited. Small car park with cycle racks, visitor trail (3 mile round trip) and two screened viewpoints. The reserve is not accessible by coach and is unsuitable for large groups.
Habitat: Wet grassland, reedbed, open water.
Key birds: *Summer:* Breeding birds include Cetti's and Grasshopper Warblers, Lapwing, Redshank, Curlew, Snipe, Yellow Wagtail, Shoveler, Gadwall, Pochard, Tufted Duck, Little and Great Crested Grebes. Hobby breeds

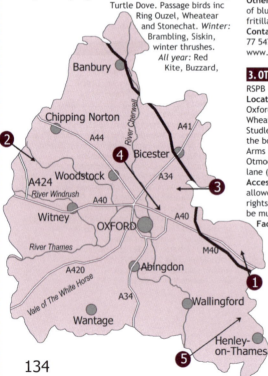

locally. *Winter*: Wigeon, Teal, Shoveler, Pintail, Gadwall, Pochard, Tufted Duck, Lapwing, Golden Plover, Hen Harrier, Peregrine, Merlin. *Autumn and spring passage*: Marsh Harrier, Short-eared Owl, Greenshank, Green Sandpiper, Common Sandpiper, Spotted Redshank and occasional Black Tern.
Contact: RSPB, c/o Folly Farm, Common Road, Bexley, OX3 9YR. 01865 351 163; www.rspb.org.uk

4. SYDLINGS COPSE

Berks, Bucks & Oxon Wildlife Trust.
Location: SP 559 096. 3.5 miles NE of Oxford. From Headington roundabout, take Bayswater Road N through Barton; turn L on B4027; after 500 m, park opposite Royal Oak Farm; take bridleway for 600m, passing two small woods; reserve on right 100m from bridleway. Parking on soft verge, 600m.
Access: Open daily.
Facilities: Public footpath. Public hide.
Habitat: Reedbed, fen, a stream, ancient woodland, heath, limestone grassland and sandy soil are all packed into the steep valley.
Key birds: Summer warblers including Grasshopper Warbler, Marsh Tit, woodpeckers and occasional Stonechat.
Other notable flora and fauna: Mammals such as badgers, deer, foxes and bats. More than 400 species of chalk grassland, woodland and heath plants. Common lizard, grass snake, slow worm. Brown and

purple hairstreak butterflies.
Contact: Trust HQ, 01865 77 5476.
e-mail: wendytobbitt@bbowt.org.uk

5. WARBURG RESERVE

Berks, Bucks & Oxon Wildlife Trust.
Location: SU 720 879. Leave Henley-on-Thames NW on A4130. Turn R at end of Fair Mile onto B480. L fork in Middle Assendon. After 1 mile, follow road round to R at grassy triangle, car park is on R after 1 mile.
Access: Open all year — visitor centre opens 9am-5pm. Please keep dogs on a lead. In some areas, only guide dogs allowed.
Facilities: Visitor Centre, toilets, car park, two hides, one with disabled access, nature trail, leaflets. Visitors with disabilities and groups should contact the warden before visits. Car park not suitable for coaches, only mini-buses.
Habitat: Scrub, mixed woodland, grassland, ponds.
Key birds: *Spring/summer*: Whitethroat, Lesser Whitethroat. *All year*: Sparrowhawk, Red Kite, Treecreeper, Nuthatch, Tawny Owl and Lesser Spotted Woodpecker. *Winter*: Redpoll, Siskin, sometimes Crossbill, Woodcock.
Other notable flora and fauna: Good for orchids, butterflies and mammals (roe, fallow and muntjac deer).
Contact: Warburg Reserve, 01491 642 001.
e-mail: wendytobbitt@bbowt.org.uk

Shropshire

T HE LONG MYND in the southern half of the county holds a good selection of upland birds such as Red Grouse, Ring Ouzel, chats and, occasionally, Merlin. Other hotspots centre round a series of lakes, gravel pits and reservoirs (see Venus Pool report), holding good numbers of wildfowl and gulls. Much of the county is farmland, with good strongholds for breeding Yellow Wagtails and Corn Buntings.

1. BUSHMOOR COPPICE

Shropshire Wildlife Trust
Location: SO 430 880. Head S from Church Stretton and take first R off A49 signed Bushmoor.
Access: Park in Bushmoor village and follow track leading from right-angled bend. Follow green lane to gate and carry onto wood along field margin. Appox half mile from road.
Facilities: None.
Public transport: Buses stop at Bushmoor village.
Habitat: Small mixed woodland and scrub.
Key birds: *Spring/summer*: Migrant warblers and flycatchers, plus common woodland species.
Other notable flora and fauna: Golden saxifrage, bluebells and yellow archangel. Dormouse.
Contact: Shropshire Wildlife Trust, 01743 284 280; www.shropshirewildlifetrust.org.uk

2. CLUNTON COPPICE

Shropshire Wildlife Trust.
Location: SO 343 806. From Craven Arms, take B4368 to Clunton village, go straight over bridge and up the hill to small car park just before reserve sign.
Access: Open at all times. Access along road and public rights of way only.
Facilities: Limited parking in small quarry entrance on R, or opposite The Crown pub.
Public transport: Buses between Craven Arms and Clun stop at Clunton. Steep one mile walk to reserve.
Habitat: Sessile oak coppice. Good for ferns, mosses and fungi.
Key birds: Buzzard and Raven regular. *Spring/summer*: Wide range of woodland birds, inc. Redstart, Wood Warbler and Pied Flycatcher, Woodcock.
Other notable flora: Hairy woodrush and bromerape, sessile oak woodland plants, bluebell, bilberry.
Contact: Trust HQ, 01743 284 280;

3. EARL'S HILL

Shropshire Wildlife Trust
Location: SJ 409 048. Near Minsterley, SW of Shrewsbury. Turn off A488 at Pontesford along lane by Rea Valley Tractors. Car park 700 yards further on.
Access: Follow green route for easier walking. Purple route leads to summit. Car park at entrance.
Facilities: None.
Public transport: Buses to Bishops Castle and

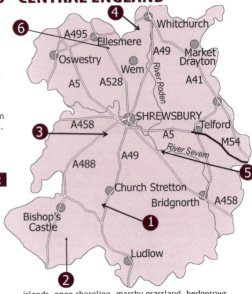

Minsterley stop at Pontesford.

Habitat: Steep-sided volcanic hill, scree slopes and crags, topped by Iron Age fort. Ancient woodland on eastern slopes.

Key birds: *Spring*: Migrants species such as Redstart, Pied Flycatcher and warblers. Dipper and Grey Wagtail on stream. Green Woodpecker common on open grassland.

Other notable flora and fauna: Dormouse. More than 30 species of butterfly recorded, yellow meadow ant. Spring ephemerals on anthills.

Contact: Trust HQ, 01743 284 280; www.shropshirewildlifetrust.org.uk

4. FENN'S WHIXALL AND BETTISFIELD MOSSES NNR

Natural England (North Mercia Team).

Location: The reserve is located four miles SE of Whitchurch, ten miles SW of Wrexham. It is to the S of the A495 between Fenn's bank, Whixall and Bettisfield. There is roadside parking at entrances, car parks at Morris's Bridge, Roundthorn Bridge, World's End and a large car park at Manor House. Disabled access by prior arrangement along the railway line.

Access: Permit required except on Mosses Trail routes.

Facilities: Panels at all main entrances to the site, and leaflets are available when permits are applied for. Three interlinking Mosses Trails explore the NNR and canal from Morris's and Roundthorn bridges.

Public transport: Bus passes nearby. Railway two miles away.

Habitat: 2,000 acres of raised peatland meres and mosses.

Key birds: *Spring/summer*: Nightjar, Hobby, Curlew, Tree Sparrow. *All year*: Skylark, Linnet. *Winter*: Short-eared Owl.

Other notable flora and fauna: Water vole, brown hare, polecat, adder, 2,000 species of moth, 27 species of butterfly, nationally important for dragonflies, inc white-faced darter.

Contact: Natural England, Attingham Park, 01743 282 000; e-mail: north.mercia@natural-england.org.uk

5. VENUS POOL

Shropshire Ornithological Society.

Location: SJ 5478 0607. 6 miles SE of Shrewsbury in angle formed by A458 Shrewsbury to Much Wenlock road and minor road leading S to Pitchford. Entrance is half a mile along minor road which leaves A458 half a mile (0.8 km) SE of Cross Houses.

Access: Public access to much of site, including four hides. Please keep to footpaths shown on notice boards at both entrances. Wheelchair-friendly paths to two public hides and Lena's Hide overlooking feeding station. Dogs not allowed anywhere.

Facilities: Car park with height barrier. Five hides (one for SOS members only). Information boards.

Public transport: Shrewsbury-Bridgnorth buses stop at Cross Houses, which is one mile walk from Venus Pool, partly along busy main road.

Habitat: Approx 27 hectares site. Pool, several islands, open shoreline, marshy grassland, hedgerows, scrub and woodland. Species-rich meadows, field growing bird-friendly crops.

Key birds: Noted for wintering wildfowl and passage waders, plus occasional county rarities, including Black-necked Grebe, Purple Heron, Spoonbill, Red Kite, Hen Harrier, Pectoral Sandpiper, Long-eared Owl, Black Redstart, and Woodlark. *All year*: Common ducks and waterfowl, passerines, including Tree Sparrow. *April-June*: Passage waders include Curlew, Ringed Plover, Dunlin, Redshank, Green and Common Sandpipers, and both godwits. Passage Black Tern. Breeding Oystercatcher, Little Ringed Plover, Lapwing, warblers, hirundines. *July-September*: Wader passage can include Little Stint, Greenshank, Green, Wood, Curlew and Common Sandpipers, and possible rarities. *October-March*: Occasional wintering Bittern, Tundra and Whooper Swans (both scarce). Geese include occasional White-fronted. Ducks include Wigeon, Teal, Pintail, Shoveler, Pochard, Goosander (up to 50 in evening roosts) and occasional Goldeneye. Water Rail, vagrant raptors and owls, winter thrushes and large passerine flocks including Lesser Redpoll, Linnet, Tree Sparrow, Reed Bunting and Yellowhammer.

Contact: www.shropshirebirds.com/venus_pool/venuspool.htm

6. WOOD LANE

Shropshire Wildlife Trust.

Location: SJ 421 331. Turn off A528 at Spurnhill, 1 mile SE of Ellesmere. Car park is three quarter miles down on R.

Access: Open at all times. Apply to Trust for permit to use hides. Reserve accessible to people of all abilities.

Facilities: Car parks signposted. Hides (permit only).

Habitat: Gravel pit restored by Tudor Griffiths.
Key birds: *Summer:* 168 species recorded since 1999.
Breeding Sand Martin, Lapwing, Little Ringed Plover
and Tree Sparrow. Osprey platforms erected to tempt
over-flying birds. Popular staging post for waders
(inc. Redshank, Greenshank, Ruff, Dunlin, Little Stint,
Green and Wood Sandpiper). *Winter:* Large flocks of
Lapwing, plus Curlew and common wildfowl.
Other notable fauna: Good range of dragonflies.
Contact: Trust HQ, 01743 284 280;
www.shropshirewildlifetrust.org.uk

Staffordshire

OUTSIDE its urban areas, the county can offer
Red Grouse on the northern moors, as well as
Lesser Spotted Woodpeckers, Pied Flycatchers and
other songbirds at RSPB Coombes Valley. Cannock
Chase is good for Nightjars, Woodlark and Goshawk,
and often has wintering Great Grey Shrikes. Belvide
Blithfield and Chasewater are the best reservoirs to
work for wintering birds.

1. BELVIDE RESERVOIR

British Waterways Board and West Midland Bird Club.
Location: SJ865 102. Entrance and car park on Shutt
Green Lane, Brewood, Staff ST19 9LX.
Access: Access only by permit from the West Midland
Bird Club.
Facilities: Five hides (3 with wheelchair access), hard
surface paths. Parking for 25-30 cars.
Public transport: Bus to Kiddermore Green (eight
minute walk to reserve).
Habitat: Reservoir with marsh, reedbeds, woodland
and scrub.
Key birds: Wintering and breeding wildfowl. Breeding
and passage waders and terns. Winter gull roost.
Recent scarcities include Sabine's Gull, White winged
and Whiskered Tern and Yellow-browed Warbler.
Other notable fauna: Dragon and damselflies.
Contact: Permit Secretary, 147 World's End Lane,
Quinton, Birmingham B32 1JX.
e-mail:permits@westmidlandbirdclub.com. For other
info: belvide@westmidlandbirdclub.com
www.westmidlandbirdclub.com/belvide

2. BLITHFIELD RESERVOIR

South Staffs Water.
Location: SK 058 237. View from causeway on B5013
(Rugeley/Uttoxeter). Close to village of Abbots
Bromley. Look for signposts to Blithfield Education
Centre.
Access: For members of WMBC only or one off
group permit. Further details from secretary@
westmidlandbirdclub.com.
Facilities: Free car park, toilets. Walk 1 has partial
wheelchair access.
Public transport: None. **Habitat:** Large reservoir.
Key birds: *Winter:* Good populations of wildfowl
(inc. Bewick's Swan, Goosander, Goldeneye), large
gull roost (can inc. Glaucous, Iceland, Mediterrean
and Caspian). Passage terns (Common, Arctic, Black)
and waders, esp. in autumn (Little Stint, Curlew
Sandpiper, Spotted Redshank regular).
Contact: WMBC Secretary
e-mail:secretary@westmidlandbirdclub.com

3. BRANSTON WATER PARK

East Staffordshire Borough Council.
Location: SK 217 207. Follow brown tourist sign from
A38 N. No access from A38 S — head to the Barton-
under-Needwood exit and return N. The park is 0.5
miles S of A5121 Burton-upon-Trent exit.
Access: Open all year, flat, wheelchair-accessible
stone path all round the lake.
Facilities: Green Flag award-winning park. Parking,
public toilets including a RADAR key-operated
disabled toilet, picnic area (some wheelchair
accessible tables), modern children's play area, dog
dip area, fishing through Burton Mutual Angling Club.
Public transport: Contact Arriva bus services.
Habitat: Reedbed, willow carr woodland, scrub,
meadow area.
Key birds: *Spring/summer:* Reed Warbler, Cuckoo,
Reed Bunting. Important roost for Swallow and
Sand Martin. *Winter:* Waders, Little Ringed Plover
occasionally, Pied Wagtail roost.
Other notable fauna: Wide
range of butterflies
and dragonflies.

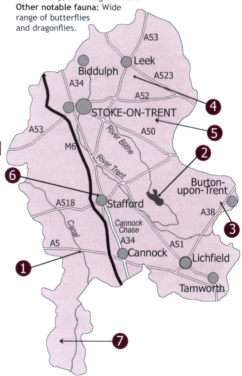

Contact: East Staffordshire Borough Council, 01283 508 000; e-mail: greenspaces@eaststaffsbc.gov.uk www.eaststaffsbc.gov.uk/Services/GreenSpaces/Pages/GreenSpacesBranstonWaterpark.aspx

4. COOMBES VALLEY

RSPB (Midlands Regional Office).
Location: SK 005 530. Three miles E of Leek. From Leek take A523 towards Ashbourne. After Bradnop, turn R on minor road (cross a railway line) to Apesford and follow signs to reserve.
Access: Open daily, no charge. Free parking. Coach groups welcome by prior arrangement. No dogs allowed. Most trails unsuitable for disabled visitors.
Facilities: Information centre, toilets, two miles of nature trail, one hide.
Public transport: 108 bus from Leek to Ashbourne, twice daily. 1.2 miles from reserve, walk towards Ashbourne then take first R, cross railway and continue to reserve.
Habitat: Sessile oak woodland, unimproved pasture and meadow.
Key birds: *Spring*: Pied Flycatcher, Redstart, Wood Warbler. *Jan-Mar*: Displaying birds of prey.
Other notable flora and fauna: Bluebells, various butterflies.
Contact: Reserve warden. 01538 384 017.
e-mail: coombes.valley@rspb.org.uk

5. COTTON DELL

Staffordshire Wildlife Trust.
Location: SK 055 450. From Cheadle take B5417 E to Oakamoor. Entering village, turn R before river bridge, following brown tourist signs for the Staffs CC parking area. Walk back and cross bridge. Take second turning on L up a gravel track next to the black and white house. Continue to reserve entrance.
Access: Park on council car park next to river and follow track north into woodland.
Facilities: None
Public transport: Infrequent bus service from nearby towns and villages.
Habitat: Ancient woodland in steep-sided valley and flower-rich grassland pasture.
Key birds: Dipper, Grey Wagtail, Wood Warbler, all three woodpeckers, Spotted Flycatcher and common woodland birds.
Other notable flora and fauna: Diverse flower-rich grasslands at northern end.
Contact: Staffordshire Wildlife Trust. 01889 880 100;

e-mail: info@staffs-wildlife.org.uk
www.staffs-wildlife.org.uk/page/cotton-dell

6. DOXEY MARSHES

Staffordshire Wildlife Trust.
Location: SJ 903 250. On W side of Stafford town centre. Parking at end of Wootton Drive ST16 1PU
Access: Open at all times. Most of site accessible by wheelchair. Dogs on leads
Facilities: One hide, three viewing platforms
Public transport: Buses and trains to Stafford town centre, walk upstream from Sainsbury's supermarket along River Sow to reserve entrance.
Habitat: Designated SSSI for wet meadow habitats. Marsh, pools, reedbeds, hedgerows, reed sweet-grass swamp
Key birds: *Spring/summer*: Breeding Lapwing, Redshank, Little Ringed Plover, Oystercatcher, Shelduck, warblers, Skylark, Water Rail. *Autumn/Winter*: Snipe, Jack Snipe, Goosander, wildfowl, Passage waders, vagrants
Other notable flora and fauna: Otter, harvest mouse, water shrew, noctule bat, musk beetle.
Contact: Staffordshire Wildlife Trust, 01889 880 100; e-mail:info@staffs-wildlife.org.uk
www.staffs-wildlife.org.uk/page/doxey-marshes

7. HIGHGATE COMMON

Staffordshire Wildlife Trust.
Location: SO 836 895. Near Wombourne, South Staffordshire. From A449 at Himley take B4176 towards Bridgnorth. After approx 1 mile, turn left at traffic lights onto Wombourne Rd, signposted towards Swindon. Continue through village of Swindon, along Chasepool Rd. At the T Junction turn R onto Camp Hill Road. About 1 mile after Camp Farm, take 1st L then R at the T junction onto Highgate Rd. Take 1st entrance on R.
Access: Several car parks, network of paths.
Facilities: Public toilets at Warden's Office (restricted opening hours).
Public transport: None.
Habitat: Lowland heath with broadleaf woodland.
Key birds: Cuckoo, Stonechat, Tree Pipit, Skylark.
Other notable flora and fauna: More than 5,000 species of insect recorded, including several red data book species of bee and wasp, also glow worm and common lizard.
Contact: Trust HQ, 01889 880 100;
www.staffs-wildlife.org.uk/page/highgate-common

Warwickshire

MORE THAN 50,000 gulls roost at Draycote Water in winter and often include the likes of Glaucous and Iceland Gulls. Look for wintering Bitterns at Ladywalk NR. Waders pass through Kingsbury Water Park in spring, and Little Ringed Plovers stay to breed. Cetti's Warblers are resident at Brandon Marsh, with Grasshopper Warblers singing there in spring.

1. BRANDON MARSH

Warwickshire Wildlife Trust.
Location: SP 386 762. Three miles SE of Coventry, 200 yards SE of A45/A46 junction (Tollbar End). Turn E off A45 into Brandon Lane. Reserve entrance 1.25 miles on R.

Access: Open weekdays (9am-4.30pm), weekends (10am-4pm). Entrance charge currently £2.50 (free to Wildlife Trust members). Wheelchair access to nature trail and Wright hide. No dogs. Parking for 2 coaches.
Facilities: Visitor centre, toilets, tea-room (open daily 10am-3pm weekdays, 10am-4pm weekends), nature trail, seven hides.
Public transport: Bus service from Coventry to Tollbar End then 1.25 mile walk. Tel Travel West Midlands 02476 817 032 for bus times.
Habitat: Ten pools, together with marsh, reedbeds, willow carr, scrub and small mixed woodland in 260 acres, designated SSSI in 1972.
Key birds: *Spring/summer*: Garden and Grasshopper Warblers, Whitethroat, Lesser Whitethroat, Hobby, Little Ringed Plover, Whinchat, Wheatear. *Autumn/winter*: Bittern (last two winters), Dunlin, Ruff, Snipe, Greenshank, Green and Common Sandpipers, Wigeon, Shoveler, Pochard, Goldeneye, Siskin, Redpoll. *All year*: Cetti's Warbler, Kingfisher, Water Rail, Gadwall, Little Grebe, Buzzard.
Other notable flora and fauna: More than 20 species of butterfly and 18 species of dragonfly recorded. Almost 500 plants species listed on www.brandonbirding.co.uk
Contact: Ken Bond, Hon. Sec. Brandon Marsh Voluntary Conservation Team, 54 Wiclif Way, Stockingford, Nuneaton, CV10 8NF. 02476 328 785.

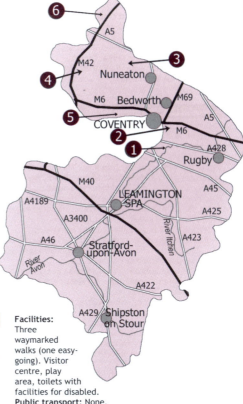

2. COOMBE COUNTRY PARK

Coventry City Council
Location: CV3 2AB. SP 402 795. Five miles East of Coventry centre, on B4027 Coventry to Brinklow road.
Access: Park opens every day, 7.30am to dusk. Entry by foot is free with pay and display system for vehicles. Paths mainly hard surfaces accessible for wheelchairs. Manual wheelchairs can be hired for a £5 returnable deposit.
Facilities: Information centre, toilets, including disabled, café, bird hide, gift shop, picnic benches and wildflower meadow (March to September).
Public transport: By rail: To Coventry City Centre, 20 minute bus journey to park. By bus: No 585 Mike de Courcey Travel (for timetable ring 024 7630 2656).
Habitat: Parkland, lake, woodland and formal gardens.
Key birds: Large heronry, plus many Cormorants. Lesser Spotted Woodpecker and Marsh Tit top the list of woodland species.
Other notable flora and fauna: More than 250 species of plant, including lesser celandine, foxglove, bluebell, red campion and herb robert. Mammals include wood mouse and muntjac deer.
Contact: Coombe Country Park, 024 7645 3720. e-mail: Coombe.countrypark@coventry.gov.uk

3. HARTSHILL HAYES COUNTRY PARK

Warwickshire County Council.
Location: SP 317 943. Signposted as `Country Park' from B4114 W of Nuneaton.
Access: Open all year except Christmas Day. Pay and display car park.

Facilities: Three waymarked walks (one easy-going). Visitor centre, play area, toilets with facilities for disabled.
Public transport: None.
Habitat: Mixed woodland, grassland hillside.
Key birds: Warblers, woodpeckers, tits, Goldcrest, Sparrowhawk, Tawny Owl.
Other notable flora and fauna: Bluebells and numerous birds. More detailed information on the wildlife can be found in the Visitor Centre.
Contact: As Kingsbury Water Park, 01827 872 660.

4. KINGSBURY WATER PARK

Warwickshire County Council.
Location: SP 203 960. Signposted `Water Park' from J9 M42, A4097 NE of Birmingham.
Access: Open all year except Christmas Day. Pay on entry car park.
Facilities: Four hides, two with wheelchair access. Miles of flat surfaced footpaths, loan scheme for mobility scooters. Cafes, Information Centre with gift shop.
Public transport: Call for advice.
Habitat: Open water; numerous small pools, some with gravel islands; gravel pits; silt beds with reedmace, reed, willow and alder; rough areas and grassland.
Key birds: *Summer*: Breeding warblers (nine species),

Little Ringed Plover, Great Crested and Little Grebes. Shoveler, Shelduck and a thriving Common Tern colony. Passage waders (esp. spring). *Winter:* Wildfowl, Short-eared Owl.
Other notable flora and fauna: Orchids.
Contact: Kingsbury Water Park, 01827 872 660. e-mail: parks@warwickshire.gov.uk
www.warwickshire.gov.uk/park

5. MARSH LANE NATURE RESERVE

Packington Estate Enterprises Limited.
Location: SP 217 804. Equidistant between Birmingham and Coventry, both approx 7-8 miles away. Off A452 between A45 and Balsall Common, S of B4102/A452 junction. Turn R into Marsh Lane and immediately R onto Old Kenilworth Road (now a public footpath), to locked gate. Two other entrances; gateway off B4102 east of Hampton-in-Arden (SP 212 814) also off Marsh Lane, Hampton-in-Arden, via bridge under railway (SP 211 805).
Access: Only guide dogs allowed. Site suitable for disabled on east side of river only. Access by day or year permit only. Contact reserve for membership rates. Day permits: adult £4, OAP £3.50, children (under 16) £3 obtained from the Somers Fishery (top end of car park to Stonebridge Golf Centre), Somers Road, Meriden, CV7 7PL.
Facilities: No toilets or visitor centre. Six hides and hard tracks between hides. Three car parks behind locked gates.
Public transport: Hampton-in-Arden railway station within walking distance on footpath loop. Bus no 194 stops at N end of Old Kenilworth Road, one mile from reserve gate.
Habitat: Two large pools with islands, three small and one large (Siden Hill) areas of woodland and crop field for finches and buntings as winter feed.
Key birds: 190 species recorded. *Summer:* Breeding birds include Little Ringed Plover, Common Tern, most species of warbler including Grasshopper. Good passage of waders in Apr, May, Aug and Sept. Hobby

and Buzzard breed locally.
Other notable flora: A wide range of wild flowers, very attractive during spring and summer.
Contact: Nicholas P Barlow or Kay Gleeson, Packington Hall, 01676 522 020.
e-mail: kay@packingtonestate.co.uk
www.packingtonestate.net

6. MIDDLETON LAKES

RSPB (Midlands Regional Office)
Location: SP 192 967. Reserve lies in the Tame Valley, S of Tamworth, next to Middleton Hall. Leave M42 at J9 onto A446, then A4091 and finally into Bodymoor Heath Road.
Access: Open dawn till dusk daily. Surfaced path from car park to Middleton Hall and heronry. Other paths are unsurfaced but generally flat. Playmeadow Trail has wheelchair access for part of the route. Car parking for 30 and bike racks on site. Dogs allowed on leads in parts of the site.
Facilities: Three viewing platforms and a viewing screen. A hide will be constructed soon. Four trails, ranging from 500m to 3km in length.
Public transport: No local bus service. Wilnecote train station is 2.5 miles from the reserve.
Habitat: This former quarry now boasts lakes, reedbeds, meadows and woodland areas.
Key birds: *All year:* Barn Owls are regularly seen and Cetti's Warbler frequently heard. *Spring/summer:* 100-strong heronry, plus common migrant warblers, Lapwing, hirundines and woodland species. *Winter:* Lesser Spotted and Great Spotted Woodpeckers and Willow Tit on the feeders, plus peak numbers of wildfowl and waders. Raptors include Hen and Marsh Harriers, Merlin, Peregrine and Short-eared Owl.
Other notable wildlife: Bluebells and spring flowers, grass snake, common butterflies and moths.
Contact: Call reserve on 01827 259 454 or e-mail: middletonlakes@rspb.org.uk

West Midlands

PEREGRINES and Black Redstarts breed in Birmingham city centre. Sandwell Valley RSPB, plus the adjoining Sandwell Valley Country Park offer a good selection of common birds throughout the year. Local reservoirs such as those at Bartley and Edgbaston are good for wildfowl and have good numbers of roosting gulls in winter.

1. LICKEY HILLS COUNTRY PARK

Location: At Rednal, 11 miles SW of Birmingham City Centre. Leave M42 at J1 or M5 at J4.
Access: Open all year, (10am-7pm in summer; 10am-4.30pm in winter). Land-Rover tours can be arranged for less able visitors.
Facilities: Car park, visitor centre with wheelchair pathway with viewing gallery, picnic site, toilets, café, shop.

Public transport: Bus: West Midlands 62 Rednal (20 mins walk to visitor centre. Rail: Barnt Green (25 mins walk through woods to the centre).
Habitat: Hills covered with mixed deciduous woodland, conifer plantations and heathland.
Key birds: *Spring/summer:* Warblers, Tree Pipit, Redstart. *Winter:* Redwing, Fieldfare. *All year:* Common woodland species.
Contact: The Visitor Centre, Lickey Hills Country Park, Warren Lane, Rednal, Birmingham, B45 8ER. 01214 477 106.
e-mail: lickey.hills@birmingham.gov.uk

2. ROUGH WOOD CHASE LNR

Walsall Metropolitan Borough Council
Location: SJ 984 007. From M6 (Jt 10) head for Willenhall and A462. Turn right into Bloxwich Road North and right again into Hunts Lane. Car park on bend.

Access: Open all year.
Facilities: Circular nature trail.
Public transport: WMT bus 341 from Walsall.
Habitat: 70 acres of oakwood, significant for West Midlands. Also meadows, ponds, pools, marsh and scrubland.
Key birds: Great Crested and Little Grebes on pools in the north end of Chase. Breeding Jay and Sparrowhawk. Common woodland species all year and warblers in summer.
Other notable flora and fauna: Great crested and smooth newts, water vole, various dragonfly species, purple hairstreak, brimstone and small heath butterflies.
Contact: Walsall Countryside Services, Walsall MBC, Top Hangar, Bosty Lane, Aldridge, Walsall WS9 0QQ. 01922 458 328. www.walsall.gov.uk
e-mail: countrysideservices@walsall.gov.uk

3. SANDWELL VALLEY COUNTRY PARK

Sandwell Metropolitan Borough Council.
Location: Entrances at SP 012 918 & SP 028 992. Located approx. 1 mile NE of West Bromwich town centre. Main entrance off Salters Lane or Forge Lane.
Access: Car parks open 8am to sunset. Wheelchair access to Priory Woods LNR, Forge Mill Lake LNR and other parts of the country park.
Facilities: 1,700 acre site. Visitor centre, toilets, café at Sandwell Park Farm (10am-4.30pm). Good footpaths around LNRs and much of the country park. Coach parking by appointment. Also 20 acre RSPB reserve (see below).
Public transport: West Bromwich bus station West Bromwich central metro stop. (Traveline 0871 200 2233).
Habitat: Pools, woodlands, grasslands, including three local nature reserves.
Key birds: Wintering wildfowl including regular flock of Goosander, small heronry. *All year:* Grey Heron, Great Crested Grebe, Lapwing, Reed Bunting, Great Spotted and Green Woodpecker, Sparrowhawk, Kestrel. *Spring:* Little Ringed Plover, Oystercatcher,

up to 8 species of warber breeding, passage migrants. *Autumn:* Passage migrants. *Winter:* Goosander, Shoveler, Teal, Wigeon, Snipe.
Other notable flora and fauna: Common spotted and southern marsh orchid. Ringlet butterfly. Water vole, weasel.
Contact: Senior Countryside Ranger, Sandwell Park Farm, Salters Lane, West Bromwich, W Midlands B71 4BG. 01215 530 220 or 2147.

4. SANDWELL VALLEY

RSPB (Midlands Regional Office).
Location: SP 035 928. Great Barr, Birmingham. Follow signs S from M6 J7 via A34. Take R at 1st junction onto A4041. Take 4th L onto Hamstead Road (B4167), then R at 1st mini roundabout onto Tanhouse Avenue.
Access: 800 metres of paths accessible to assisted and powered wheelchairs with some gradients (please ring centre for further information), centre fully accessible. Dogs on leads.
Facilities: Visitor centre, viewing screens, one hide, toilets, including disabled. Phone centre for details on coach parking. The hide and car park are open (10.30am-1.00pm Tue-Fri), (10.30am-3.30pm Sat-Sun), at other times the reserve is open to pedestrians. More facilities are being added.
Public transport: Bus: 16 from Corporation Street (Stand CJ), Birmingham City Centre (ask for Tanhouse Avenue). Train: Hamstead Station, then 16 bus for one mile towards West Bromwich from Hamstead (ask for Tanhouse Avenue).
Habitat: Open water, wet grassland, reedbed, dry grassland and scrub.
Key birds: *Summer:* Lapwing, Little Ringed Plover, Reed Warbler, Whitethroat, Sedge Warbler, Willow Tit. *Passage:* Sandpipers, Yellow Wagtail, chats, Common Tern. *Winter:* Water Rail, Snipe, Jack Snipe, Goosander, Bullfinch, woodpeckers and wildfowl.
Contact: Sandwell Valley RSPB Reserve, 0121 357 7395; e-mail: sandwellvalley@rspb.org.uk
www.rspb.org.uk

Worcestershire

BITTELL RESERVOIR is the only sizeable one in the county, but there are excellent wetlands to explore at Upton Warren and Bredon's Hardwick. There are many small woods dotted around, but for woodland species, the best area is the Wyre Forest west of Kidderminster, which features oak and coniferous woodland as well as birch heathland.

1. BEACONWOOD/THE WINSEL

Worcestershire Wildlife Trust.
Location: SO 974 759. N of Bromsgrove. Entrance near Lydiate Ash, three miles north of Bromsgrove, at end of cul-de-sac of Old Birmingham Road. Take public footpath along metalled track going N and enter through a metal gate on L after about 20 yards.

Access: The reserve is open throughout the year but please keep to the footpaths.
Facilities: None.
Public transport: Nearest station - Longbridge (three miles). Nearest bus stops in Rubery (1 mile).
Habitat: Mixed woodlands.
Key birds: Buzzard, Kestrel, Sparrowhawk, Tawny Owl, Little Owl, Great Spotted Woodpecker, Spotted Flycatcher, Nuthatch, Treecreeper and many other woodland birds are resident. *Summer:* Pied and Spotted Flycatcher, warblers.
Other notable flora and fauna: In May there is an unbroken sea of bluebells over five acres. Good variety of trees including the Great Oak, probably 250 years old.
Contact: Worcestershire Wildlife Trust, 01905 754 919; www.worcswildlifetrust.co.uk
e-mail: enquiries@worcestershirewildlifetrust.org

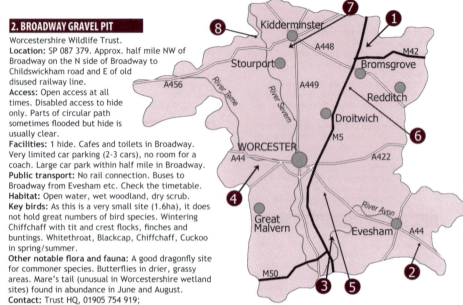

2. BROADWAY GRAVEL PIT

Worcestershire Wildlife Trust.
Location: SP 087 379. Approx. half mile NW of Broadway on the N side of Broadway to Childswickham road and E of old disused railway line.
Access: Open access at all times. Disabled access to hide only. Parts of circular path sometimes flooded but hide is usually clear.
Facilities: 1 hide. Cafes and toilets in Broadway. Very limited car parking (2-3 cars), no room for a coach. Large car park within half mile in Broadway.
Public transport: No rail connection. Buses to Broadway from Evesham etc. Check the timetable.
Habitat: Open water, wet woodland, dry scrub.
Key birds: As this is a very small site (1.6ha), it does not hold great numbers of bird species. Wintering Chiffchaff with tit and crest flocks, finches and buntings. Whitethroat, Blackcap, Chiffchaff, Cuckoo in spring/summer.
Other notable flora and fauna: A good dragonfly site for commoner species. Butterflies in drier, grassy areas. Mare's tail (unusual in Worcestershire wetland sites) found in abundance in June and August.
Contact: Trust HQ, 01905 754 919; www.worcswildlifetrust.co.uk
e-mail: enquiries@worcestershirewildlifetrust.org

3. GWEN FINCH WETLAND

Worcestershire Wildlife Trust.
Location: SO 937 421. W of Evesham. Take B4080 S off A4104. Turn L at Eckington. Park where available and view reserve from road.
Access: Due to its sensitive nature, access to this reserve is restricted to special open days or guided walks. The whole site can be viewed from the minor road between Nafford and Eckington at grid reference SO 937 417, where you can park. A footpath leads down to Nafford Lock and on to Birlingham village, the first part of which passes alongside part of the Gwen Finch reserve.
Facilities: None.
Habitat: Recently created wetland with pools and marshes.
Key birds: Redshank, Water Rail and Reed Warbler breed and, Green Sandpiper and other waders are regular passage visitors. The pools attract hundreds of House Martins and Swallows, which feed on insects over the reeds and pools before heading south on migration.
Other notable flora and fauna: Dragonflies and damselflies are abundant along the margins of the river and the pools. Regular haunt for otters.
Contact: Trust HQ, 01905 754 919;
e-mail: enquiries@worcestershirewildlifetrust.org

4. KNAPP AND PAPERMILL

Worcestershire Wildlife Trust.
Location: SO 749 522. Take A4103 SW from

Worcester; R at Bransford roundabout then L towards Suckley and reserve is approx three miles (do not turn off for Alfrick). Park at Bridges Stone layby (SO 751 522), cross road and follow path to the Knapp House.
Access: Open daily. Large parties should contact Warden.
Facilities: Nature trail, small information centre, wildlife garden, Kingfisher viewing screen.
Public transport: None.
Habitat: Broadleaved woodland, unimproved grassland, fast stream, old orchard in Leigh Brook Valley.
Key birds: *Summer:* Breeding Grey Wagtail, Kingfisher, Spotted Flycatcher nests in warden's garden, all three woodpeckers. Buzzard, Sparrowhawk and Redstart also occur.
Other notable flora and fauna: Otters have returned recently. Good numbers of dragonflies and butterflies on all three meadows include holly blue, purple hairstreak and white admiral. Bluebells, green-winged and spotted orchids.
Contact: The Warden, Knapp and Papermill reserve, The Knapp, Alfrick WR6 5HR. 01886 832 065.

5. TIDDESLEY WOOD NATURE RESERVE

Worcestershire Wildlife Trust.
Location: SO 929 462. Take B4084 from Pershore towards Worcester. Turn L towards Besford and Croome near town boundary just before the summit of the hill. Entrance is on L after about 0.75 miles.
Access: Open all year except Christmas Day. Cycles and horses only allowed on the bridleway. Please keep dogs fully under control. Military firing range at the SW corner of wood, so do not enter the area

marked by red flags. The NE plot is private property and visitors should not enter the area. Main ride stoney, with some potholes. Small pathways difficult if wet. Coach parking by appointment.
Facilities: Information board. May find numbered posts around the reserve which were described in an old leaflet. Circular trail around small pathways.
Public transport: First Midland Red services (see above).
Habitat: Ancient woodland, conifers.
Key birds: *All year:* Coal Tit, Goldcrest, Sparrowhawk, Willow Tit, Marsh Tit. *Spring:* Chiffchaff, Blackcap, Cuckoo. *Winter:* Redwing, Fieldfare.
Other notable flora and fauna: Dragonflies including club-tailed and white-legged damselflies. Good for butterflies, including white admiral, peacock and gatekeeper. Important invertebrates include nationally rare noble chafer beetle which has been recorded here for many years.
Contact: Worcestershire Wildlife Trust, 01905 754 919. e-mail:enquiries@worcestershirewildlifetrust.org www.worcswildlifetrust.co.uk

6. UPTON WARREN

Worcestershire Wildlife Trust.
Location: SO 936 675. Two miles S of Bromsgrove on A38. Leave M5 at junction 5 and head N on A38.
Access: Christopher Cadbury Wetland Reserve divided into two parts — Moors Pools and Flashes Pools. Always open except Christmas Day. Trust membership gives access, or £3 day permit from sailing centre or from wardens on site. Disabled access to hides at Moors Pools only by prior arrangement. No dogs.
Facilities: Seven hides, maps at entrances, paths can be very muddy. Coach parking at sailing centre by previous booking.
Public transport: Birmingham/Worcester bus passes reserve entrance.
Habitat: Fresh and saline pools with muddy islands, some woodland and scrub.
Key birds: *Winter:* Wildfowl. *Spring/autumn:* Passage waders. *Summer:* Breeding Avocet, Redshank, Little Ringed Plover, Oystercatcher, Common Tern, Sedge, Reed, Grasshopper and Cetti's Warblers. Hobby nearby.
Other notable flora and fauna: Saltmarsh plants, dragonflies.
Contact: A F Jacobs, 3 The Beeches, Upton Warren, Bromsgrove, Worcs B61 7EL. 01527 861 370.

7. WILDEN MARSH

Worcestershire Wildlife Trust.
Location: SO 825 730 and SO 829 735. S of Kidderminster. Take A449 S from Kidderminster. At junction with A442 go straight across roundabout into Wilden Lane. This is a very busy road with few parking spaces so park carefully. There are gated entrances off Wilden Lane.
Access: Parts of reserve accessed by gated entrances

are open at all times. Visitors to the more northerly part of the reserve should obtain a permit from the Trust's office. This reserve is complex and new visitors should consult a map. Cattle will be on the reserve at all times so ensure that all gates are secured after use. Parts of this reserve are dangerous with boggy areas, steep banks by the River Stour and deep ditches.
Facilities: None
Public transport: Nearest bus stop at Wilden, half mile from reserve.
Habitat: Dry and marshy fields with small alder and willow woods, reedbeds and many drainage ditches.
Key birds: 192 bird species have been recorded since 1968 and about 70 breed, including Yellow Wagtail, nine species of warblers and Redshank. It is one of the few wintering places for Water Pipits in Worcestershire, though numbers have declined recently.
Other notable flora and fauna: Plants include southern marsh orchids, marsh cinquefoil, marsh arrow-grass, marsh pennywort and lesser water parsnip.
Contact: Trust HQ, 01905 754 919; e-mail: enquiries@worcestershirewildlifetrust.org

8. WYRE FOREST

Natural England/Worcs Wildlife Trust.
Location: SO 750 760. 0.5 miles NW of Bewdley (on the A456) and 4.5 miles W of Kidderminster.
Access: Observe reserve signs and keep to paths. Forestry Commission visitor centre at Callow Hill. Fred Dale Reserve is reached by footpath W of B4194 (parking at SO 776 763).
Facilities: Toilets and refreshments (with disabled access) at Wyre Forest Visitor Centre (near the Discovery Centre) at Callow Hill. Several waymarked trails in (some suitable for wheelchair users) as well as regular guided walks, also family cycle routes through the reserve.
Public transport: The nearest train station is in Kidderminster. Local bus services between Bewdley and Kidderminster are provided by First Group (0871 200 2233).
Habitat: Oak forest, conifer areas, birch heath, lowland grassland, stream.
Key birds: Breeding birds include Redstart, Pied Flycatcher, Wood Warbler, Buzzard and Raven, with Dipper, Grey Wagtail and Kingfisher found on the larger streams.
Other notable flora and fauna: Mammals include fallow, roe and muntjac deer, polecat, otter and mink, yellow neck mouse, dormouse, voles and water shrew. Several bat species including pipistrelle and Daubenton's. Important site for invertebrates including England's largest colony of pearl-bordered fritillary butterflies.
Contact: Wyre Forest NNR, Natural England Office, Lodge Hill Farm, Dowles Brook, Bewdley DY12 2LY. 01299 400 686

Eastern England

Bedfordshire

THOUGH one of England's smallest counties, Bedfordshire is not devoid of birding interest. Blows Down is one of the best sites in to see Ring Ouzels on spring passage. Intense observer coverage at the RSPB's HQ at The Lodge, Sandy, has produced a series of excellent records. Exploring Country Parks such as Priory and Harold-Odell is best early in the morning before the dog-walkers are out.

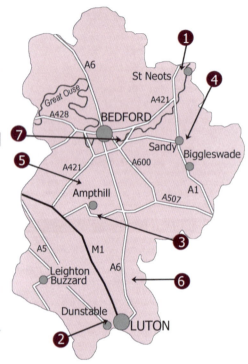

1. BEGWARY BROOK

Beds, Cambs, Northants & Peterborough Wildlife Trust.
Location: TL 169 564. 2 miles S of St Neots. From A1 S take A428 E and continue to Wyboston Lakes complex. Pass through complex and follow nature reserve signs to car park.
Access: Open all year. Partially suitable for wheelchairs.
Facilities: None.
Public transport: Bus, St Neots to Sandy, some stop in Wyboston (Saffords Coaches - 01767 677 395).
Habitat: Former gravel pit. Marsh and open pools next to Great Ouse.
Key birds: Wildfowl and wader species. *Spring:* Sedge, Reed and Willow Warblers, Blackcap. *All year:* Reed Bunting, Kingfisher, Goldcrest.
Other notable flora and fauna: Orange-tip and speckled wood butterflies, dragonflies and grass snakes. Plants include great burnet, common fleabane and marsh woundwort.
Contact: Trust HQ, 01954 713 500.
e-mail: cambridgeshire@wildlifebcnp.org
www.wildlifebcnp.org

2. BLOW'S DOWNS

Beds, Cambs, Northants & Peterborough Wildlife Trust.
Location: TL 033 216. On the outskirts of Dunstable. Take A5065 from W of Luton, cross M1, take first exit at roundabout, park with care on verge. Can also walk half mile from Dunstable centre to W entrance at Half Moon Lane off A5.
Access: Open all year, not suitable for wheelchairs.
Facilities: None. **Public transport:** None.
Habitat: SSSI, chalk downland, scrub and grassland, that is a traditional resting place for incoming spring migrants.
Key birds: *Winter:* Lapwing, Meadow Pipit, Skylark. *Spring/autumn:* Ring Ouzel, Wheatear, Whinchat, Black Redstart, Stonechat, Willow Warbler.
Other notable flora and fauna: Chalkhill blue, brown argus and marbled white butterflies. Plants include small scabious, burnet-saxifrage, squinancywort, great pignut, common spotted and bee orchids.
Contact: Trust HQ, 01954 713 500.
e-mail: bedfordshire@wildlifebcnp.org
www.wildlifebcnp.org

3. FLITWICK MOOR

Beds, Cambs, Northants & Peterborough Wildlife Trust.
Location: TL 046 354. E of Flitwick. From Flitwick town centre (Tesco roundabout) on A5120, cross railway bridge, R at roundabout, immediately L into King's Road. After 500m, L into Moulden Road towards A507. After quarter mile R at Folly Farm, follow track to small car park. Also footpath to reserve from Moor Lane.
Access: Open all year.
Facilities: Car park. Please stick to public paths.
Public transport: Frequent buses (United Counties) from Bedford and Luton to Flitwick, or take train to Flitwick and then three-quarter mile walk.
Habitat: SSSI. Important wetland for the area, blend of fen, meadow, wet woodland and fragile peaty soil. Supports mosses ferns and flowers.
Key birds: *Winter:* Siskin, Water Rail, Great Spotted Woodpecker. *Spring:* Lesser Spotted Woodpecker, Willow Warbler, Blackcap. *Summer:* Water Rail, Grasshopper and Garden Warblers, Cuckoo. *Autumn:* Brambling.
Other notable flora and fauna: Good variety of

butterflies and dragonflies, plus chimney sweeper moth and conehead bush cricket. Plants include nine species of sphagnum moss, marsh pennywort, black knapweed, water figwort plus fly agaric and yellow brain fungus in autumn.

Contact: Trust HQ, 01954 713 500.
e-mail: cambridgeshire@wildlifebcnp.org
www.wildlifebcnp.org

4. LODGE (THE)

RSPB (Central England Office).

Location: TL 191 485. Reserve lies 1 mile/1.6km E of Sandy on the B1042 road to Potton.

Access: Reserve is open daily 9am-9pm (or sunset when earlier); shop 9am-5pm weekdays, 10am-5pm weekends. Non-members: £4 per motor vehicle. Dogs only allowed on bridleway.

Facilities: Nature trails being extended to 5 miles. One bridleway (half mile) and gardens are wheelchair/pushchair accessible. One hide (wheelchair accessible), 50 yards from car park. Coach parking at weekends by arrangement. Refreshments at shop.

Public transport: Buses to Sandy Market Square from Bedford, infrequent service. One mile walk or cycle from centre of Sandy or half mile from Sandy railway station, in part along trail through heathland restoration.

Habitat: This 180-hectare reserve is a mixture of woodland, heathland and acid grassland and includes the formal gardens of the RSPB's UK headquarters. New land being restored to heathland.

Key birds: *Spring/summer:* Hobby, Spotted Flycatcher. *All year:* Woodpeckers, woodland birds. *Winter:* Winter thrushes, woodland birds.

Other notable flora and fauna: Natterjack toads, rare heathland insects. Particularly good site for fungi, and lichens. Garden pools are good for dragonflies.

Contact: RSPB, The Lodge Shop, Sandy, Beds SG19 2DL. 01767 680 541; www.rspb.org.uk/reserves/
e-mail: thelodgereserve@rspb.org.uk

5. MARSTON VALE MILLENNIUM COUNTRY PARK

Marston Vale Trust (Regd Charity No 1069229).

Location: SW of Bedford off A421 at Marston Moretaine. Only five mins from J13 of M1.

Access: Park and forest centre open seven days a week. Summer 10am-6pm, winter 10am-5pm. Forest Centre and car park closed Christmas Day, Boxing Day and New Year's Day. No dogs in wetlands reserve, rest of site OK for dogs and horses. Entry charge for wetland reserve (£2.50 for adults and £1.75 for Concessions). Main 8km trail surfaced for wheelchair and pushchair access. All-terrain wheelchair available for free loan. Coach parking available.

Facilities: Cafe bar, gift shop, art gallery, exhibition. Free parking. The 2km wetland trail is a level path with a compacted, loose stone surface inc two hand gates with top latches.

Public transport: Bedford to Bletchley line — trains to Millbrook and Stewartby station, 20 minute walk to

Forest Centre.

Habitat: Lake - 610 acres/freshwater marsh (man-made), reedbed, woodland, hawthorn scrub and grassland.

Key birds: *Winter:* Iceland and Glaucous Gulls (regular), gull roost, wildfowl, Great Crested Grebe. *Spring:* Passage waders and terns (Black Tern, Arctic Tern), Garganey. *Summer:* Nine species of breeding warblers, Hobby, Turtle Dove, Nightingale, Bearded Tit. *Autumn:* Passage waders and terns. *Rarities:* White-winged Black Tern, Laughing Gull, divers, Manx Shearwater, Bittern.

Other notable flora and fauna: Dingy and grizzled skipper butterflies, excellent for dragonflies. Also otter and brown hare, plus bee and pyramidal orchids and stoneworts.

Contact: Forest Centre, 01234 767 037.
e-mail: info@marstonvale.org
www.marstonvale.org

6. PEGSDON HILL RESERVE

Beds, Cambs, Northants & Peterborough Wildlife Trust.

Location: TL 120 295. 5 miles W of Hitchin. Take B655 from Hitchin towards Barton-le-Clay. Turn R at Pegsdon then immediately L and park in lay-by. Reserve entrance across B655 via footpath.

Access: Open all year. Dropping off point for coaches only.

Facilities: None.

Public transport: Luton to Henlow buses (United Counties) stop at Pegsdon.

Habitat: Chalk grassland, scrub and woodland.

Key birds: *Winter:* Brambling, Stonechat, winter thrushes, raptors including Buzzard. *Spring:* Wheatear, Ring Ouzel, Tree Pipit, Yellowhammer. *Summer:* Turtle Dove, Grey Partridge, Lapwing, Skylark.

Other notable flora and fauna: Dark green fritillary, dingy and grizzled skippers, chalkhill blue, brown argus and small heath butterflies. Glow worms. Plants include pasqueflower in spring, fragrant and common spotted orchids.

Contact: Trust HQ, 01954 713 500.
e-mail: cambridgeshire@wildlifebcnp.org

7. PRIORY COUNTRY PARK AND MARINA

Bedford Borough Council.

Location: TL 071 495. 1.5 miles SE from Bedford town centre. Signposted from A428 & A421. Entry point to new 'River Valley Park'

Access: Park and hides open at all times. No access to fenced/gated plantations.

Facilities: Toilets and visitor centre open daytime, all-year-round disabled access on new path around lake. Hides, nature trails, labyrinth, cycle hire, Premier Inn for meals, accommodation.

Public transport: Stagecoach (01604 676 060) 'Blue Solo 4' every 20 mins. Mon-Sat. Alight 1st stop Riverfield Drive (200 m). Rail station at Bedford (approx 2.5 miles)

Habitat: Lakes, reedbeds, scrub and woodland, meadows adjoining Great Ouse.

Key birds: Good numbers/variety of winter wildfowl, varied mix of spring passage species, with breeding warblers and woodpeckers, augmented by feeding terns, hirundines and raptors lakeside. *Winter:* Grebes, Pochard, Shoveler, Gadwall, Merlin, Water Rail, gulls, thrushes, Chiffchaff, corvids, buntings. *Passage:* Raptors, waders, terns, pipits. *Summer:* Hobby, Turtle Dove, Swift, hirundines, *acrocephalus* and *sylvia* warblers. *All year:* Cormorant, Little Egret, Heron, Stock Dove, woodpeckers, Kingfisher, Grey Wagtail, Treecreeper, Goldfinch, Bullfinch.
Other notable flora and fauna: 23 species of dragonfly, incl small red-eyed damsel & hairy hawker. 20 species of butterfly. Large plant list. Fox, muntjac and otter.
Contact: Jon Bishop, Wardens Office, Visitor Centre, Priory CP, Barkers Lane, Bedford, MK41 9SH. 01234 211 182.

Cambridgeshire

THE NENE and Ouse Washes are superb for wintering wildfowl, owls and raptors, with the former also offering the chance of Cranes, breeding Black-tailed Godwits, Spotted Crakes plus introduced Corncrakes in summer. Grafham Water attracts plenty of scarce species. Paxton Pits is probably the best place in the country to actually see Nightingales.

1. BRAMPTON WOOD

Beds, Cambs, Northants & Peterborough Wildlife Trust.
Location: TL 184 698. 4 miles W of Huntingdon. From A1 (S) at Buckden roundabout, take 3rd exit to Grafham/Kimbolton. Take 1st R to Grafham village, then 1st R on Brampton road. Car park will be on L.
Access: Open daily. Coaches able to drop passengers off but no parking space.
Facilities: Car park, interpretative shelter. The wood has wide grass rides and small mud paths. Suitable for disabled access when dry, on grassy rides.
Public transport: Bus from Huntingdon to Brampton (H&D) then 2 mile walk.
Habitat: Ancient woodland, primarily oak, ash and field maple with hazel coppice. Areas of planted conifer and species rich grassland rides and glades.
Key birds: *Autumn/winter:* Marsh Tit, Woodcock, winter thrushes. *Spring/summer:* Common woodland birds, Green Woodpecker, Spotted Flycatcher.
Other notable flora and fauna: Brown argus, white admiral and black hairstreak butterflies, pine beauty and pine hawk moths. Dormouse, glow worms, smooth and great crested newts, plus various dragonfly species. Plants include meadow grasses, cowslip, yellow rattle, devil's-bit scabious.
Contact: Trust HQ, 01954 713 500.
e-mail: cambridgeshire@wildlifebcnp.org
www.wildlifebcnp.org

2. FEN DRAYTON

RSPB (Eastern England Office).
Location: TL 352 680. NW of Cambridge. Leave A14 at Junction 28; follow signs to Swavesey. Turn L in Boxworth End (signed to Fen Drayton). Turn R onto minor road (signed to Swavesey), then L into entrance to Fen Drayton Lakes. Follow signs to car park.
Access: Open at all times. Dogs are only allowed on public footpaths and bridleways. Disabled birders can get car access to one viewing screen.
Facilities: Several public and permissive rights of way around lakes and two open access fields. Information boards giving access details. Free trail guides and events leaflets are available from the Elney car park.
Public transport: Huntingdon: Stagecoach service 553 (with change to service 15 at St Ives), alight at Fen Drayton High Street. Cambridge: Stagecoach service 15 to Swavesey Middle Watch or Whippet No 15 to Fenstanton, alight in Fen Drayton High Street. Walk north (600 m) from Fen Drayton High Street onto Holywell Ferry Road, past recreation ground on left. Cambridgeshire Guided Bus service has a request stop in reserve.
Habitat: A complex of lakes and traditional riverside meadows next to the River Great Ouse that used to be gravel workings.
Key birds: At least 213 species have been recorded in the area with some 65 species being regular breeders, including Common Tern. Hobby, waders on passage. Rarities include Great White Egret, Purple Heron, Glossy Ibis, Common Crane, Red-Footed Falcon, Honey Buzzard and Whiskered Tern. Bitterns are now a regular sight, with Holywell Lake and Elney Lake being the favoured sites. *Winter:* Nationally important numbers of Gadwall and Coot.
Other notable fauna: Good site for butterflies, dragonflies and mammals.
Contact: Fen Drayton, 01954 233 260;
e-mail: fendraytonlakes@rspb.org.uk

3. FERRY MEADOWS COUNTRY PARK

Nene Park Trust.
Location: TL 145 975. Three miles W of Peterborough and two miles E of A1. On all major routes into city, follow brown tourist signs for Nene Park or country park symbol. Also signed on Oundle Road (A605).
Access: Open all year, 7am to dusk (summer, 8am until sunset in winter. Electric scooters and wheelchair available for loan — call to book in advance. Coach parking free at all times. Car parking charges apply at weekends and Bank Holidays between April - Oct.
Facilities: Car park, visitor centre, toilets (inc disabled), café, two wheelchair-accessible hides in nature reserve area. Hard surface paths in park's central areas, but steep slopes in Bluebell Wood.
Public transport: Stagecoach X14 stops on A605 by Notcutts Nursery. Half mile walk to park entrance. Tel. Traveline 0870 6082 608 or www.traveline.org.uk
Habitat: Lakes, meadows, scrub, broadleaved woodland and small wetland nature reserve.

Key birds: *Spring*: Terns, waders, Yellow Wagtail. *Winter*: Grebes, Siskin, Redpoll, Water Rail, occasional Hawfinch. *All year*: Good selection of woodland and water birds, Kingfisher.
Other notable flora and fauna: Bluebell, wood anenome, wild garlic in woodland.
Contact: Visitor Services Officer, Nene Park Trust, 01733 234 443;
e-mail: visitor.services@ neneparktrust.org.uk
www.nene-park-trust.org.uk

4. FOWLMERE

RSPB (Eastern England Office).
Location: TL 406 461. 7 miles S of Cambridge. From A10, turn towards Fowlmere at Fowlmere-Shepreth crossroads (no RSPB sign); after 1 mile, turn R by cemetery (RSPB sign); after another 0.6 mile, turn L into reserve.
Access: Access at all times along marked trail.
Facilities: 1.5 miles of trails. Three hides, toilets. Space for one coach, prior booking essential. Wheelchair access to one hide, toilet and some of the trails.
Public transport: Shepreth railway station 2 miles. By Bus: Dunsbridge Turnpike (outside Country Homes & Gardens), 1 mile. Walk towards Melbourn; after 300 m, cross road and turn left on to single track road to Fowlmere (beware of traffic); after 0.75 mile (1.2 km), turn right into reserve (RSPB sign).
Habitat: Reedbeds, meres, woodland, scrub.
Key birds: *Summer*: Ten breeding warblers. *All year*: Water Rail, Kingfisher. *Winter*: Snipe, raptors.
Other notable flora and fauna: Healthy population of water shrews and otters. 18 species of dragonfly.
Contact: Fowlmere, 01763 208 978;
e-mail:fowlmere@rspb.org.uk

5. GRAFHAM WATER

Beds, Cambs, Northants & Peterborough Wildlife Trust.
Location: TL 143 671. Follow signs for Grafham Water from A1 at Buckden or A14 at Ellington. Follow B661 road towards Perry and Staughtons to West Perry. As you leave village, Anglian Water's Mander car park is signposted on R. Car parking charges apply.
Access: Open all year. Dogs barred in wildlife garden only, on leads elsewhere. Car parking £2 for day ticket.
Facilities: Five bird hides in nature reserve, two in the bird sanctuary area. Two in wildlife garden accessible to wheelchairs. Cycle track through reserve also accessible to wheelchairs. Visitor centre with restaurant, shop and toilets. Disabled parking. Use Plummer car park for lagoons and Marlow car park for dam area (good for waders and vagrants).
Public transport: Bus, St Neots to Bedford. Get off at Great Staughton then 2 mile walk.
Habitat: Open water, settlement lagoons ranging from reedbeds, open water, wet mud and willow carr, ancient and plantation woodland, scrub, species rich grassland.
Key birds: *Resident*: Common woodland birds,

wildfowl. *Winter*: Waders including Common Sandpiper and Dunlin, Great Crested Grebe, Wildfowl including large flocks of Tufted Duck and Coot, Pochard, Shoveler, Shelduck, Goldeneye, Goosander and Smew, gulls (can be up to 30,000 roosting in mid-winter). *Spring/summer*: Breeding Nightingale, Reed, Willow and Sedge Warblers, Common and Black Terns. *Autumn*: Passage waders. *Rarities*: Have included Wilson's Phalarope (2007), Ring-necked Duck, Great Northern Diver, Glaucous, Iceland and Mediterranean Gulls.
Other notable flora and fauna: Bee and common spotted orchids, early purple orchid, common twayblade (in woods), cowslip. Common blue and marbled white butterflies, dragonflies including broad-bodied chaser, voles, grass snakes.
Contact: The Warden, Grafham Water Nature, 01480 811 075; www.wildlifetrust.org.uk/bcnp

6. NENE WASHES

RSPB (Eastern England Office).
Location: TL 318 991. Reserve is 8 miles E of Peterborough, and NE of Whittlesey. Car park at end of Eldernell Lane, off A605 east of Coates. There is currently no signposting to the reserve.
Access: Open at all times along South Barrier Bank, accessed at Eldernell, one mile NE of Coates, off A605. No access to fields or for wheelchairs along bank.
Facilities: Small car park - one coach max. Information board. No toilets or hide.

Public transport: Bus and trains to Whittlesey, bus to Coates -Stagecoach 01733 554 575.
Habitat: Wet grassland with ditches. Often flooded.
Key birds: *Spring/early summer*: Corncrake release scheme. Breeding waders (inc Black-tailed Godwit), duck (inc Garganey), Marsh Harrier and Hobby. *Winter*: Waterfowl in large numbers (inc Bewick's Swan, Pintail, Shoveler), Barn and Short-eared Owls, Hen Harrier.
Other notable flora and fauna: Water vole, otter, water violet, flowering rush and fringe water lily.
Contact: Charlie Kitchin, RSPB Nene Washes, 21a East Delph, Whittlesey, Cambs PE7 1RH. 01733 205 140.

7. OUSE WASHES

RSPB (Eastern England Office).
Location: TL 471 860. Between Chatteris and March on A141, take B1093 to Manea. Reserve signposted from Manea. Reserve office and visitor centre located off Welches Dam. Approximately ten miles from March or Chatteris.
Access: Access at all times from visitor centre (open 9am-5pm daily except Dec 25/26). Welches Dam to public hides approached by marked paths behind boundary bank. No charge. Dogs on leads at all times. Disabled access to Welches Dam hide, 350 yards from car park. Track between Kingfisher and Stevens Hides very muddy following maintenance work. Groups welcome, but large coaches (36+ seats) cannot traverse final bend to reserve.
Facilities: Car park (inc 2 disabled bays) and toilets. Space for up to two small coaches. Visitor centre - unmanned but next to reserve office. Ten hides overlooking the reserve: nearest 350 yards from visitor centre (with disabled access) up to 1.8 miles from visitor centre. Boardwalk over pond — good for dragonflies in summer.
Public transport: None to reserve entrance. Buses and trains stop at Manea — three miles from reserve.
Habitat: Lowland wet grassland — seasonally flooded. Open pool systems in front of some hides, particularly Stockdale's hide.
Key birds: *Summer*: Around 70 species breed including Black-tailed Godwit, Lapwing, Redshank, Snipe, Shoveler, Gadwall, Garganey and Spotted Crake. Also Hobby and Marsh Harrier. *Autumn*: Passage waders including Wood and Green Sandpipers, Spotted Redshank, Greenshank, Little Stint, plus terns and Marsh and Hen Harriers. *Winter*: Large number of wildfowl (up to 100,000 birds) including Bewick's and Whooper Swans, Wigeon, Teal, Shoveler, Pintail, Pochard.
Other notable flora and fauna: Good range of dragonflies, butterflies and fenland flora.
Contact: Site Manager, Ouse Washes Reserve, 01354 680 212; e-mail: ouse.washes@rspb.org.uk

8. PAXTON PITS NATURE RESERVE

Huntingdonshire District Council.
Location: TL 196 629. Satnav PE19 6ET. Access from A1 at Little Paxton, two miles N of St Neots.

Access: Free entry. Open 24 hours. Visitors' centre open 7 days a week. Dogs allowed under control. Heron trail suitable for wheelchairs during summer. Coaches by arrangement.
Facilities: Visitors' centre provides information about the surrounding area. Books, bird feeders and seed etc are on sale and light refreshments are available. Leaflets for the Nature Reserve can also be purchased. Toilets (including disabled) are available when the visitors' centre is open. Two bird hides (always open), marked nature trails.
Public transport: Buses run from St Neots and Huntingdon to Little Paxton (enquiries 0845 045 5200). The nearest train station is St Neots (enquiries 0845 748 4950).
Habitat: Grassland, scrub, lakes. Site being expanded over the next 10 years, to include extensive reedbed.
Key birds: *Spring/summer*: Nightingale, Kingfisher, Common Tern, Sparrowhawk, Hobby, Grasshopper, Sedge and Reed Warblers, Lesser Whitethroat. *Winter*: Smew, Goldeneye, Goosander, Gadwall, Pochard.
Other notable flora and fauna: Wildflowers, butterflies and dragonflies are in abundance. Along the meadow trail there are common spotted orchids. Bee orchids are found around the car park. Otters are known to use the reserve.
Contact: The Rangers, Paxton Pits Nature Reseve, High Street, Little Paxton, St Neots, Cambs PE19 6ET. 01480 406 795. e-mail: paxtonpits@btconnect.com www.paxton-pits.org.uk

9. WICKEN FEN

The National Trust.
Location: TL 563 705. Lies 17 miles NE of Cambridge and ten miles S of Ely. From A10 drive E along A1123.
Access: Reserve is open daily except Christmas Day. Visitor centre is open daily all year round . Cafe open daily March - Oct, Weds to Sun Nov - Feb. Boardwalk suitable for wheelchairs, with 2 hides. Disabled toilet
Facilities: Toilets , visitor centre, café, hides, boardwalk, footpaths, cycle route (NCN Route 11 passes through the reserve) , coach and disabled parking. Dragonfly Centre open weekends during the summer months.
Public transport: Nearest rail link either Cambridge or Ely. Buses only on Thu and Sun. No buses to Wicken.
Habitat: Open fen, cut hay fields, sedge beds, grazing marsh, partially flooded wet grassland, reedbed, scrub, woodland.
Key birds: *Spring*: Passage waders and passerines. *Summer*: Marsh Harriers, waders and warblers. *Winter*: Wildfowl, Hen Harrier, Bittern.
Other notable flora and fauna: More than 8,000 species recorded: 22 species of dragonfly/damselfly, 27 species of butterfly and 1,000-plus species of moth. Water vole, otter.
Contact: The Warden, Wicken Fen, 01353 720 274. e-mail: wickenfen@nationaltrust.org.uk www.wicken.org.uk

Essex

THIS HUGE county offers a wide range of habitats. As well as woodland at Epping Forest, the reservoirs at Abberton and Hanningfield, plus coastal marshes such as Rainham Marshes RSPB and Old Hall Marshes RSPB, are all rich in birds. Try the migration hotspots at the Naze, a bird observatory at Bradwell and even seawatching along the Thames off Southend Pier.

1. ABBERTON RESERVOIR

Essex Wildlife Trust.
Location: TL 963 174. Six miles SW of Colchester on B1026 (Colchester - Maldon). Follow signs from Layer-de-la-Haye or Great Wigborough.
Access: Open daily (9am-5pm). Closed Christmas Day and Boxing Day.
Facilities: New visitor centre and nature reserve are now open as part of Essex & Suffolk Water's reservoir enhancement scheme. Facilities include toilets, viewing verandah, nature trails with panoramic views, bird hides, gift shop and light refreshments. Ample parking, including disabled and coaches. Also good viewing where roads cross reservoir.
Habitat: 60 acres on edge of expanding 1,200-acre reservoir.
Key birds: *Winter:* Nationally important for Coot, Mallard, Teal, Wigeon, Shoveler, Gadwall, Pochard, Tufted Duck, Goldeneye, Smew, Bittern and Goosander regular. Passage waders, terns, birds of prey. Tree-nesting Cormorant colony; raft-nesting Common Tern. *Summer:* Hobby, Yellow Wagtail, warblers, Nightingale, Turtle Dove, Skylark, Corn Bunting. *Autumn:* Red-crested Pochard, waders.
Other notable flora and fauna: Dragonflies including broad-bodied chaser, small red-eyed damselfly, butterflies including green and purple hairstreak, roesel's bush-cricket. Brown hare.

Contact: Centre Manager, Essex Wildlife Trust, Church Road, Layer-de-la-Haye, Colchester CO2 0EU. 01206 738 172; e-mail:abberton@essexwt.org.uk

2. ABBOTTS HALL FARM

Essex Wildlife Trust.
Location: TL 963 145. Seven miles SW from Colchester. Turn E off B1026 (Colchester-Maldon road) towards Peldon. Entrance is 0.5 mile on R.
Access: Weekdays (9am-5pm). Two hides with wheelchair ramps. No dogs please. Working farm so please take care.
Facilities: Toilets, hides, guided walks, fact-sheets, information boards.
Public transport: None.
Habitat: Saltmarsh, saline lagoons, grazing marsh, farmland, woodland, freshwater lakes and ponds.
Key birds: *Winter:* Waders and wildfowl. Passage migrants and summer warblers.
Other notable flora and fauna: Range of butterflies, reptiles, newts and water vole.
Contact: Trust HQ, 01621 862 960; e-mail: admin@essexwt.org.uk

3. BRADWELL BIRD OBSERVATORY

Essex Birdwatching Society
Location: 100 yards S of St Peter's Chapel, Bradwell-on-Sea. Mouth of Blackwater estuary, between Maldon and Foulness.
Access: Open all year.
Facilities: Accommodation for eight in hut; two rooms each with four bunks; blankets, cutlery, etc. supplied.
Habitat: Mudflats, saltmarsh.
Key birds: *Winter:* Wildfowl (inc. Brent Geese, Red-throated Diver, Red-breasted Merganser), large numbers of waders; small numbers of Twite, Snow Bunting and occasional Shore Lark on beaches, also Hen Harrier, Merlin and Peregrine. Good passage of migrants usual in spring and autumn. *Summer:* Small breeding population of terns and other estuarine species.
Other notable flora and fauna: A variety of dragonflies inc hairy dragonfly and scarce emerald damselfly.
Contact: Graham Smith, 48 The Meads, Ingatestone, Essex CM4 0AE. 01277 354 034.

4. FINGRINGHOE WICK

Essex Wildlife Trust.
Location: TM 046 197. The reserve is signposted from B1025 to Mersea Island, five miles S of Colchester.
Access: Winter opening: 1st Nov-31st Mar (9am-4pm), Tues to Sun (Closed Christmas Day & Boxing Day). Summer opening: 1st Apr-31st Oct (9am – 5pm) Open 7 days a week. Entry by

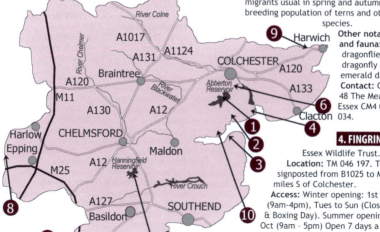

suggested donation: adult £2, child £1 and family £5.
Dogs limited to dog walk on leads
Facilities: Visitor centre: toilets inc: baby changing
facilities, easy access toilet and one wheelchair
is available, Gift shop, light refreshments, optics,
observation room with displays, observatory, car
park, Reserve: seven bird hides, nature trails.
Habitat: Old gravel pit, large lake, many ponds,
sallow/birch thickets, young scrub, reedbeds,
saltmarsh, gorse heathland.
Key birds: *Autumn/winter*: Brent Goose, waders, Hen
Harrier, Little Egret. *Spring*: 30 male Nightingales.
Good variety of warblers in scrub, thickets, reedbeds
and Turtle Dove, Green/Great Spotted Woodpeckers.
Winter: Little Grebe, Mute Swan, Teal, Wigeon,
Shoveler, Gadwall on lake.
Contact: Louise Beary, Fingringhoe Wick Visitor
Centre, 01206 729 678; www.essexwt.org.uk
e-mail: louiseb@essexwt.org.uk
www.facebook.com/EWTFingringhoe

5. HANNINGFIELD RESERVOIR

Essex Wildlife Trust.
Location: TQ 725 971. Three miles N of Wickford.
Exit off Southend Road (Old A130) at Rettendon onto
South Hanningfield Road. Follow this for two miles
until reaching the T-junction with Hawkswood Road.
Turn R and the entrance to the visitor centre and
reserve is one mile on the R.
Access: Open daily (9am-5pm) all year. Closed
Christmas and Boxing Day. Disabled parking, toilets,
and adapted birdwatching hide. No dogs. No cycling.
Facilities: Visitor centre, gift shop, optics,
refreshments, toilets, four bird hides, nature trails,
picnic area, coach parking, education room.
Public transport: Chelmsford to Wickford bus no
14 to Downham village and walk half mile down
Crowsheath Lane.
Habitat: Mixed woodland (110 acres) with grassy
glades and rides, adjoining 870-acre Hanningfield
Reservoir, designated an SSSI due to its high numbers
of wildfowl.
Key birds: *Spring*: Good numbers and mix of
woodland warblers. *Summer*: Vast numbers of Swifts,
Swallows and martins feeding over the water. Hobby
and Osprey. *Winter*: Good numbers and mix of
waterfowl. Large gull roost.
Other notable flora and fauna: Spectacular displays
of bluebells in spring. Damselflies and dragonflies
around the ponds. Grass snakes and common lizards
sometimes bask in rides.
Contact: Hanningfield Reservoir Visitor Centre, 01268
711 001; www.essexwt.org.uk

6. OLD HALL MARSHES

RSPB (Eastern England Office).
Location: TL 959 122. Overlooks River Blackwater,
SW of Colchester. From the A12 take the B1023,
via Tiptree to Tolleshunt D'Arcy. Turn L at village
maypole then R into Chapel Road (back road to
Tollesbury). After approx 1 mile (1.6 km), turn L into

Old Hall Lane. Continue up Old Hall Lane, through
iron gates, then follow signs straight ahead to car
park.
Access: By permit only (free in advance from Warden.
Write to address below). Open 9am-9pm or dusk. No
wheelchair access or facilities. No coaches.
Facilities: Two trails — one of three miles and one of
6.5 miles. Viewing screens overlooking saline lagoon
area at E end of reserve. No visitor centre or toilets.
Public transport: Limited bus service to Tollesbury
(one mile). Train to Kelvedon followed by bus to
Tollesbury or cycle.
Habitat: Coastal grazing marsh, reedbed, open water,
saline lagoon, saltmarsh and mudflat.
Key birds: *Summer*: Breeding Avocet, Redshank,
Lapwing, Pochard, Shoveler, Gadwall, Marsh Harrier
and Barn Owl. *Winter*: Large assemblies of wintering
wildfowl: Brent Goose, Wigeon, Teal, Shoveler,
Goldeneye, Red-breasted Merganser, all the expected
waders, Hen Harrier, Merlin, Short-eared Owl and
Twite. *Passage*: All expected waders inc Spotted
Redshank, Green Sandpiper and Whimbrel. Yellow
Wagtail, Whinchat and Wheatear.
Other notable fauna: Brown hare, water vole, hairy
dragonfly, scarce emerald damselfly, ground lackey
moth, cream spot tiger, white letter hairstreak.
Contact: Site Manager, 01621 869 015.
e-mail: oldhallmarshes@rspb.org.uk

7. RAINHAM MARSHES

Location: TQ 552 792. Off New Tank Hill Road
(A1090) in Purfleet, just off the A1306 between
Rainham and Lakeside. This is accessible from the
Aveley, Wennington and Purfleet junction off A13 and
J30/31 of M25.
Access: 1 Nov-31 Mar (9.30am-4.30pm). 1 April-31
Oct (9.30am-5pm). Closed Christmas Day and Boxing
Day. Programme of guided walks — check RSPB
website for details. Approx 2.5 miles of boardwalks
suitable for wheelchairs and pushchairs.
Facilities: Visitor centre, disabled toilets, car park on
site, picnic area, shop, refreshments available. Three
bird hides. Entry charges for non-RSPB members.
Public transport: Route 44 (Ensignbus – 01708 865
656) runs daily between Grays and Lakeside via
Purfleet. Nearest train station is Purfleet. Reserve is
a 15 min walk.
Habitat: Former MoD shooting range, largest
remaining area of lowland wetland along the Thames.
Key birds: *Spring*: Marsh Harrier, Hobby, Wheatear,
hirundines and other migrants. *Summer/Autumn*:
Many waders, including Black-tailed Godwit,
Whimbrel, Greenshank, Snipe, Lapwing, Avocet.
Yellow-legged Gull. Hunting Merlin and Peregrine.
Winter: Waders, wildfowl, Water Pipit, Short-eared
Owl, Little Egret & Penduline Tit most winters.
Other notable flora and fauna: 21 species of
dragonfly, including hairy hawker, scarce emerald
and small red-eyed damselfly. Marsh frog, water
vole, water shrew, fox, stoat, weasel, 32 species
of butterfly, and 13 species of orthoptera. Deadly
nightshade, flowering rush.

Contact: The Warden, The Visitor Centre, 01708 899 840; www.rspb.org.uk/rainham

8. RIVER LEE COUNTRY PARK

Lee Valley Regional Park
Location: The Country Park spreads from Waltham Abbey in Essex to Broxbourne in Hertfordshire. Car parks at Waltham Abbey Gardens (EN9 1XD), Fishers Green (EN9 2EF), Cheshunt (EN9 1XQ) and Broxbourne (EN10 6LX).
Access: All hides open daily (except Christmas Day). Hides and paths are suitable for wheelchair users.
Facilities: Café, toilet and shop at Lee Valley Park Farms and toilet facilities are also available at Fishers Green, Cheshunt and Broxbourne car parks.
Public transport: All sites served by buses — call Arriva on 0871 200 2233.
Habitat: Former gravel pits now flooded, with wooded islands, reedbeds and marshy corners.
Key birds: *Winter:* Bittern at Fishers Green. Wide variety of wildfowl incl. Smew, Goosander, Shoveler and Gadwall. *Summer:* Breeding warblers, Nightingale, Little Ringed Plover, Turtle Dove and various birds of prey. Wide variety of species on spring/autumn passage.
Other notable flora and fauna: Two orchid meadows within the Country Park, and a dragonfly sanctuary in the south of the Country Park.
Contact: Lee Valley Regional Park Authority, 08546 770 600; e-mail: info@leevalleypark.org.uk www.leevalleypark.org.uk

9. STOUR ESTUARY

RSPB (Eastern England Office).
Location: TM 190 310. Between Manningtree and Harwich. From Manningtree, stay on B1352 past Strangers Home pub in Bradfield, then look for brown sign to reserve just past Wrabness village.
Access: Open all year. Stour Wood walk (1 mile) OK for wheelchairs in dry conditions. Walks to estuary and furthest hide not suitable for wheelchairs, due to terrain and kissing gates. Dogs only allowed in Stour Wood and on public footpaths.
Facilities: Information Centre, car park, two hides, one viewing screen. Two picnic tables.
Public transport: Nearest train station (One Railway) at Wrabness is 1 mile away (08457 484 950). Hourly buses (Mon - Sat) running between Colchester and Harwich will stop at entrance to woods on request or

at new bus stop at SW corner of Stour Wood.
Habitat: Extensive woodland leading down to the River Stour estuary, saltmarsh at Deep Fleet and mudflats at Copperas Bay.
Key birds: *Spring/autumn:* Black-tailed Godwit, Dunlin, Pintail. *Summer:* Nightingale and warblers. *Winter:* Brent Goose, plus nationally important numbers of wildfowl and waders.
Other notable flora: Woodland wildflowers in spring.
Contact: The Warden, 01206 391 153; e-mail:stourestuary@rspb.org.uk www.rspb.org.uk/reserves/

10. TOLLESBURY WICK MARSHES

Essex Wildlife Trust.
Location: TL 970 104. On Blackwater Estuary eight miles E of Maldon. Follow B1023 to Tollesbury via Tiptree, leaving A12 at Kelvedon. Then follow Woodrolfe Road S towards the marina. Use small public car park at Woodrolfe Green (TL 964 107), 500m before reserve entrance on sea wall. Car park suitable for mini-buses and small coaches.
Access: Open all times along public footpath on top of sea wall. Exposed to the elements so be prepared with adequate clothing and footwear. Motorised wheelchair access possible to Block House Bay.
Facilities: Bird hide. Public toilets at Woodrolfe Green car park.
Public transport: Hedingham bus services run to Tollesbury from Maldon, Colchester and Witham — call 01621 869 214 for information.
Habitat: Estuary with fringing saltmarsh and mudflats with some shingle. Extensive freshwater grazing marsh, brackish borrowdyke and small reedbeds.
Key birds: *Winter:* Large numbers of wintering wildfowl and waders, particularly Brent Geese and Wigeon, Lapwing and Golden Plover. Short-eared Owl, Hen Harrier and, increasingly, Marsh Harrier. *Summer:* Breeding Avocet, Redshank, Lapwing, Little Tern, Reed and Sedge Warblers, Reed Bunting, Barn Owl. *Passage:* Whimbrel, Spotted Redshank, Green Sandpiper.
Other notable flora and fauna: Plants include spiny restharrow, grass vetchling, yellow horned-poppy, slender hare's-ear. Hairy dragonfly, Roesel's and great green bush-crickets. Hares and occasional common seals can be seen from the sea wall.
Contact: Reserve Manager, Tollesbury, Maldon, Essex, CM9 8RJ. 01621 868 628. www.essexwt.org.uk

Hertfordshire

VARIOUS GRAVEL PITS such as those at Tyttenhanger, Amwell and Tring are the best places to watch for birds, the latter holding a special place in the history of British birding as the site where Little Ringed Plovers first bred in this country. Look for wildfowl such as Goosander and Goldeneye and flocks of Golden Plovers in winter, plus breeding Yellow Wagtails in summer.

1. AMWELL NATURE RESERVE

Herts Wildlife Trust.
Location: TL 376 127. From A10, leave at junction signposted A414 to Harlow. At first roundabout, take B181 to St Margarets and Stanstead Abbotts. On entering St Margarets, just before railway, turn L on Amwell Lane. Reserve is on the R (signposted).
Access: Open all year. Dragonfly Trail open May-Sept.
Facilities: Public hide and viewing area.
Public transport: St Mary's Church, Hoddesdon Road,

St Margarets (310, 311, C4) 5 minute walk from railway station. Rail: St Margarets (0.75 miles). From station waslk E along B181 to towpath of River Lee Navigation, then walk N for 0.5 miles to reserve. **Habitat:** Disused gravel pit with reedbeds and woodland.
Key birds: *Spring/summer:* Ringed Plover, Little Ringed Plover. *Winter:* Smew, ducks, Bittern. In process of becoming SSSI for wintering Gadwall and Shoveler.
Other notable fauna: All 19 species of dragonflies and damselflies known in Herts have been recorded.
Contact: Trust HQ, 01727 858 901;
e-mail: info@hmwt.org www.hertswildlifetrust.org.uk

2. CASSIOBURY PARK

Welwyn & Hatfield Council.
Location: TL 090 970. Close to Watford town centre.
Access: Open all year.
Facilities: Car park, footpaths.
Public transport: Watford Metropolitan Underground station.
Habitat: Municipal park, wetland, river, alder/willow wood.
Key birds: *Spring/summer:* Kingfisher, Grey Wagtail. *Winter:* Snipe, Water Rail, occasional Bearded Tit.
Contact: Welwyn & Hatfield Council, 01707 357 000. e-mail: council.services@welhat.gov.uk

3. KINGS MEADS

Herts & Middlesex Wildlife Trust /various owners.
Location: From Ware head SE on A1170 High Street, turn R into Burgage Lane shortly after Ware Museum. Park in public car park. From here pedestrian access is via the River Lee - go over the bridge, turn R and walk 250 yards. Turn L into the reserve.
Access: Open all year.
Facilities: None.
Public transport: Bus stops on Hertford Road (A119). Trains to Ware station and Hertford East Station.
Habitat: Largest remaining area of grazed riverside flood meadow in Hertfordshire.
Key birds: *Summer:* Skylark, Reed Warbler, Reed Bunting, Sedge Warbler, Yellow Wagtail. *Winter/spring:* Gadwall, Shoveler, Wigeon, Teal, Snipe, gulls, waders.
Other notable flora and fauna: 275 species of wildflower, 19 species of dragonfly.
Contact: Herts & Middlesex Wildlife Trust, 01727 858 901. e-mail: info@hmwt.org

4. LEMSFORD SPRINGS

Herts & Middlesex Wildlife Trust.
Location: TL 222 123. Lies 1.5 miles W of Welwyn Garden City town centre, off roundabout leading to Lemsford village on B197, W of A1(M). Park in cul-de-sac next to reserve entrance.

Access: Access, via key, by arrangement with warden. Open at all times, unless work parties or group visits in progress. Keep to paths. Dogs on leads. 150m earth path to hide. Wheelchair access ramp to hide. Coaches welcome and room to park on road, but limit of 30 persons.
Facilities: Two hides, classroom, chemical toilet, paths and bridges. Circular walk.
Public transport: Bus: The Sun Inn, Lemsford Village (36, 61). Nearest railway station Welwyn Garden City (25 minute walk).
Habitat: Former water-cress beds, open shallow lagoons. Stretch of the River Lea, marsh, hedgerows. Nine acres.
Key birds: *Spring/summer:* Breeding warblers, Grey Wagtail, Kestrel, Green Woodpecker. *Autumn/winter:* Green Sandpiper, Water Rail, Snipe, Siskin, Little Egret, occasional Jack Snipe. *All year:* Mandarin Duck, Kingfisher, Grey Heron, Sparrowhawk.
Other notable flora and fauna: Muntjac, fox and stoat. Common butterflies and damselflies in summer.
Contact: Barry Trevis, Warden, 11 Lemsford Village, Welwyn Garden City, Herts, AL8 7TN. 01707 335 517. e-mail: info@hmwt.org www.hertswildlifetrust.org.uk

5. MAPLE LODGE NATURE RESERVE

Thames Water/Maple Lodge Conservation Society
Location: TQ 036 925. South of Ricksmanworth, close to village of Maple Cross. From M25 (Jt 17) turn L at traffic lights. Drive down Maple Lodge Close and park in social club car park.
Access: Restricted to members of MLCS. Visits by non-members and groups can be arranged in advance. Site can be boggy — please keep to designated paths.
Facilities: Information centre, toilets. Ten bird hides - two wheelchair-friendly. Winter feeding stations.

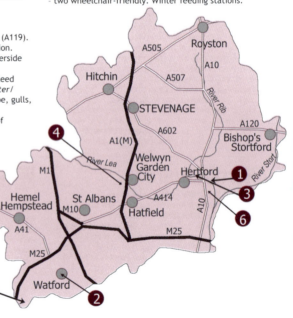

Public transport: Bus services are available from Rickmansworth train station to Maple Cross.
Habitat: A man-made wetland habitat formed from two gravel pits and a sludge settlement area. Two lakes and a reedbed. Mixed broadleaf plantation on eastern side.
Key birds: Wildfowl throughout year, numbers building in winter. All three woodpeckers, plus variety of finches, thrushes and woodland species. Nesting species include Kingfisher, Tawny Owl and migrant warblers. Snipe, Green and Common Sandpipers on passage. Birds of prey regularly seen including Sparrowhawk, Hobby, Red Kite and Common Buzzard.
Other notable flora and fauna: 250 species of moth recorded, plus many butterflies and aquatic insects. 125 species of wildflower recorded. Seven of the nine bat species found in Herts recorded on the reserve.
Contact: Chairman Mr Keith Pursall, 07850 535 986. e-mail:keith.pursall@ntlworld.com www.maplelodge.org

6. RYE MEADS

RSPB/Hertfordshire & Middlesex Wildlife Trust.
Location: TL 389 103. Take Hoddesdon turn off A10 and follow brown duck signs. Near Rye House railway station.
Access: Open every day 10am-5pm (or dusk if earlier), except Christmas Day and Boxing Day. Gates are locked when the reserve is closed.
Facilities: Disabled access and toilets. Drinks machine, staffed reception, classrooms, picnic area, car park, bird feeding area. Nature trails, 10 hides. RSPB reserve has close-circuit TV on Kingfisher and Common Tern nests in summer. Car parking charge for non members.
Public transport: Rail (Rye House) 370 metres, bus (310) stops 600 metres from entrance.
Habitat: Marsh, willow scrub, pools, scrapes, lagoons and reedbed.
Key birds: *Summer:* Breeding Tufted Duck, Gadwall, Common Tern, Kestrel, Kingfisher, nine species of warblers. *Winter:* Bittern, Shoveler, Water Rail, Teal, Snipe, Jack Snipe, Redpoll and Siskin.
Other notable flora and fauna: Fen vegetation, invertebrates and reptiles.
Contact: RSPB Rye Meads Visitor Centre, 01992 708 383; e-mail:rye.meads@rspb.org.uk

7. TRING RESERVOIRS

All four reservoirs – British Waterways / Herts & Middlesex Wildlife Trust / Friends of Tring Res. WTW lagoon – Thames Water/FOTR.
Location: Wilstone Res. SP 905 134. Other reservoirs SP 920 135. WTW Lagoon SP 923 134 adjacent to Marsworth Res. Reservoirs 1.5 miles due N of Tring, all accessible from B489 which crosses A41 Aston Clinton by-pass. NB: exit from by-pass only Southbound.
Access: Reservoirs — open at all times. Events need to be cleared with British Waterways. WTW Lagoon & Hide — open at all times by permit from FoTR. Coaches can only drop off and pick up, for advice contact FoTR. Wilstone Res. has restricted height access of 2.1 metres Disabled access available for Startops & Marsworth Reservoirs from car park, as well as FoTR Lagoon Hide.
Facilities: Café and pubs adjacent to Startops Res. car park, safe parking for cycles. Wilstone Res: Pub 0.5 mile away in village. Cafe and farm shop 0.25 mile from car park. Hides on all reservoirs.
Public transport: Buses from Aylesbury & Tring including a weekend service, tel. 0871 200 2233. Tring Station is 2.5 miles away via canal towpath.
Habitat: Four reservoirs with surrounding woodland, scrub and meadows. Two of the reservoirs have extensive reedbeds. WTW Lagoon with islands and dragonfly scrape, surrounding hedgerows and scrub.
Key birds: *Spring/summer:* Breeding water birds Common Terns and heronry. Regular Hobby, Black Terns and Red Kite, warblers including Cetti's. Occasional Marsh Harrier, Osprey *Autumn/winter passage:* Waders, occasional White-winged Black Tern. *Winter:* Gull roost, large wildfowl flocks, bunting roosts, Bittern.
Other notable flora and fauna: Black poplar trees, some locally rare plants in damp areas. 18 species of dragonfly include black-tailed skimmer, ruddy darter and emerald damselfly. Holly blue and specked wood butterflies. Chinese water deer, Daubenton's, Natterer's and both pipistrelle bats.
Contact: Herts & Middsx Wildlife Trust (www.hertswildlifetrust.org.uk)
Friends of Tring Reservoir (www.fotr.org.uk).

Norfolk

THERE ARE more birdwatchers in Norfolk than in any other county in Britain and for one very good reason; the quality of birding here is second to none. Here you can find scarce breeding birds, wonderful spring and, especially, autumn passage including plenty of rarities and huge numbers of wintering birds such as 250,000 birds on the Wash and 180,000 Pinkfeet along the north coast.

1. CLEY MARSHES NNR

Location: TG 054 441. NWT Cley Marshes is situated four miles N of Holt on A149 coast road, half a mile E of Cley-next-the-Sea. Visitor centre and car park on inland side of road.
Access: The reserve and centre are open every day, except Christmas Day as follows: Mar-Oct inc. (10am-5pm). Nov-Feb inc. (10am- 4.30pm). The café closes 30 minutes before the centre. Admission to the visitor centre is free and to the reserve is currently £5.00 with Gift Aid (£4.50 without). NWT members and

NATURE RESERVES - EASTERN ENGLAND

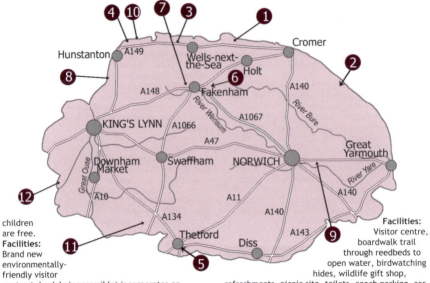

children are free.
Facilities: Brand new environmentally-friendly visitor centre (wheelchair accessible) incorporates an observation area, interactive interpretation, including remote controllable wildlife camera, café and sales area. Five hides (three with excellent wheelchair access). Audio trail. Wildlife Detective Bumbags for children, free to hire. Boardwalk and information boards. Reserve leaflet. Regular events.
Public transport: Coasthopper bus service stops outside, every two hours. Connections for train and bus services at Sheringham. Special discounts to visitors arriving by bus. Call 01603 223 800 for info.
Habitat: Reedbeds, salt and freshwater marshes, scrapes and shingle ridge with international reputation as one of the finest birdwatching sites in Britain.
Key birds: Bittern, Avocet, Marsh Harrier, Spoonbill, Bearded Tit and large numbers of wildfowl, including Wigeon, Teal, Pintail and Brent Goose. Migrating waders such as Ruff and Temminck's Stint. Many rarities.
Contact: NWT Cley Marshes Visitor Centre, 01263 740 008. e-mail: cleyvisitorcentrestaff@ norfolkwildlifetrust.org.uk www.norfolkwildlifetrust.org.uk

2. HICKLING BROAD NNR

Norfolk Wildlife Trust
Location: TG 428 222. Approx four miles SE of Stalham, just off A149 Yarmouth Road. From Hickling village, follow the brown badger tourist signs into Stubb Road at the Greyhound Inn. Take first turning L to follow Stubb Road for another mile. Turn R at the end for the nature reserve. The car park is ahead.
Access: Open all year. Visitor centre open Apr-Sep (10am-5pm daily), October (weekends and half-term). Cost: adults £4.50 (with Gift Aid), children under 16 and NWT members free.

Facilities: Visitor centre, boardwalk trail through reedbeds to open water, birdwatching hides, wildlife gift shop, refreshments, picnic site, toilets, coach parking, car parking, disabled access to broad, boardwalk and toilets. Groups welcome. Water trail mid-May to mid-Sept (additional charge — booking essential).
Public transport: Morning bus service only Mon-Fri from Norwich (Neaves Coaches) Cromer to North Walsham (Sanders). Buses stop in Hickling village, a 25 minute walk away.
Habitat: Hickling is the largest and wildest of the Norfolk Broads with reedbeds, grazing marshes and wide open skies.
Key birds: Marsh Harriers, Bittern, warblers. From October to March the raptor roost at Stubb Mill, provides excellent views of raptors flying in to roost. Likely birds include Marsh Harriers, Hen Harriers, Merlins, Cranes and Pink-footed Geese.
Other notable flora and fauna: Swallowtail butterfly, Norfolk hawker (rare dragonfly)
Contact: Hickling Broad Visitor Centre, 01692 598 276; e-mail: info@norfolkwildlifetrust.org.uk www.norfolkwildlifetrust.org.uk

3. HOLKHAM NNR

Natural England (Norfolk and Suffolk Team).
Location: TF 890 450. From Holkham village turn N off A149 down Lady Ann's Drive to park.
Access: Access unrestricted, but keep to paths and off grazing marshes and farmland. Pay-and-display parking.
Facilities: Two hides. Disabled access.
Public transport: Bus Norbic Norfolk bus information line 0845 3006 116.
Habitat: Sandflats, dunes, marshes, pinewoods.
Key birds: *Passage:* Migrants. *Winter:* Wildfowl, inc. Brent, Pink-footed and White-fronted Geese. *Summer:* Breeding Little Tern.
Other notable flora and fauna: Seablite bushes,

attractive to incoming migrant birds, sea aster and sea lavender.
Contact: M. Rooney, Hill Farm Offices, Main Road, Holkham, Wells-next-the-Sea, NR23 1AB. 01328 711 183; Email: michael.rooney@naturalengland.org.uk

4. HOLME BIRD OBSERVATORY

Norfolk Ornithologists' Association (NOA).
Location: TF 717 450. E of Hunstanton, signposted from A149. Access from Broadwater Road, Holme. The reserve and visitors centre are beyond the White House at the end of the track.
Access: Reserve open daily to members dawn to dusk; non-members (9am-5pm) by permit from the Observatory. Please keep dogs on leads in the reserve. Parties by prior arrangement.
Facilities: Accredited Bird Observatory operating all year for bird ringing, MV moth trapping and other scientific monitoring. Visitor centre, car park and several hides (seawatch hide reserved for NOA members), together with access to beach and coastal path.
Public transport: Coastal bus service runs from Hunstanton to Sheringham roughly every 30 mins but is seasonal and times may vary. Phone Norfolk Green Bus, 01553 776 980.
Habitat: In ten acres of diverse habitat: sand dunes, Corsican pines, scrub and reed-fringed lagoon make this a migration hotspot.
Key birds: Species list over 320. Ringed species over 150. Recent rarities have included Red Kite, Common Crane, Osprey, Red-flanked Bluetail, Yellow-browed, Pallas's, Arctic and Barred Warblers.
Other notable flora and fauna: Moth trap run March 1st to Oct 31st - migrant moths and butterflies recorded yearly.
Contact: Sophie Barker, Holme Bird Observatory, Broadwater Road, Holme, Hunstanton, Norfolk PE36 6LQ. 01485 525 406; e-mail: info@noa.org.uk www.noa.org.uk

5. NUNNERY LAKES

British Trust for Ornithology.
Location: TL 873 815. On the S edge of Thetford, adjacent to the BTO's headquarters at The Nunnery. Main access point is via Nun's Bridges car park, across pedestrian bridge at TL 874 821.
Access: Open dawn to dusk. Public access along permissive paths. Keep dogs on leads at all times. Call reception in advance to arrange wheelchair access to the lakes and hide.
Facilities: Waymarked paths, information panels, bird hide, boardwalk through wet woodland. Pre-booked coaches can park in grounds.
Public transport: Thetford railway station approx 1 mile (0845 7484 950). Thetford bus terminal approx 0.5 mile (0870 6082 608).
Habitat: Flood meadows, scrape, flooded gravel pits, scrub and woodland.
Key birds: Wide range of species present throughout the year including Heron, Egyptian Goose, Kingfisher,

Green Woodpecker. *Spring*: Passage waders, hirundines, Swift, passerines. *Summer*: Warblers, Cuckoo, Oystercatcher, Lapwing, Hobby. *Winter*: Goosander, Teal, Water Rail, Snipe, Siskin.
Other notable flora and fauna: Otter, brown hare, muntjac, grass snake, common lizard. Emperor dragonfly, red-eyed damselfly. Speckled wood and orange tip butterflies. Mossy stonecrop.
Contact: Chris Gregory, The British Trust for Ornithology, The Nunnery, Thetford, Norfolk, IP24 2PU. 01842 750 050; e-mail: chris.gregory@bto.org www.bto.org

6. PENSTHORPE NATURE RESERVE AND GARDENS

Private ownership /Pensthorpe Conservation Trust.
Location: TG 950 295. Take A1067 Norwich road E from Fakenham. After 1 mile look for signs for Pensthorpe Nature Reserve & Gardens. Look for Brown Tourist signs from all major roads.
Access: Route for wheelchair users to both hides overlooking wader scrape. Paths are firm, but those S of River Wensum can be muddy. Toilets for disabled at cafe and main toilet block. Designated Blue Badge parking. Admission charges (see website).
Facilities: Cafe. Shop sells bird food, nest boxes, natural history books and optical equipment.
Public transport: Bus stops at top of drive; Norfolk Green's X29 is an hourly service between Norwich and Fakenham. The X10 connects to King's Lynn; the 'Coast Hopper' service links Fakenham to the north Norfolk coast.
Habitat: Woodland, farmland, the River Wensum, eight large lakes, gardens and wildflower meadows.
Key birds: *Spring/summer*: Little Ringed Plover, Lapwing, Oystercatcher and Redshank breed, with Green Sandpipers and other waders on migration. Warblers include Reed and Sedge Warblers, Blackcap, Chiffchaff, Willow Warbler, Whitethroat and smaller numbers of Garden Warbler. Linnets nest in the gorse. Hobbies are over wader scrape and wildflower meadow, while Buzzards, Kestrels, Sparrowhawks and Barn Owls all breed. Marsh Harriers breed nearby. *Winter*: Large flocks of Wigeon and Teal, plus Shoveler and Gadwall. Birds of prey inc. Buzzard, Marsh Harrier and Peregrine. Bittern is regularly seen. The woodland and its feeders attract finches in winter including Brambling, Nuthatch and Treecreeper.
Other notable flora and fauna: 21 species of butterfly and 19 species of dragonfly. Southern marsh and common spotted orchid.
Contact: Pensthorpe Nature Reserve and Gardens, Fakenham Norfolk NR21 0LN. 01328 851 465. e-mail: info@pensthorpe.com www.pensthorpe.com

7. SCULTHORPE MOOR COMMUNITY RESERVE

Hawk and Owl Trust.
Location: TF 900 305. In Wensum Valley, just W of Fakenham, on A148 to King's Lynn, brown sign signposted 'Nature Reserve' opposite village of Sculthorpe. Follow Turf Moor Road to Visitor Centre.
Access: Open Tue-Sun plus Bank Holiday Mondays

(except Christmas Day). April to September: Tues-Wed (8am-6pm), Thur-Sun (8am-dusk). October to March: Tues-Sun (8am-4pm). £3 suggested donation for adult visitors. A car park at visitor and education centre. Guide dogs only.

Facilities: Visitor centre open 9am-5pm (9am-4pm in winter) Tuesday - Sunday, with adapted toilets, hot drinks dispenser, interpretive displays and live CCTV coverage from around the reserve. Base for specialist courses, school visits and other events. Reserve and 2 hides accessible to wheelchairs and buggies via a mile of boardwalk. Additional hides accessed by bark chipping path. Coach parking available.

Public transport: Norfolk Green (01553 776 980 www.norfolkgreen.co.uk) bus X8 Fakenham to King's Lynn stops at end of Turf Moor Road. Sustrans no.1 cycle route from Harwich to Hull runs within 200 metres of end of Turf Moor Road.

Habitat: Wetland reserve, with fen containing saw sedge (a European priority habitat), reedbed, wet woodland, pools, ditches and riverbank.

Key birds: More than 80 species recorded, including breeding Marsh Harrier, Barn Owl and Tawny Owl, visiting Buzzard, Goshawk, Hobby, Kestrel, Osprey, Sparrowhawk, also Water Rail, Kingfisher, Marsh Tit, Lesser Spotted Woodpecker and Willow Tit and Golden Pheasant.

Other notable flora and fauna: Mammals include otter, water vole and roe deer, 19 species of dragonfly/damselfly, butterflies including white admiral, glow-worms, fungi including scarlet elf cup and a host of plants including marsh fern and saw sedge.

Contact: The Hawk and Owl Trust, Sculthorpe Moor Community Nature Reserve, Turf Moor Road, Sculthorpe, Fakenham NR21 9GN. 01328 856 788. e-mail: leanne.thomas@hawkandowl.org

8. SNETTISHAM

RSPB (Eastern England Office).

Location: TF 651 330. Car park two miles along Beach Road, signposted off A149 (King's Lynn to Hunstanton), opposite Snettisham village.

Access: Open at all times. Dogs to be kept on leads. Two hides are suitable for wheelchairs. Disabled access is across a private road. Please phone office number for permit and directions. Coaches welcome, but please book in advance as a height barrier needs to be removed.

Facilities: Four birdwatching hides, connected by reserve footpath. No toilets on site. Closest hide 1 mile from car park, furthest c1.5 miles from car park.

Public transport: Nearest over two miles away.

Habitat: Intertidal mudflats, saltmarsh, shingle beach, brackish lagoons, and unimproved grassland/scrub. Highest tides best for good views of waders.

Key birds: *Autumn/winter/spring:* Waders (particularly Knot, Bar and Black-tailed Godwits, Dunlin, Grey Plover), wildfowl (particularly Pink-footed and Brent Geese, Wigeon, Gadwall, Goldeneye), Peregrine, Hen Harrier, Merlin, owls. Migrants in season. *Summer:* Breeding Mediterranean

Gull, Ringed Plover, Redshank, Avocet, Common Tern. Marsh Harrier regular.

Other notable flora and fauna: Yellow horned poppies and other shingle flora along the beach.

Contact: Jim Scott, RSPB, Barn A, Home Farm Barns, Common Road, Snettisham, King's Lynn, Norfolk PE31 7PD. 01485 542 689; www.rspb.org.uk e-mail: snettisham@rspb.org.uk

9. STRUMPSHAW FEN

RSPB (Eastern England Office).

Location: TG 33 06. Seven miles ESE of Norwich. Follow signposts. Entrance across level-crossing from car park, reached by turning sharp R and R again into Low Road from Brundall, off A47 to Great Yarmouth.

Access: Open dawn-dusk. RSPB members free, adults £3.50, children £1.50, family £7. Guide dogs only. Limited wheelchair access — please phone for advice.

Facilities: Toilets, reception hide and two other hides, two walks, five miles of trails.

Public transport: Brundall train station about one mile from reserve. Bus 17A from Norwich stops 0.5 mile from reserve - First Buses (0845 602 0121).

Habitat: Reedbed and reedfen, wet grassland and woodland.

Key birds: *Summer:* Bittern, Little Egret, Bearded Tit, Marsh Harrier, Hobby, Kingfisher, Cetti's Warbler and other reedbed birds. *Winter:* Bittern, wildfowl, Marsh and Hen Harrier.

Other notable flora and fauna: Rich fen flora inc marsh pea, milk parsley, marsh sowthistle, six species of orchid, inc marsh helleborine and narrow-leaved marsh orchid. Otter, Chinese water deer and water vole. Swallowtail, white admiral and small heath butterflies, Norfolk hawker, scarce chaser and variable damselfly among 20 dragonfly species.

Contact: Tim Strudwick, Staithe Cottage, Low Road, Strumpshaw, Norwich, Norfolk, NR13 4HS. 01603 715 191; e-mail: strumpshaw@rspb.org.uk

10. TITCHWELL MARSH

RSPB (Eastern England Office).

Location: TF 749 436. E of Hunstanton, off A149.

Access: Wheelchairs available free of charge. All paths and trails suitable for wheelchairs. Reserve and hides open at all times. Coach parking — pre-booking essential. Titchwell Coastal Project now complete with full access and fabulous new Parrinder Hides.

Facilities: Visitor centre, shop with large selection of binoculars, telescopes and books, open every day 9.30am-5pm (Nov- mid Feb, 9.30-4pm). Tearoom open from (9.30am-4.30pm) every day (Nov-mid Feb, 9.30-4pm). Visitor centre and tearoom closed on Christmas Day and Boxing Day.

Public transport: Phone Traveline East Anglia on 0871 200 22 33.

Habitat: Freshwater reedbed and fresh water lagoons, extensive salt marsh, dunes, sandy beach with associated exposed peat beds.

Key birds: Diverse range of breeding reedbed and wetland birds with good numbers of passage waders during late summer/autumn. *Spring/summer:*

Breeding Avocet, Bearded Tit, Bittern, Marsh Harrier, Reed Sedge and Cetti's Warbler, Redshank, Ringed Plover and Common Tern. Summer/*Autumn:* Passage waders including Knot, Wood and Green Sandpiper, Little Stint, Spotted Redshank, Curlew Sandpiper and many more. *Winter:* Brent Goose, Hen/Marsh Harrier roost, Snow Bunting. Offshore Common and Velvet Scoter, Long-tailed Duck, Great Northern and Red throated Divers.
Other notable flora and fauna: 25 species of butterfly, including all the common species plus Essex skipper and annual clouded yellow. 21 species of dragonfly, including small red-eyed damselfly. Good diversity of salt marsh plants including shrubby sea-blite and three species of sea lavender.
Contact: Centre Manager, 01485 210 779.
e-mail:titchwell@rspb.org.uk

11. WEETING HEATH

Norfolk Wildlife Trust.
Location: TL 756 881. Weeting Heath is signposted from the Weeting-Hockwold road, two miles W of Weeting near to Brandon in Suffolk. Nature reserve can be reached via B1112 at Hockwold or B1106 at Weeting.
Access: Open daily from Apr-Sep. Cost: £4.00 with gift aid, £3.50 without, children free. NWT members free. Disabled access to visitor centre and hides.
Facilities: Visitor centre open daily Apr-Aug, birdwatching hides, wildlife gift shop, refreshments, toilets, coach parking, car park, groups welcome (book first).
Public transport: Train services to Brandon and bus connections (limited) from Brandon High Street.
Habitat: Breckland, grass heath.
Key birds: Stone Curlew, migrant passerines, Wood Lark, Spotted Flycatcher.
Contact: *In season:* The Summer Warden, Weeting Heath, Hockwold Road, Weeting, Brandon, Norfolk. *Out of season:* Darrell Stevens, Norfolk Wildlife Trust, Bewick House, 22 Thorpe Road, Norwich NR1 1RY. 01603 625 540; www.norfolkwildlifetrust.org.uk
e-mail: DarrellS@norfolkwildlifetrust.org.uk

12. WELNEY

The Wildfowl & Wetlands Trust.
Location: TL 546 944. Ten miles N of Ely, signposted from A10 and A1101.
Access: Open daily except Christmas Day. (Nov – Feb) Mon-Wed 10am – 5pm, Thurs-Sun 10am – 8pm; (Mar – Oct) Mon-Sun 9.30am – 5pm. Free admission to WWT members, otherwise £7.30 (Adult), £5.50 (Concession), £3.60 (Child), £19.50 (Family). Wheelchair accessible. During wet winter, paths to remote hides may be flooded.
Facilities: Visitor centre (wheelchair-friendly), café open daily (Nov – Feb: Mon-Wed 10am – 4.30pm, Thurs-Sun 10am – 6.15pm; Mar – Oct: Mon-Sun 9.30am – 4.30pm). Large, heated observatory, additional 5 hides. Free parking and coach parking. Provision for disabled visitors, e.g. reserved parking, wheelchairs for hire (1 electric scooter and 2 manual chairs), lifts, disabled toilets, ramps, all access windows in hides.
Public transport: Poor. Train to Littleport (6 miles away), but from there, taxi or cycling is only option — Welney is on the National Cycle route.
Habitat: 1,000 acres of washland reserve, spring damp meadows, winter wildfowl marsh (SPA, RAMSAR site, SSSI, SAC). Additional 200 acres of recently created wetland habitat next to visitor centre.
Key birds: Large numbers of wintering wildfowl are replaced by breeding waders, terns and warblers. *Winter:* Bewick's and Whooper Swans, wintering wildfowl e.g. Wigeon. *Spring/summer:* Common Tern, Avocets, Lapwing, Black-tailed Godwit, House Martin, occasional rarities.
Other notable flora and fauna: Key flora includes: purple loosestrife, meadow rue, mixed grasses. Dragonflies include scarce chaser, emperor, banded demoiselle, small red-eyed damselfly. Approx. 400 species of moth including goat moth. Butterflies include brown argus.
Contact: WWT Welney, 01353 860 711.
e-mail:info.welney@wwt.org.uk
www.wwt.org.uk

Suffolk

MINSMERE is one of the RSPB's flagship reserves and in spring, it is possible to see more than 100 species in a day, including more or less guaranteed Bitterns. Inland, Lakenheath Fen is turning into a fine reserve too with late spring/early summer offering breeding Golden Orioles, Cranes, Bitterns, Garganeys, Bearded Tits and up to 60 Hobbies in the air at once.

1. BOYTON MARSHES

RSPB (Eastern England Office).
Location: TM 387 475. Approx. seven miles E of Woodbridge. Follow B1084 to village of Butley. Turn R and follow road through to Capel St. Andrew. Turn L and follow road towards Boyton village. Approximately 0.25 mile (400 m) before village, bear L down concrete track on sharp right-hand turn.
Access: Open at all times. Entrance free but donations welcome. Public footpath on site not suited to wheelchair use.
Facilities: Car park too small for coaches. No toilets or hides.
Public transport: None.
Habitat: 57 ha of coastal grazing marsh. Also, saltmarsh.
Key birds: *Spring:* Breeding waders and wildfowl, such as Lapwing, Avocet, Shoveler and Gadwall. Spring migrants inc Yellow Wagtail and Whitethroat. Barn and Little Owls. *Autumn:* Wintering wildfowl

such as Teal and Wigeon. Migrating waders inc Whimbrel, Black-tailed Godwit and Greenshank. *Winter:* Wintering wildfowl and wading birds, including Wigeon, Teal, Curlew, Dunlin and Redshank. **Other notable flora and fauna:** Grassland butterflies such as skippers, wall and meadow browns and dragonflies.
Contact: RSPB Havergate, 01394 450 732. www.rspb.org.uk/reserves/guide/b/boytonmarshes/ e-mail:Kieren.Alexander@rspb.org.uk

2. BRADFIELD WOODS NNR

Suffolk Wildlife Trust.
Location: TL 935 581. W of Stowmarket. From J46 on A14 take road through Beyton and Hessett towards Felsham. Turn R on Felsham road towards Cargate. Wood and parking is on L.
Access: Often wet and muddy, Wheelchair/pushchair accessible in parts, please phone 01449 737 996. Dogs on leads only.
Facilities: Visitor centre open April 6 to Oct half-term (10am-5pm). Disabled toilet. Three coloured trails of different lengths, trail guide available.
Habitat: Broadleaved woodland.
Key birds: Good range of woodland birds and migrant warblers.
Other notable flora and fauna: Badger, yellow-necked mouse, 370 species of plant.
Contact: Suffolk Wildlife Trust, 01473 890 089. e-mail: info@suffolkwildlifetrust.org www.suffolkwildlifetrust.org

3. CARLTON MARSHES

Suffolk Wildlife Trust.
Location: TM 508 920. SW of Lowestoft, at W end of Oulton Broad. Take A146 towards Beccles and turn R after Tesco garage.
Access: Open during daylight hours. Keep to marked paths. Dogs allowed in some areas, on leads at all times. Car park suitable for coaches.
Facilities: education centre with disabled toilet. Firm path around part of the marsh, including easy access gates. Disabled access route along the river wall from Oulton Broad to Carlton Marshes. Free car park.
Public transport: Bus and train in walking distance.
Habitat: 120 acres of grazing marsh, peat pools and fen.
Key birds: Wide range of wetland and Broadland birds, including Reed, Sedge and Cetti's Warblers, Bearded Tit, Hobby and Marsh Harrier.
Other notable flora and fauna: Water vole, 15 species of dragonfly including Norfolk Hawker, rare water soldier and raft spider. Plants include common spotted and southern marsh orchids.
Contact: Reserve warden, e-mail: carlton.reserve@

suffolkwildlifetrust.org www.suffolkwildlifetrust.org Education centre - 01502 564 250.

4. DINGLE MARSHES

Location: TM 48 07 20. Eight miles from Saxmundham. Follow brown signs from A12 to Minsmere and continue to Dunwich. Forest car park (hide) TM 467 710. Beach car park TM 479 707. The reserve forms part of the Suffolk Coast NNR.
Access: Open at all times. Access via public rights of way and permissive path along beach. Dogs on lead please. Coaches can park on beach car park.
Facilities: Toilets at beach car park, Dunwich. Hide in Dunwich Forest overlooking reedbed, accessed via Forest car park. Circular trail marked from car park.
Public transport: Via Coastlink, Dial-a-ride service to Dingle (01728 833 546) links to buses and trains.
Habitat: Grazing marsh, reedbed, shingle beach and saline lagoons
Key birds: *All year:* In reedbed, Bittern, Marsh Harrier, Bearded Tit. *Winter:* Hen Harrier, White-fronted Goose, Wigeon, Snipe, Teal on grazing marsh. *Summer:* Lapwing, Avocet, Snipe, Black-tailed Godwit, Hobby. Good for passage waders.
Other notable flora and fauna: Site is internationally important for starlet sea anemone — the rarest sea anemone in Britain. Otter and water vole.
Contact: Alan Miller, Suffolk Wildlife Trust, Moonrakers, Back Road, Wenhaston, Halesworth Suffolk IP16 4AP; www.suffolkwildlifetrust.org e-mail: alan.miller@suffolkwildlifetrust.org www.suffolkwildlifetrust.org

5. HAVERGATE ISLAND

RSPB (Eastern England Office).
Location: TM 425 496. Part of the Orfordness-Havergate Island NNR on the Alde/Ore estuary. Orford is 17km NE of Woodbridge, signposted off the A12.
Access: Open on first Saturday of every month throughout the year and special event weekends (See website). Book in advance through Minsmere RSPB visitor centre, 01728

LOWESTOFT
A144
Diss
A143
Southwold
Newmarket
Bury St Edmunds
Saxmundham
A14
Stowmarket
River Debden
River Alde
A134
Woodbridge
A12
Aldeb
Orford Nes
Sudbury
IPSWICH
A12
River Orwell
A1071
Felixstowe

648 281. Park in Orford at the large pay and display car park next to the quay.
Facilities: Toilets, picnic area, five birdwatching hides, viewing platform, visitor trail (approx 2km).
Public transport: Orford served by local buses (route 160). For timetable info call 0870 608 2608. Bus stop is 0.25 miles from quay. Boat trips from Orford (one mile)
Habitat: Shallow brackish water, lagoons with islands, Mudflats, saltmarsh.
Key birds: *Summer:* Breeding gulls, terns, Shelduck and Oystercatcher. A large flock of summering Spoonbills is present from mid July onwards. *Winter:* Wildfowl and waders including Wigeon, Teal, Pintail, Shoveler, Avocets, Lapwing and Black tailed Godwits. Also, Short-eared Owls, Marsh Harriers and Barn Owls.
Other notable fauna: Brown hares.
Contact: RSPB Havergate Reserves, Unit 7 and 10, Richmond Old Dairy, Gedgrave, Woodbridge, Suffolk IP12 2BU. 01394 450 732. www.rspb.org.uk/reserves/guide/h/havergate/index.aspx
e-mail:Kieren.Alexander@rspb.org.uk

6. HEN REEDBED NNR

Suffolk Wildlife Trust.
Location: TM 470 770. Three miles from Southwold. Turn off A12 at Blythburgh and follow along A1095 for two miles where brown signs guide you to the car park. Not suitable for coaches. The reserve forms part of the Suffolk Coast NNR.
Access: Open at all times.
Facilities: Two hides and two viewing platforms on waymarked trails.
Public transport: Bus service between Halesworth and Southwold.
Habitat: Reedbed, grazing marsh, scrape and estuary.
Key birds: *Spring/summer:* Marsh Harrier, Bittern, Bearded Tit, Hobby, Lapwing, Snipe, Avocet, Black-tailed and Bar-tailed Godwits. *Passage:* Wood and Green Sandpipers. *Winter:* Large flocks of waders on estuary, inc Golden and Grey Plovers, Bar and Black-tailed Godwits, Avocet and Dunlin.
Other notable flora and fauna: Otters and water voles frequently seen. Hairy dragonfly, occasional Norfolk hawker. Brown argus butterfly colony close to car park.
Contact: As Dingle Marshes.

7. LACKFORD LAKES NATURE RESERVE

Suffolk Wildlife Trust.
Location: TL 803 708. Via track off N side of A1101 (Bury St Edmunds to Mildenhall road), between Lackford and Flempton. Five miles from Bury.
Access: Visitor centre open winter (10am-4pm), summer (10am-5pm) Wed to Sun (closed Mon and Tues). Tea and coffee facilities, toilets. Visitor centre and 4 hides with wheelchair access.
Facilities: Visitor centre with viewing area upstairs. Tea and coffee facilities, toilets. Eight hides. Coaches should pre-book.
Public transport: Bus to Lackford village (Bury St Edmunds to Mildenhall service) — walk from church.

Habitat: Restored gravel pit with open water, lagoons, islands, willow scrub, reedbeds.
Key birds: *Winter:* Bittern, Water Rail, Bearded Tit. Large gull roost. Wide range of waders and wildfowl (inc. Goosander, Pochard, Tufted Duck, Shoveler). *Spring/autumn:* Migrants, inc. raptors. Breeding Shelduck, Little Ringed Plover and reedbed warblers.
Other notable flora and fauna: 17 species of dragonfly including hairy and emperor. Early marsh and southern orchid.
Contact: Lackford Lakes Visitor Centre, Lackford, Bury St Edmunds, Suffolk, IP28 6HX. 01284 728 706; www.suffolkwildlifetrust.org
e-mail: lackford@suffolkwildlifetrust.org

8. LAKENHEATH FEN

RSPB (Eastern England Office).
Location: TL722 864. W of Thetford, straddling the Norfolk/Suffolk border. From A11, head N on B1112 to Lakenheath and then two miles further. Entrance is 200 metres after level crossing.
Access: Dawn to dusk, year round. Group bookings welcome. Visitor centre accessible to wheelchair users and a few points on the reserve. £2 car park fee for non-RSPB members.
Facilities: Visitor centre, toilets (inc disabled). Coach parking (must book). Hard and grass paths. Viewpoints. Picnic area with tables. Events programme.
Public transport: Limited weekend stops at Lakenheath train station.
Habitat: Reedbed, riverside pools, poplar woods.
Key birds: Principally a site for nesting migrants but ducks and some wild swans in winter. *Spring:* Marsh Harrier, Crane. *Summer:* Bittern, Golden Oriole, Hobby, Reed and Sedge Warblers. *Autumn:* Harriers, Bearded Tit. *Winter:* Ducks, swans, Peregrine.
Other notable flora and fauna: More than 15 species of dragonflies and damselflies, inc hairy dragonfly and scarce chaser. Range of fenland plants e.g. water violet, common meadow rue and fen ragwort. Roe deer, otter and water vole.
Contact: David White (Information Officer), Visitor Centre, RSPB Lakenheath Fen, Lakenheath, Norfolk IP27 9AD. 01842 863 400; www.rspb.org.uk/reserves
e-mail: lakenheath@rspb.org.uk

9. LANDGUARD BIRD OBSERVATORY

Landguard Conservation Trust
Location: TM 283 317. Road S of Felixstowe to Landguard Nature Reserve and Fort.
Access: Visiting by appointment.
Facilities: Migration watch point and ringing station.
Public transport: Call for advice.
Habitat: Close grazed turf, raised banks with holm oak, tamarisk, etc.
Key birds: Unusual species and common migrants.
Other notable flora and fauna: 18 species of dragonfly and 29 species of butterfly have been recorded on the site. Several small mammal species plus sightings of cetaceans and seals off-shore.
Contact: Landguard Bird Observatory, View Point

Road, Felixstowe IP11 3TW. 01394 673782;
e.mail: landguardbo@yahoo.co.uk www.lbo.co.uk

10. MINSMERE

RSPB (Eastern England Regional Office)
Location: TM 452 680. Six miles NE of Saxmundham.
From A12 at Yoxford or Blythburgh. Follow brown
tourist signs via Westleton village. Car park is two
miles from the village.
Access: Open dawn to dusk every day except Dec
25/26. Visitor centre open 9am-5pm (9am-4pm Nov-
Jan). Shop and tea-room open from 10am. Adults
£7.50, concessions £5, children £3, families £15. RSPB
members free. Free entry to visitor centre.
Facilities: Car park, hides, toilets (inc disabled and
nappy changing), visitor centre with RSPB shop and
cafe. Volunteer guides. Guided walks and family
events (see website for details). Wild Zone and Wild
Wood Adventure for families. Discovery Centre for
educational programme. Coaches by appointment
only.
Public transport: Train to Saxmundham or Darsham
(6 miles) then Suffolk Link (book in advance on 01728
833 526.
Habitat: Coastal lagoons, 'the scrape', freshwater
reedbed, grazing marsh, vegetated dunes, heathland,
arable reversion and woodland.
Key birds: *All year:* Marsh Harrier, Bearded Tit,
Bittern, Cetti's and Dartford Warblers, Little Egret,
Green and Great Spotted Woodpeckers. *Summer:*
Breeding Hobby, Avocet, Lapwing, Redshank,
Common, Sandwich and Little Terns, Mediterranean
Gull, Sand Martin, warblers, Nightingale, Nightjar,
Wood Lark, Stone Curlew (sometimes visible). *Winter:*
Wildfowl inc White-fronted Goose, Bewick's Swan,
Smew, Hen Harrier (scarce), Water Pipit, Siskin.
Autumn/spring: Passage waders inc Black-tailed
Godwit, Spotted Redshank, Ruff. Regular Wryneck,
Red-backed Shrike, Yellow-browed Warbler.
Other notable flora and fauna: Red and muntjac
deer, otter, water vole, badger. Dragonflies inc
emperor, Norfolk hawker and small red-eyed
damselfly. 27 species of butterflies inc purple and
green hairstreaks and brown argus. Adder. Antlion.
Marsh mallow, southern marsh orchid.
Contact: Reserve Manager, RSPB Minsmere NR, 01728
648 281; e-mail: minsmere@rspb.org.uk
www.rspb.org.uk/minsmere

11. NORTH WARREN & ALDRINGHAM WALKS

RSPB (Eastern England Office).
Location: TM 467 575. Directly N of Aldeburgh on
Suffolk coast. Use signposted main car park on beach.
Access: Open at all times. Please keep dogs under
close control. Beach area suitable for disabled.
Facilities: Three nature trails, leaflet available from
Minsmere RSPB. Toilets in Aldeburgh and Thorpeness.
Three spaces for coaches at Thorpeness beach car
park.
Public transport: Bus service to Aldeburgh. First
Eastern Counties (08456 020 121). Nearest train
station is Saxmundham.

Habitat: Grazing marsh, lowland heath, reedbed,
woodland.
Key birds: *Winter:* White-fronted Goose, Tundra
Bean Goose, Wigeon, Shoveler, Teal, Gadwall,
Pintail, Snow Bunting. *Spring/summer:* Breeding
Bittern, Marsh Harrier, Hobby, Nightjar, Wood Lark,
Nightingale, Dartford Warbler.
Other notable flora and fauna: Hairy dragonfly,
Norfolk hawker and red-eyed damselfly, green and
purple hairstreak butterflies and southern marsh
orchid.
Contact: As Minsmere above.

12. REDGRAVE AND LOPHAM FENS

Suffolk Wildlife Trust.
Location: TM 0528 803. Five miles from Diss,
signposted and easily accessed from A1066 and A143.
Access: Reserve open all year (10am - 5pm summer,
10am - 4pm winter), dogs strictly on short leads. The
visitor centre is a fully accessible education centre.
Five waymarked circular trails (wheelchair-accessible
gates on 'spider' trail). Circular trails can be muddy
after heavy rain (not wheelchair accessible).
Facilities: Education centre with café, gift shop and
light refreshments, toilets, including disabled, car
park with coach space. Bike parking area, boardwalk
and viewing platform/short boardwalk. Regular
events and activities — see website or call for details.
Public transport: Buses and trains to Diss — Coaches
to local villages of Redgrave and South Lopham from
Diss. Simonds Coaches 01379 647 300 and Galloway
Coaches 01449 766 323.
Habitat: Calcareous fen with open water areas, wet
acid heath, river corridor, scrub and woodland.
Key birds: *All year:* Water Rail, Snipe, Teal,
Shelduck, Gadwall, Woodcock, Sparrowhawk, Kestrel,
Great Spotted and Green Woodpeckers, Tawny,
Little and Barn Owls, Kingfisher, Reed Bunting,
Bearded Tit, Willow and Marsh Tits, Linnet. *Summer:*
Hobby, Blackcap, Chiffchaff, Willow, Reed, Sedge
and Grasshopper Warblers, Spotted Flycatcher,
Whitethroat, Willow Warbler, Whitethroat, Hobby
plus large Swallow and Starling roosts. *Winter/
occcasionals on passage:* Marsh Harrier, Greenshank,
Green Sandpiper, Shoveler, Pintail, Garganey, Jack
Snipe, Bittern, Little Ringed Plover, Oystercatcher,
Wheatear, Stonechat and Whinchat.
Other notable flora and fauna: Otter, water
vole, roe, muntjac and Chinese water deer, stoat,
pipistrelle and Natterer's bats. Great crested newts,
grass snake, adder, slow worm, common lizard. More
than 300 flowering plants. 27 species of butterflies
inc purple and green hairstreaks and brown argus.
More than 20 species of dragonfly inc emperor, hairy
dragonfly, black-tailed skimmer and scarce emerald
damselfly. Fen raft spider population on site. Visit
website for more species information.
Contact: Redgrave and Lopham Fens, 01379 688 333.
e-mail: redgrave.centre@suffolkwildlifetrust.org

13. WALBERSWICK

Natural England (Suffolk Team).
Location: TM 475 733. Good views from B1387 and from lane running W from Walberswick towards Westwood Lodge; elsewhere keep to public footpaths, open access heathland or shingle beach.
Access: Parties and coach parking by prior arrangement.
Facilities: Hide on S side of Blyth estuary, E of A12.
Public transport: Call for advice.
Habitat: Tidal estuary, shingle and saline shore pools, fen, freshwater marsh and reedbeds, heath, mixed woodland, carr.
Key birds: *Spring/summer:* Marsh Harrier, Bearded Tit, Water Rail, Bittern, Nightjar. *Passage/winter:* Wildfowl, waders and raptors.
Other notable flora and fauna: Shingle vegetation and lagoons.
Contact: Natural England, The Barn, Frostenden Hall Farm, Church Lane, Frostenden, Beccles, Suffolk NR34 7HS. 01502 676 171; e-mail:enquiries.east@ naturalengland.org.uk

14. WESTLETON HEATH NNR

Natural England (Suffolk team)
Location: Lies either side of Dunwich-Westleton minor road, E of A12.
Access: Open all year — please keep dogs on leads between March-August breeding season.
Facilities: Car park next to minor road.
Public transport: Train station in Darsham, 5km to W, served by One Railway. First Group bus services on A12 (also 5km distance).
Habitat: Lowland heath with heather-burning regime.
Key birds: Breeding Tree Pipit, Stonechat, Dartford Warbler and Nightjar on open heathland, Nightingale in woods.
Other notable flora and fauna: Silver-studded blue and white admiral butterflies, solitary bees and wasps, adder.
Contact: Natural England (Suffolk team), 110 Northgate Street, Bury St Edmunds, IP33 1HP. 01284 762 218..
E-mail: enquiries.east@naturalengland.org.uk

Northern England

Cheshire, Cleveland and Co. Durham, Cumbria, Lancashire, Manchester (Greater), Merseyside, Northumberland, East Yorkshire, North Yorkshire, South Yorkshire, West Yorkshire

Cheshire

IN THE EAST, Macclesfield Forest holds Goshawk and Crossbill, with Red Grouse on the moors. High tide on the Dee Estuary can bring spectacular wader numbers. Black-necked Grebes breed in good numbers at Woolston Eyes.

1. DEE ESTUARY (BURTON MERE WETLANDS)

RSPB Dee Estuary Office, (formerly known as Inner Marsh Farm).
Location: SJ 31927 73914 Located on the Wirral. From Chester High Road (A540) follow signs for Burton Mere Wetlands. Turning down Puddington Lane, the reserve's entrance is just outside Burton Village.
Access: Open between 9am and 9pm (or dusk if earlier) each day. £4 admission for non-RSPB members. Guide dogs only.
Facilities: 97-berth car park, 3 hides overlooking a series of pools and wetland area. Wheelchair access to much of the footpaths and two of the hides. Toilets including disabled facilities. Picnic tables.
Guided walks available.
Public transport: Trains stop at Neston and Hooton. Buses between Neston and Hooton stop at Burton post office, from where it is a 600m walk to reserve entrance. Contact Traveline on 0871 200 2233.
Habitat: Former farm and fishery now converted to wetland and meadow habitats.
Key birds: *All year:* Little Egret. Great Spotted and Green Woodpecker *Spring/summer:* Avocet, Grasshopper Warbler, Lesser Whitethroat and other commoner warblers, passage Black-tailed Godwit, Spotted Redshank and regular Mediterranean Gulls. Hobby, Marsh Harrier, Spoonbill. *Autumn:* Passage waders (inc Little Stint, Ruff, Spotted Redshank, Green, Curlew and Wood Sandpipers). *Winter:* Linnet, Brambling, Fieldfare, Redwing, Whooper and Bewick's Swans, Teal, Water Rail, Hen Harrier.
Other notable flora and fauna: Extensive butterfly list. Pipistrelle, noctule, Daubenton's bats, water vole, wide array of orchids. Red-eyed damselfly.
Contact: Burton Point Farm, Station Road, Burton, Nr Neston CH64 5SB, 0151 353 8478.
e-mail:deeestuary@rspb.org.uk

2. DEE ESTUARY (PARKGATE)

RSPB Dee Estuary Office.
Location: SJ 27370 78952. On W side of Wirral, S of Birkenhead. View high tide activity from Old Baths car park near Boathouse pub, Parkgate, off B5135.
Access: Open at all times. Viewing from public footpaths and car parks. Please do not walk on the saltmarsh — the tides are dangerous and nesting birds should not be disturbed.
Facilities: Shared car park (closes at 5pm in winter and 8pm in summer), picnic area, group bookings, guided walks, special events, wheelchair access. Toilets at Parkgate village opposite the Square.
Public transport: Bus to Parkgate every hour. Rail station at Neston, two miles from reserve.
Habitat: Estuary, saltmarsh, pools, mud, sand.
Key birds: *Spring/summer/autumn:* Little Egret, Greenshank, Spotted Redshank, Curlew Sandpiper, Skylark, Reed Bunting. *Winter:* Pink-footed Goose, Shelduck, Teal, Wigeon, Pintail, Oystercatcher, Black-tailed Godwit, Curlew, Redshank, Merlin, Peregrine, Water Rail, Short-eared Owl, Hen Harrier.
Other notable flora and fauna: On very high tides, the incoming water displaces several mammal species inc pygmy shrew, water shrew, harvest mouse, weasel and stoat.
Contact: Burton Point Farm, Station Road, Burton, Nr Neston, Cheshire CH64 5SB, 0151 3367 681.
e-mail:deeestuary@rspb.org.uk

3. GOWY MEADOWS

Cheshire Wildlife Trust.
Location: SJ 435 740. From the A56 travelling S, turn R at Bridge Trafford. Drive N on B5132 over the M56. At the end of the road turn L onto the A5117. Take the third road on your L, which is the main road into Thornton-le-Moors.
Access: Park next to church in Thornton-le-Moors and take public footpath opposite into reserve. Open all year.
Facilities: None.
Public transport: The

Arriva bus service stops on the Thornton Green Lane opposite the church.
Habitat: 410 acres of lowland grazing marsh, rich in flora.
Key birds: Approx 100 species recorded, inc Barn Owl, Buzzard, Peregrine, Merlin, Hobby. *Spring/summer:* Wildfowl, warblers, Whinchat, Green Sandpiper, Lapwing, Jack Snipe, Snipe. *Winter:* Pintail, Shoveler, Reed Bunting. *Passage:* Stonechat, Wheatear.
Contact: Cheshire Wildlife Trust, 01948 820 728; e-mail: info@cheshirewt.org.uk
www.cheshirewildlifetrust.org.uk

4. MOORE NATURE RESERVE

Waste Recycling Group.
Location: SJ 577 854. SW of Warrington, via A56 Warrington-to-Chester road. At traffic lights at Higher Walton, follow signs for Moore. Take Moore Lane over swing bridge to reserve. Sat Nav users follow WA4 6XE.
Access: Open all year. One hide suitable for wheelchairs, other parts of site unsurfaced or gravel paths.
Facilities: Car park, coaches by prior arrangement. Paths, ten bird hides, bird feeding area. Guided walks available on request. See website for wildlife events throughout the year.
Public transport: 62 and 66 buses from Warrington and Runcorn stop in Moore village, less than 1km from reserve. Call 0870 608 2608 for times.
Habitat: Wetland, woodland, grasslands, five pools.
Key birds: More than 130 species every year, inc. occasional rarities. *Spring/summer:* Breeding wildfowl and waders, warblers. *Autumn/winter:* Wide variety of wildfowl, Bittern. Also good for gulls, woodpeckers, owls and raptors. See website for list and latest sightings.
Other notable flora and fauna: Wildflowers including some rarities. Great crested newts.
Contact: The Site Manager, Moore Valley Nature Reserve, 01925 444 689;
www.wrg.co.uk/moorenaturereserve

5. SANDBACH FLASHES

Privately owned.
Location: SJ 720 590. Series of flashes S and W of Sandbach. Leave M6 at junction 17 for Sandbach.
Access: No public access – view from roadside. Elton Hall Flash from new road at SJ 716 595; The Moat (also known as Foden's Flash) from road at SJ 730 614; Watch Lane Flash from car park at SJ 728 608.
Facilities: None.
Habitat: Fresh and brackish water, reedbed, carr woodland, inland saltmarsh.
Key birds: Wildfowl including Mallard, Teal, Shoveler, Wigeon, Gadwall, Barnacle

Goose, Shelduck, occasional Garganey, Mandarin. Waders inc Black-tailed Godwit, Lapwing, Common Sandpiper, Dunlin, Green Sandpiper, Curlew, Snipe, Ringed and Little Ringed Plovers, Little Stint, Ruff, Oystercatcher, Greenshank, Spotted Redshank. Raptors inc Sparrowhawk, Kestrel, Buzzard, Hobby. Warblers: Lesser Whitethroat, Blackcap, Garden Warbler. Ravens, Water Rail, Kingfisher, Wheatear, Stonechat, Turtle Dove, Swift, Yellow Wagtail. Many rarities.

6. WOOLSTON EYES

Woolston Eyes Conservation Group.
Location: SJ 654 888. E of Warrington between the River Mersey and Manchester Ship Canal. Off Manchester Road down Weir Lane or from Latchford to end of Thelwall Lane. Do not park at the bottom end of Weir Lane.
Access: Open all year. Permits required from Chairman, £10 each, £20 per family (see address below).
Facilities: Toilets located at No 3 bed.
Public transport: Buses along A57 nearest stop to

Weir Lane, or Thelwell Lane, Latchford. The bus to Weir Lane, Martinscroft (To access reserve from the N) along A57 is No3 from Central Station and Terminus.
To access reserve from South take either No1 or No2 bus to Westy, Whitley Avenue and walk to the East end of Thelwall Lane. For further info go to www. warrington borough transport.co.uk
Habitat: Wetland, marsh, scrubland, wildflower meadow areas.
Key birds: Breeding Black-necked Grebe, warblers (including Grasshopper Warbler), all raptors (Merlin, Peregrine, Marsh Harrier). SSSI for wintering wildfowl, many duck species breed.
Other notable flora and fauna: 19 mammal species recorded, plus 241 species of lepidoptera, four species of bat. Wide variety of butterflies and 22 species of dragonfly. Notable plants include marsh and bee orchids, helleborine, snakeshead fritillary and cowslip.
Contact: BR Ankers, Chairman, 9 Lynton Gardens, Appleton, Cheshire, WA4 1PD. 01925 267 355. Please enclose A5 S.A.E. for reply.
www.woolstoneyes.co.uk

Cleveland /Co Durham

THESE neighbouring areas have much to offer birdwatchers. Coastal headlands such as Hartlepool, North and South Gare and the observatory at Whitburn are at their best in autumn for seawatching and searching for displaced migrants. The RSPB is turning Saltholme into one of its flagship reserves with good birding and facilities to match. The Tees Estuary attracts large numbers of waders including several scarcities.

1. BEACON HILL AND HAWTHORN DENE MEADOW

Durham Wildlife Trust and National Trust
Location: NZ 427 458. Hawthorn Dene and Meadow located between Easington and Seaham on Durham coast. Leave A19 at Easington or Seaham and join B1432, turn into Hawthorn Village. From N end of village, follow minor road E, signposted 'Quarry Traffic'. After quarter mile, road ends at two metal gates, with a cottage and farmhouse on the right. Park on grass verge on opposite side to cottage, taking care not to obstruct gateways. Access is by foot taking the right-hand path. Access to Beacon Hill (NZ 440 455) is along Coastal Footpath or through southern end of Hawthorn Dene.
Access: Open all year, dogs on leads in spring.
Facilities: Information point. Footpaths.
Public transport: Regular bus services from Durham to Hawthorn.
Habitat: Extensive area of semi-natural habitat situated on magnesian limestone escarpment. Steep-sided ravine woodland and limestone grassland.
Key birds: *Summer:* Skylark (important conservation site), Twite, Linnet, Yellowhammer, Goldfinch, Whitethroat, Blackcap, Wren, Long-tailed Tit, Grasshopper Warbler, Reed Bunting, Green

Woodpecker, Kestrel, Sparrowhawk. *Winter:* Wide variety of waders inc Turnstone, Purple Sandpiper, Redshank, Curlew, Oystercatcher. Seabirds inc Red-throated Diver, Common Scoter, Guillemot, Cormorant and Great Crested Grebe. *Passage:* Wheatear, Fieldfare, Redwing, Waxwing, Buzzard, Ringed Plover, Dunlin, Knot, Lapwing.
Other notable flora and fauna: Good variety of butterflies. Snowdrops, bluebells and numerous species of orchid grow here, including early purple, bird's nest, lesser butterfly and bee orchids. Grassland plants include field scabious, greater knapweed, wild carrot, cowslip and bee, fragrant, common spotted and northern marsh orchids. Roe deer, badger and brown hare.
Contact: Durham Wildlife Trust, 0191 584 3112.
e-mail: mail@durhamwt.co.uk www.durhamwt.co.uk

2. BISHOP MIDDLEHAM QUARRY

Durham Wildlife Trust.
Location: NZ 331 326. Half mile N of Bishop Middleham Village, to W of A177. Car parking restricted to two lay-bys on the W side of the road adjacent to the reserve entrances.
Access: Open all year. Parking for up to 6 cars on roadside verge adjacent to W entrance. Keep to footpaths, dogs on leads in spring and summer.
Facilities: None.
Public transport: Regular bus service from Durham and Darlington to Coxhoe and Sedgefield.
Habitat: A large magnesian limestone quarry noted for its very rich flora.
Key birds: Good range of farmland birds plus rare breeding record of Bee-eater.
Other notable flora and fauna: Butterflies including northern brown argus, dingy skipper, ringlet and small and large skippers. Internationally rare habitat,

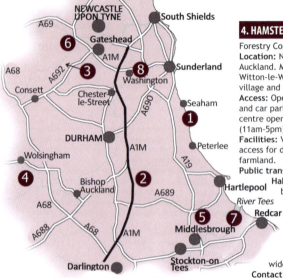

rich in orchid species such as pyramidal, common spotted, fragrant and bee plus large numbers of dark red helleborines.
Contact: Trust HQ, 0191 584 3112.
e-mail: mail@durhamwt.co.uk www.durhamwt.co.uk

3. DERWENT WALK COUNTRY PARK AND DERWENTHAUGH PARK

Gateshead Council.
Location: NZ 178 604. Along River Derwent, four miles SW of Newcastle and Gateshead. Several car parks along A694.
Access: Site open all times. Thornley visitor centre open Mon-Fri (10am-2pm), weekends and Bank Holidays (1pm-4pm). Keys for hides available from Thornley Woodlands Centre. Swalwell visitor centre open daily (9am-5pm). Both centres are closed between Christmas and New Year.
Facilities: Toilets at Thornley and Swalwell visitor centres. Hides at Far Pasture Ponds and Thornley feeding station.
Public transport: 45, 46, 46A, 47/47A/47B buses from Newcastle/Gateshead to Swalwell/Rowlands Gill. Bus stop Thornley Woodlands Centre. (Regular bus service from Newcastle). Information from Nexus Travel Information, 0919 203 3333. www.nexus.org.uk
Habitat: Mixed woodland, river, ponds, meadows.
Key birds: *Summer:* Red Kite, Grasshopper Warbler, Lesser Whitethroat, Kingfisher, Dipper, Great Spotted and Green Woodpeckers, Blackcap, Garden Warbler, Nuthatch. *Winter:* Teal, Tufted Duck, Brambling, Marsh Tit, Bullfinch, Great Spotted Woodpecker, Nuthatch, Goosander, Kingfisher.
Contact: Thornley Woodlands Centre, 01207 545 212.
e-mail: countryside@gateshead.gov.uk
www.gatesheadbirders.co.uk www.gateshead.gov.uk

4. HAMSTERLEY FOREST

Forestry Commission
Location: NZ 091 312. Eight miles W of Bishop Auckland. Main entrance is five miles from A68, S of Witton-le-Wear and signposted through Hamsterley village and Bedburn.
Access: Open all year. Toll charge (£3). Forest drive and car park close 8pm (dusk in winter). Visitor centre open weekdays (10am-4pm) and weekends (11am-5pm).
Facilities: Visitor centre, tearoom, toilets, shop, access for disabled. Visitors should not enter fenced farmland.
Public transport: None.
Habitat: Commercial woodland, mixed and broadleaved trees.
Key birds: *Spring/summer:* Willow Warbler, Chiffchaff, Wood Warbler, Redstart, Pied Flycatcher. *Winter:* Crossbill, Redwing, Fieldfare. *All year:* Jay, Dipper, Green Woodpecker.
Other notable flora: Hay meadows have wide variety of plants including globe flower.
Contact: Forestry Commission, 01434 220 242.
e-mail: enquiries.hamsterley@forestry.gsi.gov.uk

5. SALTHOLME, THE WILDLIFE RESERVE AND DISCOVERY PARK

RSPB.
Location: NZ 506 231 N of River Tees between Middlesbrough and Billingham. From A19, take A689 north of Stockton and then A1185. After four miles join A178 at mini roundabout. Take third exit and reserve is 250 yards on right.
Access: Open every day bar Dec 25. Apr 1 to Sept 30 (10am-5pm), Oct 1 to Mar 31 (10am-4pm). £3 per car, RSPB members, users of public transport and cyclists free.
Facilities: Award-winning visitor centre with cafe and shop, large car park, including wheelchair-friendly and coach parking, toilets (inc disabled), picnic area. Crushed stone paths ¬ wheelchair users may need assistance to reach bird hides. Walled garden designed by TV gardener Chris Beardshaw.
Habitat: Wet grasslands, reedbeds, pools with tern islands, wader scrapes.
Key birds: *All year:* Lapwing, Peregrine, Water Rail. *Spring/summer:* Snipe, Common Tern, Yellow Wagtail. *Autumn:* Varied waders inc Black-tailed Godwits and Green Sandpipers, occasional rarer species. *Winter:* Large numbers of wildfowl and waders.
Contact: The Warden, Saltholme, 01642 546 625;
e-mail: saltholme@rspb.org.uk
www.rspb.org.uk/reserves

6. SHIBDON POND

Gateshead Council.
Location: NZ 192 628. E of Blaydon, S of Scotswood Bridge, close to A1. Car park at Blaydon swimming

baths. Open access from B6317 (Shibdon Road).
Access: Open at all times. Disabled access to hide.
Facilities: Hide in SW corner of pond. Free leaflet available.
Public transport: At least six buses per hour from Newcastle/Gateshead to Blaydon (bus stop Shibdon Road). Nexus Travel Line (0191 232 5325).
Habitat: Pond, marsh, scrub and damp grassland.
Key birds: *Winter*: Wildfowl, Water Rail, occasional white-winged gulls. *Summer*: Reed Warbler, Sedge Warbler, Lesser Whitethroat, Grasshopper Warbler, Water Rail. *Autumn*: Passage waders and wildfowl, Kingfisher.
Other notable flora and fauna: 18 species of butterfly, inc dingy skipper. Dragonflies inc ruddy darter, migrant hawker.
Contact: Thornley Woodlands Centre, 1209 545 212. e-mail: countryside@gateshead.gov.uk
www.gatesheadbirders.co.uk

7. TEESMOUTH NNR

Natural England (North East Region).
Location: Two components, centred on NZ 535 276 and NZ 530 260, three and five miles S of Hartlepool, E of A178. Access to northern component from car park at NZ 534 282, 0.5 miles E of A178. Access to southern part from A178 bridge over Greatham Creek at NZ 510 254. Car park adjacent to A178 at NZ 508 251. Both car parks can accommodate coaches.
Access: Open at all times. In northern component, no restrictions over most of dunes and North Gare Sands (avoid golf course, dogs must be kept under close control). In southern component, disabled access path to public hides at NZ 516 255 and NZ 516 252 (no other access).
Facilities: Nearest toilets at Seaton Carew, one mile to the N. Disabled access path and hides (see above), interpretive panels and leaflet. Teesmouth Field Centre (Tel: 01429 264 912).
Public transport: Half-hourly bus service (service 1) operates Mon-Sat between Middlesbrough and Hartlepool (hourly on Sundays), along A178,

Stagecoach Hartlepool, Tel: 01429 267 082.
Habitat: Grazing marsh, dunes, intertidal flats.
Key birds: Passage and winter wildfowl and waders. Passage terns and skuas in late summer. Scarce passerine migrants and rarities. *Winter*: Merlin, Peregrine, Snow Bunting, Twite, divers, grebes.
Other notable flora and fauna: Northern component has large marsh orchid populations in damp dune grassland. Seal Sands supports a colony of 70 common seals.
Contact: Senior Reserve Manager: 01429 853 325/0300 060 1729; www.naturalengland.org.uk email: northeast@naturalengland.org.uk

8. WASHINGTON

The Wildfowl & Wetlands Trust.
Location: NZ 331 566. In Washington. On N bank of River Wear, W of Sunderland. Signposted from A195, A19, A1231 and A182.
Access: Open 9.30am-5pm (summer), 9.30am-4pm (winter). Free to WWT members. Admission charge for non-members. No dogs except guide dogs. Good access for people with disabilities.
Facilities: Visitor centre, toilets, parent and baby room, range of hides. Shop and café.
Public transport: Buses to Waterview Park (250 yards walk) from Washington, from Sunderland, Newcastle-upon-Tyne, Durham and South Shields. Tel: 0845 6060 260 for details.
Habitat: Wetlands, woodland and meadows.
Key birds: *Spring/summer*: Nesting colony of Grey Heron, other breeders include Common Tern, Oystercatcher, Lapwing. *Winter*: Bird-feeding station visited by Great Spotted Woodpecker, Bullfinch, Jay and Sparrowhawk. Goldeneye and other ducks.
Other notable flora and fauna: Wildflower meadows - cuckoo flower, bee orchid and yellow rattle. Dragonfly and amphibian ponds.
Contact: Dean Heward, (Conservation Manager), Wildfowl & Wetlands Trust, 01914 165 454 ext 231. e-mail: dean.heward@wwt.org.uk www.wwt.org.uk

---

More detailed reports on 54 sites in Cleveland and Co. Durham in Best Birdwatching Sites: North-East England, available from Buckingham Press Ltd

Cumbria

THE LAKE DISTRICT holds a typical range of upland birds, with one Golden Eagle still hanging on at Haweswater. There is an Osprey watchpoint at Lake Bassenthwaite. Bowness-on-Solway sees a major skua passage in spring. Black Guillemots are at St Bees Head, just about the only place in England to see them. Walney bird observatory is the best place for migrants.

1. CAMPFIELD MARSH

RSPB (Northern England office)
Location: NY 197 615. At North Plain Farm, on S shore of Solway estuary, W of Bowness-on-Solway. Signposted on unclassified coast road from B5307 from Carlisle.
Access: Open at all times, no charge. Disabled visitors can drive to wheelchair-friendly hide to view high-tide roosts.

Facilities: Hide overlooking wetland areas, along nature trail (1.5 miles). No toilets or visitor centre.
Public transport: Nearest railway station at Carlisle (13 miles). Bus No 93 from Carlisle terminates at reserve's eastern end — 1.5 mile walk to North Plain Farm.
Habitat: Saltmarsh/intertidal areas, open water, peat bog, wet grassland.
Key birds: *Winter:* Waders and wildfowl include Barnacle and Pinkfooted Geese, Shoveler, Scaup, Grey Plover. *Spring/summer:* Breeding Lapwing, Curlew, Redshank, Snipe, Tree Sparrow and warblers. *Spring and autumn:* Passage waders such as Black-tailed Godwit, Whimbrel. Look for Pomarine, Arctic, Great and Long-tailed Skuas over the Solway. *Autumn/winter:* Up to 10,000 Oystercatchers among large roosting wader flocks. Hen Harrier.
Other notable flora and fauna: Roe deer, brown hare. Bog rosemary, bog asphodel, sundews and cotton grass. Large numbers of dragonflies (inc azure and emerald damselflies and four-spotted chaser).
Contact: North Plain Farm, Bowness-on-Solway, Wigton, Cumbria, CA7 5AG. 01697 351 330.
e-mail: campfield.marsh@rspb.org.uk
www.rspb.org.uk

2. DRUMBURGH MOSS NNR

Cumbria Wildlife Trust.
Location: NY 255 586 (OS Landranger 85). From Carlisle city centre, head W on B5307 to Kirkbride. After about one mile, turn R to Burgh by Sands. Follow road for 7.5 miles to Drumburgh village. Turn L by post office, continue down track and park on R past Moss Cottage.
Access: Open all year. Difficult terrain, so it is best to walk on bunds built to re-wet the site.
Facilities: None.
Public transport: Bus service between Carlisle and Bowness-on-Solway stops in Drumburgh.
Habitat: Raised bog, woodland, grassland.
Key birds: *Summer:* Red Grouse, Curlew, Grasshopper Warbler. *Winter:* Geese from the Solway.
Other notable flora and fauna: Large heath butterfly,emperor moth, adder and lizards, roe deer, brown hare. Specialist plants include 13 species of sphagnum moss, sundews, cotton grass and bog rosemary.
Contact: Trust HQ, 01539 816 300;
e-mail: mail@cumbriawildlifetrust.org.uk
www.cumbriawildlifetrust.org.uk

3. FOULNEY ISLAND

Location: SD 246 640. Three miles SE of Barrow town centre on the A5087 from Barrow or Ulverston. At a roundabout 2.5 miles S of Barrow take a minor road through Rampside to Roa Island. Turn L into reserve car park. Walk to main island along stone causeway.
Access: Open all year. Access restricted to designated paths during bird breeding season. Slitch Ridge is closed at this time. No dogs allowed during bird breeding season. The island may be cut off for several hours around high-tide, so please consult tide tables.

Facilities: None.
Public transport: Bus: regular service from Barrow to Roa Island.
Habitat: Shingle, sand, grassland.
Key birds: *Summer:* Arctic and Little Terns, Oystercatcher, Ringed Plover, Eider Duck. *Winter:* Brent Goose, Redshank, Dunlin, Sanderling.
Other notable flora and fauna: Sea campion, yellow horned poppy. Six spot burnet and common blue butterfly.
Contact: Trust HQ, 01539 816 300;
e-mail: mail@cumbriawildlifetrust.org.uk

4. HAWESWATER

RSPB and United Utilities.
Location: NY 469 108. For the eagle viewpoint, go to Bampton village, 10 miles S of Penrith and five miles NW of Shap. From Bampton, head S towards Haweswater reservoir. Drive down unclassified road alongside Haweswater reservoir, the road ends at a car park. From here you will need to walk.
Access: Visitors are asked not to go beyond the viewpoint, which is always open. There is no wheelchair access.
Facilities: Golden Eagle viewpoint, manned Sat/Sun, plus bank holidays, Apr to end Aug (11am-4pm), telescopes available. There is no coach parking.
Habitat: Fells with rocky streams, steep oak and birch woodlands.
Key birds: *Upland breeders:* Golden Eagle, Peregrine, Raven, Ring Ouzel, Curlew, Redshank, Snipe. *Woodlands:* Pied Flycatcher, Wood Warbler, Tree Pipit, Redstart, Buzzard, Sparrowhawk.
Contact: RSPB Office, 01931 713 376.
e-mail:haweswater@rspb.org.uk

5. ST BEES HEAD

RSPB (Northern England).
Location: NX 959 118. S of Whitehaven via the B3545 road to St Bees village.
Access: Open at all times, no charge. Access via coast-to-coast footpath. The walk to the viewpoints is long and steep in parts.
Facilities: Three viewpoints overlooking seabird colony. Public toilets in St Bees beach car park at entrance to reserve.
Public transport: Nearest trains at St Bees (0.5 mile).
Habitat: Three miles of sandstone cliffs up to 300 ft high.
Key birds: *Summer:* Largest seabird colony on W coast of England: Guillemot, Razorbill, Puffin, Kittiwake, Fulmar and England's only breeding pairs of Black Guillemot.
Contact: North Plain Farm, Bowness-on-Solway, Wigton, Cumbria CA7 5AG. 01697 351 330.
e-mail: stbees.head@rspb.org.uk www.rspb.org.uk

6. SMARDALE GILL NNR

Cumbria Wildlife Trust.
Location: NY 727 070. NNR occupies a 6km stretch of the disused railway between Tebay and Darlington. Approx 2.5 miles NE of Ravenstonedale on A685 or

0.5 miles S of Kirkby Stephen station. Take turning signed to Smardale. Cross over railway and turn L to junction, ignoring turn to Waitby. Cross over railway and turn L at junction ignoring sign for Smardale. Cross disued railway, turn L immediately and L again to car park.
Access: Railway line is open to all, non-members should obtain a permit before visiting other parts of the reserve.
Facilities: None.
Public transport: Train: nearest station Kirkby Stephen. Buses from here to Kendal, Brough and Sedburgh.
Habitat: Limestone grassland, river, ancient semi-natural woodland, quarry.
Key birds: *Summer:* Redstart, Pied Flycatcher, Wood Warbler and commoner woodland species. *All year:* Usual woodland birds, Buzzard, Sparrowhawk.
Other notable flora and fauna: Scotch argus, northern brown argus, common blue and dark green fritillary butterflies. Fragrant orchid, common rockrose, bluebell and bloody cranesbill. Red squirrel.
Contact: Trust HQ, 01539 816 300;
e-mail: mail@cumbriawildlifetrust.org.uk

7. SOUTH WALNEY

Cumbria Wildlife Trust.
Location: SD 225 620. Six miles S of Barrow-in-Furness. From Barrow, cross Jubilee Bridge onto Walney Island, turn L at lights. Continue through Biggar village to South End Caravan Park. Follow road for 1 mile to reserve.
Access: Open daily (10am-5pm, 4pm in winter) plus Bank Holidays. No dogs except assistance dogs. Day permits: £2 adults, 50p children. Cumbria Wildlife Trust members free.
Facilities: Toilets, nature trails, eight hides (two are wheelchair accessible), 200m boardwalk, cottage available to rent – sleeps 10. Electric wheelchair for hire. Coach parking available. Small admission fee for non-Trust members.
Public transport: Bus service as far as Biggar.
Habitat: Shingle, lagoon, sand dune, saltmarsh.
Key birds: *Spring/autumn:* Passage migrants. *Summer:* 14,000 breeding pairs of Herring, Greater and Lesser Black-backed Gulls, Shelduck, Eider. *Winter:* Teal, Wigeon, Goldeneye, Redshank, Greenshank, Curlew, Oystercatcher, Knot, Dunlin, Merlin, Short-eared Owl, Twite.
Other notable flora and fauna: 450 species of flowering plants. Natterjack toad at North Walney.
Contact: The Warden, No 1 Coastguard Cottages, South Walney Nature Reserve, Walney Island, Barrow-in-Furness LA14 3YQ. 01229 471 066. e-mail: mail@cumbriawildlifetrust.org.uk

8. TALKIN TARN COUNTRY PARK

Carlisle City Council
Location: NY544 591. Twelve miles E of Carlisle. From A69 E at Brampton, head S on B6413 for two miles. Talkin Tarn is on E just after level crossing.

Access: All year. Wheelchair access around tarn, two kissing gates accessible. Tearoom has lift. Coaches welcome.
Facilities: Tearoom open all year (10.30am-4pm). Mon - Wed, takeaway only, during winter. Dogs allowed. Angling by day permit (with closed season).
Public transport: Bus: infrequent. Tel: 0870 608 2608. Train: nearest station is Brampton Junction. Tel: 0845 748 4950. One mile away by footpath.
Habitat: Natural glacial tarn, mature oak/beech woodland, orchid meadow (traditionally managed), wet mire and farmland.
Key birds: *Spring/summer:* Pied Flycatcher, Spotted Flycatcher, Redstart, Chiffchaff, Wood Warbler. *Winter:* Grebes, Smew, Long-tailed Duck, Goosander, Gadwall, Wigeon, Brambling, swans.
Other notable flora and fauna: Common blue damselfly, common darter, small copper butterfly, otter, red squirrel.
Contact: Greenspaces Team, Carlisle City County, Civic Centre, Carlisle CA3 8QG. 01228 817 200; e-mail: parks@carlisle.gov.uk

9. WALNEY BIRD OBSERVATORY

Location: Walney Island, Barrow-in-Furness, Cumbria.
Access: Several areas, notably the golf course and airfield, are restricted but the island's narrow width means most sites are viewable from the road or footpaths. Access to South Walney Nature Reserve (10am-5pm) is along permitted trails.
Facilities: Monitoring and ringing of breeding and migrant birds occurs across the island, with ringing opportunities for qualified

ringers. For availability write to Walney Bird Observatory (address below).

Public transport: Barrow-in-Furness connects to the rail network and local bus routes serve Walney Island. Routes 1 and 1A cover the central area while 6 and 6A cover the north end of the island. No bus route is available for the southern end.

Habitat: Estuarine, maritime, dunes, freshwater and brackish pools, scrub and farmland.

Key birds: Renowned Eider and gull colonies at south end. The winter months provide a wildfowl and wader spectacular across the island. Migrants aplenty appear during both passage periods — the island has a proven pedigree for attracting rare and unusual species.

Other notable flora and fauna: Famed for Walney geranium, but also important for coastal shingle species such as sea holly, sea rocket and sea kale. More than 500 species of moth recorded, inc sand dune specialities such as coast dart and sand dart.

Contact: Walney Bird Observatory, Coastguard Cottages, Walney Island, Barrow-in-Furness, Cumbria LA14 3YQ.

Lancashire

THE COUNTY'S mosses attract huge numbers of wintering Pink-footed Geese, Bewick's and Whooper Swans, while tens of thousands of waders winter in Morecambe Bay. Pendle Hill attracts regular Dotterel on spring passage. Bitterns, Marsh Harriers and Avocets are at Leighton Moss.

1. CUERDEN VALLEY PARK

Cuerden Valley Park Trust.

Location: SD 565 238. S of Preston on A49. Easy access from J28 and J29 of the M6, J8 and J9 on M61 and the end of M65.

Access: 650-acre site open all year.

Facilities: Visitor centre at Berkeley Drive, Bamber Bridge with toilets available between 9am and 5pm on weekdays. Sunday afternoon opening dependent on volunteer help. Track from Town Brow to lake is wheelchair friendly.

Public transport: None.

Habitat: 650 acres of mixed woodland, river, pond, lake, wildflower meadow, agricultural grassland.

Key birds: All year: Great Crested Grebe, Little Grebe, Kingfisher, Dipper, Great Spotted Woodpecker, Goldcrest, Little Owl and usual woodland and river birds.

Other notable flora and fauna: Dragonflies including emperor, emerald, black darter and migrant hawker. Butterflies including large and small skipper, holly blue, small copper, comma and gatekeeper. Roe deer and seven species of bat. Common spotted and marsh orchid, moschatel.

Contact: Cuerden Valley Park Trust, 01772 324 436. e-mail: rangers@cuerdenvalleypark.org

2. HEYSHAM NATURE RESERVE AND BIRD OBSERVATORY

The Wildlife Trust for Lancashire, Manchester and North Merseyside in conjunction with British Energy Estates.

Location: SD 406 599 W of Lancaster. Take A683 to Heysham port. Turn L at traffic lights by Duke of Rothesay pub, then first R after 300m.

Access: Gate to reserve car park usually open 9.30am-6pm (longer in summer and shorter in winter). Pedestrian access at all times. Dogs on lead. Limited disabled access.

Facilities: Hide overlooking Power Station outfalls. Map giving access details at the reserve car park. No manned visitor centre or toilet access, but someone usually in reserve office, next to the main car park, in the morning. Latest sightings board can be viewed through the window if office is closed.

Public transport: Train services connect with nearby Isle of Man ferry. Plenty of buses to Lancaster from various Heysham sites within walking distance (ask for nearest stop to the harbour).

Habitat: Varied: wetland, acid grassland, alkaline grassland, foreshore.

Key birds: Passerine migrants in the correct conditions. Good passage of seabirds in spring, especially Arctic Tern. Storm Petrel and Leach's Petrel during strong onshore (SW-WNW) winds in midsummer and autumn respectively. Good variety of breeding birds (e.g. eight species of warbler on the reserve itself). Two-three scarce land-birds each year, most frequent being Yellow-browed Warbler.

Other notable flora and fauna: Notable area for dragonflies: red-veined darter breeds at nearby Middleton Community Woodland main pond SD 418 592 (mid June - mid July). Bee orchid.

Contact: Reserve Warden, Heysham Nature Reserve. 01524 855 030; www.lancswt.org.uk http://heyshamobservatory.blogspot.com; Annual report from Leighton Moss RSPB reserve shop.

3. LEIGHTON MOSS

RSPB (Northern England).

Location: SD 478 750.Post code LA5 0SW. Four miles NW of Carnforth, Lancs. Leave M6 at J35. Take the A6 N towards Kendal and follow brown signs for Leighton Moss off A6.

Access: Reserve open daily dawn-dusk. Visitor centre open daily 9.30am-5pm (9.30am-4.30pm Nov-Dec inclusive), except Christmas Day. No charge to RSPB members or those who arrive by public transport or bike (you also get 10% off in our cafe if you come by public transport or bike).

Facilities: Visitor centre, shop, cafe and toilets, disabled toilet. Nature trails and five hides (four have wheelchair access), plus two hides at saltmarsh pools. Stairlift to café for those with mobility issues.

Public transport: Silverdale train station 250 metres from reserve.

Habitat: Reedbed, shallow meres and woodland. Saltmarsh pools approx 1 mile.

NATURE RESERVES - NORTHERN ENGLAND

Key birds: *All year*: Bittern, Bearded Tit, Water Rail, Shoveler, Gadwall, Marsh Tit, Little Egret. *Summer*: Marsh Harrier, Reed and Sedge Warbler. Avocet at saltmarsh pools. *Winter*: Large flocks of Starlings roosting.
Other notable flora and fauna: Common reed, otter, red deer.
Contact: RSPB Leighton Moss Nature Reserve, Myers Farm, Silverdale, Carnforth, LA5 0SW. 01524 701601. e-mail: leighton.moss@rspb.org.uk
www.rspb.org.uk/leightonmoss

4. MARTIN MERE

The Wildfowl & Wetlands Trust.
Location: SD 428 145. Six miles N of Ormskirk via Burscough Bridge (A59), 20 miles from Liverpool and Preston.
Access: Opening times: 9.30am-5pm (Nov-Feb), 9.30am-5.30pm (rest of year). Special dawn and evening events. Guide dogs only allowed. Admission charge except for members. Special rates for coach parties. Fully accessible to disabled, all hides suitable for wheelchairs. Coach park available.
Facilities: Visitor centre with toilets, gift shop, restaurant, education centre, play area, nature reserve and nature trails, hides, waterfowl collection and sustainable garden.
Public transport: Bus service to WWT Martin Mere from Ormskirk. Train to Burscough Bridge or New Lane Stations (both 1.5 miles from reserve). For bus times contact Traveline 0870 608 2608.
Habitat: Open water, wet grassland, moss, copses, reedbed, parkland.
Key birds: *Winter*: Whooper and Bewick's Swans, Pink-footed Goose, various ducks, Ruff, Black-tailed Godwit, Peregrine, Hen Harrier, Tree Sparrow. *Spring*: Ruff, Shelduck, Little Ringed and Ringed Plovers, Lapwing, Redshank.

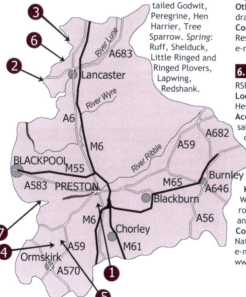

Summer: Marsh Harrier, Garganey, hirundines, Tree Sparrow. Breeding Avocet, Lapwing, Redshank, Shelduck. *Autumn*: Pink-footed Goose, waders on passage.
Other notable flora and fauna: Whorled caraway, golden dock, tubular dropwort, 300 species of moth.
Contact: WWT Martin Mere Wetland Centre, 01704 895 181; e-mail: info.martinmere@wwt.org.uk

5. MERE SANDS WOOD

The Wildlife Trust for Lancashire, Manchester and North Merseyside.
Location: SD 44 71 57. 12 miles by road from Southport, 0.5 miles off A59 Preston - Liverpool road, in Rufford along B5246 (Holmeswood Road).
Access: Visitor centre open 9.30am-4.30pm - closed Fridays and Christmas Day. Car park open until 8pm in summer. Three miles of wheelchair-accessible footpaths. All hides accessible to wheelchairs.
Facilities: Visitor centre with toilets (disabled), six viewing hides, three trails, exhibition room, latest sightings board. Feeding stations. Booking essential for two motorised buggies.
Public transport: Bus: Southport-Chorley 347 and Preston-Ormskirk 2B stop in Rufford, 0.5 mile walk. Train: Preston-Ormskirk train stops at Rufford station, one mile walk.
Habitat: 40h inc freshwater lakes, mixed woodland, sandy grassland/heath.
Key birds: *Winter*: Regionally important for Teal and Gadwall, good range of waterfowl, Kingfisher. Feeding stations attract Tree Sparrow, Bullfinch, Reed Bunting, Water Rail. *Woodland*: Treecreeper, Nuthatch. *Summer*: Kingfisher. *Passage*: Most years, Osprey, Crossbill, Green Sandpiper, Greenshank.
Other notable flora and fauna: 18 species of dragonfly recorded annually.
Contact: Reserve Manager, Mere Sands Wood Nature Reserve, 01704 821 809. www.lancswt.org.uk e-mail: meresandswood@lancswt.org.uk

6. MORECAMBE BAY (HEST BANK)

RSPB (Northern England).
Location: SD 468 667. Two miles N of Morecambe at Hest Bank.
Access: Open at all times. Do not venture onto saltmarsh or intertidal area, as there are dangerous channels and quicksands.
Facilities: Viewpoint at local council car park. **Public transport:** No 5 bus runs between Carnforth and Morecambe. Tel: 0870 608 2608. **Habitat:** Saltmarsh, estuary.
Key birds: *Winter*: Wildfowl (Pintail, Shelduck, Wigeon) and waders. This is an important high tide roost for Oystercatcher, Curlew, Redshank, Dunlin and Bar-tailed Godwit.
Contact: RSPB Leighton Moss & Morecambe Bay Nature Reserves, 01524 701601; e-mail:leighton.moss@rspb.org.uk
www.rspb.org.uk/morecambebay

7. RIBBLE ESTUARY

Natural England (NNRs North Team).
Location: SD 380 240. W of Preston.
Access: Open at all times.
Facilities: No formal visiting facilities.
Public transport: None.
Habitat: Saltmarsh, mudflats.
Key birds: High water wader roosts (of Knot, Dunlin, Black-tailed Godwit, Oystercatcher and Grey Plover) are best viewed from Southport, Marshside, Lytham and St Annes. Pink-footed Geese and wintering swans are present in large numbers from Oct-Feb on Banks Marsh and along River Douglas respectively. Banks Marsh can be viewed from the public footpath which runs along the sea defence embankment from Crossens Pumping Station to Hundred End. The large flocks of Wigeon, for which the site is renowned, can be seen on high tides from Marshside but feed on saltmarsh areas at night. Good numbers of raptors also present in winter.
Contact: Senior Reserve Manager, Natural England, Ribble Estuary NNR, 01704 578 774.
e-mail:Dave.mercer@naturalengland.org.uk

Manchester, Greater

FOR A largely urban area, there are good places for birdwatching. Pennington Flash is the area's best all-round birding site, while Peregrines and Black Redstarts breed in the city centre and urban regeneration has cleaned up the water to such an extent that increasing numbers of ducks are wintering in Salford Docks. Etherow CP holds Dipper, Grey Wagtail, Pied Flycatcher and all three woodpeckers.

1. ASTLEY MOSS

The Wildlife Trust for Lancashire, Manchester and North Merseyside.
Location: SJ 692 975. Seven km S of Leigh and 14km W of Manchester. Turn off A580(T) onto Higher Green Road, signposted on a through road. After Lower Green, the road bends sharply L and then R. Reserve is accessible from the second track on the R, approx 150m before the railway crossing.
Access: Permit from Trust required.
Facilities: None. **Public transport:** None.
Habitat: Remnant peat bog, scrub, oak/birch woodland.
Key birds: *Spring/summer:* Breeding Tree Pipit. *Winter:* Raptors (inc. Merlin, Hen Harrier), finch flocks, thrush flocks; Long- and Short-eared Owls.
Other notable flora and fauna: Sphagnum mosses, 10 species of dragonfly recorded.
Contact: Trust HQ, 01772 324 129; www.lancswt.org.uk

2. ETHEROW COUNTRY PARK

Stockport Metropolitan Borough Council.
Location: SJ 965 908. B6104 into Compstall near Romiley, Stockport SK6 5JD.
Access: Open at all times; permit required for conservation area. Keep to paths.
Facilities: Reserve area has SSSI status. Hide, nature trail, visitor centre, scooters for disabled.
Public transport: None.
Habitat: River Etherow, woodlands, marshy area.
Key birds: Sparrowhawk, Buzzard, Dipper, all three woodpeckers, Pied Flycatcher, warblers. *Winter:* Brambling, Siskin, Water Rail. Frequent sightings of Merlin and Raven over hills.
Other notable flora and fauna: 200 species of plant.
Contact: John Rowland, Etherow Country Park, Compstall, Stockport, Cheshire SK6 5JD. 01614 276 937; e-mail: parks@stockport.gov.uk

3. HOLLINGWORTH LAKE

Hollingworth Lake – Rochdale MBC.
Location: SD 939 153 (visitor centre). Four miles NE of Rochdale, signed from A58 Halifax Road and J21 of M62 – B6225 to Littleborough.
Access: Access open to lake and surroundings at all times.
Facilities: Cafes, hide, trails and education service, car parks, coach park by prior arrangement. Free wheelchair hire, disabled toilets and baby changing facilities, fishing. Visitor centre open 10.30am-6pm each day in summer, 11am-4pm (Mon-Fri), 10.30am-5pm (Sat & Sun) in winter.
Public transport: Bus Nos 452, 450. Train to Littleborough or Smithy Bridge.
Habitat: Lake (116 acres, includes 20 acre nature reserve), woodland, streams, marsh, willow scrub.
Key birds: *All year:* Great Crested Grebe, Kingfisher, Lapwing, Little Owl, Bullfinch, Cormorant. Occasional Peregrine, Sedge Warbler, Water Rail, Snipe. *Spring/autumn:* Passage waders, wildfowl, Kittiwake. *Summer:* Reed Bunting, Dipper, Common Sandpiper, Curlew, Oystercatcher, Black Tern, 'Commic' Tern, Grey Partridge, Blackcap. *Winter:* Goosander, Goldeneye, Siskin, Redpoll, Golden Plover.
Contact: The Ranger, Hollingworth Lake Visitor Centre, Rakewood Road, Littleborough, OL15 0AQ. 01706 373 421. www.rochdale.gov.uk

4. PENNINGTON FLASH COUNTRY PARK

Wigan Leisure and Culture Trust
Location: SJ 640 990. One mile from Leigh town centre. Main entrance on A572 (St Helens Road).
Access: Park is signposted from A580 (East Lancs Road) and is permanently open. Five largest hides, toilets and information point open 9am-dusk (except Christmas Day). Main paths flat and suitable for disabled. Main car park pay & display with coach parking available if booked in advance.
Facilities: Toilets (including disabled) and information point. Total of eight bird hides. Site leaflet available and Rangers based on site. Group visits welcome but please book your visit in advance.

Public transport: Only 1 mile from Leigh bus station. Several services stop on St Helens Road near entrance to park. Tel: 01942 883 501 for more details.
Habitat: Lowland lake, ponds and scrapes, fringed with reeds, rough grassland, scrub and young woodland.
Key birds: Waterfowl all year, waders (14-plus species) and terns (4-plus species) mainly on passage in both spring and autumn. Breeding birds include 9 species of warbler. Feeding station attracts Willow Tit, Stock Dove and up to 40 Bullfinch all year. Large gull roost in winter. More than 240 species recorded, including 7 county firsts in the last decade alone.
Other notable flora and fauna: Several species of orchid including bee orchid. Wide variety of butterflies and dragonflies.
Contact: Site Manager, Pennington Flash Country Park, St Helens Road, Leigh, WN7 3PA. 01942 605 253 e-mail: pfcp@wlct.org www.wlct.org/open-spaces/parks/park-information.htm

5. WIGAN FLASHES LNR

Lancashire Wildlife Trust/Wigan Council.
Location: SD 580 035. Leave M6 at J25 head N on A49, turn R on to Poolstock Lane (B5238). There are several entrances to the site; at end of Carr Lane near Hawkley Hall School, one off Poolstock Lane, two on Warington Road (A573). Also accessible from banks of Leeds and Liverpool Canal.
Access: Free access, open at all times. Areas suitable for wheelchairs but there are some motorcycle barriers (gates can be opened by reserve manager for large groups). Paths being upgraded. Access for coaches - contact reserve manager for details.
Facilities: Six hide screens.
Public transport: 610 bus (Hawkley Hall Circular). Local timetable info - call 0161 228 7811.
Habitat: Wetland with reedbed.
Key birds: Black Tern on migration. *Summer:* Nationally important for Reed Warbler and breeding Common Tern. Willow Tit, Cetti's and Grasshopper Warblers, Kingfisher. *Winter:* Wildfowl, especially diving duck and Gadwall. Bittern (especially winter).
Other notable flora and fauna: Interesting orchids, with the eight species including marsh and dune helleborine. One of the UK's largest feeding assemblage of noctule bats. Eighteen species of dragonfly which has included red-veined darter.
Contact: Mark Champion, Lancashire Wildlife Trust, Highfield Grange, Wigan, Lancs WN3 6SU. 01942 233 976; e-mail: wiganflashes@lancswt.org.uk

Merseyside

SEAFORTH DOCKS has a good reputation for rare gulls, while north-westerly gales in autumn bring Leach's Petrels to the tip of the Wirral peninsula, probably the best place in Britain to see them away from their breeding sites.

1. DEE ESTUARY

Metropolitan Borough of Wirral.
Location: SJ 255 815. Leave A540 Chester to Hoylake road at Heswall and head downhill (one mile) to the free car park at the shore end of Banks Road. Heswall is 30 mins from South Liverpool and Chester by car.
Access: Open at all times. Best viewpoint 600 yards along shore N of Banks Road. No disabled access along shore, but good birdwatching from bottom of Banks Road. Arrive 2.5 hours before high tide. Coach parking available.
Facilities: Information board. No toilets in car park. Wirral Country Park Centre three miles N, off A540 has toilets, hide, café, kiosk (all accessible to wheelchairs). Sheldrakes Restaurant at the end of Banks Road with an outside terrace overlooking the foreshore. tel 0151 342 1556.
Public transport: Bus service to Banks Road car park from Heswall bus station, or bus to Irby village then walk one mile. Mersey Travel (0151 236 7676).
Habitat: Saltmarsh and mudflats.
Key birds: *Autumn/winter:* Large passage and winter wader roosts — Redshank, Curlew, Black-tailed Godwit, Oystercatcher, Golden Plover, Knot, Shelduck, Teal, Red-breasted Merganser, Peregrine, Merlin, Hen Harrier, Short-eared Owl. Smaller numbers of Pintail, Wigeon, Bar-tailed Godwit, Greenshank, Spotted Redshank, Grey and Ringed Plovers, Whimbrel, Curlew Sandpiper, Little Stint, occasional Scaup and Little Egret.
Contact: Wirral Country Park Visitors Centre, Station Road, Thustaston, Wirral CH61 0HN. 0151 648 4371; e-mail: wirralcountrypark@wirral.gov.uk

2. HILBRE ISLAND LNR

Metropolitan Borough of Wirral.
Location: SJ 184 880. Three tidal islands in the mouth of the Dee Estuary. Park in West Kirby on A540 Chester-to-Hoylake road – 30 minutes from Liverpool, 45 minutes from Chester. Follow the brown Marine Lake signs to Dee Lane pay and display car park or free parking along the promenade. Coach parking available at West Kirby. Groups are asked to provide an indication of numbers and a mobile phone contact number for someone within the group in case of emergency.
Access: Two mile walk across the sands from Dee Lane slipway. No disabled access. Do not cross either way within 3.5 hours of high water – tide times and suggested safe route on noticeboard at slipway.
Facilities: Hilbre Bird Observatory by prior appointment only. Composting toilets on the main island (Hilbre) and at Wirral Sailing Centre (end of Dee Lane, West Kirby). Leaflets and tide times from Thurstaston Visitor Centre.
Public transport: Bus and train station (from Liverpool) within 0.5 mile of Dee Lane slipway. Contact Mersey Travel, 0151 236 7676.
Habitat: Sandflats, rocky shore and open sea.
Key birds: *Late summer/autumn:* Seabird passage — Gannets, terns, skuas, shearwaters and after NW

gales good numbers of Leach's Petrel. *Winter:* Wader roosts at high tide, Purple Sandpiper, Turnstone, sea ducks, divers, grebes. Passage migrants.
Other notable flora and fauna: Nationally scarce rock sea lavender.
Contact: As Dee Estuary (above).

3. MARSHSIDE

RSPB (Northern England).
Location: SD 353 205. From Southport, follow minor coast road N (1.5 miles from Southport Pier) to small car park by sand works.
Access: Open 8.30am-5pm all year. No dogs. Coach parties please book in advance. No charges but donations welcomed. Park in Sefton Council car park along Marine Drive.
Facilities: Information centre, toilets (inc disabled), two hides and trails accessible to wheelchairs. Two viewing screens and a viewing platform.
Public transport: Bus service to Elswick Road/ Marshside Road half-hourly, bus No 44, from Lord Street. Contact Traveline (0870 608 2608).
Habitat: Coastal grazing marsh and lagoons.
Key birds: *Winter:* Pink-footed Goose, wildfowl, waders, raptors. *Spring:* Breeding waders, inc. Avocet and wildfowl, Garganey, migrants. *Autumn:* Migrants. *All year:* Black-tailed Godwit.
 Other notable flora and fauna: Hares, various plants including marsh orchid, migrant hawker dragonfly.
Contact: Marshside RSPB Reserve, 01704 226 190.

4. N.WIRRAL COASTAL PARK

Location: SJ 241 909. Located between the outer Dee and Mersey Estuaries. From Moreton take A553 E then A551 N. Turn left onto Tarran Way South then R onto Lingham Lane. Parking available by lighthouse. Foreshore can be viewed from footpath which runs alongside.

Access: Open at all times.
Facilities: Visitor centre, several car parks, 3 toilet blocks (one summer-only), extensive footpath network and public bridleways, 4 picnic areas.
Public transport: The area being served by Grove Road (Wallasey), Leasowe, Moreton, and Meols Merseyrail Stations, and with bus routes along Leasowe Road, Pasture Road and Harrison Drive.
Habitat: Saltmarsh.
Key birds: Important as a feeding and roosting site for passage and wintering flocks of waders, wildfowl, terns and gulls. Wintering populations of Knot (20,000+), Bar-tailed Godwit (2,000+) and Dunlin (10,000). Redshank (1,000+) and Turnstone (500+) feed on the rocky shore at Perch Rock and on the rocky sea walls. Oystercatcher (500+), Curlew, Grey Plover and Black-tailed Godwit also regularly roost here in relatively high numbers. Small populations of wildfowl, including Common Scoter, Scaup and Goldeneye, Red-throated Divers and Great Crested Grebes also frequently winter on this site.
Other notable flora and fauna: Sea holly, marram grass, storksbill, burnet rose and rarities like the Isle of Man cabbage can be found. This area is one of only two known sites in the world for the very rare British sub-species of the belted beauty moth.
Contact: Ranger Service, North Wirral Coastal Park, 0151 678 5488. www.wirral.gov.uk
e-mail: coastalpark@wirral.gov.uk

5. SEAFORTH NATURE RESERVE

Wildlife Trust for Lancs, Manchester and N Merseyside
Location: SJ 315 970. Five miles from Liverpool city centre. From M57/M58 take A5036 to docks.
Access: Only organised groups which pre-book are now allowed access. Groups should contact the reserve office (see below) at least seven days in advance of their planned trip. Coaches welcome.
Facilities: Toilets at visitor centre when open, three hides.
Public transport: Train to Waterloo or Seaforth stations from Liverpool. Buses to dock gates from Liverpool.
Habitat: Saltwater and freshwater lagoons, scrub grassland.
Key birds: Noted site for Little Gull on passage (Apr), plus Roseate, Little and Black Terns. Breeding and passage Common Tern (Apr-Sept). Passage and winter waders and gulls. Passage passerines, especially White Wagtail, pipits and Wheatear.
Contact: Seaforth Nature Reserve, Port of Liverpool, L21 1JD. 0151 9203 769; www.lancswt.org.uk

6. WIRRAL COUNTRY PARK

Metropolitan Borough of Wirral.
Location: SJ 237 835. SW of Birkenhead. Take coast road E off A540 at Thurstaton (Station Road), visitor centre and parking is at end of road. Other car parking available at West Kirby and Caldy or close

to the park at Banks Road or Riverbank Road (Lower Heswall).
Access: Visitor Centre open all year (10am – 4.45pm) except Christmas Day.
Facilities: Visitor centre with toilets, hide, café, kiosk (all accessible to wheelchairs).
Public transport: No public transport to Thurstaston Centre. (Buses stop on A540 by Thurstaston Village 0.75 miles away. Train stations at West Kirby or Heswall.
Habitat: Hedgerows, fields and woodland overlooking large open estuary and shoreline.
Key birds: In hedgerows and grassland, Wren, Dunnock, tits and finches joined by summer warblers and winter thrushes. Skylarks, Barn Owls over grassland with Kestrels along cliff edge. Nearby Dee Estuary is feeding area for migrating birds like Knot, Dunlin and Oystercatcher. Redshank, Shelduck, Lapwing and terns and, particularly at high spring-tides, possible raptors like Peregrine, Hen Harrier and daytime-hunting Short-eared Owls.
Other notable flora and fauna: Up to 10 species of butterfly recorded, locally rare grassland wildflowers along the Dee Cliffs SSSI. Ragworm, Lugworm, cockles, shrimp-like creatures and tiny spire-shells in the adjacent Dee Estuary.
Contact: As Dee Estuary (above).

Northumberland

A STUNNING county, with a fantastic range of habitats. The seabird colonies on the Farne Islands are world famous, while Holy Island (Lindisfarne) attracts a range of migrants in spring and autumn, plus huge numbers of wintering birds. Kielder Forest is good for Crossbills and raptors, including Goshawk. The nearby moors hold a good selection of upland species.

1. ARNOLD MEMORIAL, CRASTER

Northumberland Wildlife Trust.
Location: NU 255 197. Lies NE of Alnwick and SW of Craster village.
Access: Public footpath from car park in disused quarry. Open all year.
Facilities: Information centre (not NWT) open in summer. Interpretation boards.Toilets (incl disabled) and picnic site in quarry car park. Easy going access along path through site. Coach parking in adjacent public car park (charges). Dogs on lead.
Public transport: Arriva Northumberland nos. 500, 505. Travelsure No 401
Habitat: Semi-natural woodland and scrub near coast.
Key birds: Good site for migrant passerines to rest and feed. Interesting visitors can inc. Bluethroat, Red-breasted Flycatcher, Barred and Icterine Warblers, Wryneck; moulting site for Lesser Redpoll. Breeding warblers in summer.
Other notable flora and fauna: Spring flora including primrose and non-native periwinkle.
Contact: Northumberland Wildlife Trust, 01912 846 884; e-mail: mail@northwt.org.uk www.nwt.org.uk

2. DRURIDGE POOLS - CRESSWELL POND

Northumberland Wildlife Trust.
Location: Two sites lying on coast between Newbiggin and Amble, off A1068. 1. Druridge Pools NZ 272 965. 2. Cresswell Pond NZ 283 945. Half mile N of Cresswell.
Access: Day permits needed for both reserves. Wheelchair users can view northern part of Cresswell Pond from public footpath or roadside.
Facilities: 1. Three hides. 2. Hide.
Public transport: Arriva No 420 (to within 2 miles).
Habitat: 1. Deep lake and wet meadows with pools behind dunes. 2. Shallow brackish lagoon behind dunes fringed by saltmarsh and reedbed, some mudflats.
Key birds: 1. Especially good in spring. Winter and breeding wildfowl; passage and breeding waders. 2. Good for waders, esp. on passage.
Other notable flora and fauna: The sheltered sunny banks are good for a range of butterflies and dragonflies in summer at Druridge Pools. Otters are often seen by the lakes.
Contact: Northumberland Wildlife Trust, 01912 846 884; e-mail: mail@northwt.org.uk www.nwt.org.uk

3. EAST CHEVINGTON

Northumberland Wildlife Trust.
Location: NZ 270 990. Overlooking Druridge Bay, off A 1068 between Hauxley and Cresswell.
Access: Main access from overflow car park at Druridge Bay Country Park (signed from main road).
Facilities: Four public hides, café, toilets and information at Country Park (County Council). ID boards for coastal plants.
Public transport: Arriva 420 and 423 bus services.
Habitat: Ponds and reedbeds created from former open cast coal mine. Areas of scrub and grassland.
Key birds: Large numbers of wildfowl, including Greylag and Pinkfooted Geese in winter. Breeding Skylark, Stonechat, Reed Bunting, plus Reed, Sedge and Grasshopper Warblers. Capable of attracting rarities at any time of year. Marsh Harriers around the reedbeds.
Other notable flora and fauna: Coastal wildflowers.
Contact: Northumberland Wildlife Trust, 01912 846 884; e-mail: mail@northwt.org.uk www.nwt.org.uk

4. FARNE ISLANDS

The National Trust.
Location: NU 230 370. Access by boat from Seahouses Harbour, which is reached from A1.
Access: Apr, Aug-Oct: Inner Farne and Staple 10.30am-6pm (majority of boats land at Inner Farne

when conditions are calm). May-Jul: Staple Island 10.30am-1.30pm, Inner Farne: 1.30pm-5pm. Disabled access possible on Inner Farne, telephone Property Manager for details. Dogs allowed on boats but not on islands.
Facilities: Toilets on Inner Farne.
Public transport: Nearest rail stations at Alnmouth and Berwick. Hourly Travelsure buses between Budle and Beadnell Bays (Mon-Sat). Call 01665 720 955.
Habitat: Maritime islands – between 15-28 depending on height of tide.
Key birds: 18 species of seabirds/waders, four species of tern (including Roseate), 40,000-plus pairs of Puffin, 33,000 pairs of Guillemots, 800 Eider, Rock Pipit, Pied Wagtail etc.
Contact: David Steel, Farne Islands, Seahouses NE68 7SR. 01665 720 651.
e-mail:farneislands@nationaltrust.org.uk

5. HAUXLEY

Northumberland Wildlife Trust
Location: NU 285 023. Near Low Hauxley village, at the N end of Druridge Bay.
Access: Day permit required. Access through High Hauxley village. Site is signposted off A1068. Dogs on leads.
Facilities: Reception hide open daily from 10am-5pm (summer) or 10am-3pm (winter) and six public hides. Toilets and information.
Public transport: Arriva 420 and 423 bus services.
Habitat: Ponds created from former opencast coal mine. Areas of woodland and grassland.
Key birds: Large numbers of wildfowl use the site in winter, waders use the site at high tide. Roseate Terns sometimes join commoner species in late summer. Waders and migrants on passage. *Winter*: Bewick's Swan, Shoveler, Lapwing and Purple Sandpiper.
Other notable flora and fauna: A variety of invertebrates, including butterflies, dragonflies and amphibians such as great crested newt.
Contact: Northumberland Wildlife Trust, 01912 846 884; e-mail: mail@northwt.org.uk
www.nwt.org.uk

6. KIELDER FOREST PARK

Forestry Commission
Location: NY 632 934. Kielder Castle is situated at N end of Kielder Water, NW of Bellingham.
Access: Forest open all year. Toll charge on 12 mile forest drive and car park charge applies. Visitor centre has limited opening in winter.
Facilities: Visitor centre, exhibition, toilets, shop, access for disabled, licensed café. Local facilities include youth hostel, camp site, pub and garage.
Public transport: Bus: 814, 815, 816 from Hexham and seasonal service 714 from Newcastle.
Habitat: Commercial woodland, mixed and broadleaved trees.
Key birds: *Spring/summer*: Goshawk, Chiffchaff, Willow Warbler, Redstart, Siskin. *Winter*: Crossbill.

Resident: Jay, Dipper, Great Spotted Woodpecker, Tawny Owl, Song Thrush, Goldcrest.
Other notable flora and fauna: Impressive display of northern marsh orchids at entrance to Kielder Castle.
Contact: Forestry Commission, 01434 220 242.
e-mail: kieldercastle@forestry.gsi.gov.uk

7. LINDISFARNE NNR

Natural England (Northumbria Team).
Location: NU 090 430. Island access lies two miles E of A1 at Beal, 10 miles S of Berwick-on-Tweed.
Access: Causeway floods at high tide, so check when it is safe to cross. Some restricted access (bird refuges). Coach parking available on Holy Island.
Facilities: Toilets, visitor centre in village. Hide on island (new hide with disabled access at Fenham-le-Moor). Self-guided trail on island.
Public transport: Irregular bus service to Holy Island, mainly in summer. Main bus route follows mainland boundary of site north-south.
Habitat: Dunes, sand, mudflats and saltmarsh.
Key birds: *Passage and winter*: Wildfowl and waders, including pale-bellied Brent Goose, Long-tailed Duck and Whooper Swan. Rare migrants.
Other notable flora and fauna: Butterflies include dark green fritillary (July) and grayling (August). Guided walks advertised for 9 species of orchid including coralroot and Lindisfarne helleborine.
Contact: Reserve Manager, Beal Station, Berwick-on-Tweed, TD15 2PB. 01289 381 470.

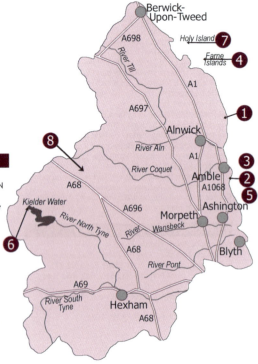

8. WHITELEE MOOR

Northumberland Wildlife Trust
Location: NT 700 040. Reserve located at head of Redesdale, south of A68 Newcastle to Jedburgh road where it crosses Scottish Border at Carter Bar.
Access: There is parking at tourist car park at Carter Bar and on laybys on forest track at reservoir end. A public footpath leads along old track to Whitelee Limeworks and then southwards. This footpath extends to southern boundary of site and eastwards along it to link up with a bridleway from White Kielder Burn via Girdle Fell to Chattlehope Burn. Additionally there is access on foot via Forest Enterprise road near eastern corner of reserve.

Reserve is remote and wild, and weather can change quickly. Visitors should have hill-walking experience if attempting long walks.
Facilities: Car park and laybys.
Habitat: Active blanket bog and heather heath.
Key birds: The River Rede and its tributaries add to the habitat and bird diversity. Notable breeding birds include Merlin and Stonechat. Black Grouse, Skylark, Meadow Pipit, Dunlin, Curlew, Golden Plover, Grey Wagtail, Dipper and Ring Ouzel regularly visit the reserve.
Other notable flora and fauna: Otters often hunt along the Rede and a herd of feral goats may be seen.
Contact: Trust HQ, 01912 846 884;
e-mail: mail@northwt.org.uk www.nwt.org.uk

Yorkshire, East Riding

COASTAL birding dominates here, with Bempton Cliffs probably the best seabird colony in England, with Puffins in front of your face and a Gannetry to boot. Two headlands — Flamborough Head and Spurn Point — attract migrants, including scarce vagrants, in autumn. Book a boat trip from Bridlington to see shearwaters and skuas in autumn.

1. BEMPTON CLIFFS

RSPB (Northern England).
Location: TA 197 738. Near Bridlington. Take Cliff Lane N from Bempton Village off B1229 to car park and visitor centre.
Access: Visitor centre open year round - 10am-5pm Mar - Oct; 10am-4pm Nov - Feb. Public footpath along cliff top with observation points. Access for wheelchairs to main observation points along gravel paths.
Facilities: Visitor centre, toilets, light refreshments, observation points, picnic area, limited coach parking. Four miles of stunning chalk cliffs, highest in county.
Public transport: Bempton railway station (limited service) 1.5 miles — irregular bus service to village 1.25 miles.
Habitat: Seabird nesting cliffs, farmland, grassland, coastal scrub.
Key birds: Largest mainland seabird colony in UK; only Gannet colony in England. Birds present January to October with peak Apr - Jun. Includes Kittiwake, Gannet, Puffin, Guillemot, Razorbill and Fulmar. Nesting Tree Sparrow and Corn Bunting. Passage skuas, shearwaters, terns and passerine migrants.
Other notable flora and fauna: Harbour porpoise and grey seal regularly offshore. Also bee and northern marsh orchids can occur.
Contact: RSPB Bempton Cliffs Nature Reserve, Cliff Lane, Bempton YO15 1JF. 01262 851 179.
e-mailbempton.cliffs@rspb.org.uk

2. BLACKTOFT SANDS

RSPB (Northern England).
Location: SE 843 232. Eight miles E of Goole on minor road between Ousefleet and Adlingfleet.
Access: Open 9am-9pm or dusk if earlier. RSPB members free, £3 permit for non-members, £2 concessionary, £1 children, £6 family.
Facilities: Car park, toilets, visitor centre (open 9am to 5pm April to Oct and weekends between Nov and March), six hides, footpaths suitable for wheelchairs.
Public transport: Goole/Scunthorpe bus (Sweynes' Coaches stops outside reserve entrance). Bus timetable on main RSPB website (see Blacktoft Reserve details).
Habitat: Reedbed, saline lagoons, lowland wet grassland, willow scrub.
Key birds: *Summer:* Breeding Avocet, Marsh Harrier, Bittern, Bearded Tit, passage waders (exceptional list inc many rarities). *Winter:* Hen Harrier, Merlin, Peregrine, wildfowl.
Other notable flora and fauna: Good place to see water vole. Small number of dragonflies and damselflies including black-tailed skimmer, four-spotted chaser, large red damselfly. Marsh sow thistle easily seen from footpaths in summer.
Contact: Visitor Development Officer, Blacktoft Sands RSPB reserve, Hillcrest, Whitgift, Nr Goole DN14 8HL. 01405 704 665; e-mail: blacktoft.sands@rspb.org.uk

3. FLAMBOROUGH CLIFFS

Yorkshire Wildlife Trust
Location: TA 240 722. The reserve is part of the Flamborough headland, approx 4 miles NE of Bridlington. From Bridlington take B1255 to Flamborough and follow the signs for the North Landing.
Access: Open all year. Public pay and display car park at North Landing gives access to both parts of the reserve. Paths not suitable for wheelchairs.
Facilities: Car park (pay and display), trails, refreshments available at café at North Landing (open Apr-Oct 10am-5pm), toilets.
Public transport: Flamborough is served by buses

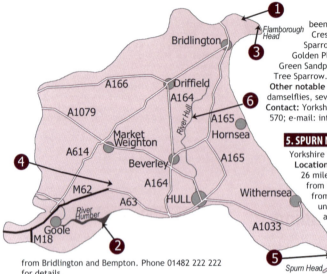

been recorded including Great Crested Grebe, Gadwall, Pochard, Sparrowhawk, Avocet, Ringed Plover, Golden Plover, Dunlin, Ruff, Redshank, Green Sandpiper, Common Sandpiper and Tree Sparrow.

Other notable flora and fauna: Dragon and damselflies, several butterfly species.

Contact: Yorkshire Wildlife Trust, 01904 659 570; e-mail: info@ywt.org.uk

5. SPURN NNR

Yorkshire Wildlife Trust.

Location: Entrance Gate TA 417 151. 26 miles from Hull. Take A1033 from Hull to Patrington then B1445 from Patrington to Easington and unclassified roads on to Kilnsea and Spurn Point.

Access: Normally open at all times. Vehicle admission fee (at present £3). No charge for pedestrians. No dogs allowed under any circumstances, not even in cars. Coaches by permit only (must be in advance).

Facilities: Reserve open all year, Blue Bell café open daily. Four hides. Public toilets in Blue Bell car park.

Public transport: Nearest bus service is at Easington (3.5 miles away). 2011 Sunday service to the Point, hail and ride, Easter to last weekend of October.

Habitat: Sand dunes with marram and sea buckthorn scrub. Mudflats around Humber Estuary.

Key birds: *Spring:* Many migrants on passage and often rare birds such as Red-backed Shrike, Bluethroat etc. *Autumn:* Passage migrants and rarities such as Wryneck, Pallas's Warbler. *Winter:* Waders and Brent Goose.

Other notable flora and fauna: Unique habitats and geographical position makes Spurn a very interesting site in Yorkshire for butterflies (25 species recorded) and moths.

Contact: Outer Humber Officer, Spurn NNR, Blue Bell, Kilnsea, Hull HU12 0UB; e-mail: info@ywt.org.uk

6. TOPHILL LOW NATURE RESERVE

Yorkshire Water.

Location: TA 071 482. Signposted from village of Watton on A164.

Access: Open daily (9am-6pm). Charges: £2.80 per person. £1.20 concessions. No dogs. Provision for disabled visitors (paths, ramps, hides, toilet etc). Coaches welcome.

Facilities: Visitor Centre with toilets open every weekend/ most week days. Disabled toilet open at all times. 12 hides (five with wheelchair access), paths and sightings board.

Public transport: None.

Habitat: Open water (two reservoirs), marshes, wader scrapes, woodland and thorn scrub.

Key birds: 160 species annually. *Winter:* SSSI for

---

from Bridlington and Bempton. Phone 01482 222 222 for details.

Habitat: Coastal cliffs, species-rich rough grassland and scrub, farmland. Spectacular views of this chalk coastline and living seas beyond.

Key birds: *Summer:* Puffin, Guillemot, Razorbill, Kittiwake, Shag, Fulmar, Skylark, Meadow Pipit, Linnet, Whitethroat, Yellowhammer, Tree Sparrow, occasional Corn Bunting. *Passage migrants:* Fieldfare, Redwing and occasional rarities such as Wryneck and Red-backed Shrike.

Other notable flora and fauna: Pyramidal and northern marsh orchids, harebell, thrift on cliff tops. Migrant butterflies such as painted ladies.

Contact: Yorkshire Wildlife Trust, 01904 659 570; e-mail: info@ywt.org.uk www.ywt.org.uk

4. NORTH CAVE WETLANDS

Yorkshire Wildlife Trust.

Location: SE 887 328. At NW of North Cave village, approx 10 miles W of Hull. From junction 28 of M62, follow signs to North Cave on B1230. In village, turn L and follow road to next crossroads where you go L, then take next L onto Dryham Lane.

Access: Open all year with car parking on Dryham Lane. Some of the footpaths are suitable for all abilities.

Facilities: Five bird-viewing hides and screen including unique straw bale constructions, four are accessible to wheelchair users. Portaloo available on site and Wild Bird Café open seven days a week for refreshments on Dryham Lane, adjacent to reserve.

Public transport: Buses serve North Cave from Hull and Goole: telephone 01482 222 222 for details.

Habitat: Former gravel pits have been converted into various lagoons for wetland birds, including one reedbed. There are also, scrub and hedgerows, and since 2010 a large area of wet grassland.

Key birds: More than 200 different species have

wildfowl, plus one of the UK's largest Black-head and Common Gull roosts. Regular wintering Bittern and Smew. Active feeding station with Brambling and Woodcock. *Spring/early summer*: Hirundines, Black Tern and Black-necked Grebe. Breeding Little Ringed Plover, Common Tern, Kingfisher and Barn Owl with variety of warblers. *Late summer/autumn*: Up to 20 species of passage wader.

Other notable flora and fauna: 400+ Sp. flora, 365+ Sp. fungi 16 Sp.odonata inc. hairy hawker. Grass snake, otter, water vole and roe deer.
Contact: Richard Hampshire, Tophill Low Nature Reserve, Hutton Cranswick, Driffield, East Yorkshire YO25 9RH. 01377 270 690. e-mail:richard.hampshire@yorkshirewater.co.uk, www.tophilllow.blogspot.com

Yorkshire, North

SEAWATCHING in autumn from Filey Brigg can produce a range of skuas and shearwaters, with divers and grebes becoming more noticeable as the season progresses. The North York Moors hold breeding waders, chats, raptors and Red Grouse. There are several areas to explore in the Lower Derwent Valley, with first class birding throughout the year.

1. COATHAM MARSH

Tees Valley Wildlife Trust.
Location: NZ 585 250. Located on W edge of Redcar. Access from minor road to Warrenby from A1085/A1042.
Access: Reserve is open throughout daylight hours. Please keep to permissive footpaths only.
Facilities: Good footpaths around site. Facilities available in Redcar close by.
Public transport: Very frequent bus service between Middlesbrough and Redcar. Nearest stops are in Coatham 0.25 mile from reserve (Arriva tel 0871 200 2233). Redcar Central Station one mile from site. Frequent trains from Middlesbrough and Darlington.
Habitat: Freshwater wetlands, lakes, reedbeds.
Key birds: *Spring/autumn*: Wader passage (including Wood Sandpiper and Greenshank). *Summer*: Passerines (including Sedge Warbler, Yellow Wagtail). *Winter*: Ducks (including Smew). *Occasional rarities*: Water Rail, Great White Egret, Avocet, Bearded Tit and Bittern.
Other notable flora and fauna: The lime-rich soil allows wildflowers to grow around the site, including northern marsh orchid. Also good for insects including migrant hawker dragonfly.
Contact: Steve Ashton, Tees Valley Wildlife Trust, 01287 636 382; e-mail: info@teeswildlife.org www.teeswildlife.org

2. FILEY BRIGG ORNITHOLOGICAL GROUP BIRD OBSERVATORY

FBOG and Yorkshire Wildlife Trust (The Dams).
Location: TA 10 68 07. Two access roads into Filey from A165 (Scarborough to Bridlington road). Filey is ten miles N of Bridlington and eight miles S of Scarborough.
Access: Opening times - no restrictions. Dogs only in Parish Wood and The Old Tip (on lead). Coaches welcome. Park in the North Cliff Country Park.
Facilities: No provisions for disabled at present. Two

hides at The Dams, one on The Brigg (open most weekends from late Jul-Oct, key can be hired from Country Park café). Toilets in Country Park (Apr-Nov 1) and town centre. Nature trails at The Dams, Parish Wood/Old Tip. Cliff top walk for seabirds along Cleveland Way.
Public transport: All areas within a mile of Filey railway station. Trains into Filey tel. 08457 484 950; buses into Filey tel 01723 503 020
Habitat: The Dams — two freshwater lakes, fringed with some tree cover and small reedbeds. Parish Wood — a newly planted wood which leads to the Old Tip, the latter has been fenced (for stock and crop strips) though there is a public trail. Carr Naze has a pond and can produce newly arrived migrants.
Key birds: *The Dams*: Breeding and wintering water birds, breeding Sedge Warbler, Reed Warbler and Tree Sparrow. *The Tip*: Important for breeding Skylark, Meadow Pipit, common warblers and Grey Partridge. *Winter*: Buntings, including Lapland. *Seawatch Hide*: (Jul-Oct). All four skuas, shearwaters, terns. *Winter*: Divers and grebes. *Totem Pole Field*: A new project should encourage breeding species and wintering larks, buntings etc. Many sub-rare/rare migrants possible at all sites.
Contact: e-mail: secretary@fbog.co.uk www.fbog.co.uk

3. FYLINGDALES MOOR CONSERVATION AREA

Hawk and Owl Trust /Strickland Estate/Fylingdales Moor ESS Co Ltd.
Location: NZ 947 003. Off A171 S of Whitby. On eastern side of North York Moors National Park, stretching between Sneaton High Moor (Newton House Plantation) and the coast at Ravenscar. Crossed by A171 Scarborough to Whitby road.
Access: Open access. Parking (inc for coaches) available at Jugger Howe layby (OS NZ 947 003) on A171 Scarborough to Whitby road.
Facilities: Numerous footpaths including the Jugger Howe Nature Trail, Lyke Wake Walk and Robin Hood's Bay Road.
Public transport: Half-hourly bus service (No. 93 and X93) between Scarborough and Whitby, nearest stop at Flask Inn (approx. 1 mile N of Jugger Howe layby). Services run by Arriva (0191 281 1313) www.arrivabus.co.uk
Habitat: About 6,800 acres (2,750 hectares) of heather moorland (former grouse moor), with scattered trees and wooded valleys and gulleys. Managed exclusively for wildlife and archaeological remains, the moor is an SSSI and SPA (Merlin and

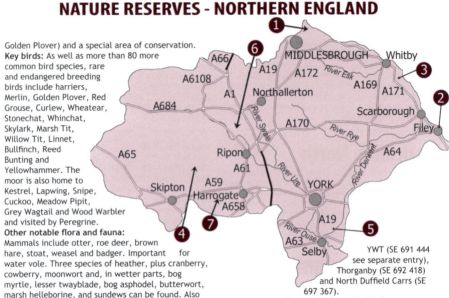

Golden Plover) and a special area of conservation.
Key birds: As well as more than 80 more common bird species, rare and endangered breeding birds include harriers, Merlin, Golden Plover, Red Grouse, Curlew, Wheatear, Stonechat, Whinchat, Skylark, Marsh Tit, Willow Tit, Linnet, Bullfinch, Reed Bunting and Yellowhammer. The moor is also home to Kestrel, Lapwing, Snipe, Cuckoo, Meadow Pipit, Grey Wagtail and Wood Warbler and visited by Peregrine.
Other notable flora and fauna: Mammals include otter, roe deer, brown hare, stoat, weasel and badger. Important for water vole. Three species of heather, plus cranberry, cowberry, moonwort and, in wetter parts, bog myrtle, lesser twayblade, bog asphodel, butterwort, marsh helleborine, and sundews can be found. Also rare orchids and sedges. Insect species include large heath and small pearl-bordered fritillary butterflies and emperor moth.
Contact: Professor John Edwards, The Hawk and Owl Trust., 01751 417 398. www.hawkandowl.org
e-mail: john.edwards@wildfylingdales.co.uk

4. GOUTHWAITE RESERVOIR

Yorkshire Water.
Location: SE 12 69. 2.5miles NW of Pately Bridge on the B6265 on the Lofthouse road.
Access: Open all hours, all year.
Facilities: Three viewing areas on edge of reservoir.
Public transport: Nidderdale Rambler route 24/25 (summer Sundays and bank holidays). Harrogate and District Travel 01423 566 061.
Habitat: Reservoir, deciduous woodland shoreline, moors, pasture.
Key birds: Green Woodpecker, Nuthatch, Merlin and Buzzard all year. Summer warblers with passage Osprey. *Winter:* Goosander, Goldeneye and Whooper Swan. Waders including Oystercatcher, Curlew, Redshank, Lapwing and waterfowl.
Contact: Geoff Lomas, Catchment & Recreation Officer, Yorkshire Water, Western House, Halifax Road, Bradford BD6 2LZ.
e-mail:Geoff.D.Lomas@yorkshirewater.co.uk
www.yorkshirewater.co.uk (turn to recreation page).

5. LOWER DERWENT VALLEY

Natural England (Yorkshire and Humber Region), Yorkshire Wildlife Trust and Countryside Trust.
Location: Six miles SE of York, stretching 12 miles S along the River Derwent from Newton-on-Derwent to Wressle and along the Pocklington Canal. Visitor facilities at Bank Island (SE 691 448), Wheldrake Ings

YWT (SE 691 444 see separate entry), Thorganby (SE 692 418) and North Duffield Carrs (SE 697 367).
Access: Open all year. No dogs. Disabled access at North Duffield Carrs.
Facilities: Bank Island — two hides, viewing tower. Wheldrake Ings — four hides. Thorganby — viewing platform. North Duffield Carrs — two hides and wheelchair access. Car parks at all sites, height restriction of 2.1m at Bank Island and North Duffield Carrs. Bicycle stands in car parks at Bank Island and North Duffield Carrs.
Public transport: Bus from York/Selby — contact First (01904 622 992).
Habitat: Hay meadow and pasture, swamp, open water and alder/willow woodland.
Key birds: *Spring/summer:* Breeding wildfowl and waders, incl. Garganey, Snipe and Ruff. Barn Owl and warblers. *Winter/spring:* 20,000-plus waterfowl including Whooper Swan, wild geese, Teal and Wigeon. Large gull roost, incl. white-winged gulls. Also passage waders, incl. Whimbrel.
Other notable flora and fauna: A walk alongside the Pocklington Canal is particularly good for a wide range of aquatic plants and animals.
Contact: Senior Reserve Manager, Natural England Yorkshire and Humber Region, 01904 435 500.
email: york@naturalengland.org.uk
www.naturalengland.org.uk Pocklington Canal: www.pocklington.gov.uk/pcas

6. NOSTERFIELD LOCAL NATURE RESERVE

Lower Ure Conservation Trust
Location: SE 278 795 Six miles N of Ripon, between West Tanfield and Nosterfield, via A6108 (Ripon to Masham road) and approx 4 miles W of A1.
Access: Open all year, two hides, one roofed viewing screen. Main car park, a lower 'viewing area' beyond car park permits viewing from cars only. Please keep to permissive footpath at all times. Dogs permitted,

NATURE RESERVES – NORTHERN ENGLAND

on short lead, only on part of permissive footpath network.
Facilities: Permissive footpath from Main Hide to Tanfield Hide (500 m) is disabled-friendly. Terrain is more uneven from car park to Northern Viewing Screen (1000 m). Two disabled-friendly hides, interpretation panels (Main Hide), comfortable "woolly" seats, lowered windows for wheelchair users. No other on-site facilities.
Habitat: Wetland grassland and open water. Also Magnesian limestone grassland, gravel banks, hedgerows and scrub.
Key species: Annually 150 species recorded – more than 225 species recorded overall (including rarities). Spring/autumn: Wader passage between 25 to 30 species recorded annually, also terns. Summer: Breeding species include Redshank, Lapwing, Avocet, Oystercatcher, Curlew, Ringed Plover, Shoveler, Gadwall, Barn Owl, Skylark, Lesser Whitethroat, Tree Sparrow, Linnet, Reed Bunting. Autumn: Passage waders including regular Pectoral Sandpiper. Winter: Wildfowl (Wigeon, Teal, Greylag and rarer geese), waders (Golden Plover, Lapwing, Curlew) and Peregrine.
Other notable flora and fauna: Specialist grassland and wetland flora, including seven species of orchid, mudwort, yellow rattle, golden dock. Butterflies include white-letter hairstreak, brown argus, wall and large colony of common blue. Dragonflies include emperor, black-tailed skimmer, red-veined darter

(has bred). At least 450 species of moths have now been recorded. Also, brown hare and water shrew.
Contact: email:luct@luct.org.uk www.luct.org.uk

7. TIMBLE INGS

Yorkshire Water
Location: SE 15 53. West of Harrogate, north of Otley. Off the A59 south of Blubberhouses, near Timble village.
Access: Open at all times, all year.
Facilities: Toilets, cafes, pubs, coach parking all nearby. Hard forest tracks.
Public transport: None.
Habitat: Woodland and nearby reservoir.
Key birds: Bradford OG species list stands at 134. Habitat management work by Yorkshire Water makes site attractive to Long-eared and Tawny Owls, Nightjars and Tree Pipits. Buzzards now nest and Red Kites seen regularly. Goshawk numbers in decline. *Summer:* Breeding species inc Redpoll, Siskin, Crossbill, Woodcock, Redstart and Grasshopper Warbler. Short-eared Owls hunt adjacent moorland. *Winter:* Fieldfare, Redwing, Brambling, occasional Waxwings and Hawfinches.
Other notable flora and fauna: Roe deer, badger, brown hare, shrew, vole and mouse species (all detected from owl pellets). Ponds attractive to amphibians and dragonflies, inc broad-bodied chaser, emperor and black darter.
Contact: As Gouthwaite Reservoir above.

Yorkshire South & West

RSPB FAIRBURN INGS, right next to the A1 makes for a much better coffee stop than some overpriced service station, with its mix of woodland and wetland species. Breeding birds at Potteric Carr include Kingfisher, Water Rail and all three woodpeckers. Peregrines hunt at Old Moor RSPB in winter, attracted by huge numbers of ducks, Lapwings and Golden Plovers.

1. BOLTON INGS (DEARNE VALLEY)

RSPB (Northern England)
Location: SE 425 020. Park at RSPB Old Moor and walk east along Trans-Pennine Trail to Bolton Ings. By car, Old Moor is just off Manvers Way (A633). From the M1, take junction 36 then follow the A6195. From the A1M, take junction 37 then follow the A635 towards the A6195.
Access: Open all year round. Dearne Way footpath and Trans-Pennine Trail open at all times, but not suitable for wheelchair users.
Facilities: Cormorant View hide. More facilities at RSPB Old Moor.
Public transport: Wombwell and Swinton train stations approximatley 3 miles from reserve. Buses run to Old Moor reserve from Barnsley, Doncaster

and Meadowhall – call Traveline on 01709 515 151 for details. Trans-Pennine Trail runs along southern edge of reserve.
Habitat: 43 hectares of reedbed and scrub. Excellent warbler habitat.
Key birds: *All year:* Kingfisher, Grey Heron. *Winter:* Stonechat. *Spring/summer:* Reed Bunting. breeding waders and warblers, Cuckoo, Garganey. *Autumn:* Passage waders including Greenshank, Green Sandpiper, Golden Plover. *Winter:* Wildfowl, including Goosander, Wigeon and Teal.
Other notable flora and fauna: Dragonflies inc. banded demoiselle, brown hare.
Contact: RSPB Old Moor, Old Moor Lane, Wombwell, Barnsley, South Yorkshire, S73 0YF. 01226 751 593 e-mail: old.moor@rspb.org.uk - www.rspb.org.uk

2. DENABY INGS NATURE RESERVE

Yorkshire Wildlife Trust.
Location: Reserve on Pastures Rd, off A6023 near Mexborough. Junction signed Denaby Ings Nature Reserve. Proceed along Pastures Road for 0.5 miles and watch for a sign on R marking entrance to car park. From car park, climb flight of concrete steps to enter reserve.
Access: Open all year.
Facilities: Car park, 2 hides, interpretation panels, circular trail.

179

Public transport: None.
Habitat: Water, deciduous woodland, marsh, willows.
Key birds: *Spring/summer:* Waterfowl, Barn Owl, Tawny Owl, Sand Martin, Swallow, Whinchat, Grasshopper Warbler, Lesser Whitethroat, Whitethroat, other warblers, Kingfisher. *Passage:* Waders, Common, Arctic and Black Terns, Redstart, Wheatear. *Winter:* Whooper Swan, wildfowl, Jack Snipe and other waders, Grey Wagtail, Fieldfare, Redwing, Brambling, Siskin. *All year:* Corn Bunting, Yellowhammer, all three woodpeckers, common woodland birds, possible Willow Tit.
Contact: Yorkshire Wildlife Trust, 01904 659 570. e-mail:info@ywt.org.uk - www.ywt.org.

3. FAIRBURN INGS

RSPB (Northern England).
Location: SE 452 277. 12 miles from Leeds, six miles from Pontefract, three miles from Castleford, situated next to A1246 from J42 of A1.
Access: Reserve and hides open every day except Dec 25/26. Centre and shop open each day (9am-5pm). Dogs on leads welcome. Boardwalks leading to Pickup Pool, feeding station and Kingfisher viewpoint are all wheelchair-friendly.
Facilities: Five hides open at all times. Toilets open 9am-5pm. Disabled toilets and baby-changing facilities. Hot and cold drinks, snacks available. Wildlife garden, pond-dipping and mini beast areas, plus duck feeding platform. Coach parking for club visits.
Public transport: Nearest train stations are Castleford, Micklefield and Garforth. No bus service.
Habitat: Open water, wet grassland, marsh and fen scrub, reedbed, reclaimed colliery spoil heaps.
Key birds: *All year:* Tree Sparrow, Willow Tit, Green Woodpecker, Bullfinch. *Winter:* Smew, Goldeneye, Goosander, Wigeon, Peregrine. *Spring:* Osprey, Little Gull, Wheatear, five species of tern inc annual Black Tern. *Summer:* Nine species of breeding warbler, Grey Heron, Gadwall, Little Ringed Plover.
Other notable flora and fauna: Brown hare, harvest mouse, roe deer, Leisler's and Daubenton's bats, 28 species of butterfly and 20 species of dragonfly.
Contact: Laura Bentley, Visitor Services Manager, Fairburn Ings Visitor Centre, 01977 628 191.

4. HARDCASTLE CRAGS

National Trust.
Location: From Halifax, follow A646 W for five miles to Hebden Bridge and pick up National Trust signs in town centre to the A6033 Keighley Road. Follow this for 0.75 miles. Turn L at the National Trust sign to the car parks. Alternate pay-and-display car park at Clough Hole on Widdop Road, Heptonstall.
Access: Open all year. NT car park charges: £3.50 all day weekdays and for up to 3 hours at weekends, £5 at weekends and bank holidays. No charge for NT members and disabled badge holders.
Facilities: 2 small pay car parks, cycle racks and several way-marked trails. Gibson Mill visitor centre (not NT property) has toilets, café, exhibitions.

Not connected to any mains services, in extreme conditions the mill may be closed for health and safety reasons.
Public transport: Good public transport links. Trains to Hebden Bridge from Manchester or Leeds every 30 minutes. Call 08457 484 950. Weekday buses every 30 minutes to Keighley Road, then 1 mile walk to Midghole. Summer weekend bus 906 Widdop-Hardcastle Crags leaves Hebden Bridge rail station every 90 minutes 9.20am-6.05pm. Tel: 0113 245 7676.
Habitat: 400 acres of unspoilt wooded valleys, ravines, streams, hay meadows and moorland edge.
Key birds: *Spring/summer:* Cuckoo, Redstart, Lesser Whitethroat, Garden Warbler, Blackcap, Wood Warbler, Chiffchaff, Spotted Flycatcher, Pied Flycatcher, Curlew, Lapwing, Meadow Pipit. *All year:* Sparrowhawk, Kestrel, Green and Greater Spotted Woodpeckers, Lesser Spotted Woodpecker, Tawny Owl, Barn Owl, Little Owl, Jay, Coal Tit, Dipper, Grey Wagtail and other woodland species. Goshawk in Crimsworth Dean.
Other notable flora and fauna: Northern hairy wood ant, moss carder bee, tree bumble bee, killarney fern, brittle bladder fern.
Contact: National Trust, Hardcastle Crags, 01422 844 518. www.nationaltrust.org.uk

5. INGBIRCHWORTH RESERVOIR

Yorkshire Water.
Location: Leave the M1 at J37 and take the A628 to Manchester and Penistone. After five miles you reach a roundabout. Turn R onto the A629 Huddersfield road. After 2.5 miles you reach Ingbirchworth. At a sign for The Fountain Inn, turn L. Pass a pub. The road bears L to cross the dam, proceed straight forward onto the track leading to the car park.
Access: Open all year. One of the few reservoirs in the area with footpath access.
Facilities: Car park, picnic tables.
Public transport: None.
Habitat: Reservoir, small strip of deciduous woodland.
Key birds: *Spring/summer:* Whinchat, warblers, woodland birds, House Martin. *Spring/autumn passage:* Little Ringed Plover, Ringed Plover, Dotterel, other waders, Common Tern, Arctic Tern, Black Tern, Yellow Wagtail, Wheatear. *Winter:* Wildfowl, Golden Plover, waders, occasional rare gull such as Iceland or Glaucous, Grey Wagtail, Fieldfare, Redwing, Brambling, Redpoll.
Other notable flora: Woodland wildflowers, inc bluebells.
Contact: www.yorkshirewater.co.uk (turn to recreation page).
e-mail: Geoff.D.Lomas@yorkshirewater.co.uk

6. OLD MOOR (DEARNE VALLEY)

RSPB (Northern England).
Location: SE 422 022. By car, Old Moor is just off Manvers Way (A633). From the M1, take junction 36 then follow the A6195. From the A1M, take junction 37 then follow the A635 towards the A6195.

NATURE RESERVES - NORTHERN ENGLAND

Access: Open Visitor centre and cafe open daily, except Christmas Day and Boxing Day, (9.30am- 5pm) from Feb to end of Oct, (9.30am- 4pm) Nov to end of Jan. The reserve is open until 8 pm from April to October. RSPB Members free. Non-members (adults) £4, (family) £8, (children) £2, (concessions) £2.50.
Facilities: Visitor centre, café, shop, education and meeting rooms. Accessible toilets. Two trails with seven hides, all suitable for wheelchair users. Free electric scooters available on request.
Public transport: Wombwell and Swinton train stations approximately 3 miles from reserve. Buses run to Old Moor reserve from Barnsley, Doncaster and Meadowhall - Traveline (01709 515 151).
Habitat: Lakes and flood meadows, wader scrape and reedbeds.
Key birds: *All year:* Kingfisher, Little Owl. *Winter:* Large numbers of wildfowl, spectacular flocks of Lapwing and Golden Plover, Peregrine, Tree Sparrow in garden feeding area. *Summer:* Breeding waders, inc drumming Snipe, and wildfowl.
Other notable flora and fauna: Water vole, brown hare, pygmy shrew, wildflowers including orchids and adders tongue fern.
Contact: RSPB Old Moor, 01226 751 593; e-mail: old.moor@rspb.org.uk www.rspb.org.uk

7. POTTERIC CARR

Yorkshire Wildlife Trust.
Location: SE 589 007. From M18 junction 3 take A6182 (Doncaster) and at first roundabout take third exit (roadworks are in progress during 2012 so the roundabout may no longer be there — look for signposts to reserve in 2013); entrance and car park are on R after 50m.
Access: Open daily 9am-5pm. Obtain ticket on arrival, YWT members free; Single £3.00; family £6.50 (a family is up to two adults and up to three

children); concession £2.50; child £1.50. Groups of ten or more should book in advance.
Facilities: The reserve has around 8 km of paths (5 km accessible to wheelchairs, unassisted), 14 viewing hides (10 suitable for the disabled) and a Field Centre with café, open daily (10am-4pm) with hot and cold drinks, snacks and meals. Toilets at entrance reception, in Field Centre (during café opening times), and outside Field Centre.
Public transport: Nearest railway station is Doncaster. From Frenchgate Interchange, take bus number 72 or 75, and alight at B&Q on Woodfield Way. Cross White Rose Way, walk down Mallard Way. Cross car park to reserve entrance in Sedum House.
Habitat: Reed fen, subsidence ponds, artificial pools, grassland, woodland.
Key birds: 96 species have bred. Nesting waterfowl (inc. Shoveler, Gadwall, Pochard), Water Rail, Kingfisher, all three woodpeckers, Lesser Whitethroat, Reed and Sedge Warblers, Willow Tit. *Passage/winter:* Bittern, Marsh Harrier, Black Tern, waders, wildfowl.
Other notable flora and fauna: 20 species of dragonfly recorded, 28 species of butterfly including purple hairstreak and dingy skipper. Palmate and great crested newt.
Contact: Potteric Carr Nature Reserve, 01302 570 077. e-mail: potteric.carr@ywt.org.uk www.potteric-carr.org.uk

8. SPROTBOROUGH FLASH RESERVE AND THE DON GORGE

Yorkshire Wildlife Trust.
Location: Leave A1(M) at junction 36 onto A630 towards Rotherham. After 0.8km, turn R at traffic lights to Sprotborough. After approx 1.6km the road drops down into Don Gorge. Cross a bridge over river, then another over a canal, turn immediately L. Public car park on left.
Access: Open all year.
Facilities: Three hides, footpaths, interpretation panels.
Public transport: River bus from Doncaster in summer months. Bus service from Doncaster to Sprotbrough village (10 minute walk to reserve).
Habitat: River, reed, gorge, woodland, limestone grassland
Key birds: *Summer:* Hirundines, Lesser Whitethroat, Whitethroat, Garden Warbler, Blackcap, Chiffchaff, Willow Warbler, Cuckoo. *Spring/autumn passage:* Little Ringed Plover, Dunlin, Greenshank, Green Sandpiper, waders, Yellow Wagtail. *Winter/all year:* Wildfowl, Water Rail, Snipe, Little Owl, Tawny Owl, all three woodpeckers, thrushes, Siskin, possible Corn Bunting.
Contact: Trust HQ . 01904 659 570. e-mail:info@ywt.org.uk www.ywt.org.uk

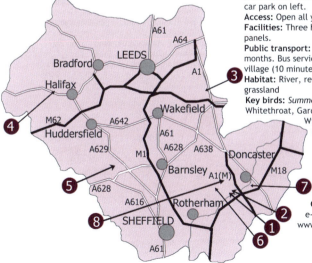

South East England

Berkshire, Buckinghamshire, Hampshire, Kent, London (Greater), Surrey, East Sussex, West Sussex

Berkshire

DESPITE its proximity to London, Berkshire offers a surprisingly wide range of habitats including heathland and downland. It is the gravel pits that attract the widest range of bird species though, including good numbers of wintering Smew. The areas around Heathrow Airport are good for Ring-necked Parakeets.

1. DINTON PASTURES

Wokingham District Council.
Location: SU 784 718. Country Park, E of Reading off B3030 between Hurst and Winnersh.
Access: Open all year, dawn to dusk. Car parking charges apply 8am to 6pm each day. Dogs allowed.
Facilities: Three hides (one adapted for wheelchairs), information centre, car park, café, toilets (suitable for wheelchairs). Electric buggies for hire. Various trails between one and three miles in length.
Habitat: Mature gravel pits and banks of River Loddon. Sandford Lake managed for wildfowl, Lavell's Lake best for waders and scrub species.
Key birds: *All year:* Kingfisher, Water Rail. *Spring/summer:* Hobby, Little Ringed Plover, Common Tern, Nightingale, common warblers. *Winter:* Bittern, wildfowl (inc. Goldeneye, Wigeon, Teal, Gadwall), thrushes. Waders include Green and Common Sandpipers, Snipe, Redshank.
Other notable flora and fauna: Water vole, harvest mouse, great crested newt, Loddon pondweed and Loddon lily. Dragonflies inc emperor, black-tailed skimmer, white-legged and banded agrion damselfies and migrant hawker.
Contact: Dinton Pastures Country Park, 0118 934 2 016; e-mail: countryside@wokingham.gov.uk www.wokingham.gov.uk/parks/parks/countryparks/dintonpastures/

2. HUNGERFORD MARSH

Berks, Bucks & Oxon Wildlife Trust.
Location: SU 333 687. On W side of Hungerford,

beside the Kennet and Avon Canal. From town centre, go along Church Street past the town hall. Turn R under the railway. Follow public footpath over swing bridge on the canal near the church. The reserve is separated from Freeman's Marsh by a line of willows and bushes.
Access: Open all year. Please keep to the footpath. Dogs on leads please.
Facilities: Car park.
Public transport: Hungerford railway station half mile from reserve.
Habitat: An idyllic waterside site with chalk stream, unimproved rough grazing and reedbed.
Key birds: 120 species recorded. *Spring/summer:* Reed and Grasshopper Warblers. *Winter:* Siskin and Water Rail. *All year:* Kingfisher, Mute Swan, Mallard, Little Grebe.
Other notable flora and fauna: Water vole, otter and grass snake.
Contact: Berks, Bucks & Oxon Wildlife Trust, 01865 775 476; e-mail:wendytobbitt@bbowt.org.uk www.bbowt.org.ukreserves/Hungerford-Marsh

3. LAVELL'S LAKE

Wokingham District Council.
Location: SU 785 727. Via Sandford Lane off B3030 between Hurst and Winnersh E of Reading.
Access: Dawn to dusk. No permit required. Dogs on leads all year.
Facilities: Car park, two public hides, one with disabled access, one members-only hide (see below), viewing screen.
Public transport: Thames Travel bus services 128/129 run between Reading and Wokingham, stopping outside Dinton Pastures main entrance. Nearest train services are at either Winnersh, or Winnersh Triangle.
Habitat: Gravel pits, two wader scrapes, reed beds, rough grassland, marshy area, sand martin banks, between River Loddon & Emm Brook. To N of Lavell's Lake gravel pits are being restored to attract birds. The lake at Lea Farm is viewable walking N along the River Loddon from Lavell's Lake over small green

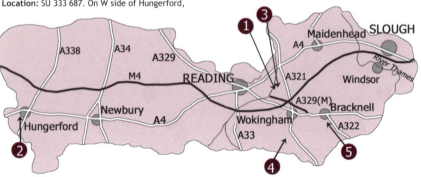

bridge. It is on R and can be seen through a viewing screen and a members-only hide for Friends of Lavell's Lake (see www.foll.org.uk). No access.
Key birds: *All year*: Great Crested Grebe, Gadwall, Sparrowhawk, Kingfisher, Red Kite, Buzzard, Cetti's Warbler. *Summer*: Common Tern, Redshank, Lapwing, Hobby, warblers include Reed, Sedge, Whitethroat. *Passage*: Garganey, Little-ringed Plover, Common and Green Sandpiper and Greenshank. *Winter*: Water Rail, Bittern, Little Egret, Teal, Shoveler, Pochard, Goldeneye, occasional Smew and Goosander, along River Loddon - Siskin, Lesser Redpoll, Fieldfare and Redwing.
Contact: As for Dinton Pastures, 0118 934 2 016.

4. MOOR GREEN LAKES

Blackwater Valley Countryside Partnership.
Location: SU 805 628. Main access and parking off Lower Sandhurst Road, Finchampstead (RG40 3TH). Alternatively, Rambler's car park, Chandlers Lane, Yateley near junction with Mill Lane (SU 820 619).
Access: Car parks open dawn-dusk. Dogs on leads. Site can be used by wheelchairs, though surface not particularly suitable.
Facilities: Two bird hides open to members of Moor Green Lakes Group (contact BVCP for details), two viewing screens. Feeder station viewable from bench on adjacent path. Footpaths along western, southern and eastern perimeter of site: Blackwater Valley long distance footpath passes alongside site.
Public transport: Nearest railway station, South West Trains Crowthorne.
Habitat: Thirty-six hectares (90 acres) in total. Three lakes with gravel islands, beaches and scrapes. River Blackwater, grassland, surrounded by willow, ash, hazel and thorn hedgerows.
Key birds: *Spring/summer*: Redshank, Little Ringed

Plover, Willow Warbler. Also Whitethroat, Sedge Warbler, Common Sandpiper, Common Tern. Lapwings and Barn Owl breed on site. Dunlin and Green Sandpiper on passage. *Winter*: Wigeon, Teal, Gadwall and of particular interest, a flock of Goosander.
Other notable flora and fauna: 27 species of butterfly and 15 species of dragonfly have been recorded. See www.mglg.org.uk for more details.
Contact: Blackwater Valley Countryside Partnership, 01252 331 353; www.blackwater-valley.org.uk e-mail: blackwater.valley@hants.gov.uk

5. WILDMOOR HEATH

Berks, Bucks & Oxon Wildlife Trust.
Location: SU 842 627. Between Bracknell and Sandhurst. From Sandhurst shopping area, take the A321 NW towards Wokingham. Turn E at the mini-roundabout on to Crowthorne Road. Continue for about one mile through one set of traffic lights. Car park is on the R at the bottom of the hill.
Access: Open all year. No access to woodland N of Rackstraw Road at Broadmoor Bottom. Please keep dogs on a lead.
Facilities: Car park.
Public Transport: The reserve is one mile north of Sandhurst railway station.
Habitat: Wet and dry lowland heath, bog, mixed woodland and mature Scots pine plantation.
Key birds: *Spring/summer*: Wood Lark, Nightjar, Dartford Warbler and Stonechat.
Other notable flora and fauna: Dragonflies, slow worm, adder, grass snake, lizard. Bog plants inc sundews.
Contact: Trust HQ, 01865 775 476. e-mail:wendytobbitt@bbowt.org.uk www.bbowt.org.uk/reserves/Wildmoor-Heath

Buckinghamshire

BORDERED by the River Thames to the south and River Ouse to the north, Buckinghamshire offers a good selection of woods, lakes and gravel pits. The high ground of the Chiltern escarpment is an excellent place to watch Red Kites. There is a good breeding population of Firecrests in the county.

1. BURNHAM BEECHES NNR

City of London.
Location: SU 950 850. N of Slough and on W side of A355, running between J2 of the M40 and J6 of M4. Entry from A355 via Beeches Road. Also smaller parking areas in Hawthorn Lane and Pumpkin Hill to the S and Park Lane to the W.
Access: Open all year, except Dec 25. Main Lord Mayor's Drive open from 8am-dusk. Beeches Café, public toilets and information point open 10am to 5pm. Motorised buggy available for hire. Network of wheelchair accessible roads and paths.
Facilities: Car parks, toilets, café, visitor information

centre. Easy access path network, suitable for wheelchairs, most start at Victory Cross. Coach parking possible, additional coach parking on request.
Public transport: Train - nearest station is Slough on main line from Paddington. Arriva, First and Jason Tours bus numbers 74 and 40, tel 0871 200 22 33 (Traveline).
Habitat: Ancient woodland, streams, pools, heathland, grassland, scrub.
Key birds: *Spring/summer*: Cuckoo, possible Turtle Dove. *Winter*: Siskin, Crossbill, regular large flocks c100 Brambling. Possible Woodcock. *All year*: Mandarin (good population), all three woodpeckers, Sparrowhawk, Marsh Tit, possible Willow Tit, Red Kite and Buzzard.
Other notable flora and fauna: Ancient beech and oak pollards with associated wildlife. Rich array of fungi.
Contact: City of London Corporation, Burnham Beeches Office, Hawthorn Lane, Farnham Common, SL2 3TE. 01753 647 358. e-mail: burnham.beeches@cityoflondon.gov.uk www.cityoflondon.gov.uk

2. CALVERT JUBILEE

Berks, Bucks & Oxon Wildlife Trust.
Location: SP 849 425. Near Steeple Claydon, NW of
Aylesbury, Bucks.
Access: Access by permit (free) only. Apply to Trust
which provides map and information with permit.
Please keep to network of paths.
Facilities: Two hides, small car park.
Public transport: None.
Habitat: Ex-clay pit, railway and landfill site. Now
with deep lake, marginal reedbed and scrub habitat.
Key birds: *Summer:* Nesting Common Tern on
rafts, Kingfisher, Hobby, warblers and occasional
Nightingale. *Passage migrants:* Include Black Tern and
flyover waders. *Winter:* Bittern, Water Rail and large
gull roost with occasional Glaucous and Iceland Gull.
Rarer birds turn up regularly.
Other notable flora and fauna: Rare butterflies,
including dingy and grizzled skippers and black
hairstreak.
Contact: Wildlife Trust HQ, 01865 775 476.
e-mail:wendytobbitt@bbowt.org.uk
www.bbowt.org.uk/reserves/Calvert-Jubilee

3. CHURCH WOOD RESERVE

RSPB (Midlands Regional Office).
Location: SU 971 872. Reserve lies three miles from
J2 of M40 in Hedgerley. Park in village, walk down
small track beside pond for approx 200m. Reserve
entrance is on L.
Access: Open all year. Not suitable for wheelchairs.
Facilities: Two marked paths with some inclines.
Public transport: None.
Habitat: Mixed woodland.
Key birds: *Spring/summer:* Red Kite, Buzzard,
Blackcap, Garden Warbler, Swallow. *Winter:* Redpoll,
Siskin. *All year:* Marsh Tit, Willow Tit, Nuthatch,
Treecreeper, Great Spotted and Green Woodpeckers.
Other notable flora and fauna: Wood anenome,
wood sorrel, bluebell and other woodland plants.
Brimstone, comma, white admiral and peacock
butterflies. Good range of fungi species.
Contact: RSPB central England Office, 01865 351 163.
www.rspb.org.uk/wildlife/reserves

4. COLLEGE LAKE

Berks, Bucks & Oxon Wildlife Trust.
Location: SU 934 140. 2 miles N of Tring on B488,
quarter mile N of canal bridge at Bulbourne turn L
into gated entrance. Marked with brown tourist signs.
Access: Open Apr-Oct (9.30am-5pm); Nov-Mar
(9.30am-4pm), seven days a week. Wheelchair access
to some hides and disabled toilets. Electric tramper
available for disabled visitors, please phone to book.
Facilities: Large car park, coach park, many hides,
interpretive buildings. Network of wheelchair-friendly
paths, visitor centre, toilets.
Public transport: Tring railway station, two miles
walk mostly on canal towpath.
Habitat: Deep lake in former chalk pit, shallow pools,

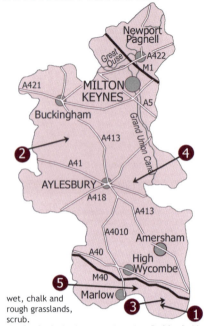

wet, chalk and
rough grasslands,
scrub.
Key birds: *Spring/summer:* Lapwing, Redshank, Little
Ringed Plover, Sand Martin, Hobby, Common Tern,
Skylark. *Winter:* Wildfowl (Wigeon, Shoveler, Teal,
Gadwall), waders, inc. Snipe, Peregrine Falcon. Rarer
birds turn up regularly.
Other notable flora and fauna: Chalk grassland
flowers. Arable weeds. Butterflies include small blue
and green hairstreak. Good numbers of dragonflies
(16 species). Brown hare.
Contact: The Warden, College Lake. 01442 826 7740
ext 208; (M)07711 821 303; www.bbowt.org.uk
e-mail:collegelake@bbowt.org.uk

5. LITTLE MARLOW GRAVEL PITS

Lefarge Redland Aggregates.
Location: SU 880 880. NE of Marlow from J4 of M40.
Use permissive path from Coldmoorholm Lane to
Little Marlow village. Follow path over a wooden
bridge to N end of lake. Permissive path ends just
past the cottages where it joins a concrete road to
sewage treatment works. Be careful at all times when
walking round the lake.
Access: Open all year. Do not enter the gravel works.
Facilities: Paths.
Habitat: Gravel pit, lake, scrub.
Key birds: *Spring:* Passage migrants, Sand Martin,
Garganey, Hobby. *Summer:* Reed warblers, Kingfisher,
wildfowl. *Autumn:* Passage migrants. *Winter:*
Wildfowl, possible Smew, Goldeneye, Yellow-legged
Gull, Lapwing, Snipe.
Contact: Ranger Service, Wycombe District Council,
01494 421 825.

Hampshire

DOMINATED by the New Forest, this huge county holds many scarce breeding birds including Honey Buzzard, Goshawk, Red Kite (north of the county), Firecrest, Hawfinch, Dartford Warbler and Nightjar, with Great Grey Shrikes regular in winter. Keyhaven and Farlington Marshes are the best sites for migrants. Blashford Lakes holds a good selection of waterbirds including wintering Bitterns.

1. BLASHFORD LAKES

Hampshire & Isle of Wight Wildlife Trust/Wessex Water/Bournemouth & West Hampshire Water/New Forest District Council.
Location: SU 151 079. From Ringwood take A338 for two miles towards Fordingbridge/Salisbury, pass Ivy Lane R and take next R to Moyles Court / Linwood at Ellingham Cross, into Ellingham Drove. The main car park for hides is first L (entrance shared with Hanson works) after 400 yards.
Access: Car park, hides and visitor centre (with toilets) open daily (9am-4.30pm) except Dec 25. Paths accessible outside these hours but without vehicle access.
Facilities: Parking, footpaths, six hides, viewing screens, toilets and information including recent sightings board, webcams. Coach parking by arrangement.
Public transport: Bus, the X3 Bournemouth-Salisbury service stops at Ellingham Cross 500yds W of the main reserve entrance.
Habitat: Flooded gravel pits, areas of wet woodland, also dry grassland and lichen heath.
Key birds: *Winter:* Large number of over-wintering wildfowl, inc. internationally important numbers of Gadwall. Also a large gull roost. *Spring/summer:* Breeding birds include Common Tern, Lapwing, Redshank, Oystercatcher, Kingfisher, Garden Warblers are especially common. *Autumn:* Waders on migration including Green and Common Sandpipers and Greenshank, also Hobby, Black Tern and passerines.
Other notable flora and fauna: Dragonflies (23 species recorded) including brown hawker, scarce chaser and large and small red-eyed damselfly. Roe deer, badgers, otters, foxes, reptiles include adders and grass snakes.
Contact: Blashford Lakes Centre, 01425 472 760 or 07917 616 695; e mail: feedback@hwt.org.uk

2. FARLINGTON MARSHES

Hants & Isle of Wight Wildlife Trust
Location: SU 685 045. North of Langstone Harbour. Main entrance off roundabout junction A2030/A27.
Access: Open at all times, no charge or permits, but donations welcome. Dogs welcome but must be on leads at all times. Wheelchair access via RADAR gates. Short slopes up to sea wall. Paths around site are mostly level but the main path running along the sea wall can be uneven in places and muddy in wet weather.

Facilities: 2.5 mile circular walk around sea wall. Information at entrance and shelter. No toilets.
Public transport: By bus: Several bus routes pass along the A2030 (Easter Road), close to the western entrance to the marsh. Contact First bus service on 023 8058 4321. By train: Hilsea station is one mile from reserve. Contact South West Trains on 0845 6000 650.
Habitat: Coastal grazing marsh with pools and reedbed within reserve. Views over intertidal mudflats/saltmarshes of Langstone Harbour.
Key birds: *Summer:* Breeding waders and wildfowl (including Lapwing, Redshank and Shelduck) also breeding Cetti's, Sedge and Reed Warbler, Bearded Tit. *Late summer:* Passage migrants (Yellow Wagtail, Whimbrel, etc) and returning waders, chance of rarities such as Spotted Crake, Curlew Sandpiper, stints. *Autumn/winter:* waders and wildfowl, good numbers of Teal, Wigeon, Pintail, Marsh Harrier, Short-eared Owl regular visitors. Notable numbers of Dark-bellied Brent Goose. Important high tide roost site best viewed over spring high tide.
Other notable flora and fauna: Corky fruited water dropwort, slender hares-ear, southern marsh and early marsh orchids. Water vole in ditches.
Contact: Jamie Marsh, Solent Reserves Officer. 01489 774 429. www.hwt.org.uk - go to 'Reserves' and then 'news' for sightings, etc

3. FLEET POND LNR

Hart District Council Service/Fleet Pond Society.
Location: SY 85. Located in Fleet, W of Farnborough. From the B3013, head to Fleet Station. and park in the long-stay car park. Parking also available in Chestnut Grove and Westover Road. Pond car park off B3013.
Access: Open all year.
Facilities: Some surfaced paths, boardwalks in wet areas.
Public transport: Fleet railway station lies N of site.
Habitat: Lake, marshes, reedbeds, heathland, wet and dry woodland.
Key birds: *Spring/autumn:* Migrant waders incl. Little Ringed Plover, Dunlin, Greenshank, Little Gull, Lesser Spotted Woodpecker, occasional Kittiwake, terns, Wood Lark, Skylark, occasional Ring Ouzel, Firecrest, Pied Flycatcher. *Summer:* Hobby, Common Tern, Tree Pipit, occasional Red Kite and Osprey. *Winter:* Bittern, wildfowl, occasional Smew, Snipe, occasional Jack Snipe, Siskin, Redpoll.
Other notable flora and fauna: Dragonflies and damselflies in wet areas of marshes and heathlands. Butterflies, roe deer. Plants include ling and bell heather, phragmites reeds.
Contact: Hart District Council, 01252 623 443; e-mail: countryside@hart.gov.uk

4. LOWER TEST

Hampshire & Isle of Wight Wildlife Trust.
Location: SU 364 150. Area bounded by M27, M271 and A35 west of Southampton.

NATURE RESERVES - SOUTH EAST ENGLAND

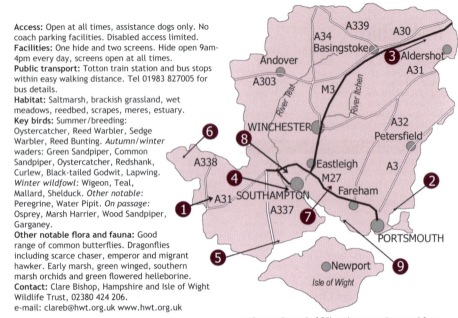

Access: Open at all times, assistance dogs only. No coach parking facilities. Disabled access limited.
Facilities: One hide and two screens. Hide open 9am-4pm every day, screens open at all times.
Public transport: Totton train station and bus stops within easy walking distance. Tel 01983 827005 for bus details.
Habitat: Saltmarsh, brackish grassland, wet meadows, reedbed, scrapes, meres, estuary.
Key birds: *Summer/breeding:* Oystercatcher, Reed Warbler, Sedge Warbler, Reed Bunting. *Autumn/winter* waders: Green Sandpiper, Common Sandpiper, Oystercatcher, Redshank, Curlew, Black-tailed Godwit, Lapwing. *Winter wildfowl:* Wigeon, Teal, Mallard, Shelduck. *Other notable:* Peregrine, Water Pipit. *On passage:* Osprey, Marsh Harrier, Wood Sandpiper, Garganey.
Other notable flora and fauna: Good range of common butterflies. Dragonflies including scarce chaser, emperor and migrant hawker. Early marsh, green winged, southern marsh orchids and green flowered helleborine.
Contact: Clare Bishop, Hampshire and Isle of Wight Wildlife Trust, 02380 424 206.
e-mail: clareb@hwt.org.uk www.hwt.org.uk

5. LYMINGTON REEDBEDS

Hampshire & Isle of Wight Wildlife Trust.
Location: SZ 324 965. From Lyndhurst in New Forest take A337 to Lymington. Turn L after railway bridge into Marsh Lane. Park in the lay-by next to allotments. The reserve entrance is on opposite side, to R of the house and over railway crossing. The footpath exits the reserve near the Old Ampress Works, leading to a minor road between the A337 and Boldre.
Access: Open all year. The best viewpoint over the reedbeds is from Bridge Road or from the Undershore leading from the B3054.
Facilities: None.
Public transport: Bus: at either end of the footpath through site, Marsh Lane and on the A337 (route 112). Five minutes walk from train station.
Habitat: One of largest reedbeds on S coast, fringed by alder and willow woodland.
Key birds: One of highest concentrations of Water Rail in the country; resident but most evident in winter. *Spring/summer:* Cetti's Warbler, Bearded Tit, Yellow Wagtail, Swallow, martins, Reed Warbler. *Passage:* Snipe, ducks.
Other notable fauna: Otters are in the area.
Contact: Trust HQ, 01489 774 400;
e-mail: jamiem@hwt.org.uk www.hwt.org.uk

6. MARTIN DOWN

Natural England (Wiltshire Team).
Location: SU 05 19. Fourteen miles SW of Salisbury, 1km W of Martin village. The N part of the site is crossed by the A354. A car park is on the A354 and

another at the end of Sillens Lane, a minor road from Martin village.
Access: Open access, organised groups of 10+ should book in advance. Car park height barrier of 7ft 6 ins. Coaches only by prior arrangement. Hard flat track from A354 car park suitable for wheelchairs.
Facilities: Two car parks, interpretative boards.
Public transport: One bus Salisbury/Blandford. Call 01722 336 855 or visit www.wdbus.co.uk
Habitat: Chalk downland and scub.
Key birds: *Spring/summer:* Grey Partridge, Turtle Dove, warblers, Nightingale. *Winter:* Occasional Merlin, Hen Harrier.
Other notable flora and fauna: Species-rich chalk downland with a variety of orchids.
Contact: South Wiltshire NNR Office, 01980 620 485, www.naturalengland.org.uk
e-mail: wiltshire@naturalengland.org.uk

7. SWANWICK LAKES NATURE RESERVE

Hampshire & Isle of Wight Wildlife Trust.
Location: SU 505 098. SE from Southampton. About 2 miles from Bursledon and 7 miles from Fareham. From M27 J8, follow signs to A3024 Southampton and Hamble and then Park Gate A27. At lights by 'The Spinnaker' pub turn L onto Swanwick Lane. Cross motorway then L onto Sopwith Way. Turn R at mini roundabout by security gates. From J9 follow signs for Southampton A27 up to Park Gate. Take road to Botley. At Elm Tree pub turn L onto Swanwick Lane. After about a mile, turn R onto Sopwith Way. Turn R at mini roundabout by security gates.
Access: Some surfaced paths for wheelchairs, plenty of benches.

Facilities: Network of surfaced and unsurfaced paths, 3 waymarked trails of varying lengths, frequent benches, fantastic viewpoints, reserve leaflet including a trail guide available.

Public transport: *By train:* About 30 mins walk from Swanwick. From station turn R at end of access road then continue to Elm Tree Pub. Turn L onto Swanwick Lane then continue as above. *By bus:* Several First Group buses stop on A27, at the bottom of Swanwick Lane. www.firstgroup.com/ukbus/hampshire/

Habitat: Mixed woodland, flower-rich meadows and deep lakes.

Key birds: Good range of birds including Little Grebe, Gadwall, Buzzard, Kingfisher, Great Spotted and Green Woodpecker, Nuthatch, Treecreeper, finches and tits.

Other notable flora and fauna: Common butterflies, with occasional silver-washed fritillary and purple emperor, common dragonflies and damselflies and other insects including mining bees. Great crested newts. Common spotted orchid. Rich variety of different fungi. Roe Deer.

Contact: Trust HQ, 01489 774 400 or Swanwick Lakes Education Officer, 01489 570 240;
e-mail: dawnp@hwt.org.uk www.hwt.org.uk

8. TESTWOOD LAKES

Southern Water
Hampshire & Isle of Wight Wildlife Trust
Location: SU 347 155. M271 West J2 towards Totton. L at first roundabout, then left onto A36. L at next roundabout onto Brunel Rd. Entrance on L after ¼ mile.

Access: Car parks open 8am until 4pm in winter and from 8am until 6pm in summer. Surfaced paths around lakes and to hides are relatively flat. Dogs under control allowed in some parts of the reserve but not the conservation and education areas.

Facilities: Two hides and two screens. Hides open

10am-4pm daily. Disabled toilet in Education Centre.
Public transport: Totton rail station is 1.5 miles from the reserve. Bluestar and Wilts & Dorset buses stop ¼ mile from entrance. Tel 01983 827 005.

Habitat: Flooded gravel pits, scrapes, wet and dry grasslands, woodland and hedgerows.

Key Birds: *Winter:* Various wildfowl (inc. Tufted Duck, Wigeon, Pochard, Teal, Gadwall, Goosander), Siskin, Hawfinch, Meadow Pipit, Common Sandpiper, Green Sandpiper, Pochard, Redwing, Fieldfare. *Spring:* Shelduck, Sand Martin, Little Ringed Plover, Willow Warbler. *Summer:* Swift, Swallow, Blackcap, Whitethroat. *Autumn:* Wheatear, Yellow Wagtail, Goldfinch.

Other notable flora and fauna: Good range of butterflies. Dragonflies including emperor, scarce chaser, southern and migrant hawker and golden ring.

Contact: Clare Bishop, Trust HQ, 02380 424 206. e-mail: clareb@hwt.org.uk www.hwt.org.uk

9. TITCHFIELD HAVEN

Hampshire County Council.
Location: SU 535 025. From A27 W of Fareham; public footpath follows derelict canal along W of reserve and road skirts S edge.

Access: Open Wed-Sun all year (9.30am- 5pm summer, 9.30am-4pm winter), plus Bank Hols, except Christmas and Boxing Days.

Facilities: Centre has information desk, toilets, tea room and shop. Eight hides.

Habitat: Shoreline, reedbeds, freshwater scrapes, wet grazing meadows.

Key birds: *Spring/summer:* Waders (inc. Avocet and Black-tailed Godwit), wildfowl, Common Tern, breeding Cetti's Warbler, Water Rail. *Autumn/winter:* Bittern, Bearded Tit, Brent Geese, Wigeon, Teal, Shoveler and Snipe.

Contact: Reserve Manager, Titchfield Haven, 01329 662 145; e-mail:countryside@hants.gov.uk

Kent

A FABULOUS county for birders. Being so close to France, the shingle spit at Dungeness offers excellent seawatching, an RSPB reserve and bird observatory. There is another observatory at Sandwich Bay, marshes all along the north coast and reedbeds at Stodmarsh. The Isle of Sheppey holds a wide selection and good numbers of birds of prey in winter.

1. BLEAN WOODS NNR

Location: TR 126 592 (postcode CT2 9DD). From Rough Common (off A290, one and a half miles NW of Canterbury).

Access: Open 8am-9pm for cars, open at all times for visitors on foot. No parking for coaches — please drop passengers off in Rough Common village. Green Trail suitable for wheelchair users.

Facilities: Public footpaths and five waymarked trails.

Public transport: No 27 from Canterbury hourly, stops at reserve entrance (ask for Lovell Road). No 4/4A every 20 minutes from Canterbury to Whitstable. Ask for Rough Common Road, 500m walk from site entrance. Local bus company Stagecoach 0870 243 3711.

Habitat: Mature oak woodland, plus birch, sweet chestnut, hazel and hornbeam coppice. Grazed and ungrazed heathland.

Key birds: Good for woodpeckers, warblers and Nightingale in spring, fairly quiet the rest of the year. *All year:* Woodpecker (3 species), Nuthatch, Treecreeper, tits (5 species). *Spring:* Nightingale, Blackcap, Garden Warbler, Hobby, Nightjar.

Other notable flora and fauna: Badger, dormouse. Heath fritillary, white admiral and silver-washed fritillary butterflies. Common spotted orchid.

Contact: Jason Mitchell, Warden, 07770 683 971. e-mail: blean.woods@rspb.org.uk

2. BOUGH BEECH RESERVOIR

Kent Wildlife Trust.
Location: TQ 496 494. Lying SW of Sevenoaks, Bough Beech is situated 3.5 miles S of Ide Hill, signposted off B2042.
Access: Apr-Oct Wed, Sat, Sun and Bank Hols, 10am-5pm. Nov-Mar, Sun, 10am-4pm. Dogs on leads at all times.
Facilities: Visitor centre, gift shop, picnic facilities, toilets (inc disabled). Paths are uneven and can be muddy.
Public transport: Rail service to Penshurst Station (two miles south)
Habitat: Reservoir and adjacent woodland and farmland.
Key birds: Approx 60 species of birds breed in and around the reserve annually, with Mallard, Tufted Duck, Mandarin, Canada Goose, Coot and Great Crested Grebe notable among the waterfowl. Little Ringed Plover nest most years. *Autumn:* Good for numbers of waders like Green and Common Sandpipers and Greenshank. Many rarities have been recorded. Ospreys recorded most years. Winter wildfowl numbers are much higher than summer and include Goldeneye and Goosander.
Other notable flora and fauna: Great crested newt, toad, dragonflies (black-tailed skimmer, ruddy darter, emperor, southern aeshna, migrant hawker, red-eyed damselfly), common lizard, Roesel's bush cricket, long-winged conehead, dormouse, water shrew, white admiral butterfly, glow-worm, bats (pipistrelle, Daubenton, noctule, brown long-eared).
Contact: Visitor Centre Manager Peter Bassett (01732 750 624), Reserve Manager Paul Glanfield (01732 456 407); e-mail: info@kentwildlife.org.uk
www.kentwildlifetrust.org.uk

3. CLIFFE POOLS

RSPB (South East Region Office).
Location: TQ 722 757. From coastbound A2, take A289 near Strood. From the A289 follow signs for Wainscott and Cliffe onto B2000. At T-junction turn L to Cliffe. At crossroads, turn L to Higham. Before you enter Cliffe, take 2nd L after Cliffe sign. Turn L at next T-junction and L again into Salt Road. Car park is on L just past a sharp R bend.
Access: Free admission at all times, but donations welcome. Group bookings welcome. Car park open daily from 8.30am-5pm, except Christmas Day. Monthly guided walks available. Dogs only on public footpaths.
Facilities: Six viewing points. Public rights of way encircle reserve and bisect it. Pushchair friendly.
Public transport: Nearest bus stop at Six Bells pub in Cliffe.
Habitat: A mix of saline lagoons, freshwater pools, grassland, saltmarsh and scrub.
Key birds: Massed flocks of waders in winter, plus a wide range of wildfowl. A great variety of passage birds in spring and autumn. Breeding species include Lapwing, Redshank, Avocet, Ringed Plover, Shelduck. Also look out for Nightingale, Hobby and Turtle Dove.
Other notable flora and fauna: Good range of insects (rare bees include shrill carder bee, brown-banded carder bee). Butterflies, inc. marbled white, common blue, Essex skipper and the migrant clouded yellow, grasshoppers and bush crickets, including Roesel's.
Contact: Reserve Manager 01634 222 480; e-mail:northkentmarshes@rspb.org.uk

4. DUNGENESS NATURE RESERVE

RSPB (South East Region Office).
Location: TR 062 197. One mile out of Lydd on the Dungeness Road, turn R for main site. Visitor centre and car park are one mile along entrance track. Entrance to Hanson ARC site and car park is opposite main reserve entrance on L of Dungeness Road.
Access: Open daily (9am-9pm) or sunset when earlier. Visitor centre open (10am-5pm, or 4pm Nov-Feb). Parties over 12 by prior arrangement. Closed Dec 25 & 26.
Facilities: Visitor centre, toilets (including disabled access), seven hides, viewing screen, two nature trails, wheelchair access to visitor centre and six hides. Fully equipped classroom/meeting room. Coach parking available.
Public transport: Limited service. Bus 11 from Ashford stops at reserve

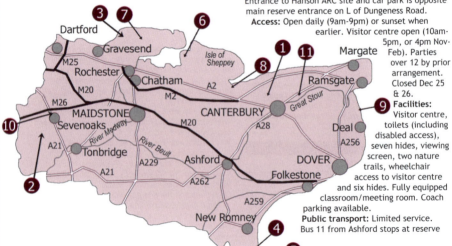

entrance on request — one mile walk to visitor centre.
Habitat: Shingle, flooded gravel pits, sallow scrub, reedbed, wet grassland.
Key birds: *All year:* Bittern, Marsh Harrier, Bearded Tit. *Spring:* Little Ringed Plover, Wheatear, Yellow Wagtail, Lesser Whitethroat. *Autumn:* Migrant waders and passerines. *Winter:* Smew, Goldeneye, Slavonian Grebe, Wigeon, Goosander and Bewick's Swan.
Other notable flora and fauna: Jersey cudweed, Nottingham catchfly, brown hare.
Contact: Reserve Manager, 01797 320 588;
e-mail: dungeness@rspb.org.uk www.rspb.org.uk

5. DUNGENESS BIRD OBSERVATORY

Dungeness Bird Observatory Trust.
Location: TR 085 173. Three miles SE of Lydd. Turn south off Dungeness Road at TR 087 185 and continue to end of road.
Access: Observatory open throughout the year. No wheelchair access.
Facilities: Accommodation available. Bring own sleeping bag/sheets and toiletries. Shared facilities including fully-equipped kitchen. Coach parking available at railway station.
Public transport: Bus service between Rye and Folkestone, numbers 11, 12, 711, 712. Alight at the Pilot Inn, Lydd-on-Sea. Tel: 01227 472 082.
Habitat: Shingle promontory with scrub and gravel pits. RSPB reserve nearby.
Key birds: Breeding birds include Wheatear and Black Redstart and seabirds on RSPB Reserve. Important migration site. Excellent seawatching when weather conditions are suitable. Power station outfall, 'The Patch' good for gulls and terns.
Other notable flora and fauna: Long Pits are excellent for dragonflies, including small red-eyed damselfly. Moth trapping throughout the year.
Contact: David Walker, Dungeness Bird Observatory, 01797 321 309, www.dungenessbirdobs.org.uk
e-mail: dungeness.obs@tinyonline.co.uk

6. ELMLEY MARSHES

RSPB (South East Region Office).
Location: TQ 924 698. From J5 on the M2, follow A249 towards Sheerness. Reserve signposted from the exit for Iwade and Ridham Dock, immediately before the Sheppey bridge. At the roundabout, take second exit onto the old road bridge. On the Isle of Sheppey, after 1.25 miles (2 km), turn R following the RSPB sign. Follow the rough track for approximately 2 miles (3 km) to the car park at Kingshill Farm.
Access: Open every day (9am-9pm or dusk if earlier) except Tue, Christmas and Boxing days. No charge to RSPB members. Dogs are not allowed on the reserve. Less able may drive closer to the hides.
Facilities: Five hides. Disabled access to Wellmarsh hide. No visitor centre. Toilets located in car park 1.25 miles from hides. Pushchair friendly.
Public transport: Swale Halt nearest railway station on Sittingbourne to Sheerness line. From there it is a three mile walk to reserve.

Habitat: Coastal grazing marsh, ditches and pools alongside the Swale Estuary with extensive intertidal mudflats and saltmarsh.
Key birds: *Spring/summer:* Breeding waders — Redshank, Lapwing, Avocet, Yellow Wagtail, passage waders, Hobby. *Autumn:* Passage waders. *Winter:* Spectacular numbers of wildfowl, especially Wigeon and White-fronted Goose. Waders. Hunting raptors - Peregrine, Merlin, Hen Harrier and Short-eared Owl.
Contact: Reserve Manager, 01795 665 969;
e-mail:northkentmarshes@rspb.org.uk

7. NORTHWARD HILL

RSPB (South East Region Office).
Location: TQ 781 757. Adjacent to High Halstow, off A228, approx four miles NE of Rochester.
Access: Open all year, free access, trails in public area of wood joining Saxon Shoreway link to grazing marsh. Dogs allowed in public area on leads. Trails often steep and not suitable for wheelchair users.
Facilities: Four trails vary in length from 0.5 to 4km. The Toddler trail is surfaced and suitable for 'off-road' push-chairs. Heron trail takes in heronry viewpoints.
Public transport: Buses to village of High Halstow. Contact Arriva buses (01634 283 600).
Habitat: Ancient and scrub woodland (approximately 130 acres), grazing marsh (approximately 350 acres).
Key birds: *Spring/summer:* Wood holds UK's largest heronry, with c.130 pairs of Grey Heron and c.120 pairs of Little Egret (in 2009), breeding Nightingale, Turtle Dove, scrub warblers and woodpeckers. Marshes — breeding Lapwing, Redshank, Avocet, Marsh Harrier, Shoveler, Pochard. *Winter:* Wigeon, Teal, Shoveler. Passage waders (ie Black-tailed Godwit), raptors, Corn Bunting. Long-eared Owl.
Other notable flora and fauna: Good range of dragonflies over the marsh, white-letter hairstreak butterfly in the woods.
Contact: Jason Mitchell, RSPB North Kent Marshes, 01634 222 480.

8. OARE MARSHES LNR

Kent Wildlife Trust.
Location: TR 01 36 48 (car park). Two miles N of Faversham. From A2 follow signs to Oare and Harty Ferry.
Access: Open at all times. Access along marked paths only. Dogs under strict control to avoid disturbance to birds and livestock.
Facilities: Three hides. Roadside viewpoint of East Hide accessible to wheelchair users.Those with pneumatic tyres can reach seawall path and hide. Small car park, restricted turning space, not suitable for coaches.
Public transport: Bus to Oare Village one mile from reserve. Arriva service (Mon-Sat), Jaycrest (Sun) — call Traveline on 0870 608 2608. Train: Faversham (two miles distance).
Habitat: Grazing marsh, mudflats/estuary.
Key birds: *All year:* Waders and wildfowl. *Winter:* Merlin, Peregrine. Divers, grebes and sea ducks on

Swale. *Spring/summer*: Avocet, Garganey, Green, Wood and Curlew Sandpipers, Little Stint, Black-tailed Godwit, Little Tern, Marsh Harrier.
Contact: Tony Swandale, Kent Wildlife Trust, 01622 662 012. e-mail: info@kentwildlife.org.uk www.kentwildlifetrust.org.uk

9. SANDWICH BAY BIRD OBSERVATORY

Sandwich Bay Bird Observatory Trust.
Location: TR 355 575. 2.5 miles from Sandwich, five miles from Deal. A256 to Sandwich from Dover or Ramsgate. Follow signs to Sandwich Station and then Sandwich Bay.
Access: Open daily. Disabled access.
Facilities: New Field Study Centre. Visitor centre, toilets, refreshments, hostel-type accommodation, plus self-contained flat.
Public transport: Sandwich train station two miles from Observatory.
Habitat: Coastal, dune land, farmland, marsh, two small scrapes.
Key birds: *Spring/autumn passage*: Good variety of migrants and waders, specially Corn Bunting. Annual Golden Oriole. *Winter*: Golden Plover.
Other notable flora and fauna: Sand dune plants such as lady's bedstraw and sand sedge.
Contact: The Secretary, Sandwich Bay Bird Observatory, Guildford Road, Sandwich Bay, Sandwich, Kent, CT13 9PF. 01304 617 341. e-mail: sbbot@talk21.

10. SEVENOAKS WILDLIFE RESERVE

Kent Wildlife Trust/Lafarge plc.
Location: TQ 519 568. From A25 at Bradbourne Vale Road, immediately N of Sevenoaks.
Access: Reserve open daily from dawn to dusk. Acess by car for disabled visitors and two designated accessible parking spaces.
Facilities: Bike racks, car park, nature trail, hides, refreshments. Visitor centre open: Oct-Apr, Wed, Sat,

Sun and Bank Hols (excl Christmas and New Year), 10am-4pm. Apr-Oct, Sat-Wed and Bank Holidays, 10am-5pm.
Public transport: 15 minutes walk from Bat & Ball station, 20 minutes from Sevenoaks station.
Habitat: Flooded gravel pits, reedbed and woodland (designated SSSI status).
Key birds: A good range of wetland, reedbed and woodland birds including passage migrants and waders.
Other notable flora: Several species of orchid and a good range of terrestrial and acquatic flora.
Contact: Wardens: Paul Glanfield or Susanna Clerici. Visitor Centre Manager: Amanda Hedges, 01732 456 407; www.kentwildlifetrust.org.uk

11. STODMARSH NNR

Natural England (Kent Team).
Location: TR 222 618. Lies alongside River Stour and A28, five miles NE of Canterbury.
Access: Open at all times. Keep to paths. No dogs.
Facilities: Fully accessible toilets are available at the Stodmarsh entrance car park. Five hides (one fully accessible), easy access nature trail, footpaths and information panels. Car park, picnic area and toilets adjoining the Grove Ferry entrance with easily accessible path, viewing mound and two hides.
Public transport: There is a regular Stagecoach bus service from Canterbury to Margate/Ramsgate. Alight at Upstreet for Grove Ferry. Hourly on Sun.
Habitat: Open water, reedbeds, wet meadows, dry meadows, woodland.
Key birds: *Spring/summer*: Breeding Bearded Tit, Cetti's Warbler, Garganey, Reed, Sedge and Willow Warblers, Nightingale. Migrant Black Tern, Hobby, Osprey, Little Egret. *Winter*: Wildfowl, Hen Harrier, Bittern.
Other notable flora and fauna: Nationally rare plants and invertebrates, including shining ram's horn snail.
Contact: David Feast, Natural England, 07767 321 058 (mobile).

London, Greater

WITH SO many tall buildings, it is little surprise that Peregrines are colonising with birds on Tate Modern, Battersea Power Station and the O2 Arena to name but a few. Black Redstarts are present too. Recent attentions have been devoted to impressive visible migration over the city. There are many parks to explore. Common Terns fish along the cleaned-up Thames.

1. BEDFONT LAKES COUNTRY PARK

Continental Landscapes Ltd.
Location: TQ 080 728. OS map sheet 176 (west London). 0.5 miles from Ashford, Middx, 0.5 miles S of A30, Clockhouse Roundabout, on B3003 (Clockhouse Lane).
Access: Park open (7.30am-9pm or dusk, whichever

is earlier), all days except Christmas Day. Disabled friendly. Dogs on leads. Main nature reserve only open Sun (2pm-4pm). Keyholder membership available.
Facilities: Toilets, information centre, several hides, nature trail, free parking, up-to-date information.
Public transport: Train to Feltham and Ashford. Bus — H26 and 116 from Hounslow.
Habitat: Lakes, reedbed, wildflower meadows, wet woodland, scrub.
Key birds: *Winter*: Water Rail, Bittern, Smew and other wildfowl, Meadow Pipit. *Summer*: Common Tern, Willow, Garden, Reed and Sedge Warblers, Whitethroat, Lesser Whitethroat, hirundines, Hobby, Blackcap, Chiffchaff, Skylark. *Passage*: Wheatear, Wood Warbler, Spotted Flycatcher, Ring Ouzel, Redstart, Yellow Wagtail.
Other notable flora and fauna: 140 plant species inc bee and pyramidal orchid. Nathusius pipistrelle

bat, emperor dragonfly plus other butterflies and dragonflies.
Contact: James Herd, Ranger, BLCP, Clockhouse Lane, Bedfont, Middx, TW14 8QA. 0845 456 2796.
e-mail: bedfont.lakes@continental-landscapes.co.uk

2. CHASE (THE) LNR

London Wildlife Trust.
Location: TQ 515 860. Lies in the Dagenham Corridor, an area of green belt between the London Boroughs of Barking & Dagenham and Havering.
Access: Open throughout the year and at all times. Reserve not suitable for wheelchair access. Eastbrookend Country Park which borders The Chase LNR has surfaced footpaths for wheelchair use.
Facilities: Millennium visitor centre, toilets, ample car parking, Timberland Trail walk.
Public transport: Rail: Dagenham East (District Line) 15 minute walk. Bus: 174 from Romford five minute walk.
Habitat: Shallow wetlands, reedbeds, horse-grazed pasture, scrub and wetland. These harbour an impressive range of animals and plants, including the nationally rare black poplar tree. A haven for birds, with approx 190 different species recorded.
Key birds: *Summer:* Breeding Reed Warbler, Lapwing, Water Rail, Lesser Whitethroat, Little Ringed Plover, Kingfisher, Reed Bunting. *Winter:* Significant numbers of Teal, Shoveler, Redwing, Fieldfare and Snipe dominate the scene. *Spring/autumn migration:* Yellow Wagtail, Wheatear, Ruff, Wood Sandpiper, Sand Martin, Ring Ouzel, Black Redstart and Hobby regularly seen.
Other notable flora and fauna: 140 plant species, wasp spider, butterflies and dragonflies.
Contact: The Millennium Centre, 02085 938 096, e-mail: lwtchase@cix.co.uk
www.wildlifetrust.org.uk/london/

3. LONDON WETLAND CENTRE

The Wildfowl & Wetlands Trust.
Location: TQ 228 770. Less than 1 mile from South Circular (A205) at Roehampton. In London, Zone 2/3, one mile from Hammersmith.
Access: Winter (9.30am-5pm; last admission 4pm), summer (9.30am-6pm; last admission 5pm). Charge for admission for non-WWT members. Coach parking by arrangement.
Facilities: Visitor centre, hides, nature trails, discovery centre and children's adventure area, restaurant (hot and cold food), cinema, shop, observatory building, six hides (all wheelchair

accessible), sustainable gardens, interactive pond zone, three interpretative buildings.
Public transport: Train: Barnes. Tube: Hammersmith then bus 283 (comes into centre). Other buses from Hammersmith are 33, 72, 209; from Richmond, 33.
Habitat: Main lake, reedbeds, wader scrape, open water lakes, wet woodland, grazing marsh.
Key birds: Nationally important numbers of wintering waterfowl, including Gadwall and Shoveler. Important numbers of wetland breeding birds, including grebes, swans, a range of duck species such as Pochard, plus Lapwing, Little Ringed Plover, Redshank, warblers, Reed Bunting and Bittern. Cetti's Warblers remain on site all year round and bred for the first time in 2010.
Other notable flora and fauna: Water voles, slow worm, grass snake, common lizard. Seven species of bat. 22 species of dragonfly and 25 of butterfly. Notable plants inc snake's head fritillaries, cowslip, pyramidal and bee orchids.
Contact: London Wetland Centre 020 8409 4400. email:info.london@wwt.org.uk - www.wwt.org.uk/london Twitter:@wwtlondon.

4. SYDENHAM HILL WOOD

London Wildlife Trust.
Location: TQ 335 722. Forest Hill, SE London, SE26, between Forest Hill and Crystal Palace, just off South Circular (A205). Entrances at Crescent Wood Road and Coxs Walk.
Access: Open at all times, no permits required. Some steep slopes, so wheelchair access is difficult.
Facilities: Nature trail, information boards. No toilets.
Public transport: Train stations: Forest Hill (from London Bridge) or Sydenham Hill (from Victoria). Buses 363, 202, 356, 185, 312, 176, P4. Call Transport for London 0207 5657 299 for details.
Habitat: Ancient woodland, reclaimed Victorian gardens, meadow and small pond.
Key birds: Woodland and gardens species all year round. *All year:* All three woodpeckers, Tawny Owl, Kestrel, Sparrowhawk, Goldcrest, Nuthatch, Treecreeper, Stock Dove. *Summer:* Blackcap, Chiffchaff, Willow Warbler. *Winter:* Fieldfare, Redwing.
Other notable flora and fauna: Five species of bat, including noctule and brown long-eared. Bluebell, wood anemone, dog violet and primrose. Oak and hornbeam. Speckled wood, comma, painted lady and orange-tip butterflies.
Contact: Chantal Brown, London Wildlife Trust, 0207 252 9186; e-mail: cbrown@wildlondon.org.uk

Surrey

LONDON'S Wetland Centre at Barnes is developing an excellent reputation for quality birding in the centre of suburbia. Slightly less salubrious is the sewage farm at Beddington. To the west of the county, heathland at Thursley Common and around Frensham are good for the likes of Nightjar, Hobby, Woodlark and Dartford Warbler.

1. BRENTMOOR HEATH LNR

Surrey Wildlife Trust.
Location: SU 936 612. The reserve runs along the A322 Guildford to Bagshot road, at the intersection with the A319/B311 between Chobham and Camberley. Best access is by Brentmoor Road, which runs W from West End past Donkey Town.
Access: Open all year.
Facilities: None.
Public transport: Local buses, nos 34, 590 and 591 stop less than half a miles away.
Habitat: Heathland, woodland, grassland, ponds.
Key birds: *Spring/summer:* Stonechat, Nightjar, Hobby. *All year:* Usual woodland birds.
Contact: Surrey Wildlife Trust, 07799 894 154. e-mail: info@surreywt.org.uk
www.surreywildlifetrust.org.uk

2. FARNHAM HEATH

RSPB (South East Region Office).
Location: SU 859 433. SE of Farnham. Take the B3001 SE from Farnham. Take the R hand fork, signposted Tilford, immediately past level crossing. Keep to that road. Just outside Tilford village it is signed to the Rural Life Centre. Follow those signs. Entrance is on the R after 0.5 mile.
Access: Reserve open at all times. Car park opens 9.30 am weekdays and 10.30 am weekends. Parking lay-bys on adjacent roads outside those hours. Rural Life Centre open Wed-Fri and Sundays all year. Open on Saturdays April-Sept. Tea room opens at 11 am.
Facilities: Large grass car park, shared with Rural Life Centre. No height barrier, but gates may be locked outside opening hours. No bike racks. Toilets (including disabled), picnic area, refreshments. Group bookings accepted, guided walks available. Good for walking, pushchair friendly.
Public transport: Bus route is number 19 (Farnham to Hindhead service). Nearest stop is in Millbridge village, outside entrance to Pierrepont House. Reserve is a mile away, along Reeds Road (follow signs to the Rural Life Centre). Train - Farnham.
Habitat: Heathland

and pine woodland.
Key birds: *Spring:* Blackcap, Tree Pipit, Woodcock, Woodlark. *Summer:* Woodcock and Nightjar, woodland birds, including Stock Dove and Green and Great Spotted Woodpeckers. *Winter:* Crossbills in the pine woods, winter finches, including Brambling around the feeders, winter thrushes.
Other notable flora and fauna: Fungi — more than 150 species. Bats in summer.
Contact: Mike Coates, c/o The Rural Life Centre, 01252 795 632.

3. FRENSHAM COMMON AND COUNTRY PARK

Waverley BC and National Trust.
Location: SU 855 405. Common lies on either side of A287 between Farnham and Hindhead.
Access: Open at all times. Car park (locked 9pm-9am). Keep to paths.
Facilities: Information rooms, toilets and refreshment kiosk at Great Pond.
Public transport: Call Trust for advice.
Habitat: Dry and humid heath, woodland, two large ponds, reedbeds.
Key birds: *Summer:* Dartford Warbler, Wood Lark, Hobby, Nightjar, Stonechat. *Winter:* Wildfowl (inc. occasional Smew), Bittern, Great Grey Shrike.
Other notable flora and fauna: Tiger beetle, purple hairstreak and silver-studded blue butterflies, sand lizard, smooth snake.
Contact: The Rangers Office, 01252 792 416.

4. LIGHTWATER COUNTRY PARK

Surreyheath Council
Location: SU 921 622. From J3 of M3, take the A322 and follow brown Country Park signs. From the Guildford Road in Lightwater, turn into The Avenue. Entrance to the park is at the bottom of the road.
Access: Open all year, dawn-dusk.
Facilities: Car park, toilets, waymarked trails with leaflets available.
Public transport: Train: Bagshot two miles. Tel SW Trains 0845 6000 650. Arriva Bus: No 34. Tel: 01483 306 397.
Habitat: Heathland, woodland, three ponds and meadows.
Key birds: *All year:* All three woodpeckers, Goldcrest in woods, Coot, Moorhen, Grey Heron

and Kingfisher on ponds. *Summer*: Nightjar, Willow Warbler, Chiffchaff, Blackcap, Whitethroat. *Winter*: Fieldfare, Redwing, Siskin.
Other notable flora and fauna: Flora includes ox-eye daisies, knapweed and common spotted orchid in meadow, three heathers and two gorse species on heath. Wood ant nests in woodlands. Good range of dragonflies and butterflies.
Contact: Surreyheath Ranger Service, Lightwater Country Park, 01276 479 582; e-mail: rangers@surreyheath.gov.uk
www.surreyheath.gov.uk

5. THURSLEY COMMON

Natural England (NNR Delivery Team South East).
Location: SU 900 417. From Guildford, take A3 SW to B3001 (Elstead/Churt road). Use the Moat car park, S of Elstead village.
Access: Open access. Parties must obtain prior permission.

Facilities: Boardwalk in wetter areas.
Public transport: None.
Habitat: Wet and dry heathland, woodland, bog.
Key birds: *Winter*: Hen/Marsh Harriers, Great Grey Shrike and passage/migrant waders such as Redshank, Greenshank, Wood and Common Sandpipers. *Summer*: Hobby, Woodlark, Lapwing, Stonechat, Curlew, Snipe, Nightjar, Spotted Flycatcher, Redstart, Crossbill.
Other notable flora and fauna: Large populations of silver-studded blue, grayling and purple emperor butterflies can be seen here, alongside 26 recorded dragonfly species. Sandier sites on the reserve provide homes for many species of solitary bees and wasps and tiger beetles. Damp areas support carnivorous sundews and a large population (in the thousands) of early marsh orchid.
Contact: James Giles, Natural England, T01483 307 703; e-mail: james.giles@naturalengland.org.uk
www.naturalengland.org.uk

Sussex, East

THE AREA around Rye Harbour, and the nearby Pett Level, guarantees a good day's birdwatching, with an interesting mix of wildfowl, waders, raptors, terns and Bitterns, depending on the season. If you enjoy finding your own migrants, then a spring or autumn visit to Beachy Head is a must. Ashdown Forest offers a fine mix of woodland heathland birds.

1. CASTLE WATER, RYE HARBOUR

Sussex Wildlife Trust.
Location: TQ 942 189. Reserve is one mile SE of Rye along Harbour Road.
Access: Open at all times, entry is free. Information centre at Limekiln Cottage open every day 10am-4pm. The site is quite flat with some wheelchair access to all four hides, although there are stiles where the sheep are grazing the fields.
Facilities: Information centre, large car park at Rye Harbour with nearby toilets.
Habitat: Intertidal, saltmarsh, marsh, drainage ditches, shingle ridges, pits, sand, scrub, woodland.
Key birds: Many birds occur here in nationally important numbers, such as Shoveler and Sanderling in the winter and breeding Little Tern and Mediterranean Gull. Nesting Black-headed Gull colony, Common and Sandwich Terns and a good range of waders and ducks. Barn and Short-eared Owls.
Other notable flora and fauna: The saltmarsh supports such unusual plants as sea-heath and marsh mallow, and even highly specialised insects including the star-wort moth and saltmarsh bee.
Contact: Sussex Wildlife Trust, 01273 492 630; e-mail: enquiries@sussexwt.org.uk
www.sussexwt.org.uk

2. FORE WOOD

RSPB (South East Region Office).
Location: TQ 752 127. From the A2100 (Battle/Hastings) take lane to Crowhurst at Crowhurst Park Caravan Park. Park at Crowhurst village hall and walk up Forewood Lane for 500 yards. Look for the finger post on L and follow the public footpath across farmland to reserve entrance.
Access: Open all year. No disabled facilities. No dogs. No coaches.
Facilities: Two nature trails. Not suitable for pushchairs or wheelchairs.
Public transport: Station at Crowhurst, about 0.5 mile walk. Charing Cross/Hastings line. No buses within one mile.
Habitat: Semi-natural ancient woodland.
Key birds: A wide range of woodland birds. *Spring*: Chiffchaff, Greater Spotted Woodpecker, Nuthatch, Treecreeper. *Summer*: Blackcap, Bullfinch, Mistle Thrush, Green Woodpecker. *Autumn*: Goldcrest, Jay, Marsh Tit. *Winter*: Fieldfare, Rook, Redwing.
Other notable flora and fauna: Rare ferns, bluebells, wood anemonies, purple orchid. Butterflies include silver-washed fritillary and white admiral.
Contact: Reserve Manager, RSPB Broadwater Warren, 01273 775 333.

3. LULLINGTON HEATH

Natural England (NNR Delivery Team South East).
Location: TQ 525 026. W of Eastbourne, between Jevington and Litlington, on northern edge of Friston Forest.
Access: Via footpaths and bridleways. Site open for access on foot as defined by CROW Act 2000.
Facilities: None. Nearest toilets/refreshmenst at pubs in Jevington, Litlington or Seven Sisters CP, 2km to S.

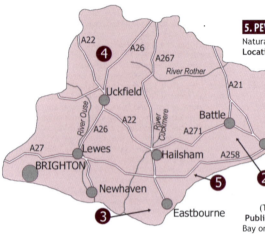

5. PEVENSEY LEVELS

Natural England (NNR Delivery Team South East).
Location: TQ 665 054. A small reserve of 12 fields, within the 3,500 ha SSSI/Ramsar site of Pevensey Levels. NE of Eastbourne. S of A259, one mile along minor road from Pevensey E towards Norman's Bay.
Access: Please view from road to avoid disturbance to summer nesting birds and sheltering flocks in winter. Access on foot allowed at Rockhouse Bank (TQ 675 057) — panoramic view of whole reserve.
Facilities: None. Nearest toilets at Star Inn (TQ 687 062) or petrol station (TQ 652 052).
Public transport: Nearest railway stations: Pevensey Bay or Cooden Beach. Eastbourne buses to Pevensey Bay — call 01323 416416.
Habitat: Freshwater grazing marsh with extensive ditch system, subject to flooding.
Key birds: *Summer:* Breeding Reed and Sedge Warblers, Yellow Wagtail, Snipe, Redshank, Lapwing. Raptors include Peregrine and Hobby. Passage migrants include Whimbrel, Curlew, Brent Geese. *Winter:* Flocks of wildfowl and waders, Short-eared Owl, Merlin and other raptors.
Other notable flora and fauna: Variable damselfly, many rare snails and other molluscs, the most important site in the UK for fen raft spider. Unusual wetland plants.
Contact: East Sussex NNRs, Natural England, 07971 974 401 or reserve manager 07825 386 620. email: malcolm.emery@naturalengland.org.uk www.naturalengland.org.uk

Public transport: Nearest bus stop is Seven Sisters Country Park. Phone Brighton & Hove services on 01273 886 200 or visit: www.buses.co.uk/bustimes/
Habitat: Grazed chalk downland and heath, with mixed scrub and gorse.
Key birds: *Summer:* Breeding Nightingale, Turtle Dove, Nightjar and diverse range of grassland/scrub-nesting species. Passage migrants include Wheatear, Redstart, Ring Ouzel. *Winter:* Raptors (inc. Hen Harrier), Woodcock.
Other notable flora and fauna: Bell heather, ling and gorse on chalk heath; orchid species in grassland.
Contact: East Sussex NNRs, Natural England, 07971 974 401 or reserve manager 07825 386 620. email: malcolm.emery@naturalengland.org.uk www.naturalengland.org.uk

4. OLD LODGE RESERVE

Sussex Wildlife Trust.
Location: TQ 469 306 (postcode TN22 3JD). On W side of B2026 between Maresfield and Hartfield, about 0.75 miles N of junction with B2188 at Kings Standing.
Access: Open all year. Dogs must be kept on a short, fixed lead between Jan-end Sept and when livestock is present.
Facilities: Car park, nature trail. Steep paths.
Public transport: None.
Habitat: Heath, pine and deciduous woodlands.
Key birds: *All year:* Heathland specialists inc Dartford Warbler. *Spring/summer:* Breeding Nightjar, Redstart, Woodlark, Tree Pipit, Stonechat. *Autumn/winter:* Raven, Crossbill.
Other notable flora and fauna: Good for dragonflies including black darter, golden ringed and small red damselfly. Small colony of silver-studded blue butterflies.
Contact: Sussex Wildlife Trust, 01273 492 630; e-mail: enquiries@sussexwt.org.uk www.sussexwt.org.uk

6. RYE HARBOUR

Rye Harbour Local Nature Reserve Management Committee.
Location: TQ 941 188. One mile from Rye off A259 signed Rye Harbour. From J10 of M20 take A2070 until it joins A259.
Access: Open at all times by footpaths. Organised groups please book.
Facilities: Car park in Rye Harbour village. Information kiosk in car park. Shop, two pubs, toilets and disabled facilities near car park, four hides (wheelchair access), information centre open most days (10am-4pm) by volunteers.
Public transport: Train stations at Rye and Winchelsea, (08457 484 950), bus (0870 608 2608), tourist information (tel: 01797 226 696).
Habitat: Sea, sand, shingle, pits and grassland.
Key birds: *Spring:* Passage waders, especially roosting Whimbrel. *Summer:* Turtle Dove, terns (3 species), waders (7 species), gulls (6 species), Garganey, Shoveler, Cetti's Warbler, Bearded Tit. *Winter:* Wildfowl, Water Rail, Bittern, Smew.
Other notable flora and fauna: Good shingle flora

including sea kale, sea pea, least lettuce and stinging hawksbeard. Excellent range of dragonflies including breeding red-veined darter and scarce emerald damselfly.

Contact: Barry Yates, (Manager), 01797 223 862.
e-mail: rhnr.office@eastsussex.gov.uk
www.wildrye.info

Sussex, West

PAGHAM HARBOUR is worth a visit at any time of year. Nearby Selsey Bill is good for migrants and there is a noticeable skua passage in the spring. The WWT reserve at Arundel is good for Mandarins and Cetti's Warblers, while further inland, RSPB Pulborough Brooks holds important numbers of wintering wildfowl including the chance of Bewick's Swans.

1. ARDUR ESTUARY

RSPB (South East Region Office).
Location: TQ 215 049. On W side of Shoreham-on-Sea.
Access: Good views from riverside paths between footbridge in Shoreham town centre and A259 Norfolk bridge (car park).
Facilities: None.
Public transport: Trains: Shoreham-by-Sea. Bus: Shoreham-by-Sea town centre. Brighton and Hove buses (01273 886 200).
Habitat: Mudflats and saltmarsh.
Key birds: A small area but a haven for waders and wildfowl. *Summer:* Dunlin, Snipe and Redshank. *All year:* Oystercatcher.
Contact: Tim Callaway, RSPB Pulborough Brooks, Wiggonholt, Pulborough, West Sussex RH20 2EL. 01798 875 851.
e-mail: pulborough.brooks@rspb.org.uk
www.rspb.org.uk/adurestuary

2. ARUNDEL

Wildfowl and Wetland Trust
Location: TQ 020 081. Centre clearly signposted from Arundel, just N of A27.
Access: Summer (9.30am-5.30pm) winter (9.30am-4.30pm). Closed Christmas Day. Approx 1.5 miles of level footpaths, suitable for wheelchairs. No dogs except guide dogs. Admission charges for non-WWT members.
Facilities: Visitor centre, restaurant, shop, hides, picnic area, seasonal nature trails. Eye of The Wind Wildlife Gallery. Corporate hire facilities.
Public transport: Arundel station, 15-20 minute walk. Tel: 01903 882 131.
Habitat: Lakes, wader scrapes, reedbed.
Key birds: *Summer:* Nesting Redshank, Lapwing, Oystercatcher, Common Tern, Sedge, Reed and Cetti's Warblers, Peregrine, Hobby. *Winter:* Teal, Wigeon, Reed Bunting, Water Rail, Cetti's Warbler and occasionally roosting Bewick's Swan.
Contact: WWT Arundel Wetland Centre, 01903 883 355; e-mail: info.arundel@wwt.org.uk
www.wwt.org.uk

3. KINGLEY VALE

Natural England (Sussex & Surrey Team).
Location: SU 825 088. West Stoke car park. Approx five miles NW of Chichester town centre (as the crow flies). Travel N from Chichester on A286 to Lavant, then turn L (W) by the church on to Downs Road. Follow for West Stoke. Turn R at the junction after the church to West Stoke car park.
Access: Always open, no permits, no disabled access. All dogs on a lead please - grazing stock.
Facilities: There is a nature trail (posts 1-24) and an unmanned information centre - no toilets, plenty of trees and bushes!
Public transport: Nearest railway station approx five miles walking distance. Nearest main bus route just over one mile on A286 at Mid Lavant. No 60 from Chichester Bus Station next to the Rail Station.
Habitat: Greatest yew forest in Europe (more than 30,000 trees). Chalk grassland, mixed oak/ash woodland and scrub. Chalk heath.
Key birds: *Spring/summer:* Nightingale, Whitethroat, Blackcap, Lesser Whitethroat. *Autumn/winter:* Hen Harrier, Buzzard, Hobby on migration, Red Kite. Barn and Tawny Owls, Hawfinch, Ravens, Goldcrest, Firecrest, Redwing, Fieldfare, Osprey (passing over on migration), Green Woodpecker, Nuthatch.
Contact: Natural England, 01243 575353; e-mail enquiries.southeast@naturalengland.org.uk; www.naturalengland.org.uk;

4. PAGHAM HARBOUR

West Sussex County Council/RSPB
Location: SZ 857 966. Five miles S of Chichester on B2145 towards Selsey. After 0.5miles turn R at first roundabout still following Selsey. Look for entrance just after leaving Sidlesham after speed limit increases to 50mph.
Access: Open at all times, dogs must be on leads, disabled trail with accessible hide. All groups and coach parties must book in advance.
Facilities: Visitor Centre open weekends in winter (10-4) and in summer (10-5). Open most of the week throughout the year (10-4) but check first. Toilets (including disabled), three hides, one nature trail.
Public transport: Bus stop by visitor centre.
Habitat: Mudflats, intertidal saltmarsh, shingle beaches, lagoons and farmland.
Key birds: *Spring:* Passage migrants. *Autumn:* Passage waders, other migrants. *Winter:* Brent Goose, Slavonian Grebe, wildfowl and waders. *All year:* Little Egret.
Other notable flora and fauna: Wide range of grasses, butterflies and dragonflies.
Contact: Reserve Manager 01243 641 508; e-mail: pagham.harbour@rspb.org.uk

NATURE RESERVES - SOUTH EAST ENGLAND

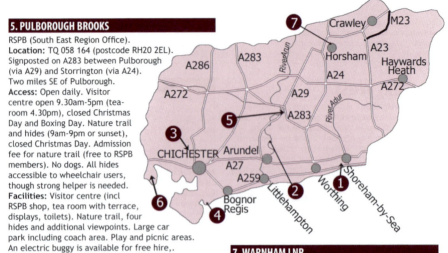

5. PULBOROUGH BROOKS

RSPB (South East Region Office).
Location: TQ 058 164 (postcode RH20 2EL).
Signposted on A283 between Pulborough
(via A29) and Storrington (via A24).
Two miles SE of Pulborough.
Access: Open daily. Visitor
centre open 9.30am-5pm (tea-
room 4.30pm), closed Christmas
Day and Boxing Day. Nature trail
and hides (9am-9pm or sunset),
closed Christmas Day. Admission
fee for nature trail (free to RSPB
members). No dogs. All hides
accessible to wheelchair users,
though strong helper is needed.
Facilities: Visitor centre (incl
RSPB shop, tea room with terrace,
displays, toilets). Nature trail, four
hides and additional viewpoints. Large car
park including coach area. Play and picnic areas.
An electric buggy is available for free hire,.
Public transport: Two miles from Pulborough train
station. Connecting bus service regularly passes
reserve entrance (not Sun). Compass Travel (01903
690 025). Cycle stands.
Habitat: Lowland wet grassland (wet meadows and
ditches). Heathland, hedgerows, scrub and woodland.
Key birds: *Winter*: Wintering waterbirds, Bewick's
Swan. *Spring/summer*: Breeding wading birds and
songbirds (inc Lapwing and Nightingale), Nightjar,
Lesser-spotted Woodpecker. *Autumn*: Passage wading
birds, Redstart, Whinchat.
Other notable flora and fauna: Good range of
butterflies and dragonflies.
Contact: The Administrator, Pulborough Brooks NR,
01798 875 851; www.rspb.org.uk/pulboroughbrooks
e-mail: pulborough.brooks@rspb.org.uk

6. THORNEY/PILSEY

RSPB (South East Region Office).
Location: W of Chichester. Take A259 and park in
Prinstead, near Emsworth. Walk over sea walls to
view both Thorney and Pilsey islands.
Access: No vehicle access to Thorney Island, viewing
from footpaths only. Pilsey Island can also be viewed
from coastal path (the Sussex Border Path) that runs
around the Thorney Island MoD base. Long, exposed
walk.
Facilities: Footpath.
Habitat: Intertidal sandflats and mudflats, fore dunes
and yellow dunes, bare and vegetated shingle and
saltmarsh.
Key birds: The reserve, together with the adjacent
area of Pilsey Sand, forms one of the most important
pre-roost and roost site for passage and wintering
waders in the area. Brent Geese in winter, plus Merlin
and Peregrine possible
Contact: Site Warden, 01798 875 851.
e-mail: pilsey.island@rspb.org.uk

7. WARNHAM LNR

Horsham District Council.
Location: TQ 167 324. One mile from Horsham town
centre, just off A24 'Robin Hood' roundabout on
B2237.
Access: Open all year (except Dec 25 and 26) Mar -
Oct (10am-6pm), Nov-Feb (10am-5pm). Day permits:
Adults £1, children under 16 free. Annual permits
also available. No dogs or cycling allowed. Good
wheelchair access over most of the Reserve.
Facilities: Visitor centre and café. Also Stag Beetle
Loggery. Ample car park – coaches by request.
Toilets (including disabled), two hides, reserve
leaflets, millpond nature trail, bird feeding station,
boardwalks, benches and hardstanding paths.
Public transport: One mile from Horsham Railway
Station, along Hurst Road, with a R turn onto
Warnham Road. Buses from 'CarFax' in Horsham
Centre stop within 150 yards of the reserve. Travel
line, 0870 608 2608.
Habitat: 17 acre millpond, reedbeds, marsh, meadow
and woodland (deciduous and coniferous).
Key birds: *Summer*: Common Tern, Kingfisher,
woodpeckers, Mandarin Duck, Marsh Tit, Goldcrest,
hirundines, Hobby, warblers. *Winter*: Cormorant,
gulls, Little Grebe, Water Rail, Brambling, Siskin,
Lesser Redpoll, thrushes and wildfowl. *Passage*:
Waders, pipits, terns and hirundines.
Other notable flora and fauna: Extensive
invertebrate interest, including 33 species of
butterfly and 25 species of dragonfly. Mammals
including harvest mouse, water vole and badger. More
than 450 species of plant, including broad-leaved
helleborine and common spotted orchid.
Contact: The Site Manager, 01403 256 890; e-mail:
leisure@horsham.gov.uk www.visithorsham.co.uk

South West England

Cornwall, Devon, Dorset, Somerset, Wiltshire

Cornwall

LOCATION, location, location…. Cornwall is ideally placed to attract overflying migrants in both spring and, particularly, autumn. Valleys near Land's End such as Cot and Nanquidno are just as likely to hold a Siberian vagrant next to an American bird and the Scilly Isles remain an autumn hotspot for twitchers. Headlands at St Ives and Porthgwarra are ideal for autumn seawatching, while Choughs have recently started recolonizing the Lizard.

1. BRENEY COMMON

Cornwall Wildlife Trust.
Location: SX 054 610. 2.5 miles S of Bodmin. Take minor road off A390 one mile W of Lostwithiel to Lowertown. For Breney Common entrance, turn R at Reperry Cross, then L fork to Trebell Green and on towards Gurtla. The entrance track is on the left in Gurtla, after the Methodist church, opposite The Barn.
Access: Open at all times but please keep to paths. Disabled access from small car park at Breney.
Facilities: Wilderness trail. Boardwalk sections the only suitable surface for wheelchairs.
Public transport: None.
Habitat: Huge site (536 acres) includes wetland, grassland, heath and scrub.
Key birds: Willow Tit, Nightjar, Tree Pipit, Sparrowhawk, Lesser Whitethroat, Curlew.
Other notable flora and fauna: Royal fern, sundews and other bog plants. Butterflies (inc marsh and small pearl-bordered fritillaries, silver-studded blue).
Contact: Sean O'Hea, Cornwall Wildlife Trust, 01872 273 939. e-mail: info@cornwt.demon.co.uk www.cornwallwildlifetrust.org.uk

2. CROWDY RESERVOIR

South West Lakes Trust.
Location: Follow signs from A39 at Camelford to Davidstow Airfield and pick up signs to reservoir. On edge of forestry plantation, park in pull-in spot near cattle grid. A track leads to a hide via stiles. Main car park located a little further down the lane.
Access: Open all year.
Facilities: Hide. **Public transport:** None.
Habitat: Reservoir, bog, moorland, forestry.
Key birds: *Spring*: Passage migrants, inc Wheatear, Whimbrel, Ruff. *Summer*: Black-headed Gull, Reed and Sedge Warblers, returning waders. *Autumn*: Waders, raptors possible inc Peregrine, Goshawk,

Merlin. *Winter*: Wild swans, wildfowl, possible Smew. Golden Plover, Woodcock, Fieldfare, Redwing.
Other notable flora: Mire floral communities.
Contact: South West Lakes Trust, 01566 771 930. www.swlakestrust.org.uk

3. HAYLE ESTUARY

RSPB (South West England Office).
Location: SW 550 370. In town of Hayle. Follow signs to Hayle from A30. Take B3301 through Hayle past the Tempest factory, turn L into Chenells Rd and R into Ryans Field.
Access: Open at all times. No permits required. No admission charges. Not suitable for wheelchair users. Dogs on leads please. Sorry — no coaches.
Facilities: Eric Grace Memorial Hide at Ryan's Field has parking and viewing, but birds here only at high tide. Nearest toilets in town of Hayle. No visitor centre but information board at hide.
Public transport: Buses and trains at Hayle. Call 0871 200 2233 for details.
Habitat: Intertidal mudflats, saltmarsh, lagoon and islands, sandy beaches and sand dunes.
Key birds: *Winter*: Wildfowl, gulls, Kingfisher, Great Northern Diver and waders. *Spring/summer*: Migrant waders, breeding Shelduck. *Autumn*: Rare waders, often from N America. Terns, gulls.
Contact: RSPB South West Regional Office, 01392 432 691; www.rspb.org.uk

4. MARAZION MARSH

RSPB (South West England Office).
Location: SW 510 315. Reserve is one mile E of Penzance, 500 yards W of Marazion. Entrance off seafront road near Marazion.
Access: Open at all times. No

197

permits required. No admission charges. Not suitable for wheelchair users. Dogs on leads please. Sorry — no coaches.

Facilities: No toilets or visitor centre. Nearest toilets in Marazion and seafront car park.

Public transport: First Group Nos 2, 7 and 8, plus Sunset Bay2Bay service 340 from Penzance. Call 0871 200 2233 for details.

Habitat: Wet reedbed, willow carr.

Key birds: *Winter*: Wildfowl, Snipe, occasional Bittern. *Spring/summer*: Breeding Reed, Sedge and Cetti's Warblers, herons, swans. *Autumn*: Large roost of Swallows and martins in reedbeds, migrant warblers and Water Rail.

Other notable flora and fauna: Up to 22 species of dragonfly, plus 500 species of vascular plants, inc lawn camomile and yellow flag.

Contact: RSPB South West Regional Office, 01392 432 691; www.rspb.org.uk

5. NARE HEAD

National Trust.

Location: Approx ten miles SE of Truro. from A390 head S on A307 to two miles S of Tregony just past the garage. Follow signs to Veryan then L signposted to Carne. Go straight over at crossroad, following Carne and Pendower. Turn L on a bend following NT signs for Nare Head. Bearing R, cross over a cattle grid to the car park. From the garage, Nare Head is about four miles.

Access: Open all year.

Facilities: Car park.

Habitat: Headland.

Key birds: *Spring/summer*: Razorbill, Guillemot, Sandwich, Common and Arctic Terns, possible Whimbrel, Fulmar. *Winter*: Black-throated and Great Northern Divers. Red-throated Diver possible. Common Scoter, Velvet Scoter, Slavonian, Black-necked and Red-necked Grebes.

Contact: National Trust, Lanhydrock House, Lanhydrock, Cornwall, PL30 4DE. 01208 432 691.

6. STITHIANS RESERVOIR

South West Lakes Trust.

Location: SS 715 365. From B3297 S of Redruth.

Access: Good viewing from causeway.

Facilities: New hide near main centre open to all.

Habitat: Open water, marshland.

Key birds: County's best open water site for winter wildfowl. Good for waders such as Common, Green and Wood Sandpipers, plus rarities, eg. Pectoral and

Semipalmated Sandpipers, Lesser Yellowlegs.

Contact: South West Lakes Trust, Centre Manager, 01209 860 301. www.swlakestrust.org.uk

7. TAMAR ESTUARY

Cornwall Wildlife Trust.

Location: SX 434 631 (Northern Boundary). SX 421 604 (Southern Boundary). From Plymouth head W on A38. Access parking at Cargreen and Landulph from minor roads off A388.

Access: Open at all times. Access bird hides from China Fleet Club car park, Saltash. Follow path alongside golf course — do not walk on course itself. Combination number for hide locks available at club reception.

Facilities: Two hides on foreshore, first (0.25 miles from car park) overlooks estuary, second (0.5 miles) has excellent views across Kingsmill Lake.

Public transport: None.

Habitat: Tidal mudflat with some saltmarsh.

Key birds: *Winter*: Avocet, Snipe, Black-tailed Godwit, Redshank, Dunlin, Curlew, Whimbrel, Spotted Redshank, Green Sandpiper, Golden Plover, Kingfisher.

Contact: Cornwall Wildlife Trust, 01579 351 155.
e-mail: peter@cornwt.demon.co.uk
www.cornwallwildlifetrust.org.uk

8. TAMAR LAKES

South West Lakes Trust

Location: SS 295 115. Site lies E of A39, N of Bude. Follow brown tourist signs from Holsworthy or Kilkhampton.

Access: Open all year. Limited wheelchair access.

Facilities: Bird hides on Upper and Lower lakes. Café (limited opening) at Upper Tamar. Toilets at Upper open all year, those at Lower only open in summer.

Public transport: None.

Habitat: Two freshwater lakes, plus swamp, scrub and grassland.

Key birds: *All year*: Great Crested Grebe, Black-headed Gull, Kingfisher, Willow Tit, Reed Bunting. *Spring*: Black Tern. *Summer*: Breeding Sedge, Reed and Willow Warblers and House Martin. *Winter*: Moderate numbers of wildfowl, inc Wigeon and Teal and gulls.

Other notable flora and fauna: Badger, roe deer, otter, southern marsh orchid, wood white butterfly, grass snake.

Contact: Conservation Officer, Upper Tamar Lakes Visitor Centre, 01288 321 262.

Devon

BLESSED with two National Parks, Exmoor to the north is the prettier, with wonderful wooded valleys attractive to birds whereas Dartmoor is much bleaker. Red-backed Shrikes are attempting to re-establish themselves there. The island of Lundy in the Bristol Channel is good for vagrants. Look for waders around Exminster Marshes while the southern coast holds localised but increasing pockets of Cirl Buntings.

1. AYLESBEARE COMMON

RSPB (South West England Office).
Location: SY 058 897. Five miles E of J30 of M5 at Exeter, 0.5 miles past Halfway Inn on B3052. Turn R to Hawkerland, car park is on L. The reserve is on the opposite side of the main road.
Access: Open all year. One track suitable for wheelchairs and pushchairs.
Facilities: Car park, picnic area, group bookings, guided walks and special events. Disabled access via metalled track to private farm.
Public transport: Buses (Exeter to Sidmouth, 52a, 52b). Request stop at Joneys Cross (reserve entrance). Tel: 01392 427 711.
Habitat: Heathland, wood fringes, streams and ponds.
Key birds: *Spring/summer*: Hobby, Nightjar, Tree Pipit, Stonechat. *All year*: Dartford Warbler, Buzzard, Yellowhammer. *Winter*: Possible Hen Harrier.
Other notable flora and fauna: Good range of dragonflies and butterflies.
Contact: Toby Taylor, Hawkerland Brake Barn, Exmouth Road, Aylesbeare, Nr Exeter, Devon EX5 2JS. 01395 233 655.
www.rspb.org.uk/reserves/guide/a/aylesbearecommon/

2. BOVEY HEATHFIELD

Devon Wildlife Trust.
Location: SX 824 765. On the outskirts of Bovey Tracey on SE edge of Dartmoor. From A382 Bovey Straight take Battle Road into Heathfield Industrial estate. Turn L into Cavalier Road, then Dragoon Close — the reserve is along a gravel path.
Access: Open all year. Dogs allowed on leads. Please keep to paths. Rough paths not suitable for wheelchairs. No coach access.
Facilities: Information hut open when warden is on site.
Public transport: Buses to Battle Road, Heathfield.
Habitat: Heathland.
Key birds: Breeding Nightjar, Tree Pipit, Stonechat and Dartford Warbler, plus commoner species.
Other notable flora and fauna: Heathers, wet and dry heathland plants, more than 60 endangered insect species, plus grayling and green hairstreak butterflies, slow worm, adder.
Contact: Devon Wildlife Trust, Cricklepit Mill, Commercial Road, Exeter, EX1 4AB. 01392 279 244. e-mail: devonwt@cix.co.uk

3. BOWLING GREEN MARSH

RSPB (South West England Office).
Location: SX 972 876. On the E side of River Exe, four miles SE of Exeter, 0.5 miles SE of Topsham.
Access: Open at all times. Please park at the public car parks in Topsham village, not in the lane by the reserve.
Facilities: RSPB shop at Darts Farm, 1.5km from reserve, east of Topsham across River Clyst.
Public transport: Exeter to Exmouth railway has regular (every 30 mins) service to Topsham station (half a mile from reserve). Stagecoach Devon 57 bus has frequent service (Mon-Sat every 12 mins, Sun every half-hour) from Exeter to Topsham. Traveline 0871 200 2233.
Habitat: Coastal grassland, open water/marsh.
Key birds: *Winter*: Wigeon, Shoveler, Teal, Black-tailed Godwit, Curlew, Golden Plover. *Spring*: Shelduck, passage waders, Whimbrel, passage Garganey and Yellow Wagtail. *Summer*: Gull/tern roosts, high tide wader roosts contain many passage birds. *Autumn*: Wildfowl, Peregrine, wader roosts.
Other notable flora and fauna: Hairy dragonfly, wasp spider.
Contact: RSPB, Darts Farm Shopping Village, Clyst St. George, Exeter EX3 0QH. 01392 879 438 or the reserve on 01392 824 614.
www.rspb.org.uk

4. BURRATOR RESERVOIR

South West Lakes Trust.
Location: SX 551 681. Lies 10 miles NE of Plymouth, off A386 (Tavistock road). At Yelverton take B3212 towards Princeton. Turn R at Burrator Inn and follow signs to reservoir.
Access: Open all year. Numerous free parking areas around reservoir. Main route is suitable for disabled but is also used by motorists and cyclists. There are about 25 stiles around the reservoir but not on main route.
Facilities: Toilets (including disabled at Burrator Lodge). Snacks and ice-creams available during summer.
Public transport: Bus: daily from Plymouth to Dousland (a short walk from the reservoir). No 82 Western National or No 48 (Sun). Tel: 01752 402 060. Train: nearest station is Plymouth. Tel: 08457 484 950.
Habitat: Pine forests, wooded streams, open moorland scrub.
Key birds: *Winter*: Goosander, Dipper, Grey Wagtail, Green Sandpiper, Brambling, Crossbill, Siskin, Redpoll. *All year*: Three woodpeckers, Buzzard, Sparrowhawk, Kestrel, Barn Owl, Tree Sparrow.
Other notable flora and fauna: Marsh fritillary butterfly, dragonflies and damselflies, particularly in the arboretum, bats (various species), otter.
Contact: South West Lakes Trust, Lidn Park, Quarry Crescent, Pennygillam Industrial Estate, Launceston, Cornwall PL15 7PF. 01566 771 930.
www.swlakestrust.org.uk

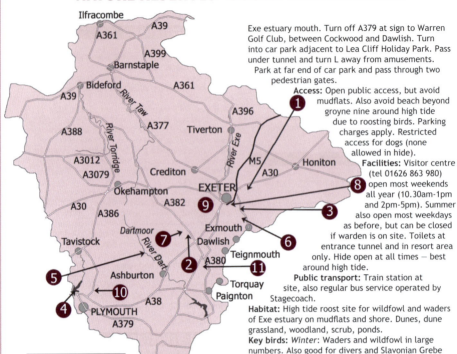

Exe estuary mouth. Turn off A379 at sign to Warren Golf Club, between Cockwood and Dawlish. Turn into car park adjacent to Lea Cliff Holiday Park. Pass under tunnel and turn L away from amusements. Park at far end of car park and pass through two pedestrian gates.

Access: Open public access, but avoid mudflats. Also avoid beach beyond groyne nine around high tide due to roosting birds. Parking charges apply. Restricted access for dogs (none allowed in hide).

Facilities: Visitor centre (tel 01626 863 980) open most weekends all year (10.30am-1pm and 2pm-5pm). Summer also open most weekdays as before, but can be closed if warden is on site. Toilets at entrance tunnel and in resort area only. Hide open at all times — best around high tide.

Public transport: Train station at site, also regular bus service operated by Stagecoach.

Habitat: High tide roost site for wildfowl and waders of Exe estuary on mudflats and shore. Dunes, dune grassland, woodland, scrub, ponds.

Key birds: *Winter*: Waders and wildfowl in large numbers. Also good for divers and Slavonian Grebe offshore. *Summer*: Particularly good for terns. Excellent variety of birds all year, especially on migration.

Contact: Visitor centre: 01626 863 980. Teignbridge District Council: 01626 361 101 (Ext 5754). www.dawlishwarren.co.uk

5. DART VALLEY

Devon Wildlife Trust.
Location: SX 680 727. On Dartmoor nine miles NW from Ashburton. From A38 'Peartree Cross' near Ashburton, follow signs towards Princetown. Access from National Park car parks at New Bridge (S) or Dartmeet (N).
Access: Designated 'access land' but terrain is rough with few paths. It is possible to walk the length of the river (eight miles). A level, well-made track runs for a mile from Newbridge to give easy access to some interesting areas. Not suitable for large coaches (narrow bridges). Probably too rough for wheelchairs.
Facilities: Dartmoor National Park toilets in car parks at New Bridge and Dartmeet.
Public transport: Enquiry line 01392 382 800. Summer service only from Newton Abbot/Totnes to Dartmeet.
Habitat: Upland moor, wooded valley and river.
Key birds: *All year*: Raven, Buzzard. *Spring/summer*: Wood Warbler, Pied Flycatcher, Redstart in woodland, Stonechat and Whinchat on moorland, Dipper, Grey Wagtail, Goosander on river.
Contact: Devon Wildlife Trust, 01392 279 244. www.devonwildlifetrust.org

6. DAWLISH WARREN NNR

Teignbridge District Council.
Location: SX 983 788. At Dawlish Warren on S side of

7. EAST DARTMOOR NNR

Natural England.
Location: SX 778 787. The NNR is two miles from Bovey Tracey on road to Becky Falls and Manaton. Road continues across Trendlebere Down, where there are roadside car parks and adjacent paths.
Access: Yarner Wood car park open from 8.30am-7pm or dusk if earlier. Outside these hours, access on foot from Trendlebere Down. Dogs welcome but must be kept under close control.
Facilities: Information/interpretation display and self-guided trails available in Yarner Wood car park also hide with feeding station (Nov-Mar).
Public transport: Nearest bus stops are in Bovey Tracey. Buses from here to Exeter and Newton Abbot (hourly).
Habitat: The reserve consists of three connected sites (Yarner Wood, Trendlebere Down and Bovey Valley Woodlands) totalling 365 hectares of upland oakwood and heathland.
Key birds: *All year*: Raven, Buzzard, Goshawk, Sparrowhawk, Lesser Spotted, Great Spotted and Green Woodpeckers, Grey Wagtail and Dartford

Warbler (on Trendlebere Down). *Spring/summer*:
Pied Flycatcher, Wood Warbler, Redstart, Tree Pipit,
Linnet, Stonechat, Cuckoo, Whitethroat, Skylark.
Autumn/winter: Good range of birds with feeding
at hide, inc Siskin, Redpoll, plus Hen Harrier on
Trendlebere Down.
Contact: Site Manager, Natural England, Yarner
Wood, 01626 832 330. www.natural-england.org.uk

8. EXMINSTER MARSHES

RSPB (South West England Office).
Location: SX 954 872. Five miles S of Exeter on W
bank of River Exe. Marshes lie between Exminster and
the estuary.
Access: Open at all times, dogs on leads only.
Facilities: No toilets or visitor centre. Information in
RSPB car park and marked footpaths across reserve.
Public transport: Exeter to Newton Abbot/Torquay
buses — stops are 400 yds from car park. Traveline
0871 200 2233. No 2 buses Mon-Sat every 15 mins,
Sun half-hourly.
Habitat: Coastal grazing marsh with freshwater
ditches and pools, reeds, scrub-covered canal banks,
winter stubbles and crops managed for farmland
birds.
Key birds: *Winter*: Brent Goose, Wigeon, Water
Rail, Short-eared Owl. *Spring*: Lapwing, Redshank
and wildfowl breed, Cetti's Warbler on canal banks.
Summer: Gull roosts, passage waders. *Autumn*:
Peregrine, winter wildfowl, finch flocks. There are
also records of Cirl Bunting and Woodlark.
Other notable flora and fauna: 23 species of
dragonfly, including hairy and scarce chaser.
Contact: RSPB, 01392 824 614.
www.rspb.org.uk

9. HALDON FOREST RAPTOR VIEWPOINT

Forestry Commission.
Location: Five miles W of Exeter. Turn off A38 at
Haldon Racecourse junction, then follow signs for
Dunchideock and Forest Walks. After just over 1 mile,
turn L into Haldon Forest Park car park. Follow all-
ability trail to the viewpoint.
Access: Open all year.
Facilities: Toilets in car park. Viewing point with
benches. Path suitable for wheelchairs.
Habitat: Plantations, clearings.
Key birds: *Summer*: Hobby, Nightjar, Turtle Dove,
Tree Pipit. *All year*: Goshawk, Sparrowhawk,
Buzzard, all woodpeckers, Crossbill, Siskin.
Contact: Forestry Commission, 01392 832 262.
www.forestry.gov.uk/england

10. PLYMBRIDGE WOOD

National Trust/Forest Enterprise.
Location: At the Estover roundabout, Plymouth (near
the Wrigley company factory), take the narrow,
steep Plymbridge Road. Park at the bridge area at
the bottom of the hill. Coming from Plympton, pick
up Plymbridge Road from either Plymouth Road or
Glen Road.
Access: Open all year.
Facilities: Car park, woodland paths, picnic area.
Public transport: None.
Habitat: Mixed woodland, river, conifers.
Key birds: *Spring/summer*: Cuckoo, Wood Warbler,
Redstart, Blackcap, possible Nightjar, Crossbill.
Winter: Woodcock, Snipe, Fieldfare, Redwing,
Brambling, Siskin, Redpoll, possible Crossbill. *All
year*: Mandarin Duck, Sparrowhawk, Buzzard, Kestrel,
Tawny Owl, all three woodpeckers, Kingfisher, Grey
Wagtail, Dipper, Goldcrest, common woodland
passerines, Marsh Tit, Raven.
Contact: National Trust, Lanhydrock House,
Lanhydrock, Cornwall, PL30 4DE. 01208 432 691.

11. STOVER LAKE COUNTRY PARK

Devon County Council.
Location: Two miles N of Newton Abbot off A38
Exeter-Plymouth road. Follow the A382 L at
Drumbridges roundabout, signed to Newton Abbot.
After 0.25 miles follow the brown tourist sign L into
the car park (fee payable).
Access: Open all year. Wheelchairs available for
visitor use.
Facilities: Car park, information centre, notice board
display, site leaflets, maps, feeding station, 90 metre
aerial walkway.
Public transport: From Newton Abbot, Exeter or
Plymouth. Info from Traveline 0871 200 2233.
Habitat: Mixed woodland, lake and lowland heath.
SSSI.
Key birds: *Spring/summer*: Sand Martin, Chiffchaff,
Willow Warbler, Spotted Flycatcher, Nightjar, Great
Crested Grebe. *Winter*: Water Rail, Marsh Tit, Snipe.
All year: Woodpeckers, Jay, Siskin, Kingfisher.
Other notable flora and fauna: More than 20 species
of dragonfly and damselfly, including hairy dragonfly,
downy, emerald and red-eyed damselflies. 34 species
of butterfly have been recorded, including white
admiral, pearl-bordered and silver-washed fritillaries.
A good site for bat watching with 10 species
identified.
Contact: Rangers Office, Stover Country Park, Stover,
Newton Abbot, Devon TQ12 6QG. 01626 835 236.
www.devon.gov.uk/stover_country_park

Dorset

WEYMOUTH makes a splendid base, with two RSPB reserves – Lodmoor and Radipole in the town itself. From there you can visit the bird observatory and migration hotspot of Portland Bill to the south and The Fleet and Jurassic coast to the west. To the east, heathland such as Arne RSPB is good for Dartford Warblers and Nightjars. Studland Bay holds all three divers and five grebes species in winter.

1. ARNE

RSPB (South West England Office).
Location: SY 973 882. Four miles SE of Wareham, turn off A351 at Stoborough.
Access: Shipstal Point and Coombe Birdwatchers' trails open all year. Coombe birdwatchers' screen on Middlebere Channel and overlooking estuary open all year. Visitor centre open all year except Christmas. Bird hides on both trails accessed from car park. Coaches and escorted parties by prior arrangement.
Facilities: Toilets in car park. Car park charge applies to non-members. Various footpaths. Visitor centre.
Public transport: None to reserve. Nearest station is Wareham.
Habitat: Lowland heath, woodland, reedbed and saltmarsh, extensive mudflats of Poole Harbour.
Key birds: *All year:* Dartford Warbler, Little Egret, Stonechat. *Winter:* Hen Harrier, Red-breasted Merganser, Black-tailed Godwit. *Summer:* Nightjar, warblers. *Passage:* Spotted Redshank, Whimbrel, Greenshank, Osprey.
Other notable flora and fauna: Sika deer, all six species of UK reptile, silver-studded blue and 32 other butterflies, 23 dragonflies, 850 moths and 500 flowering plants.
Contact: Arne Nature Reserve, RSPB Work Centre, 01929 553 360, e-mail: arne@rspb.org.uk
www.rspb.org.uk/reserves/guide/a/arne/

2. BROWNSEA ISLAND

Dorset Wildlife Trust.
Location: SZ 026 883. Half hour boat rides from Poole Quay with Greenslade Pleasure Boats (01202 631 828) and Brownsea Island Ferries (01929 462 383). Ten minutes from Sandbanks Quay (next to Studland chain-ferry).
Access: Open Apr, May, Jun, Sept and Oct. Access by self-guided nature trail. Costs £2 adults, £1 children. Jul, Aug access by afternoon guided tour (2pm daily, duration 105 minutes). Costs £2 adults, £1 children.
Facilities: Toilets, information centre and shop, six hides, nature trail.
Public transport: Poole rail/bus station for access to Poole Quay and boats. Tel: 01202 673 555.
Habitat: Saline lagoon, reedbed, lakes, coniferous and mixed woodland.
Key birds: *Spring:* Avocet, Black-tailed Godwit, waders, gulls and wildfowl. *Summer:* Common and Sandwich Terns, Yellow-legged Gull, Little Egret,

Little Grebe, Golden Pheasant. *Autumn:* Curlew Sandpiper, Little Stint.
Other notable flora and fauna: Red squirrel, water vole, Bechstein's bat found 2007.
Contact: Dorset Wildlife Trust, 01202 709 445. e-mail: brownseaisland@dorsetwildlife.co.uk
www.wildlifetrust.org.uk/dorset

3. DURLSTON NNR AND COUNTRY PARK

Dorset County Council.
Location: SZ 032 774. One mile S of Swanage (signposted).
Access: Open between sunrise and sunset. Visitor centre open weekends and holidays during winter and daily in other seasons.
Facilities: Guided walks, visitor centre, café, toilets, hide, waymarked trails.
Habitat: Grassland, hedges, cliff, meadows.
Key birds: Cliff-nesting seabird colonies; good variety of scrub and woodland breeding species; spring and autumn migrants; seawatching esp. Apr/May and Aug/Nov.
Other notable flora and fauna: 34 species of butterfly and 500-plus species of flowering plants, inc nine species of orchid.
Contact: The Ranger, Durlston Country Park, 01929 424 443, e-mail: info@durlston.co.uk
www.durlston.co.uk

4. GARSTON WOOD

RSPB (South West England Office).
Location: SU 004 194. SW from Salisbury. From A354 take turn to Sixpenny Handley then take Bowerchalke road (Dean Lane). Keeping R, proceed for approximately 1.5 miles. Garston Wood car park on L of road indicated by a finger post on R side of road.
Access: Pushchairs can be negotiated around all of the rides, though the terrain is best in dry weather. Dogs on leads are only allowed on public footpaths and bridleways.
Facilities: Car park, reserve leaflet, picnic area, group bookings accepted, guided walks available, remote location, good for walking, pushchair friendly.
Public transport: The nearest train station is in Salisbury: from the bus station, take Wilts and Dorset 184 service to Sixpenny Handley (Roebuck Inn).
Habitat: Ancient woodland includes large area of coppiced hazel and maple. Other habitats include oak woodland, scrub and mixed plantation, with important features such as glades, rides and dead wood.
Key birds: Common woodland birds plus Turtle Dove and migrant warblers including Blackcap, Willow Warbler, Garden Warbler and Nightingale. Spotted Flycatcher. Raptors include Buzzard, Sparrowhawk and Goshawk. Winter thrushes.
Other notable flora and fauna: Butterflies, including silver-washed fritillary and elusive white admiral. Adders can be seen on the ride side. Good range of fungi. Fallow deer.
Contact: As Arne Nature Reserve.

5. HAM COMMON LNR

Poole Borough Council.
Location: SY 99. W of Poole. In Hamworthy, take the Blandford Road S along Lake Road, W along Lake Drive and Napier Road, leading to Rockley Park. Park in the beach car park by Hamworthy Pier or Rockley Viewpoint car park, off Napier Road, opposite the entrance to Gorse Hill Central Park.
Access: Open all year. Not suitable for coaches.
Facilities: None.
Habitat: LNR consisting of heathland, scrub, reedbeds, lake. Views over Wareham Channel and Poole Harbour.
Key birds: *Spring/summer*: Stonechat, Dartford Warbler. *Winter*: Brent Goose, Red-breasted Merganser, occasional divers, rarer grebes, Scaup. Waders inc Whimbrel, Greenshank and Common Sandpiper. *All year*: Little Egret.
Contact: Poole Borough Council, 01202 633 633. e-mail: information@poole.gov.uk

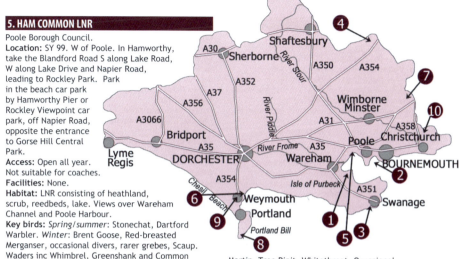

6. LODMOOR

RSPB (South West England Office).
Location: SY 686 807. Adjacent Lodmoor Country Park, in Weymouth, off A353 to Wareham.
Access: Open all times.
Facilities: One viewing shelter, network of paths.
Public transport: Local bus service.
Habitat: Marsh, shallow pools, reeds and scrub, remnant saltmarsh.
Key birds: *Spring/summer*: Breeding Common Tern, warblers (including Reed, Sedge, Grasshopper and Cetti's), Bearded Tit. *Winter*: Wildfowl, waders. *Passage*: Waders and other migrants.
Contact: Nick Tomlinson, RSPB Visitor Centre, Swannery Car Park, Weymouth, DT4 7TZ. 01305 778 313. www.rspb.org.uk

7. MOORS VALLEY COUNTRY PARK AND RINGWOOD FOREST

East Dorset District Council/Forestry Commission
Location: Two miles W of Ringwood, well-signposted from A31 between Ringwood and Three Legged Cross.
Access: Open every day (except Christmas Day) 8am-dusk. Visitor centre open 9am to 4.30pm daily. Many trails wheelchair friendly.
Facilities: Visitor centre, toilets, tea-room, country shop. Coach parking. Way-marked trails in good condition.
Public transport: Accessible by Wilts and Dorset No 36 service (01988 827 005) or visit: www.wdbus.co.uk
Habitat: River, wet meadow, lakes, scrub, broad-leaved woodland, large coniferous forest, golf course.
Key birds: *Spring/summer*: Cuckoo, Nightjar, Sand Martin, Tree Pipit, Whitethroat. Occasional Woodlark, Sedge Warbler. *Winter*: Teal, Pochard, Gadwall, Snipe, Redpoll. Occasional Brambling, Goosander. *Passage*: Whimbrel, Common Sandpiper, waders.
All year: Buzzard, Lapwing, Woodcock, Little Owl, Grey Wagtail, Kingfisher, Dartford Warbler, Crossbill, usual woodland species.
Other notable flora and fauna: 27 species of dragonfly. Good numbers of butterflies and other invertebrates. Roe deer, muntjac, badger, fox, rabbit, grey squirrel.
Contact: Moors Valley Country Park, 01425 470 721, e-mail: moorsvalley@eastdorset.gov.uk www.moors-valley.co.uk

8. PORTLAND BIRD OBSERVATORY

Portland Bird Observatory (registered charity).
Location: SY 681 690. Six miles S of Weymouth beside the road to Portland Bill.
Access: Open at all times. Parking only for members of Portland Bird Observatory. Self-catering accommodation for up to 20. Take own towels, sheets, sleeping bags.
Facilities: Displays and information, toilets, natural history bookshop, equipped kitchen.
Public transport: Bus service from Weymouth (First Dorset Transit Route 1).
Habitat: World famous migration watchpoint. Scrub and ponds.
Key birds: *Spring/autumn*: Migrants, including many rarities. *Summer*: Breeding auks, Fulmar, Kittiwake. A total of 355 species recorded.
Contact: Martin Cade, Old Lower Light, Portland Bill, Dorset, DT5 2JT. 01305 820 553. e-mail: obs@btinternet.com www.portlandbirdobs.org.uk

9. RADIPOLE LAKE

RSPB (South West England Office).
Location: SY 677 796. In Weymouth. Enter from Swannery car park on footpaths.
Access: Visitor centre and nature trail open every day, summer (9am-5pm), winter (9am-4pm). Hide open (8.30am-4.30pm). Permit (available from visitor centre) required by non-RSPB members.
Facilities: Network of paths, one hide, one viewing shelter.
Public transport: Close to train station serving London and Bristol.
Habitat: Lake, reedbeds.
Key birds: *Winter:* Wildfowl. *Summer:* Breeding reedbed warblers (including Cetti's), Bearded Tit, passage waders and other migrants. Garganey regular in spring. Good for rarer gulls.
Contact: Nick Tomlinson, RSPB Visitor Centre, Swannery Car Park, Weymouth, DT4 7TZ. 01305 778 313. www.rspb.org.uk

10. SOPLEY COMMON

Dorset Wildlife Trust.
Location: SZ 132 975. Four miles NW of Christchurch near Hurn village.
Access: Open at all times. Permits required for surveying and group visits. Dogs under close control and on leads Apr to Aug. Limited disabled access.
Facilities: None.
Public transport: None.
Habitat: Lowland heath (dry and wet) and deciduous woodland.
Key birds: *Summer:* Breeding Dartford Warbler, Nightjar, Woodlark, Stonechat. Also Hobby. *Winter:* Snipe.
Other notable flora and fauna: Rare fauna includes sand lizard, smooth snake, green and wood tiger beetles, silver-studded blue butterfly. Wide range of dragonflies on many ponds.
Contact: Dorset Wildlife Trust, 01305 264 620, e-mail: mail@dorsetwildlifetrust.org.uk www.dorsetwildlifetrust.org.uk

Somerset

THE SOMERSET LEVELS are gaining an enviable reputation, not least as an area where continental herons such as Cattle Egret, Great White Egret and Little Bittern have bred recently. The area is also famous for its massive pre-roost gatherings of Starlings in winter. There is an on-going plan to reintroduce Cranes into the area. Elsewhere, Steart Point is good for waders.

1. BREAN DOWN

National Trust (North Somerset).
Location: ST 290 590. 182 map. Juts into Bristol Channel five miles N of Burnham on Sea. J22 of M5, head for Weston-super-Mare on A370 and then head for Brean at Lympsham.
Access: Open all year. Dogs on lead. Steep slope – not suitable for wheelchair-users.
Facilities: Toilets one mile before property, not NT.
Public transport: Call Tourist Information Centre for details 01934 888 800 (bus services differ in winter/summer).
Habitat: Limestone and neutral grassland, scrub and steep cliffs.
Key birds: *All year:* Peregrine, Raven. *Summer:* Blackcap, Garden Warbler, Whitethroat, Stonechat. *Winter:* Curlew, Shelduck, Dunlin on mudflats. Migrants.
Other notable flora and fauna: Chalkhill blue, marbled white and commoner butterflies. Extremely rare white rock rose in June. Somerset hair grass, dwarf sedge.
Contact: The National Trust, Barton Rocks, 01934 844 518.

2. BRIDGWATER BAY NNR

Natural England (Dorset and Somerset Team)
Location: ST 270 470. Five kilometres N of Bridgwater and extends to Burnham-on-Sea. Take J23 or 24 off M5. Turn N off A39 at Cannington.
Access: Hides open every day except Christmas Day. Permits needed for Steart Island (by boat only). Dogs on leads to protect grazing animals/nesting birds. Disabled access to hides by arrangement, other areas accessible.
Facilities: Car park, interpretive panels and leaflet dispenser at Steart. Footpath approx 0.5 miles to tower and hides.
Public transport: Train and bus stations in Bridgwater. First Group buses on A39 stop at Stockland Bristol, 2km SW of Steart. www.firstgroup.com
Habitat: Estuary, intertidal mudflats, saltmarsh.
Key birds: *All year:* Approx 190 species recorded on this Ramsar and SPA site. Wildfowl includes large population of Shelduck and nationally important numbers of Wigeon. Internationally important numbers of Whimbrel and Black-tailed Godwit. Resident Curlews and Oystercatchers joined by many other waders on passage. Good for birds of prey. *Spring/autumn:* Passage migrants, including occasional vagrants.
Other notable flora and fauna: Saltmarsh flora. Rare invertebrates include great silver water beetle, aquatic snail and hairy dragonfly.
Contact: Senior Reserves Manager, Natural England, 0300 060 2570, www.naturalengland.org.uk

3. CATCOTT LOWS

Somerset Wildlife Trust.
Location: ST 400 415. Approx one mile N of Catcott

village (off A39 from J23 of M5).
Access: Open at all times.
Facilities: River Parrett Trail passes through reserve.
Public transport: None.
Habitat: Wet meadows with winter flooding and summer grazing.
Key birds: *Winter*: Wigeon, Teal, Pintail, Shoveler, Gadwall, Bewick's Swan, Peregrine. *Spring*: Little Egret, passage waders, breeding Lapwing, Snipe, Redshank, Yellow Wagtail.
Contact: Somerset Wildlife Trust. 01823 652 400.
e-mail: enquires@somersetwildlife.org
www.somersetwildlife.org

4. CHEW VALLEY LAKE

Avon Wildlife Trust/Bristol Water Plc.
Location: ST 570 600. Nine miles S of Bristol. Take B3114 south from Chew Stoke, bear L for West Harptree and head NE on A368. View reserve from causeway at Herriott's Bridge where there is car parking.
Access: Permit needed for access to hides (five at Chew, two at Blagdon). Best roadside viewing from causeways at Herriott's Bridge (nature reserve) and Herons Green Bay. Day, half-year and year permits from Bristol Water, Recreation Department, Woodford Lodge, Chew Stoke, Bristol BS18 8SH. Tel/Fax 01275 332 339. Parking for coaches available.
Facilities: Hides.
Public transport: Traveline, 0870 6082 608.
Habitat: Largest artificial lake in SW England with important reedbed.
Key birds: Often attracts rarities. *Winter and passage*: Wildfowl include important numbers of Shoveler, Gadwall, Teal and Tufted Duck. Large numbers of Goosander, Great Crested Grebe and Cormorant, with the grebe numbers often the highest in Britain in autumn. Plus Bewick's Swan, Goldeneye, Smew, Ruddy Duck. Huge winter gull roost (up to 50,000+), mostly Black-headed, Common and Mediterranean Gull. *Summer*: Breeding birds include Great Crested and Little Grebe, Gadwall, Tufted Duck, Shoveler, Pochard, Reed Warbler. Hobbies hunt in late summer. When the water level low, mud can attract waders such as Dunlin, Ringed Plover and Green Sandpiper.
Other notable flora and fauna:
Ruddy darter and migrant hawker dragonflies.
Contact: Avon Wildlife Trust HQ or Bristol Water Recreation Dept, 01275 332 339.
e-mail: mail@avonwildlifetrust.org.uk
www.avonwildlifetrust.org.uk

5. GREYLAKE

RSPB (South West England Office).
Location: ST 399 346. Off A361 Taunton to Glastonbury road, between Othery and Greinton.
Access: Open all year, dawn to dusk, free admission. No dogs, apart from guide-dogs. Wheelchair users can access a 700 metre-long boardwalk and viewing hide.
Facilities: Surfaced nature trail, interpretive signs. No toilets on site.
Public transport: Bus No 29 (First Group). Nearest stop is one mile along main road at Greinton phone box, but drivers may stop at reserve on request.
Habitat: A large wet grassland reserve bought by RSPB in 2003. Formerly arable farmland.
Key birds: *Spring/summer*: Kingfisher, Grey Heron, Little Egret and breeding Snipe, Lapwing, Redshank, Skylark, Meadow Pipit, Yellow Wagtail. *Autumn*: Green Sandpiper, waders on passage. *Winter*: Waders, wildfowl (including Lapwing, Golden Plover, Shoveler, Pintail, Teal and Wigeon). Peregrine, Hen Harrier.
Other notable flora and fauna: Roe deer, water vole, stoat, otter, dragonflies including four-spotted chaser.
Contact: Site Manager, 01458 252 805;
e-mail:west.sedgemoor@rspb.org.uk
www.rspb.org.uk/reserves/guide/g/greylake

6. HAM WALL

RSPB (South West England Office).
Location: ST 449 397. W of Glastonbury. From A39 turn N in Ashcott and follow road onto the moor. After three miles pass Church Farm Horticultural building. Shortly after, at metal bridge, reserve is opposite side of road to Shapwick Heath NNR.
Access: Open all year. 2m height restriction on car park. Coach parking available at Avalon Marshes Centre, Shapwick Road. Dogs only on public footpaths and disused railway line. Wheelchair users can access viewing areas

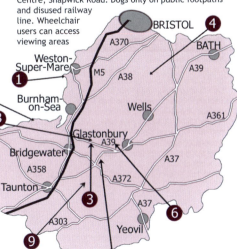

from main track (use RADAR key). Other rougher tracks cover 3.8 miles.

Facilities: Two open-air viewing platforms, four roofed viewing screens.

Public transport: By bus: Service 668 to Avalon Marshes Centre (BA6 9TT) at Westhay village, approx I mile or St Mary's Road, Meare (approx 1.2 miles from reserve entrance).

Habitat: 200-plus hectare wetland, including region's largest reedbed.

Key birds: *Spring/summer:* Bittern, Cetti's Warbler, Water Rail, warblers, Hobby, Barn Owl. *Autumn:* Migrant thrushes, Lesser Redpoll, Siskin, Kingfisher, Bearded Tit. *Winter:* Million+ Starling roost, plus large flocks of ducks, Bittern, Little Egret, Peregrine, Merlin, Short-eared Owl.

Other notable flora and fauna: Otter, water vole, dragonflies, butterflies.

Contact: RSPB Ham Wall,1458 860494.

e-mail:ham.wall@rspb.org.uk;

7. HORNER WOOD NATURE RESERVE

National Trust.**Location:** SS 897 454. From Minehead, take A39 W to a minor road 0.8km E of Porlock signed to Horner. Park in village car park.

Access: Open all year. Car parking in Horner village, extensive footpath system.

Facilities: Tea-room and toilets. Walks leaflets available from Holnicote Estate office and Porlock visitor centre. Interpretation boards in car parks.

Public transport: Bus: Porlock.

Habitat: Oak woodland, moorland.

Key birds: *Spring/summer:* Wood Warbler, Pied Flycatcher, Redstart, Stonechat, Whinchat, Tree Pipit, Dartford Warbler possible. *All year:* Dipper, Grey Wagtail, woodpeckers, Buzzard, Sparrowhawk.

Other notable flora and fauna: Silver-washed fritillary in July.

Contact: National Trust, 01643 862 452.

e-mail: holnicote@nationaltrust.org.uk
www.nationaltrust.org.uk

8. SHAPWICK MOOR RESERVE

Hawk and Owl Trust.

Location: ST417 398. On Somerset Levels. From J23 on M5 take A39 towards Glastonbury, after 6 miles turn N onto minor road, signed Shapwick. Continue straight over crossroads, through Shapwick village, towards Westhay, turn L at T-junction following signs for Peat Moors Centre, park here. Reserve is about half way between centre and Shapwick village.

Access: Open all year (except Christmas Day). Access only along public footpaths and permissive path. Dogs on leads only.

Facilities: Information panels. Public toilets at nearby Avalon Marshes Centre (ST 425 414), none on site.

Public transport: Train to Bridgwater, then First Bus (01278 434 574) No 375 Bridgwater-Glastonbury, to Shapwick village. Sustrans National Route 3 passes through Shapwick village.

Habitat: A wet grassland reserve covering 134 acres. Grazing pasture, hay meadows with rough grass edges, fen, open ditches, pollard willows and hedges.

Key birds: *Spring/summer:* Hobby, Barn Owl, Reed Bunting and Cetti's Warbler. Whimbrel and other waders on passage. Skylark. Passerines such as Skylark, Bullfinch, Greenfinch and Yellowhammer. *Autumn/winter:* Flocks of finches, Snipe, Shoveler, Gadwall, Stonechat, Brambling. Peregrine and harriers may fly over. *All year:* Buzzard, Kestrel, Sparrowhawk, Kingfisher, Lapwing, Grey Heron, Mute Swan.

Other notable fauna: Mammals include roe deer, brown hare, stoat, badger, otter and water vole.

Contact: Hawk and Owl Trust, 0844 984 2824;

e-mail: enquiries@hawkandowl.org
www.hawkandowl.org

9. SWELL WOOD

(RSPB South West England Office).

Location: ST 361 238. Entrance down by-road off A378 Taunton-Langport road, one mile E of Fivehead.

Access: Access at all times to Swell Wood car park and heronry hide. Coach parking in lay-by across main road. Heronry hide and part of woodland trail are wheelchair accessible.

Facilities: Heronry hide, two nature trails: woodland trail and scarp trail link to public footpaths, disabled parking area.

Public transport: Bus from Taunton to Fivehead. First Southern National Ltd 01823 272 033.

Habitat: Semi-natural ancient oak woodland and views across wet grassland from woodland trails. Part of the Somerset Levels and Moors.

Key birds: *Spring/summer:* Breeding Grey Heron, Little Egret, Buzzard, Bullfinch, Spotted Flycatcher, Song Thrush, warblers such as Chiffchaff, Blackcap and Garden Warbler.

On escorted walks: Curlew, Snipe, Sedge Warbler, Yellow Wagtail, Skylark, Nightingale. *Autumn:* Green Woodpecker, Robin, Wren, Coal Tit. *Winter:* Long-tailed Tit, Treecreeper, Great Spotted Woodpecker, Nuthatch.

Other notable flora and fauna: Roe deer, woodland flora such as bluebells, wood anemone, lesser celandine, plus dragonflies, damselflies, butterflies.

Contact: Site Manager, 01458 252 805.

e-mail: swell.wood@rspb.org.uk
www.rspb.org.uk/reserves/guide/s/swellwood/

Wiltshire

MUCH of Salisbury Plain, an important chalk downland habitat, is used by the Ministry of Defence as a gunnery range and access is restricted. Perversely, this reduces the amount of human disturbance and increases the biodiversity. There is an attempt to re-introduce Great Bustards here. The Cotswold Water Park is the best area for wildfowl in winter and Hobbies in summer.

LANGFORD LAKES

Wiltshire Wildlife Trust.
Location: SU 037 370. Nr Steeple Langford, S of A36, approx eight miles W of Salisbury. In centre of village, turn S into Duck Street, signposted Hanging Langford. Langford Lakes is first L just after a small bridge.
Access: Opened to the public in Sept 2002. Main gates open during the day — ample parking. Advance notice required for coaches. No dogs.
Facilities: Visitor centre, toilets, education centre. Four hides, all accessible to wheelchairs. Cycle stands provided (250m from Wiltshire Cycleway between Great Wishford and Hanging Langford).
Public transport: Nearest bus stop 500m - X4 Service between Salisbury and Warminster.
Habitat: Three former gravel pits, with newly created islands and developing reed fringes. 12 ha (29 acres) of open water; also wet woodland, scrub, chalk river.
Key birds: *Summer*: Breeding Coot, Moorhen, Mallard Tufted Duck, Pochard, Gadwall, Little Grebe, Great Crested Grebe. Also Kingfisher, Common Sandpiper, Grey Wagtail, warblers (8 species). *Winter*: Common wildfowl, sometimes also Wigeon, Shoveler, Teal, Water Rail, Little Egret, Bittern. *Passage*: Sand Martin, Green Sandpiper, waders, Black Tern.
Contact: Wiltshire Wildlife Trust, Langford Lakes, 01722 790 770; e-mail: info@wiltshirewildlife.org

RAVENSROOST WOOD

Wiltshire Wildlife Trust.
Location: SU 023 877. NW of Swindon. Take B4696 Ashton Keynes road N from Wootton Bassett. After two miles take second turn L to Minety. Go straight on when main road turns R. Go straight over next crossroads and car park is on R after 1/4 mile.
Access: Open at all times.
Facilities: Small car park, small shelter.
Habitat: Woodland, both coppice and high oak forest, and ponds.
Key birds: Breeding Willow Warblers, Blackcap, Chiffchaff and Garden Warblers. In winter mixed flocks of Nuthatches, tits and Treecreepers move noisily through the wood and Woodcock can be flushed from wet, muddy areas.
Other notable flora and fauna: Butterflies include silver-washed fritillary and white admiral, plus meadow brown, gatekeeper and peacock. Good display of spring bluebells, wood anemone, wood sorrel, sanicle, violet and primrose. In summer,

common spotted, early purple and greater butterfly orchids, hemp agrimony and betony.
Contact: Wiltshire Wildlife Trust, Langford Lakes, 01722 790 770.
e-mail: info@wiltshirewildlife.org www.wiltshirewildlife.or

SAVERNAKE FOREST

Savernake Estate Trustees.
Location: From Marlborough the A4 Hungerford road runs along side of forest. Two pillars mark Forest Hill entrance, 1.5 miles E of A346/A4 junction. The Grand Avenue leads straight through the middle of the woodland to join a minor road from Stibb.
Access: Privately owned but open all year to public. (Roads are closed occasionally).
Facilities: Car park, picnic site at NW end by A346. Only enter fenced-off areas if there is a footpath.
Habitat: Ancient woodland, with one of the largest collections of veteran trees in Britain.
Key birds: *Spring/summer*: Garden Warbler, Blackcap, Willow Warbler, Chiffchaff, Wood Warbler, Redstart, occasional Nightingale, Tree Pipit, Spotted Flycatcher. *Winter*: Finch flocks possibly inc Siskin, Redpoll, Brambling and Hawfinch. *All year*: Sparrowhawk, Buzzard, Red Kite, Woodcock, owls, all three woodpeckers, Marsh Tit, Willow Tit, Jay and other woodland birds.
Other notable flora and fauna: Rare lichens and fungi, all main deer species, badgers, foxes.
Contact: Savernake Estate, Estate Foreman: 01672 810302; savernakeestate@hotmail.com www.savernakeestate.co.uk

SWILLBROOK LAKES

Wiltshire Wildlife Trust.
Location: SU 018 934. NW of Swindon. From A419 Swindon - Cirencester road, turn L onto Cotswold Water Park Spine Road. Cross B4696 South Cerney/ Ashton Keynes road, take next L, Minety Lane, after about 1.5 miles. Parking is in the gateway on either side of road, after about 0.5 miles. Swillbrook Lakes nature reserve and information board is on E side of road.
Access: Open at all times.
Facilities: Footpath along N and E sides of lakes.
Habitat: Gravel pits with shallow pools, rough grassland and scrub around edges.
Key birds: *Winter*: Wildfowl (inc. Gadwall, Pochard, Smew, Goosander, Goldeneye). *Summer*: Breeding Nightingale, Garden, Reed and Sedge Warblers, Blackcap, Cetti's Warbler, Sand and House Martin, Swallow. One of the best sites for Hobby and Nightingale in Cotswold WP.
Other notable flora and fauna: 18 species of dragonfly including downy emerald and lesser emperor in recent years.
Contact: Wiltshire Wildlife Trust, Langford Lakes, 01722 790 770; e-mail: info@wiltshirewildlife.org www.wiltshirewildlife.org

Scottish Border Counties

Borders, Dumfries and Galloway

Borders

THE CLIFFS at St Abb's Head hold a large summer seabird colony, while migrants move past in spring and autumn. Try seawatching in autumn either there, or from Rotten Brae, Eyemouth. Ospreys have recently moved into the area and can often be seen fishing at Duns Castle. Water Rails breed at Yetholm Loch, which is also good for wildfowl.

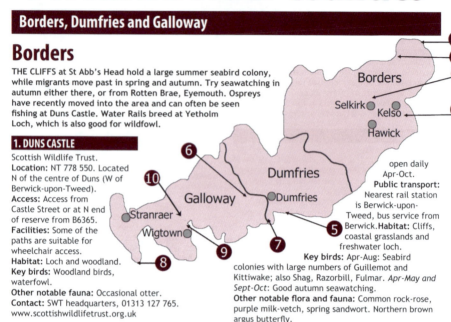

1. DUNS CASTLE

Scottish Wildlife Trust.
Location: NT 778 550. Located N of the centre of Duns (W of Berwick-upon-Tweed).
Access: Access from Castle Street or at N end of reserve from B6365.
Facilities: Some of the paths are suitable for wheelchair access.
Habitat: Loch and woodland.
Key birds: Woodland birds, waterfowl.
Other notable fauna: Occasional otter.
Contact: SWT headquarters, 01313 127 765. www.scottishwildlifetrust.org.uk

2. GUNKNOWE LOCH AND PARK

Scottish Borders Council.
Location: NT 518 345. At Tweedbank, 3.2km from Galashiels on the A6091. Park at Gunknowe Loch.
Access: Open all year. Surfaced paths suitable for wheelchair use.
Facilities: Car park, paths.
Public transport: Tweedbank is on the Melrose-to-Peebles bus route.
Habitat: River, man-made loch, parkland, scrub, woodland.
Key birds: *Spring/summer:* Grey Wagtail, Kingfisher, Sand Martin, Blackcap, Sedge and Grasshopper Warblers. *Passage:* Yellow Wagtail, Whinchat, Wheatear. *Winter:* Thrushes, Brambling, Wigeon, Tufted Duck, Pochard, Goldeneye. *All year:* Great Spotted and Green Woodpeckers, Redpoll, Goosander, possible Marsh Tit.
Contact: Ranger Service 01835 825 060. www.scotborders.gov.uk

3. ST ABB'S HEAD

National Trust for Scotland.
Location: NT 914 693 for car park and bus stop. Lies five miles N of Eyemouth. Follow A1107 from A1.
Access: Reserve open all yar. All-ability path to viewpoint at Starney Bay. Well behaved dogs welcome; keep dogs under close control and droppings taken home. Coach parking at Northfield Farm by prior arrangement.
Facilities: Visitor centre and toilets (inc disabled)

open daily Apr-Oct.
Public transport: Nearest rail station is Berwick-upon-Tweed, bus service from Berwick. **Habitat:** Cliffs, coastal grasslands and freshwater loch.
Key birds: Apr-Aug: Seabird colonies with large numbers of Guillemot and Kittiwake; also Shag, Razorbill, Fulmar. *Apr-May and Sept-Oct:* Good autumn seawatching.
Other notable flora and fauna: Common rock-rose, purple milk-vetch, spring sandwort. Northern brown argus butterfly.
Contact: Liza Cole, Ranger's Office, 01890 771 443. www.nts.org.uk, www.stabbrangers.blotspot.com and St Abb's Head NNR page on Facebook

4. THE HIRSEL

The Estate Office, The Hirsel.
Location: NT 827 403. Signposted off the A698 on the outskirts of Coldstream.
Access: Open all year. Private estate so please stick to the public paths. Coaches by appointment.
Facilities: Car parks, visitor centre, toilets, hide, walks, café.
Public transport: Bus: Coldstream, Kelso, Berwick-upon-Tweed, Edinburgh. **Habitat:** Freshwater loch, reeds, woods.
Key birds: *Spring/summer:* Redstart, Garden Warbler, Blackcap, flycatchers, possible Water Rail, wildfowl. *Autumn:* Wildfowl, Goosander, possible Green Sandpiper. *Winter:* Whooper Swan, Pink-footed Goose, Wigeon, Goldeneye, Pochard, occasional Smew, Scaup, Slavonian Grebe.
Contact: John Letham, Hirsel Estate Manager, 01890 830 293; e-mail:john.letham2@btinternet.com www.dandaestates.co.uk

Dumfries and Galloway

THE SOLWAY holds nationally important numbers of wintering Barnacle Geese, with Caerlaverock WWT and RSPB Mersehead being prime sites. Ospreys and Red Kites are colonising and there is a chance of a Golden Eagle over upland areas or Hen

Harrier on moorland. The Mull of Galloway has fine seabird cliffs. The Ken/Dee Marshes hold Willow Tit and Nuthatch.

5. CAERLAVEROCK WETLAND CENTRE

The Wildfowl & Wetlands Trust.
Location: NY 051 656. Overlooks the Solway. From Dumfries take B725 towards Bankend.
Access: Open daily (10am-5pm), except Christmas.
Facilities: 20 hides, heated observatory, four towers, Salcot Merse Observatory, sheltered picnic area. Self-catering accommodation and camping facilities. Nature trails in summer. Old Granary visitor building with fair-trade coffee shop serving light meals and snacks; natural history bookshop; binoculars & telescopes for sale. Theatre/conference room. Binoculars for hire. Parking for coaches.
Public transport: Bus 6A from Dumfries stops 30 mins walk from reserve. Stagecoach 01387 253 496.
Habitat: Saltmarsh, grassland, wetland.
Key birds: *Winter*: Wildfowl esp. Barnacle Geese (max 30,000) and Whooper Swans. *Summer*: Osprey, Barn Owl, Skylark.
Other notable flora and fauna: Natterjack toads. Northern marsh, common spotted and twayblade orchids.
Contact: WWT Caerlaverock, 01387 770 200.
e-mail: info.caerlaverock@wwt.org.uk wwt.org.uk

6. KEN-DEE MARSHES

RSPB (South & West Scotland Office).
Location: NX 699 684. Six miles from Castle Douglas — good views from A762 and A713 roads to New Galloway.
Access: From car park at entrance to farm Mains of Duchrae. Open during daylight hours. No dogs.
Facilities: Hides, nature trails. Three miles of trails available, nearer parking for elderly and disabled, but phone warden first. Part of Red Kite trail.
Public transport: None. **Habitat:** Marshes, woodlands, open water.
Key birds: *All year*: Mallard, Grey Heron, Buzzard, Nuthatch, Willow Tit. *Spring/summer*: Pied Flycatcher, Redstart, Tree Pipit, Sedge Warbler. *Winter*: Greenland White-fronted and Greylag Geese, raptors (Hen Harrier, Peregrine, Merlin, Red Kite).
Other notable flora and fauna: Red squirrel.
Contact: RSPB Ken-Dee Marshes, 01556 670 464

7. MERSEHEAD

RSPB (South & West Scotland Office).
Location: NX 928 566. From Dumfries take A710 S for about 16 miles. Reserve is signposted on L just before Caulkerbush village. Single track road with passing places runs for a mile to car park and visitor centre. From Castle Douglas, take A745, then A711 to Dalbeattie before joining A710.
Access: Open at all times. Wheelchair friendly.
Facilities: Hide, nature trails, information centre, refreshments and toilets. Visitors with restricted mobility can take vehicles to within 300 metres of the hide to designated parking spaces.

Public transport: None.**Habitat:** Wet grassland, arable farmland, saltmarsh, inter-tidal mudflats.
Key birds: *Winter*: Up to 9,500 Barnacle Geese, 4,000 Teal, 2,000 Wigeon, 1,000 Pintail, waders (inc. Dunlin, Knot, Oystercatcher). *Summer*: Breeding birds include Lapwing, Redshank, Skylark.
Contact: RSPB Mersehead, 01387 780 579;
e-mail: mersehead@rspb.org.uk

8. MULL OF GALLOWAY

RSPB (South & West Scotland Office).
Location: NX 156 304. Most southerly tip of Scotland — five miles from village of Drummore, S of Stranraer.
Access: Open at all times. Access suitable for disabled. Disabled parking by centre. Centre open summer only (Apr-Oct).
Facilities: Visitor centre, toilets, nature trails, CCTV on cliffs.
Public transport: None. **Habitat:** Sea cliffs, coastal heath.
Key birds: *Spring/summer*: Guillemot, Razorbill, Kittiwake, Black Guillemot, Puffin, Fulmar, Raven, Wheatear, Rock Pipit, Twite. Migrating Manx Shearwater. *All year*: Peregrine.
Contact: RSPB Mull of Galloway, 01988 402 130;
e-mail: mullofgalloway@rspb.org.uk

9. WIGTOWN BAY LNR

Dumfries & Galloway Council.
Location: NX 465 545. Between Wigtown and Creetown, S of Newton Stewart. It is the largest LNR in Britain at 2,845 ha. The A75 runs along E side, with A714 S to Wigtown and B7004 providing superb views of the LNR.
Access: Reserve open at all times. The hide is disabled-friendly. Main accesses: Roadside lay-bys on A75 near Creetown and parking at Martyr's Stake and Wigtown Harbour. All suitable for coaches. Visitor Centre in Wigtown County Building has coach parking and welcomes groups. It has full disabled access, including lift and toilets.
Facilities: Hide at Wigtown Harbour overlooking River Bladnoch, saltmarsh and fresh water wetland has disabled access from harbour car park. Walks and interpretation in this area. Visitor centre has a commanding view of the bay. CCTV of Ospreys breeding in Galloway during summer and wetland birds in winter. Open Mon-Sat (10am-5pm, later some days). Sun (2pm-5pm).
Public transport: Travel Information Line 08457 090 510 (local rate 9am-5pm Mon-Fri). Bus No 415 for Wigtown and W side. Bus No 431 or 500 X75 for Creetown and E side.**Habitat:** Estuary with extensive saltmarsh/merse and mudflats with developed fresh water wetland at Wigtown Harbour.
Key birds: *Winter*: Internationally important for Pink-footed Goose, nationally important for Curlew, Whooper Swan and Pintail, with major gull roost and other migratory coastal birds. *Summer*: Breeding waders and duck.
Other notable flora and fauna: Fish including smelt and shad. Lax-flowered sea-lavender, sea aster.

NATURE RESERVES - CENTRAL SCOTLAND

Contact: Visitor Centre 01988 402 673, Keith Kirk, Countryside Ranger, 01556 505 479, (M)07850 157 661; e-mail:keith.kirk@dumgal.gov.uk www.dgcommunity.net/wblr

10. WOOD OF CREE

RSPB (South & West Scotland Office).
Location: NX 382 708. Four miles N of Newton Stewart on minor road from Minnigaff, parallel to A714.
Access: Open during daylight hours. Dogs on lead. Not suitable for disabled.

Facilities: Nature trails.
Public transport: None. **Habitat:** Oak woodland, marshes, river.
Key birds: *Spring/summer:* Pied Flycatcher, Wood Warbler, Tree Pipit, Redstart, Buzzard, Great Spotted Woodpecker.
Other notable flora and fauna: Red squirrel, otter, Leisler's bat, carpet of bluebells and other spring wildflowers.
Contact: Wood of Cree, 01988 402 130;
e-mail: wood.cree@rspb.org.uk

Central Scotland

Argyll, Ayrshire, Clyde, Fife, Forth, Lothian

Argyll

TWO ISLANDS take the birding honours for this region. Islay is renowned for its wintering wildfowl, including huge numbers of Barnacle and White-fronted Geese. Choughs, raptors and Corncrakes are other island specialities. The island of Mull is home to the highest breeding densities of Golden Eagle and White-tailed Eagles in Britain.

1. COLL RESERVE

RSPB (South & West Scotland Office).
Location: NM 167 563. By ferry from Oban to island of Coll. Take the B8070 W from Arinagour for five miles. Turn R at Arileod. Continue for about one mile. Park at end of the road. Reception point at Totronald.
Access: Open all year. A natural site with unimproved paths not suitable for wheelchairs. Please avoid walking through fields and crops.
Facilities: Car park, information bothy at Totronald, guided walks in summer. Corncrake viewing bench.
Public transport: None.**Habitat:** Sand dunes, beaches, machair grassland, moorland, farmland.
Key birds: *Spring:* Gt Northern Diver offshore. Corncrakes arrive in late April. Displaying waders, inc Redshank, Lapwing, Snipe. *Summer:* Auks offshore, plus Gannet, shearwaters and terns. *Autumn:* Barnacle and Greenland White-fronted Geese arrive, thrushes on passage. Waders inc Purple Sandpiper. *Winter:* Long-tailed Duck, divers offshore. Hunting Hen Harrier and Merlin. Twite.
Other notable flora and fauna: Good for ceteceans and basking shark. Otter, 300-plus machair wildflowers inc rare orchids, great yellow bumblebee.
Contact: RSPB Coll Nature Reserve, 01879 230 301; www.rspb.org.uk

2. LOCH GRUINART, ISLAY

RSPB (South & West Scotland Office).
Location: NR 275 672. Sea loch on N coast of Islay,

seven miles NW from Bridgend.
Access: Hide open all hours, visitor centre open (10am-5pm), disabled access to hide, viewing area and toilets. Assistance required for wheelchair users. Coach parking at visitor centre only. No dogs in hides.
Facilities: Toilets (inc disabled), visitor centre (offers hot drinks), hide, trail. Two car parks — the one opposite the viewpoint is level and made from rolled stone. Group bookings accepted. Weekly guided walks every Thursday at 10am (April to Oct)
Public transport: Nearest bus stops 3 miles from reserve.
Habitat: Lowland wet grasslands, sea loch, moorland.
Key birds: *Oct-Apr:* Large numbers of Barnacle and White-fronted Geese, plus other wildfowl and waders. *May-Aug:* Breeding and displaying waders and Corncrake. *Sept-Nov:* Many passage migrants and arriving wildfowl. Birds of prey are present all year, esp Hen Harrier and Peregrine, while Chough can be seen feeding in nearby fields. *Spring:* Displaying Snipe, Lapwing, Curlew and Redshank.
Other notable flora and fauna: Otter, red and roe deer. Marsh fritillary butterflies during May and June.
Contact: RSPB Scotland, 01496 850 505.
e-mail: loch.gruinart@rspb.org.uk
www.rspb.org.uk/scotland

3. MACHRIHANISH SEABIRD OBSERVATORY

(sponsored by SNH and Leader+) Nancie Smith and Eddie Maguire.
Location: NR 628 209. Southwest Kintyre, Argyll. Six miles W of Campbeltown on A83, then B843.
Access: Daily April-Oct. Wheelchair access. Dogs welcome. Parking for three cars. Digiscoping facilities include electricity and monitor.
Facilities: Seawatching hide, toilets in nearby village. Coach parking.
Public transport: Regular buses from Campbeltown (West Coast Motors, tel 01586 552 319).**Habitat:** Marine, rocky shore and upland habitats.

210

Key birds: *Summer*: Golden Eagle, Peregrine, Storm Petrel and Twite. *Autumn*: Passage seabirds and waders. On-shore gales often produce inshore movements of Leach's Petrel and other scarce seabirds, including Balearic Shearwater, Sabine's Gull and Grey Phalarope. *Winter*: Great Northern Diver, Purple Sandpiper, Ruddy Turnstone with occasional Glaucous and Iceland Gulls.
Other notable flora and fauna: Grey and common seals, otter, wild goat.
Contact: Eddie Maguire, Warden, 07919 660 292.
e-mail:machrihanishbirds@btinternet.com
www.machrihanishbirds.org.uk

4. THE OA, ISLE OF ISLAY

RSPB (South & West Scotland Office).
Location: NR 282 423. Six miles SW of Port Ellen, Islay.
Access: Open all year. Terrain is uneven and soft underfoot.
Facilities: Car park and waymarked trail. No toilets or other facilities. Guided walk every Tuesday from April to October.
Habitat: Open moorland, freshwater loch, seacliffs, coastal grassland and heath.
Key birds: Breeding Golden Eagle, Red-throated Diver, Peregrine, Hen Harrier, Chough, Corncrake and farmland birds. *Winter*: Greenland White-fronted Goose, Merlin, Twite and winter finches and thrushes.
Other notable flora and fauna: Narrow-bordered bee hawkmoth, feral goats on cliffs.
Contact: David Wood, RSPB Scotland, 01496 300 118.
e-mail: the.oa@rspb.org.uk

Ayrshire

AILSA CRAIG boasts a huge gannetry, together with plenty of other breeding seabirds. Martnaham Loch is good for wildfowl and a good range of common species. Turnberry Point is excellent for seawatching, with Twite in the scrub there. The shore at Barassie and Troon sees a large build-up of waders in autumn, plus white-winged gulls in winter.

5. AILSA CRAIG

RSPB (South & West Scotland Office).
Location: NX 020 998. Island is nine miles offshore, nearest town on mainland is Girvan.
Access: Accessible only by boat - no landing possible. Boat trips on the MFV Glorious (tel: 01465 713 219) or Kintyre Express (tel: 01294 270 160) from Girvan during the summer period. Also from Campbeltown by Mull of Kintyre Seatours' fast rib (07785 542 811).
Facilities: None
Public transport: None. **Habitat:** Dramatic seacliffs.
Key birds: Ailsa Craig is the third largest gannetry in the UK and supports 73,000 breeding seabirds, including Guillemot, Razorbill, Puffin, Black Guillemot, Kittiwake and up to 36,000 pairs of Gannets. Twite can also be found here.
Other notable flora and fauna: Slow worm.

Contact: RSPB, 0141 331 0993.
e-mail:glasgow@rspb.org.uk

6. CULZEAN CASTLE COUNTRY PARK

National Trust for Scotland.
Location: NS 234 103. 12 miles SW of Ayr on A719.
Access: Country Park open all year during daylight hours. Restaurant/shops open daily (Apr-Oct) and weekends Nov-March. Access leaflet available.
Facilities: Car park, visitor centre, children's playground, picnic areas, 21 miles of footpath and estate tracks, ranging from unsurfaced woodland paths to metalled roads.
Public transport: Stagecoach bus No 60 (Ayr to Girvan) stops at site entrance. One mile walk downhill to visitor centre and castle.
Habitat: Shoreline, parkland, woodland, gardens, streams, ponds.
Key birds: *All year*: Good populations of common woodland species, inc Jay, Great Spotted Woodpecker and thrushes. *Spring/summer*: Arriving migrants, esp Blackcap, Chiffchaff and Willow Warbler. Nesting Raven and Gannet on cliffs, Gannet and terns offshore. *Autumn/winter*: Regular flocks of Redwing and Fieldfare, Waxwing, crossbills. Wildfowl on pond inc Little Grebe, Tufted Duck, Goldeneye. Offshore divers and Eider.
Other notable fauna: Roe deer, otter, water vole, several species of bat. Shoreline SSSI rich in rock pool life.
Contact: The Ranger Service, Culzean Castle & Country Park, 0844 493 2148.

7. GARNOCK FLOODS

Scottish Wildlife Trust.
Location: NS 306 417. From A779 N, take the one-way road to Bogside, just beyond A779 interchange. Park on roadside. Best viewed from cycle track along E boundary.
Access: Open all year. **Facilities:** Parking.
Habitat: River, ponds, rush pasture.
Key birds: *Spring/summer*: Sedge and Willow Warblers, Lesser Whitethroat, Sand Martin. *Winter*: Wildfowl inc Goldeneye, Mute Swan, occasional Garganey, waders including Ruff and Snipe.
Contact: SWT headquarters 01313 127 765.
www.scottishwildlifetrust.org.uk/garnock-floods

Clyde

THE FALLS OF CLYDE Scottish Wildlife Trust reserve has a well-known Peregrine watchpoint, with Dippers and Kingfishers along the river. Whinchats and several species of warbler breed at Baron's Haugh, with a good autumn passage of waders there. RSPB Lochwinnoch offers a good selection of commoner species throughout the year.

8. BARON'S HAUGH

RSPB (South & West Scotland Office).
Location: RSPB NS 756 553. On SW edge of

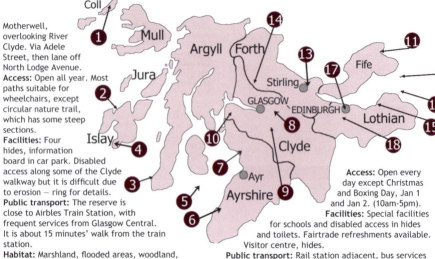

Motherwell, overlooking River Clyde. Via Adele Street, then lane off North Lodge Avenue.
Access: Open all year. Most paths suitable for wheelchairs, except circular nature trail, which has some steep sections.
Facilities: Four hides, information board in car park. Disabled access along some of the Clyde walkway but it is difficult due to erosion — ring for details.
Public transport: The reserve is close to Airbles Train Station, with frequent services from Glasgow Central. It is about 15 minutes' walk from the train station.
Habitat: Marshland, flooded areas, woodland, parkland, meadows, scrub, river.
Key birds: *Summer:* Breeding Gadwall, warblers (inc. Garden, Grasshopper); Whinchat, Common Sandpiper, Kingfisher, Sand Martin. *Autumn:* Excellent for waders (22 species). *Winter:* Whooper Swan, Pochard, Wigeon, Sparrowhawk.
Contact: RSPB, 0141 331 0993; e-mail: baronshaugh@rspb.org.uk

9. FALLS OF CLYDE

Scottish Wildlife Trust
Location: NS 883 414. Approx one mile S of Lanark. Directions from Glasgow – travel S on M74 until J7 then along A72, following brown signs for New Lanark.
Access: Reserve open daily. Disabled access limited, as reserve is not wheelchair accessible. Visitor centre is wheelchair friendly, inc toilet facilities.
Facilities: Visitor centre open daily 10am-5pm Apr-Sept, 11am-5pm Oct-Mar. Peregrine watch site open from Mar-Jun. Woodland trails and a range of guided walks inc self-guided, wildflower trail and badger watches.
Public transport: Scotrail trains run to Lanark. Local bus service from Lanark to New Lanark.
Habitat: River runs through ancient gorge woodland with waterfalls, meadow and wet woodland.
Key birds: Over 100 species of birds, unrivalled views of breeding Peregrines. Others inc Kingfisher, Dipper, Jay, Spotted Flycatcher and Goosander.
Other notable flora and fauna: Badgers, otters, bats and wildflowers.
Contact: Falls of Clyde Visitor Centre 01555 665 262; e-mail:fallsofclyde@swt.co.uk www.swt.org.uk

10. LOCHWINNOCH

RSPB (South & West Scotland Office).
Location: NS 358 582. 18 miles SW of Glasgow, adjacent to A760.

Access: Open every day except Christmas and Boxing Day, Jan 1 and Jan 2. (10am-5pm).
Facilities: Special facilities for schools and disabled access in hides and toilets. Fairtrade refreshments available. Visitor centre, hides.
Public transport: Rail station adjacent, bus services nearby.
Habitat: Shallow lochs, marsh, mixed woodland.
Key birds: *Winter:* Wildfowl (esp. Whooper Swan, Wigeon, Goosander, Goldeneye). Occasional passage migrants inc. Whimbrel, Greenshank. *Summer:* Breeding Great Crested Grebe, Water Rail, Sedge and Grasshopper Warblers, Reed Bunting.
Other notable fauna: Possible otters, roe deer, small mammals, butterflies, moths and dragon/damselflies.
Contact: RSPB Nature Centre, 01505 842 663; e-mail lochwinnoch@rspb.org.uk www.rspb.org.uk/lochwinnoch

Fife

WINTERING flocks of seaducks off Ruddons Point often hold a few Surf Scoters among the more numerous Common and Velvet Scoters, while Fife Ness is good for seawatching and autumn migrants. The Eden Estuary holds good numbers of wildfowl and waders throughout the year but especially in winter. Tentsmuir offers an unusual mix of woodland and coastal habitats.

11. EDEN ESTUARY LNR

Fife Coast and Countryside Trust
Location: 470 195 (centre of site). The Local Nature Reserve can be accessed from Guardbridge, St Andrews (2 miles) on A91, and from Leuchars via Tentsmuir Forest off A919 (4 miles). Use Outhead at St Andrews off, West Sands beach, to access Balgove Bay.
Access: Eden Estuary Centre, Guardbridge: (Entry by keypad number available from ranger service). Open (9am-5pm) all days except Dec 25, 26th and 31st and Jan 1st. Evans Hide: at GR 483 183, parking at Pilmuir Links golf course car park. Combination number required from ranger service.
Facilities: Visitor centre at Guardbridge. Viewing

platform and picnic area at Outhead. Evans Hide at Balgove Bay (number from Ranger Service).
Public transport: Leuchars train station (1.5 miles), regular bus service from Cupar and Dundee. Tel 08457 484 950.
Habitat: Intertidal mudflats, saltmarsh, river, reed, sand dunes and wetland.
Key birds: Winter and passage: Significant numbers of waders and wildfowl. Outer estuary is good place for sea duck such as Scoter, Eider and Long-tailed Duck, plus Gannet, terns and skuas. Mudflats ideal for Godwits, Plovers, Sandpipers, Redshank and Shelduck. River good for Kingfisher, Common Sandpiper and Goosander. Surrounding area is good for Short and Long-eared Owl, Peregrine, Marsh Harrier, Sea Eagle and Merlin. Osprey are regular visitors, daily throughout the season.
Other notable flora and fauna: Northern marsh orchid, dune grasses, herbs, maiden pink, saltmarsh grasses and reed systems. Harbour and Grey seal, bottle-nosed dolphin, porpoise, brown hare, stoat and otter. Butterflies include comma, grayling, small pearl- bordered, dark green fritilliary, painted lady and orange tip.
Contact: Ranald Strachan, Fife Ranger Service, 01592 656 080, 07985 707 593.
e-mail: Ranald.Strachan@fifecountryside.co.uk

12. ISLE OF MAY NNR

Scottish Natural Heritage.
Location: NT 655 995. This small island lying six miles off Fife Ness in the Firth of Forth is a National Nature Reserve.
Access: Boats run from Anstruther and North Berwick. Contact SNH for details 01334 654038 or look on the Isle of May NNR page on www.nnr-scotland.org. Keep to paths. Those using Observatory accommodation should note delays are possible, both arriving and leaving, because of weather.
Facilities: No dogs; no camping; no fires. Prior permission required if scientific work, photography or filming is to be carried out.
Public transport: Regular bus service to Anstruther and North Berwick harbour.
Habitat: Sea cliffs, rocky shoreline.
Key birds: *Early summer*: Breeding auks, gulls and terns, Kittiwake, Shag, Eider, Fulmar. Over 45,000 pairs of Puffins. *Autumn/spring*: Weather-related migrations include rarities each year.
Contact: For Observatory accomodation: look on www.isleofmaybirdsobs.org or contact Jonathan Osbourne, The Shieling, Halcombe Crescent, Earlston, Berwickshire TD4 6DA, e-mail: jonathan@osbourn108. fsnet.co.uk. For all other enquiries: SNH, 01463 725 000; www.nnr-scotland.org

Forth

CAMBUS POOLS attracts passage waders and winter wildfowl, while high tide at Kinneil produces good numbers of waders in spring and autumn. The RSPB reserve at Inversnaid is good for Black Grouse, Twite, Redstart, Wood Warbler and Pied Flycatcher.

There are large movements of finches and thrushes in autumn. A Red Kite feeding station at Argaty provides visitors with close-up views.

13. CAMBUS POOLS

Scottish Wildlife Trust.
Location: NS 846 937. Take A907 from Stirling towards Alloa, then Station Road to Cambus village. Park by river in village.
Access: Cross River Devon by bridge at NS 853 940 and walk down stream on R bank past bonded warehouses. Open all year.
Facilities: Bench on S side of western pool.
Public transport: None.
Habitat: Wet grassland with two salty pools.
Key birds: Used extensively by migrants in spring and autumn, inc. wildfowl and waders such as Black-tailed Godwit and Greenshank. Gadwall have bred here and Kingfisher is seen regularly.
Other notable flora and fauna: Brown hare, stoat, short-tailed vole, 115 species of vascular plants. Harbour porpoise seen in Forth.
Contact: SWT headquarters, 01313 127 765. www.scottishwildlifetrust.org.uk/reserve/ cambus-pools

14. INVERSNAID

RSPB (South and West Scotland Office).
Location: NN 337 088. On E side of Loch Lomond. Via B829 W from Aberfoyle, then along minor road to car park by Inversnaid Hotel.
Access: Open all year.
Facilities: New car park and trail at Garrison Farm (NN 348 095).
Habitat: Deciduous woodland rises to craggy ridge and moorland.
Key birds: *Summer*: Breeding Black Grouse, Snipe, Cuckoo, Wheatear and Twite. Raven, Grey Wagtail, Dipper, Wood Warbler, Redstart, Pied Flycatcher, Tree Pipit. The loch is on a migration route, especially for wildfowl and waders. Look for Red-throated and Black-throated Divers in spring. *Winter*: Hen Harrier and thrushes.
Other notable flora and fauna: Pine marten, slow worm, 17 species of butterfly inc small pearl-bordered fritillary on nature trail at Inversaid. Wilson's and Tunbridge filmy ferns on boulders through woodland.
Contact: RSPB South and West Scotland Office, 01413 310 993.

Lothian

THOUGH coastal locations usually grab the headlines, the Lammermuir Hills hold a range of upland species. More than 250 species have been recorded at Aberlady Bay, including many thousands of geese in winter. The seabird centre at North Berwick is a great place to take young children, or take a boat out to the gannetry at Bass Rock, while Ferny Ness sees a build-up of Red-necked Grebes in late summer.

15. ABERLADY BAY

East Lothian Council (LNR).
Location: NT 472 806. From Edinburgh take A198 E to Aberlady. Reserve is 1.5 miles E of Aberlady village.
Access: Open at all times. Please stay on footpaths to avoid disturbance. Disabled access from reserve car park. No dogs please.
Facilities: Small car park and toilets. Notice board with recent sightings at end of footbridge. SOC HQ, Waterston House, located W of Aberlady village. Includes shop, library, hot and cold drinks.
Public transport: Edinburgh to N Berwick bus service stops at reserve (request), service no 124. Nearest train station 4 miles away at Longniddry.
Habitat: Tidal mudflats, saltmarsh, freshwater marsh, dune grassland, scrub, open sea.
Key birds: *Summer:* Breeding birds include Shelduck, Eider, Reed Bunting and up to eight species of warbler. Passage waders inc. Green, Wood and Curlew Sandpipers, Little Stint, Greenshank, Whimbrel, Black-tailed Godwit. *Winter:* Divers (esp. Red-throated), Red-necked and Slavonian Grebes and geese (large numbers of Pink-footed roost); sea-ducks, waders.
Contact: John Harrison, Reserve Warden, Landscape and Countryside Management, East Lothian Council, 01875 870 588. email:jharrison@eastlothian.gov.uk
www.aberlady.org

16. BASS ROCK

Location: NT 605 875. Island NE of North Berwick.
Access: Private property. Regular daily sailings from N Berwick around Rock; local boatman has owner's permission to land individuals or parties by prior arrangement. For details contact 01620 892 838 or The Scottish Seabird Centre 01620 890 202; www.seabird.org
Facilities: None. **Habitat:** Sea cliffs.
Key birds: The spectacular cliffs hold a large Gannet colony, (up to 9,000 pairs), plus auks, Kittiwake, Shag and Fulmar.

17. BAWSINCH & DUDDINGSTON LOCH

Scottish Wildlife Trust.
Location: NT 284 725. Centre of Edinburgh, below Arthur's Seat. Use car park on Duddingston Road West and Holyrood Park Gate.
Access: Open access to north shore of loch and cavalry ground to SE. Remainder of site and hide by prior arrangement with C.McLean, 88 Gilmore Place, Edinburgh.
Facilities: Hide with bird and plant lists.
Public transport: Call SWT on 0131 312 7765 for advice.
Habitat: Reedbed, marsh, loch, ponds, mixed woodland, flower meadow and scrub. Developed from former waste area.
Key birds: Heronry. Loch has breeding swans, geese, ducks and grebes. Summer migrants, winter-roosting wildfowl.
Other notable flora and fauna: Fox and otter. Damselfly, four species of amphibian.
Contact: SWT headquarters, 01313 127 765.www. scottishwildlifetrust.org.uk/reserve/bawsinch-and-duddingston

18. GLADHOUSE RESERVOIR

Scottish Water.
Location: NT 295 535. S of Edinburgh off the A703.
Access: Open all year although there is no access to the reservoir itself. Most viewing can be done from the road (telescope required).
Facilities: Small car park on north side. Not suitable for coaches.
Habitat: Reservoir, grassland, farmland.
Key birds: *Spring/summer*: Oystercatcher, Lapwing, Curlew. Possible Black Grouse. *Winter*: Geese, including Pinkfeet, Twite, Brambling, Hen Harrier.
Contact: Scottish Water, PO Box 8855, Edinburgh, EH10 6YQ, 084 6 018 855.
e-mail:customer.service@scottishwater.co.uk
www.scottishwater.co.uk

Eastern Scotland

Angus & Dundee, Moray & Nairn, NE Scotland, Perth & Kinross

Angus & Dundee

THE ANGUS glens hold a typical range of upland species, including Ring Ouzel, grouse, chats and Golden Eagle. Ospreys fish regularly at RSPB Loch of Kinnordy, while Montreathmont Forest is a mix of coniferous and broadleaved woodland. Montrose Basin is a flagship Scottish Wildlife Trust reserve, with a good selection of wildfowl ever present and waders on passage.

1. LOCH OF LINTRATHEN

Scottish Wildlife Trust.
Location: NO 278 550. Seven miles W of Kirriemuir. Take B951 and choose circular route on unclassified roads round loch.
Access: Two public hides (one wheelchair-accessible) open 24 hours a day. Rest of reserve is private, but good viewing is possible from several places along unclassified roads.

Facilities: Viewpoint can accommodate five cars.
Public transport: None.
Habitat: Mesotrophic loch designated a Ramsar site because of its value to waterbirds. Surrounded by mainly coniferous woodland.
Key birds: *Summer*: Grey Heron, Great Crested Grebe and other water birds. Osprey. *Winter*: Internationally-important numbers of Icelandic Greylag Geese, plus Goosander, Whooper Swan, Wigeon, Teal and other wildfowl.
Other notable flora and fauna: Red squirrel.
Contact: Robert Potter, Reserves Manager North East, SWT, 01575 540 396; (M)07920 468 568.
e-mail:rpotter@swt.org.uk

2. MONTROSE BASIN

Scottish Wildlife Trust on behalf of Angus Council.
Location: NO 690 580 – centre of basin. NO 702 565 – Wildlife SWT Centre on A92. 1.5 miles from centre of Montrose.
Access: Visitor Centre open March 1st -Oct 31st, 7 days per week 10.30am-5pm and from Nov 1st-Feb 29th Fri, Sat and Sun only 10.30am-4pm. Admission: £4 Adults, £3.00 Concessions, £7.50 families, Members Free. Several hides open at all times.
Facilities: Visitor centre, gift shop, fair-trade tea, coffee and snacks, toilets, disabled access to centre, two hides open on western half of reserve.
Public transport: Train 1.5 miles in Montrose. Bus stop outside Visitor Centre.
Habitat: Estuary, saltmarsh, reedbeds, farmland.
Key birds: Pink-footed Goose – up to 65,000 arrive Oct. Wintering wildfowl and waders (Curlews at peak numbers in Aug, Dunlin in Feb). Breeding terns, gulls, Shelduck, Goldeneye, Eider Duck. Nationally important moulting site for Mute Swan.

Contact: Montrose Basin Wildlife Centre, 01674 676 336; e-mail:montrosebasin@swt.org.uk

Moray & Nairn

YEAR-ROUND variety is on offer here, with Lochindorb the best area of moorland to explore, with grouse, raptors, divers and waders all breeding. Roseisle Forest holds Crested Tits and opens out onto Burghead Bay which is superb in winter for seaducks, divers and grebes. Spey Bay can be explored from either side of the river and attracts passage waders, terns, Ospreys, seabirds and wildfowl.

3. CULBIN SANDS

RSPB (North Scotland Office).
Location: NH 900 576. Approx ½ mile NE of Nairn, overlooking Moray Firth. Access to parking at East Beach car park, signed off A96.
Access: Open at all times. 750m path to Minster's Pool suitable for all abilities.
Facilities: Toilets (inc disabled) and bike racks at car park. Track along dunes and saltmarsh.
Public transport: Buses stop in St Ninian's Road, Nairn, half mile W of site. Call Rapsons on 0870 608 2608 or Stagecoach on 01862 892 683. Train station in Nairn three-quarters mile W of reserve.
Habitat: Saltmarsh, sandflats, dunes.
Key birds: *Winter*: Flocks of Common Scoter, Long-tailed Duck, Knot, Bar-tailed Godwit, Red-breasted Merganser. Raptors including Peregrine, Merlin and Hen Harrier attracted by wader flocks. Roosting geese, Snow Bunting flocks. *Spring*: Tern flock, esp Sandwich, passage waders. *Summer*: Breeding Eider, Ringed Plover, Oystercatcher. Osprey on passage.
Other notable fauna: Dolphins in Firth. Otters sometimes seen.
Contact: RSPB North Scotland Office, 01463 715 000; e-mail:nsro@rspb.org.uk www.rspb.org.uk

4. SPEY BAY

Scottish Wildlife Trust.
Location: NJ 335 657. Eight miles NE of Elgin. From Elgin take A96 and B9015 to Kingston. Reserve is immediately E of village. Car parks at Kingston and Tugnet.
Access: Open all year.
Facilities: Car park, information board.
Public transport: None. **Habitat:** Shingle, rivermouth and coastal habitats.
Key birds: *Summer*: Osprey, waders, wildfowl. *Winter*: Seaduck and divers offshore, esp. Long-tailed Duck, Common and Velvet Scoters, Red-throated Diver.
Other notable fauna: Otter, plus dolphin offshore. Good range of dragonflies.
Contact: Robert Potter, SWT, The Kennels, 07920 468 568; e-mail:rpotter@swt.org.uk

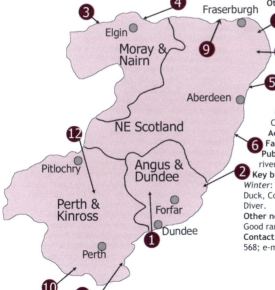

NE Scotland

SCOTLAND'S only mainland gannetry is at Troup Head, while RSPB Loch of Strathbeg is the main UK arrival point for Pink-footed Geese and Whooper Swans every autumn. The Ythan Estuary is good for breeding terns, Eiders, and passage and wintering waders. The interior holds typical Highlands species, with the notable exception of Crested Tit.

5. FORVIE NNR

Scottish Natural Heritage.
Location: NK 034 289. 12 miles N of Aberdeen. Through Newburgh off A975 road.
Access: Reserve open at all times but ternery closed Apr 1 to end of Aug annually. Stevenson Forvie Centre open every day (Apr-Sept) and, outside these months when staff are available. Centre, short trail and hide are wheelchair-accessible.
Facilities: Interpretive display and toilets at Stevenson Forvie Centre. Bird hide, waymarked trails. Coach parking at Waterside car park and Stevenson Forvie Centre.
Public transport: Bluebird No 263 to Cruden Bay. Ask for the Newburgh or Collieston Crossroads stop. Tel: 01224 591 381.
Habitat: Estuary, dunes, coastal heath.
Key birds: *Spring/summer:* Breeding Eider and terns. Migrant waders and seabirds offshore. *Autumn:* Pink-footed Goose, migrant seabirds, waders and passerines inc occasional scarce species or rarity. *Winter:* Waders and wildfowl, inc Whooper Swan, Long-tailed Duck and Golden Plover.
Other notable flora and fauna: Occasional ceteceans offshore, esp in summer.
Contact: Annabel Drysdale (Reserve Manager), 01358 751 330. www.nnr-scotland.org

6. FOWLSHEUGH

RSPB
Location: NO 879 80. Cliff top path N from Crawton, signposted from A92, three miles S of Stonehaven.
Access: Unrestricted. Not suitable for wheelchair users.
Facilities: Car park with 12 spaces, 200 yards from reserve. New stone-built viewing shelter at end of footpath.
Public transport: Request bus stop (Stonehaven to Johnshaven route). Mile walk to reserve entrance.
Habitat: Sea cliffs.
Key birds: Spectacular 130,000-strong seabird colony, mainly Kittiwake and Guillemot plus Razorbill, Fulmar and Puffin. Gannet, Eider and skuas offshore. Peregrines regular throughout year. *Autumn:* Red-throated Diver on sea, terns on passage.
Other notable flora and fauna: Grey and common seals, bottle-nosed dolphin regular, white-beaked dolphin and minke whale occasional in summer. Spring flowers, common butterflies and moths.
Contact: RSPB Fowlsheugh Warden, 01346 532 017; e-mail:strathbeg@rspb.org.uk
www.rspb.org.uk/fowlsheugh

7. HADDO COUNTRY PARK

Aberdeenshire Council.
Location: NJ 875 345. On the A90 Aberdeen-Peterhead road. After Bridge of Don, turn on to the B999. Continue to Tarves for about 20km and pick up signs for Haddo House.
Access: Open all year.
Facilities: Car parks, display boards, more than 5,000m of surfaced paths, toilets open all year (inc disabled) and bird hides with wheelchair access. Coach parking.
Public transport: Bus: Aberdeen-Tarves stop 3.2km from house. Call Stagecoach on 01224 212 266.
Habitat: Parkland, woodland, wetland, loch, ponds.
Key birds: *Spring/summer:* Osprey, Sedge Warbler, Blackcap, Chiffchaff, Lapwing. *Winter:* Canada and Greylag geese, Teal, Wigeon, Goldeneye, Goosander, Brambling. *All year:* Buzzard, Sparrowhawk, Grey Partridge, Great Spotted Woodpecker, Goosander, Grey Wagtail, Tawny Owl, herons, Cormorant.
Other notable flora and fauna: Meadow brown, ringlet and common blue butterflies, burnet moths, blue damselfly. Plants include eyebright, yellow rattle, meadow cranesbill, meadowsweet, angelica, pignut, devils' bit scabious, green alkanet, betony, rock rose, valerian, tansy and bird's foot trefoil. Fauna includes red squirrels, otters and pipistrelle and Daubenton's bats.
Contact: David Brown, Aberdeenshire Council Ranger Service, 01358 726 417.
e-mail:formartine.ranger@aberdeeshire.gov.uk

8. LOCH OF STRATHBEG

RSPB.
Location: NK 057 581. Britain's largest dune loch is near Crimond on the A90, nine miles S of Fraserburgh.
Access: Visitor Centre open daily 8am-6pm, dusk if earlier.
Facilities: Visitor centre, with toilets and coffee machine. New Willow Hide short walk from centre. Tower Pool hide accessible via 700 metre footpath. Two hides overlooking loch accessed via drive to airfield. Wildlife garden, indoor children's area. Long beach walks from St Combs.
Public transport: Access to whole reserve difficult without vehicle. Buses from Fraserburgh and Peterhead to Crimond, one mile from centre. Details at www.travelinescotland.com.
Habitat: Dune loch with surrounding marshes, reedbeds, grasslands and dunes.
Key birds: Breeding wetland species, passage waders, internationally important numbers of wintering wildfowl. Scarcities year round. *Winter:* Pink-footed and Barnacle Geese, Whooper Swan, large numbers of duck. Snow Goose and Smew annual. Raptors including Hen and Marsh Harriers. Great Northern Diver offshore. *Summer:* Common Tern, Water Rail, Corn Bunting. *Spring/autumn:* Spoonbill, Avocet, Marsh Harrier, Garganey, Little Gull, regular Pectoral Sandpiper. Osprey (seen almost daily), Common Crane (now annual on reserve).

Other notable flora and fauna: Otter, badger, stoat, roe deer. Early purple, butterfly and northern marsh orchids, dark green fritillary butterfly.
Contact: RSPB Loch of Strathbeg, 01346 532 017.
e-mail:strathbeg@rspb.org.uk www.rspb.org.uk

9. TROUP HEAD

RSPB (East Scotland).
Location: NJ 825 672. Troup Head is between Pennan and Gardenstown on B9031, E along coast from Macduff. It is signposted off B9031. Look for small RSPB signs which direct you past the farm buildings to car park.
Access: Unrestricted, but not suitable for wheelchair users.
Facilities: Parking for small number of cars. Not suitable for coaches. Live pictures are beamed from the reserve to the Macduff Marine Aquarium during the summer. Boat trips run from Macduff and Banff or Gardenstown (contact North 580 01261 819 900).
Public transport: None.
Habitat: Sea cliffs, farmland.
Key birds: Spectacular seabird colony, including Scotland's only mainland nesting Gannets. Bonxies linger in summer. Migrants occur during spring/autumn.
Other notable flora and fauna: Impressive common flower assemblage in spring. Ceteceans possible offshore in summer including minke whale. Brown hare common.
Contact: RSPB Troup Head Warden, 01346 532 017.
e-mail:troup@rspb.org.uk
www.rspb.org.uk/trouphead

Perth & Kinross

RSPB LOCH LEVEN (formerly known as Vane Farm) is the region's best known reserve and holds huge numbers of wintering geese, ducks and swans. Ospreys fish there too but the well-known watchpoint of Loch of the Lowes offers better views of birds on the nest than RSPB Loch Garten. The Hermitage at Dunkeld is good for woodland species, Dippers and raptors, possibly including Goshawk.

10. DOUNE PONDS

Stirling Council.
Location: NN 726 019. Take A820 Dunblane road E from the junction with the A84 Callander-Stirling road. First left turn to Station Wynd. Car park is second turn on the right.
Access: Wheelchair access to both hides though paths may be muddy. Open all year.
Facilities: Information board, paths, hides. Leaflet from local tourist information offices, local library.
Public transport: Bus: from Stirling and Callander to Doune. Traveline 0870 608 2608.
Habitat: Pools, scrape, birch and willow woodlands.
Key birds: All year: Grey Heron, Buzzard, Snipe, Goldcrest, Siskin, Red Kite. Spring/summer: Common Sandpiper, Whitethroat, warblers.

Other notable flora: Excellent site for fungi.
Contact: Stirling Council Ranger Service, 08452 777 000; e-mail: birdc@stirling.gov.uk
www.facebook.com/stirlingcouncilrangers

11. LOCH LEVEN NNR

SNH/Loch Leven Laboratory.
Location: Car parking at Kinross Pier (NO 122 016) and Kirkgate Park in Kinross, Findatie (NT 170 993) to the SE on the B9097, and Burleigh Sands (NO 1300 39) on the Loch's N shore (close to the A911). Reserve can also be accessed at RSPB's Vane Farm, situated 2 miles east of J5 off the M90. On leaving M90, turn L then R onto B9097 for 2 miles to car park.
Access: A 13km all-abilities trail around loch shore from Kinross as far as the RSPB on the south shore. For more information visit http://www.nnr-scotland.org.uk/loch-leven/ or pick up leaflet locally.
Facilities: 3 hides on the trail-one at Levenmouth, one at Burleigh and one at Kinross. Multiple hides at RSPB on the south shore. Cafes and facilities are located regularly around the trail. Toilets at Kirkgate, Findatie and RSPB.
Public transport: Nearest bus stops are in Kinross and Ballingry. The nearest railway station is in Cowdenbeath (7 miles) on the Edinburgh to Markinch line.
Habitat: Lowland loch with islands.
Key birds: Winter: Flocks of geese (more than 20,000 Pinkfeet), huge numbers of the full range of ducks, Whooper Swan. Summer: Greatest concentration of inland breeding ducks in Britain (10 species), Osprey and grebes. Passage: Waders (Golden Plover flocks up to 500).
Contact: The Reserve Manager, 01577 864 439; e-mail: lochleven_NNR@snh.gov.uk
www.nnt-scotland.org.uk

12. LOCH OF THE LOWES

Scottish Wildlife Trust.
Location: NO 042 435. Sixteen miles N of Perth, two miles NE of Dunkeld, just off A923 (signposted).
Access: Admission charge for non-members of SWT. Visitor centre open daily Mar-Oct (10am-5pm) and Fri-Sun only Nov-Feb (10.30am-4pm). Observation hide open all year during daylight hours. Crannog hide accessible during visitor centre opening hours. No dogs allowed. Full access for wheelchairs.
Facilities: Visitor centre with exhibition, shop & toilets. Two hides overlooking loch.
Public transport: Railway station at Birnam and Dunkeld, three miles from reserve. Buses to Dunkeld, two miles from reserve.
Habitat: Freshwater loch fringed by areas of fen, reedbeds and semi-natural woodland.
Key birds: Breeding Ospreys (Apr-end Aug). Nest 200 metres from hide. Wildfowl and woodland birds.
Other notable fauna: Red Squirrels.
Contact: Caroline Hendry, (Manager), Loch of the Lowes, Visitor Centre, 01350 727 337; e-mail:lochofthelowes@swt.org.uk www.swt.org.uk

13. RSPB LOCH LEVEN

RSPB Scotland
Location: NT 160 990. Part of Loch Leven NNR. Seven miles from Cowdenbeath, signposted two miles E of J5 from M90 onto B9097. Drive for approx two miles. Car park on R.
Access: Open daily (10am-5pm) except Christmas Day, Boxing Day, Jan 1 and 2. Cost £5 adults, £3 concessions, £1 children, £10 family. Free to RSPB members. Disabled access to shop, coffee shop, observation room area and toilets. Coach parking available for up to two coaches. Free car parking.
Facilities: Shop, coffee shop and observation room with five telescopes overlooking Loch Leven and the reserve. There is a 1.25 mile hill trail through woodland and moorland. Wetland trail with three observation hides. Toilets, including disabled. binoculars can be hired from shop.
Public transport: Trains to Cowdenbeath (7 miles), but no bus service from here. Limited bus service (Stagecoach Fife 203 & 204) runs to the reserve from Kinross (4 miles) on Wednesdays, Saturdays and Sundays. Contact Stagecoach Fife on 01383 511 911 Traveline on 0871 200 22 33 for further details. Eight-mile cycle path around loch.
Habitat: Wet grassland and flooded areas by Loch Leven. Arable farmland. Native woodland and heath moorland.
Key birds: *Spring/summer*: Breeding and passage waders (including Lapwing, Redshank, Snipe, Curlew). Farmland birds (including Skylark and Yellowhammer), Tree Pipit. *Autumn*: Migrating waders on exposed mud. *Winter*: Whooper Swan, Bewick's Swan, Pink-footed Goose, finch and tit flocks.
Other notable flora and fauna: 237 butterfly and moth species. 25 mammal species including pipstrelle bat and roe deer.
Contact: Business Visitor Services Manager, Vane Farm Nature Centre, RSPB Loch Leven, 01577 862 355; e-mail: vanefarm lochleven@rspb.co.uk

Highlands & Islands

Highlands Orkney, Outer Hebrides, Shetland

Highlands

HABITATS found nowhere else in Britain hold a range of scarce species: Dotterel, Ptarmigan and Snow Buntings on the tops, plus Crested Tit, the endemic Scottish Crossbill and Capercaillie are in the Caledonian pine forests. The boggy Flow Country of Caithness and Sutherland attracts breeding Greenshank, Common Scoter and Red- and Black-throated Divers.

1. BEINN EIGHE

Scottish Natural Heritage.
Location: NG 990 620. By Kinlochewe, Wester Ross, 50 miles from Inverness and 20 miles from Gairloch on A832.
Access: Reserve open at all times, no charge. Visitor centre open Easter-Oct (10am-5pm).
Facilities: Visitor centre, toilets, woodland trail and mountain trail (self-guided with leaflets from visitor centre). Trails suitable for all abilities.
Public transport: Very limited.
Habitat: Caledonian pine forest, dwarf shrub heath, mountain tops, freshwater loch shore.
Key birds: *All year*: Golden Eagle, Scottish Crossbill, Ptarmigan, Red Grouse, Siskin. *Summer*: Black-throated Diver, Redwing, Snow Bunting.
Other notable flora and fauna: Wide range of dragonflies, including golden ringed and common hawker.
Contact: Eoghain Maclean, Reserve Manager, 01445 760 254; e-mail:eoghain.maclean@snh.gov.uk

2. CORRIMONY

RSPB (North Scotland Office).
Location: NH 383 302. Lies SW of Inverness between Glen Affric and Loch Ness, off A 831.
Access: Open at all times. Waymarked trail suitable for wheelchairs. Unimproved paths, so terrain may not be suitable for disabled visitors.
Facilities: Way-marked trail (8.5 miles long) passes through farm. Please leave gates as you find them. Guided minibus safaris to see Black Grouse leks in April and May.
Public transport: No 17 bus from Inverness to Cannich stops 1.5 miles from reserve.
Habitat: Pine woodland, moorland, blanket bog.
Key birds: Black Grouse, Crested Tit, crossbill species, occasional Golden Eagle and Osprey. Breeding Greenshank, Red Grouse, Black-throated Diver. *Autumn*: Whooper Swan, Pinkfooted Goose, Woodcock.
Other notable flora and fauna: Red deer, pine marten. Many orchids in July.
Contact: RSPB North Scotland Office, 01463 715 000; e-mail:nsro@rspb.org.uk

3. FORSINARD

RSPB (North Scotland Region).
Location: NC 890 425. 30 miles SW of Thurso on A897. From S turn off at Helmsdale (24 miles) or from N coast road (A836) turn 2 miles E of Melvich (14 miles).

Access: Open at all times. Contact reserve office during breeding season (mid-Apr to end Jul) and during deerstalking season (Jul 1 to Feb 15) for advice. Families welcome. Two self-guided trails open all year, requested no dogs, disabled viewpoint accessed via farm track on Forsinain Trail.
Facilities: Visitor centre open Apr 1 to Oct 31 (9am-5.30pm), seven days per week. Static and AV displays, Hen Harrier nest CCTV. Wheelchair access to centre and toilet. Guided walks Tue and Thu afternoon, May-Aug. Accommodation available locally.
Public transport: Train from Inverness and Thurso (08457 484 950). RSPB visitor centre is in former Forsinard Station building.
Habitat: Blanket bog, upland hill farm.
Key birds: The best time to visit for birds is May-July. Join a guided walk for the best chance of views of Red-throated Diver, Golden Plover, Greenshank, Dunlin, Hen Harrier, Merlin, Short-eared Owl. Few birds between Sep-Feb.
Other notable fauna: Red deer, azure hawker dragonfly, emperor moth.
Contact: RSPB, Forsinard Flows Reserve, 01641 571 225; e-mail: forsinard@rspb.org.uk www.rspb.org.uk

4. HANDA

Scottish Wildlife Trust.
Location: NC 138 480. Island accessible by boat from Tarbet, near Scourie — follow A894 N from Ullapool for 40 miles. Continue another three miles, turn L down single track road another three miles to Tarbet.
Access: Open April-Sept. Boats leave 9.30am-2pm (last boat back 5pm). Dogs not allowed. Visitors are asked for a contribution of £2 towards costs. Not suitable for disabled due to uneven terrain.
Facilities: Three mile circular path, shelter (no toilets on island — use those in Tarbet car park). Visitors are given introductory talk and a leaflet with map on arrival.
Public transport: Post bus to Scourie (tel 01549 402 357 Lairg Post Office). Train to Lairg (tel 0845 484 950 National Train enquiries). No connecting public transport between Scourie and Tarbet.
Habitat: Sea cliffs, blanket bog.
Key birds: Spring/summer: Biggest Guillemot and Razorbill colony in Britain and Ireland. Also nationally important for Kittiwakes, Arctic and Great Skuas. Puffin, Shag, Fulmar and Common and Arctic Terns also present.
Contact: Handa Ranger, 07920 468 572; e-mail: handaranger@swt.org.uk Ferry operators - Roger (07780 967 800) or Paul (07775 625 890).

5. INSH MARSHES

RSPB (North Scotland Office).
Location: NN 775 998. In Spey Valley, two miles NE of Kingussie on B970 minor road.
Access: Open at all times. Disabled access to the information viewpoint. Coach parking available at car park.

Facilities: Information viewpoint, two hides, three nature trails. Access for disabled to Information Viewpoint only . No toilets.
Public transport: Nearest rail station and bus stop at Kingussie (two miles).
Habitat: Marshes, woodland, river, open water.
Key birds: Spring/summer: Waders (Lapwing, Curlew, Redshank, Snipe), wildfowl (including Goldeneye and Wigeon), Osprey, Wood Warbler, Redstart, Tree Pipit. Winter: Hen Harrier, Whooper Swan, other wildfowl.
Other notable flora and fauna: Black darter dragonflies along Invertromie trail plus northern brown argus butterflies. Five species of orchid in Tromie Meadow. Roe deer.
Contact: Pete Moore, 01540 661 518; e-mail: pete.moore@rspb.org.uk www.visitkincraig.com

6. ISLE OF EIGG

Scottish Wildlife Trust.
Location: NM 38 48. Small island S of Skye, reached by ferry from Mallaig or Arisaig (approx 12 miles).
Access: Ferries seven days per week (weather permitting) during summer. Four days per week (weather permitting) between Sept-Apr. Coach parties would need to transfer to ferries for visit to Eigg. Please contact ferry companies prior to trip. Mix of roads, hardcore tracks and rough paths on island.
Facilities: Pier centre: shop/post office, tea-room, craftshop, toilets.
Public transport: Train service from Glasgow, via Arisaig to Mallaig. Cal-Mac (01687 462 403) ferries (no sailing Wed and sun), MV Sheerwater (no sailing Thurs, (01687 450 224). Island minibus/taxi usually available at the pier.

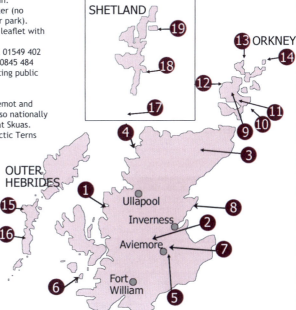

Habitat: Moorland (leading to Sgurr pitchstone ridge), extensive woodland and scrub, marshland and bog, hay meadows, sandy bays and rocky shorelines.
Key birds: *All year:* Resident species include Red-throated Diver, Golden Eagle, Hen Harrier, Woodcock and Raven. *Summer:* Cuckoo, Wheatear, Whitethroat, Whinchat, Sedge and Willow Warblers, Twite. Large numbers of Manx Shearwaters offshore with Storm-petrels regularly seen from boats between June-Sept.
Other notable flora and fauna: 17 species of butterfly recorded, including green hairstreak, small pearl-bordered and dark green fritillaries. Nine species of damsel/dragonfly occur with golden ringed, common hawker and highland darter the most numerous. Approx 500 species of 'higher' plants listed, including 12 species of orchid, and alpine/arctic species such as mountain aven and moss campion. Carpet of primroses, bluebells and wild garlic in spring. Otters not uncommon and minke whales, bottle-nosed and common dolphins and harbour porpoises regularly recorded offshore. Basking sharks fairly numerous in early summer.
Contact: John Chester, 01687 482 477. www.isleofeigg.org

7. LOCH GARTEN - ABERNETHY FOREST RESERVE

RSPB (North Scotland Office).
Location: NH 981 184. 2.5 miles from Boat of Garten, eight miles from Aviemore. Off B970, follow 'RSPB Ospreys' road signs (between Apr - Aug only).
Access: Osprey Centre open daily 10am-6pm (Apr to end Aug). Disabled access. Guide dogs only. RSPB members free. Non-members: adults £4, senior citizens £2.50, children £1.00. Family ticket £8 (up to 2 adults and four children).
Facilities: Osprey Centre overlooking nesting Ospreys, toilets, optics and CCTV live pictures, shop, toilets.
Public transport: Bus service to Boat of Garten from Aviemore, 2.5 mile footpath to Osprey Centre. Steam railway to Boat of Garten from Aviemore.
Habitat: Caledonian pine wood.
Key birds: Spring/summer: Ospreys nesting from Apr to Aug, Crested Tit, Redstart, Spotted Flycatcher, Tree Pipit, crossbills. Possible views of lekking Capercaillies from the Osprey Centre, Apr to mid-May. Autumn: Pinkfeet and Greylag Geese roost on loch, Whooper Swan and various duck species.
Other notable flora and fauna: Red squirrel, roe deer,otter, woodland plants and fungi.
Contact: The Warden, 01479 831 476;
e-mail:abernethy@rspb.co.uk

8. UDALE BAY RSPB RESERVE

RSPB (North Scotland Office).
Location: NH 712 651. On the Black Isle, one mile W of Jemimaville on the B9163.
Access: Open all year. View wader roost from lay-by. Nearest adapted unisex toilet in Allen Street, Cromarty (one mile away).
Facilities: Hide, large lay-by. No coach parking.
Public transport: No 26 bus stops in Jemimaville six times a day (approx 5 min walk to reserve). Bus Info

Contact: Rapsons, 0870 608 2608 or Stagecoach on 01862 892 683.
Habitat: Mudflat, saltmarsh and wet grassland.
Key birds: *Spring/summer:* 10,000 Pinkfeet on passage each year, other wildfowl, Oystercatcher, Redshank, waders. Possible Osprey fishing. *Autumn/winter:* Large flocks of wildfowl (approx 10,000 Wigeon), geese, waders.
Contact: RSPB North Scotland Office, 01463 715 000; e-mail: nsro@rspb.org.uk

Orkney

A LACK of managed grouse moors means that Hen Harriers breed here in excellent numbers. Other scarce breeders include Whimbrels, Great and Arctic Skuas, and Red-throated Divers. There are excellent seabird colonies such as the one at Marwick Head. North Ronaldsay attracts good numbers of migrants.

9. BRODGAR

RSPB (East Scotland).
Location: HY 296 134. Reserve surrounds Ring of Brodgar, part of Heart of Neolithic Orkney World Heritage Site on B9055 off Stromness-Finstown Road.
Access: Open all year.
Facilities: Footpath, circular route approx one mile.
Public transport: Stagecoach – 01856 878 014. Service within 0.5 mile of reserve. Occasional service past reserve.
Habitat: Wetland and farmland including species-rich grassland, loch shores.
Key birds: *Spring/summer:* Breeding waterfowl on farmland and nine species of waders breed here. The farmed grassland is suitable for Corncrake and provides water, food and shelter for finches, larks and buntings. *Winter:* large numbers of Golden Plover, Curlew and Lapwing.
Other notable fauna: Good for great yellow bumblebee in August. Otter possible, common seals haul out nearby on Loch of Stenness.
Contact: The Warden, 01856 850 176.
e-mail:orkney@rspb.org.uk www.rspb.co.uk

10. COPINSAY

RSPB (East Scotland).
Location: HY 610 010. Small island accessed by private boat or hire boat from mainland Orkney.
Access: Open all year round.
Facilities: House on island open to visitors, but no facilities, toilets or hides.
Public transport: None.
Habitat: Sea cliffs, farmland.
Key birds: *Summer:* Stunning seabird-cliffs with breeding Kittiwake, Guillemot, Black Guillemot, Puffin, Razorbill, Shag, Fulmar, Rock Dove, Eider, Twite, Raven and Greater Black-backed Gull, Great Skua (new breeding species in recent years). Passage migrants esp. during periods of E winds.
Other notable fauna: The island is a key breeding

location for Atlantic grey seals from Oct-Dec. 2,385 pups counted in 2006.
Contact: The Warden, 01856 850 176; e-mail:orkney@rspb.org.uk www.rspb.co.uk
S Foubisher (boatman) 01856 741 252. Boats cannot sail if wind is in the east

11. HOBBISTER

RSPB (East Scotland).
Location: HY 396 070 or HY 381 068. Near Kirkwall.
Access: Open access between A964 and the sea. Dogs on leads please.
Facilities: A council-maintained footpath to Waulkmill Bay, two car parks. New circular walk from RSPB car park along cliff top and Scapa Flow.
Public transport: Stagecoach– 01856 878 014.
Habitat: Orkney moorland, bog, fen, saltmarsh, coastal cliffs, scrub.
Key birds: *Summer:* Breeding Hen Harrier, Merlin, Short-eared Owl, Red Grouse, Red-throated Diver, Eider, Red-breasted Merganser, Black Guillemot. Wildfowl and waders at Waulkmill Bay. *Autumn/winter:* Waulkmill for sea ducks, divers, auks and grebes (Long-tailed Duck, Red-throated, Black-throated and Great Northern Divers, Slavonian Grebe).
Other notable fauna: Otter occasionally seen from Scapa trail. Grey and common seal both possible from footpath looking towards Scapa Flow.
Contact: The Warden, 01856 850 176; e-mail:orkney@rspb.org.uk www.rspb.co.uk

12. MARWICK HEAD

RSPB (East Scotland).
Location: HY 229 242. On W coast of mainland Orkney, near Dounby. Path N from Marwick Bay, or from council car park at Cumlaquoy at HY 232 252.
Access: Open all year. Rough terrain not suitable for wheelchairs.
Facilities: Cliff top path.
Public transport: Stagecoach – 01856 878 014, nearest stop one mile from reserve. **Habitat:** Rocky bay, sandstone cliffs.
Key birds: May-Jul best. Huge numbers of Kittiwakes and auks, inc. Puffins, also nesting Fulmar, Rock Dove, Raven, Rock Pipit.
Other notable fauna: Cetaceans are a possibility from Marwick with porpoise and minke whale occasionally seen. Beach path good place for great yellow bumblebee in Aug.
Contact: The Warden 01856 850 176; e-mail:orkney@rspb.org.uk www.rspb.co.uk

13. NORTH HILL, PAPA WESTRAY

RSPB (East Scotland).
Location: HY 495 538. From the pier or airfield travel N along main road. From shop/hostel, travel up the road to the junction at Holland Farm, turn R onto main road. Continue past Rose Cottage until the road bends sharply R at reserve entrance.
Access: Access at all times. During breeding season report to summer warden at Rose Cottage, 650 yards S of reserve entrance (01857 644 240) or use trail guide.
Facilities: Nature trails, hide/info hut. Limited parking. Not suitable for wheelchairs or pushchairs.
Public transport: Orkney Ferries (01856 872 044), Loganair (01856 872 494).
Habitat: Sea cliffs, maritime heath.
Key birds: *Summer:* Close views of colony of Puffin, Guillemot, Razorbill and Kittiwake. Black Guillemot nest under flagstones around reserve's coastline. One of UK's largest colonies of Arctic Tern, also Arctic Skua.
Other notable flora and fauna: One of the best areas to see 'Scottish primrose' (*primula scotica*), with two flowering periods that just overlap (May-Aug).
Contact: Apr-Aug, The Warden at Rose Cottage, Papay Westray DW17 2BU. 01857 644240., 2. RSPB Orkney Office, 01856 850 176; e-mail:orkney@rspb.org.uk www.rspb.co.uk

14. NORTH RONALDSAY BIRD OBSERVATORY

Location: HY 64 52. 35 miles from Kirkwall, Orkney mainland.
Access: Open all year except Christmas.
Facilities: Three star guest house and hostel accommodation, restaurant, cafe, fully licenced, croft walk.
Public transport: Daily subsidised Loganair flights from Kirkwall from Mainland Orkney to North Ronaldsay. 15 minute flight gives stunning views of several islands. See Loganair website (www.loganair.co.uk/reservations/) for full information.
Habitat: Crofting island with a number of eutrophic and oligotrophic wetlands. Coastline has both sandy bays and rocky shore. Walled gardens concentrate passerines.
Key birds: *Spring/autumn:* Prime migration site including regular BBRC species. Wide variety of breeding seabirds, wildfowl and waders. *Winter:* Waders and wildfowl include Whooper Swan and hard weather movements occur.
Contact: Alison Duncan, North Ronaldsay Bird Observatory, 01857 633 200; www.nrbo.f2s.com e-mail:alison@nrbo.prestel.co.uk

Outer Hebrides

THESE ISLANDS are the Corncrake stronghold of Britain, though having large numbers of birds doesn't make them any easier to see! There is a strong passage of Long-tailed and Pomarine Skuas past RSPB Balranald in May. The area's ability to attract rare migrants is only just being discovered with recent autumnal trips to Barra turning up trumps.

15. BALRANALD

RSPB (North Scotland Office).
Location: NF 705 707. From Skye take ferry to Lochmaddy, North Uist. Drive W on A865 for 20 miles to reserve. Turn off main road three miles NW of

Bayhead at signpost to Houghharry.
Access: Open at all times, no charge. Dogs on leads. Circular walk not suitable for wheelchairs.
Facilities: Visitor Centre and toilets (disabled access). Marked nature trail. Group bookings welcome.
Public transport: Post bus service (01876 560 244).
Habitat: Freshwater loch, machair, coast and crofts.
Key birds: *Spring:* Skuas and divers at sea, Purple Sandpiper and other waders on shore. Dotterel. *Summer:* Corncrake, Corn Bunting, Lapwing, Oystercatcher, Dunlin, Ringed Plover, Redshank, Snipe, terns. *Autumn:* Hen Harrier, Peregrine, Greylag Goose. *Winter:* Twite, Snow Bunting, Whooper Swan, Greylag Goose, Wigeon, Teal, Shoveler, sightings of Golden and White-tailed Eagles becoming commoner. *Passage:* Barnacle Goose, Pomarine Skua, Long-tailed Skua.
Other notable flora: Blanket bog and machair plants reach their peak in July.
Contact: The Warden, 01463 715000;
e-mail: nsro@rspb.org.uk www.rspb.org.uk

16. LOCH DRUIDIBEG NNR

SNH (Western Isles Area).
Location: NF 782 378. Reserve of 1,577 ha on South Uist. Turn off A865 at B890 road for Loch Sgioport. Track is 1.5 miles further on — park at side of road.
Access: Open all year. Several tracks and one walk covering a range of habitats — most not suitable for wheelchairs. Stout footwear essential. Observe Scottish Outdoor Access Code in all areas with livestock. View E part of reserve from public roads but parking and turning areas for coaches is limited.
Facilities: None.
Public transport: Regular bus service stops at reserve. Hebridean Coaches 01870 620 345, MacDonald Coaches 01870 620 288. Large print timetable — call 01851 709 592.
Habitat: Range of freshwater lochs and marshes, machair, coast and moorland.
Key birds: *Summer:* Breeding waders, Corncrake, wildfowl, terns and raptors. *Spring and autumn:* Migrant waders and wildfowl. *Winter:* Waders, wildfowl and raptors.
Contact: SNH Area Officer, 01870 620 238;
e-mail:western.isles@snh.gov.uk

Shetland

BRITAIN'S most northerly archipelago is always going to attract large numbers of vagrants, with the observatory on Fair Isle boasting a phenomenal list of species. Seabird colonies here are truly spectacular and include such unusual species as Leach's Petrels; an overnight stay on Mousa is the best way to catch up with this largely nocturnal species.

17. FAIR ISLE BIRD OBSERVATORY

Fair Isle Bird Observatory.
Location: HZ 2172. Famous island for rarities located

SE of mainland Shetland.
Access: Open from end Apr-end Oct. No access restrictions.
Facilities: Public toilets at Airstrip and Stackhoull Stores (shop). Accommodation at Fair Isle Bird Observatory (phone/e-mail: for brochure/details). Guests can be involved in observatory work and get to see birds in the hand. Slide shows, guided walks through Ranger Service.
Public transport: Tue, Thurs, Sat — ferry (12 passengers) from Grutness, Shetland. Tel: Neil or Pat Thomson on 01595 760 363. Mon, Wed, Fri, Sat — air (7 seater) from Tingwall, Shetland. Tel: Direct Flight 01595 840 246.
Habitat: Heather moor and lowland pasture/crofting land. Cliffs.
Key birds: Large breeding seabird colonies (auks, Gannet, Arctic Tern, Kittiwake, Shag, Arctic Skua and Great Skua). Many common and rare migrants Apr/May/early Jun, late Aug-Nov.
Other notable flora and fauna: Northern marsh, heath spotted and frog orchid, lesser twayblade, small adders tongue, oyster plant. Orcas, minke whale, white-backed, white-sided and Risso's dolphins. Endemic field mouse.
Contact: Fair Isle Bird Observatory, 01595 760 258.
e-mail:fairisle.birdobs@zetnet.co.uk
www.fairislebirdobs.co.uk

18. FETLAR

RSPB Scotland
Location: HU 603 917. Small island lying E of Yell. Take car ferry from Gutcher, N Yell. Booking advised (01957 722 259).
Access: Apart from the footpath to Hjaltadance circle, Vord Hill, the Special Protection Area is closed mid May to end July. Entry during this period is only by arrangement with warden.
Facilities: Hide at Mires of Funzie open Apr-Nov. Toilets and payphone at ferry terminal, interpretive centre at Houbie, campsite, shop.
Public transport: None.
Habitat: Serpentine heath, rough hill lane, upland mire.
Key birds: *Summer:* Breeding Red-throated Diver, Eider, Shag, Whimbrel, Golden Plover, Dunlin, skuas, Manx Shearwater, Storm Petrel. Red-necked Phalarope on Loch of Funzie (HU 655 899) viewed from road or RSPB hide overlooking Mires of Funzie.
Other notable flora and fauna: Heath spotted orchid and autumn gentian. Otters are common, harbour and grey seals breed.
Contact: RSPB North Isles Warden, 01957 733 246;
e-mail: fetlar@rspb.org.uk

19. NOSS NNR

Scottish Natural Heritage (Shetland Office).
Location: HU 531 410. Take car ferry to Bressay from Lerwick and follow signs for Noss (5km). At end of road walk to shore (600 mtrs) where inflatable ferry (passenger only) to island will collect you. If red flag is flying, island is closed due to sea

conditions. Information updated daily in season on 0800 107 7818.
Access: Open Tue, Wed, Fri, Sat, Sun (10am-5pm) between late Apr-late Aug. Access by zodiac inflatable. No dogs on ferry. Steep rough track down to ferry. Anyone requiring asistance to board ferry should contact SNH as far in advance as possible.
Facilities: Visitor centre, toilets. Bike rack/car park on Bressay side. Parking for small coaches.
Public transport: None. Cycle hire in Lerwick.
Habitat: Dune and coastal grassland, moorland, heath, blanket bog, sea cliffs.

Key birds: *Spring/summer*: Breeding Fulmar, Shag, Gannet, Arctic Tern, Kittiwake, Herring and Great Black-backed Gull, Great Skua, Arctic Skua, Guillemot, Razorbill, Puffin, Black Guillemot, Eider, Lapwing, Dunlin, Snipe, Wheatear, Twite plus migrant birds at any time.
Other notable fauna: Grey and common seals, otter porpoise regularly seen, killer whales annual in recent years.
Contact: Glen Tyler, SNH, 01595 693 345; e-mail:noss_nnr@snh.gov.uk www.nnr-scotland.org

Eastern Wales
Breconshire, Montgomeryshire, Radnorshire

OSPREYS are just beginning to colonise, breeding in Montgomeryshire. The area around Rhayadar was the last stronghold of Red Kites before the re-introduction schemes; now hundreds can be seen daily, coming to food at Gigrin Farm. Lake Vrynwy has a fine mix of habitats for a day's birding, with woodland birds, waterfowl and upland species.

1. BRECHFA POOL
Brecknock Wildlife Trust.
Location: SO 118 377. Travelling NE from Brecon look for lane off A470, 1.5 miles SW of Llyswen; on Brechfa Common, pool is on R after cattle grid.
Access: Open dawn to dusk. Road runs around three-quarters of pool, giving good access.
Facilities: None.
Public transport: None.
Habitat: Marshy grassland, large shallow pool.
Key birds: Good numbers of wintering wildfowl are replaced by breeding gulls and commoner waterfowl. Species recorded inc Teal, Gadwall, Tufted Duck, Shoveler, Wigeon, Little Grebe, Black-headed Gull, Lapwing, Dunlin, Redshank, Kestrel.
Other notable flora and fauna: Rare pillwort around pond margins, plus crowfoot, penny royal and orange foxtail.
Contact: Trust HQ, 01874 625 708.
e-mail:enquiries@brecknockwildlifetrust.org.uk
www.brecknockwildlifetrust.org.uk

2. CARNGAFALLT
RSPB Wales
Location: SN 935 653. From Rhayader take the B4518 W to Elan village. Turn into village and carry on over bridge into Elan village. Continue through village to cattle grid where nature trail starts.
Access: The nature trail is open at all times.
Facilities: Nature trail.
Public transport: None.
Habitat: Ancient oak woodland, grassland and moorland. Spectacular upland scenery.

Key birds: Red Kite, Buzzard, Sparrowhawk, Peregrine, Raven, Green Woodpecker, Grey Wagtail and Marsh Tit are joined in the summer by Pied Flycatcher, Spotted Flycatcher, Wood Warbler, Redstart, Tree Pipit and Cuckoo.
Other notable flora and fauna: Golden-ringed dragonfly, silver-washed, small pearl-bordered and dark-green fritillaries and purple hairstreak butterflies.
Contact: RSPB Ynys-Hir Reserve, 01654 700 222.
e-mail:ynyshir@rspb.org.uk

3. ELAN VALLEY
Dwr Cymru /Welsh Water.
Location: SN 928 646 (visitor centre). Three miles SW of Rhayader, off B4518.
Access: Mostly open access.
Facilities: Visitor centre and toilets (open every day except Christmas Day). 10am-5.30pm (1st Mar-31st Oct), 10am-4pm (1st Nov-28th Feb). Nature trails all year and hide at SN 905 617.
Public transport: None.
Habitat: 45,000 acres of moorland, woodland, river and reservoir.
Key birds: *Spring/summer*: Birds of prey, upland birds including Golden Plover and Dunlin. Woodland birds include Redstart and Pied Flycatcher.
Other notable flora and fauna: Internationally important oak woodlands. More than 3,000 species of flora and fauna recorded.
Contact: Site Manager, 01597 810 880.
www.elanvalley.org.uk (contains contact form for enquiries) www.dwrcymru.com

4. GIGRIN FARM
Location: Farm lies half a mile south of Rhayader, Powys off A470.
Access: Open for kite feeding sessions from 1pm each day, except Dec 25. Feeding at 2pm (winter) and 3pm (summer). No booking required. See website for admission charges.

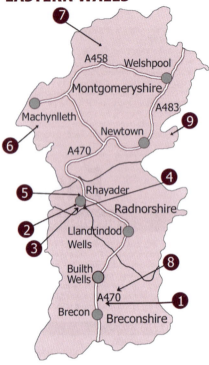

Facilities: Red Kite Shop, five hides (three with disabled access), plus specialist photography hides.
Habitat: 200-acre upland sheep farm rising to 1,200 feet above sea level.
Details: Brilliant views of Red Kites. For the past 18 years, Gigrin has been the official Red Kite feeding station for Wales, helping young birds survive in winter. By attracting large numbers of birdwatchers it relieves pressure on nest sites in summer.
Key birds: Daily feeds attract a wide range of species including Carrion Crow, Raven, Jackdaw, Buzzard and Red Kite. Kite numbers vary from a few dozen to around 400 when weather is bad . Other feeding stations attract smaller birds such as Brambling, Yellowhammer and Siskin. A 1.5ml trail links to the RSPB Dyffryn reserve while a wetland area attracts wild ducks, Grey Heron and wagtails.
Contact: Chris Powell, Gigrin Farm, South Street, Rhayader, Powys LD6 5BL. 01597 810 243; www.gigrinfarm.co.uk

5. GILFACH

Radnorshire Wildlife Trust.
Location: SN 952 714. Two miles NW from Rhayader/Rhaeadr-Gwy. Take minor road to St Harmon from A470 at Marteg Bridge.
Access: Open every day, all year.
Facilities: Visitor centre opening times may vary — contact Trust for details.
Public transport: None.
Habitat: Upland hill farm, river, oak woods, meadows, hill-land.
Key birds: *Spring/summer*: Pied Flycatcher, Redstart. *All year*: Dipper, Red Kite.
Other notable flora and fauna: Green hairstreak, wall brown and ringlet butterflies, mountain pansy, bloody-nosed beetle.
Contact: Reserve manager, 01597 823 298. e-mail:info@rwtwales.org www.radnorshirewildlifetrust.org.uk

6. GLASLYN, PLYNLIMON

Montgomeryshire Wildlife Trust.
Location: SN 826 941. Nine miles SE of Machynlleth. Off minor road between the B4518 near Staylittle and the A489 at Machynlleth. Go down the track for about a mile to the car park.
Access: Open at all times — dogs on lead at all times.
Facilities: Footpath.
Public transport: None.
Habitat: Heather moorland and upland lake.
Key birds: Red Grouse, Short-eared Owl, Meadow Pipit, Skylark, Wheatear and Ring Ouzel, Red Kite, Merlin, Peregrine. Goldeneye occasional.
Contact: Montgomeryshire Wildlife Trust, 555 654. e-mail:info@montwt.co.uk www.montwt.co.uk

7. LAKE VYRNWY

RSPB Mid-Wales Office
Location: SJ 020 193. Located WSW of Oswestry. Nearest village is Llanfyllin on A490. Take B4393 to lake.
Access: Reserve open all year. Visitor centre open Apr-Oct (10.30am-5.00pm), Nov-March (10.30am-4.00pm).
Facilities: Toilets, visitor centre, hides, nature trails, coffee shop, RSPB shop, craft workshops.
Public transport: Train and bus Welshpool (25 miles away).
Habitat: Heather moorland, woodland, meadows, rocky streams and large reservoir.
Key birds: Dipper, Kingfisher, Pied Flycatcher, Wood Warbler, Redstart, Peregrine and Buzzard.
Other notable flora and fauna: Mammals include otter, polecat, brown hare. Golden-ringed dragonflies frequent in summer.
Contact: Centre Manager, 1691 870 278; e-mail: vyrnwy@rspb.org.uk

8. PWLL-Y-WRACH

Brecknock Wildlife Trust.
Location: SO 165 326. From Talgarth town centre take Bell Street and then Hospital Road. After 1.5 miles, reserve is on the right.
Access: Reserve open all year. Please keep to footpaths. Level wheelchair-friendly path runs half way into site. Elsewhere, paths can be muddy and there are steps in places.
Facilities: No facilities.
Public transport: No local services.

Habitat: 17.5 hectares of ancient woodland, river and spectacular waterfall.
Key birds: Large variety of resident woodland birds, with migrant boost in spring. Dipper, Kingfisher, Pied Wagtail, Great Spotted Woodpecker, Chiffchaff, Wood Warbler, Pied Flycatcher, Mistle and Song Thrushes, Nuthatch.
Other notable flora and fauna: Otter, dormouse, bats, common lizard. Early purple and birds' nest orchids, herb paris, bluebell, wood anenome.
Contact: Brecknock Wildlife Trust, 01874 625 708. e-mail:enquiries@brecknockwildlifetrust.org.uk www.brecknockwildlifetrust.org.uk

9. ROUNDTON HILL

Montgomeryshire Wildlife Trust.
Location: SO 293 947. SE of Montgomery. From Churchstoke on A489, take minor road to Old Churchstoke, R at phone box, then first R.
Access: Open access. Tracks rough in places. Dogs on lead at all times.
Facilities: Car park. Waymarked trails.
Public transport: None.
Habitat: Ancient hill grassland, woodland, streamside wet flushes, scree, rock outcrops.
Key birds: Buzzard, Raven, Wheatear, all three woodpeckers,Tawny Owl, Redstart, Linnet, Goldfinch.
Contact: Trust HQ, 01938 555 654; e-mail:info@montwt.co.uk www.montwt.co.uk

Northern Wales

Anglesey, Caernarfonshire, Denbighshire, Flintshire, Merioneth

HIGHLIGHTS on Anglesey include a seabird colony and Choughs at South Stack, terns at Cemlyn Bay and waders at Malltraeth. RSPB Valley Lakes, Newborough Warren and Llyn Alaw are all worth exploring too. Conwy is one of the RSPB's flagship reserves. There is an observatory on Bardsey Island. Red and Black Grouse are on the moors, with Crossbills in coniferous woodland.

1. BARDSEY BIRD OBSERVATORY

Bardsey Bird Observatory.
Location: SH 11 21. Private 444 acre island. Twenty minute boat journey from Aberdaron.
Access: Mar-Nov. No dogs. Visitor accommodation in 150-year-old farmhouse (two single, two double, two x four bed dorm). To stay at the Observatory contact Alicia Normand (tel 01626 773 908) e-mail; stay@bbfo.org.uk). Day visitors by Bardsey Ferries (07971760895)
Facilities: Public toilets available for day visitors. Three hides, one on small bay, two seawatching. Gift shops and payphone.
Public transport: Trains from Birmingham to Pwllheli. Tel: 0345 484 950. Arriva bus from Bangor to Pwllheli. Tel: 0870 6082 608.
Habitat: Sea-birds cliffs viewable from boat only. Farm and scrubland, Spruce plantation, willow copses and gorse-covered hillside.
Key birds: *All year:* Chough, Peregrine. *Spring/summer:* Manx Shearwaters 16,000 pairs, other seabirds. Migrant warblers, chats, Redstart, thrushes. *Autumn:* Many rarities including Eye-browed Thrush, Lanceolated Warbler, American Robin, Yellowthroat, Summer Tanager.
Other notable flora and fauna: Autumn ladies' tresses.

Contact: Steven Stansfield, 07855 264 151. e-mail:warden@bbfo.org.uk www.bbfo.org.uk

2. CEMLYN

North Wales Wildlife Trust.
Location: SH 329 936 and SH 336 932. Cemlyn is signposted from Tregele on A5025 between Valley and Amlwch on Anglesey.
Access: Open all the time. Dogs on leads. No wheelchair access. During summer months walk on seaward side of ridge and follow signs.
Facilities: Car parks at either end of reserve.
Public transport: None within a mile.
Habitat: Brackish lagoon, shingle ridge, salt marsh, mixed scrub.
Key birds: Wintering wildfowl and waders, breeding terns, gulls and warblers, pipits and passing migrants. *Spring:* Wheatear, Whitethroat, Sedge Warbler, Manx Shearwater, Sandwich Tern, Whimbrel, Dunlin, Knot and Black-tailed Godwit. *Summer:* Breeding Arctic, Common and Sandwich Terns, Black-headed Gull, Oystercatcher and Ringed Plover. *Autumn:* Golden Plover, Lapwing, Curlew, Manx Shearwater, Gannet, Kittiwake, Guillemot. *Winter:* Little and Great Crested Grebes, Shoveler, Shelduck, Wigeon, Red-breasted Merganser, Coot, Turnstone, Purple Sandpiper.
Other notable flora and fauna: 20 species of butterfly recorded. Sea kale, yellow horned poppy, sea purslane, sea beet, glasswort. Grey seal, harbour porpoise, bottlenose dolphin.
Contact: North Wales Wildlife Trust, 01248 351 541; e-mail: nwwt@wildlifetrustswales.org www.northwaleswildlifetrust.org.uk

Access: Open daily (9.30am-5pm). Closed for Christmas Day. Ample parking for coaches. Toilets, buildings and trails accessible to pushchairs and wheelchairs.

Facilities: Visitor centre, gift shop, coffee shop, toilets including disabled. Four hides (accessible to wheelchairs) two viewing screens. Trails firm and level, though a little rough in places and wet in winter.

Public transport: Train service to Llandudno Junction, 10 minute walk. Bus service to Tesco supermarket, Llandudno Junction 5 minutes walk. Tel: 0871 200 2233.

Habitat: Lagoons, islands, reedbed, scrub, estuary.

Key birds: Wildfowl and waders in winter, warblers and wetland breeding birds in summer. *Spring*: Passage waders, hirundines and wagtails. *Summer*: Lapwing, waterbirds and warblers. *Winter*: Kingfisher, Goldeneye, Water Rail, Red-breasted Merganser, wildfowl, huge Starling roost.

Other notable flora and fauna: Common butterflies through summer, especially common blues. Great display of cowslips in March, bee orchids in summer. Otters seen early mornings.

Contact: Conwy RSPB Nature Reserve, 01492 584 091. e-mail:conwy@rspb.org.uk www.rspb.org.uk/conwy

3. CONNAHS QUAY POWER STATION NR

Location: SJ 275 715. From England: Take A550 from Liverpool/N Wirral or A5117 from Ellesmere Port/M56, follow road to Queensferry. 200 metres after junction of A550 and A5117, turn L at A548 and follow signs to Flint. Cross Dee Bridge and turn off dual carriageway at B5129, signed Connah's Key. Turn R under A548 then L, following signs to power station. From Flint: Take A548 towards Connah's Quay/Queensferry. After 2.5 miles, take B5129 (Connah's Quay exit). Turn L following signs to power station. From Connah's Quay: Take B5129 towards Flint. Go under A548, turn L following signs to power station.

Access: Advance permit required (group bookings only). Wheelchair access. Public welcome on open days — see website for details.

Facilities: Field studies centre, five hides.

Public transport: Contact Arriva Cymru on 01745 343 492.

Habitat: Saltmarsh, mudflats, grassland scrub, open water, wetland meadow.

Key birds: *Summer*: Small roosts of non-breeding estuarine birds. *Winter*: High water roosts of waders and wildfowl including, Black-tailed Godwit, Oystercatcher, Redshank, Spotted Redshank, Curlew, Lapwing, Teal, Pintail and Wigeon.

Contact: Pauline Moulton, Secretary, 01244 313 404. e-mail:secretary@deesidenaturalists.org.uk www.deesidenaturalists.org.uk

4. CONWY

RSPB (North Wales Office).

Location: SH 799 773. On E bank of Conwy Estuary. Access from A55 at exit 18 signed to Conwy and Deganwy. Footpath and cycleway accessed from Conway Cob.

5. LLYN ALAW

Welsh Water/United Utilities.

Location: SH 390 865. North Anglesey, SW of Amlwch. Signposted from J5 of A55. Main car park at SH 375 856.

Access: Open all year. No dogs to hides or sanctuary area but dogs allowed (maximum two per adult) in other areas. Limited wheelchair access. Coach parking in main car park (SH 373 856).

Facilities: Visitor centre, Toilets (including disabled), earth paths, boardwalks. Two hides, car parks, network of mapped walks, picnic sites, information boards. Coach parking at main car park.

Public transport: Not to within a mile.

Habitat: Large area of standing water, shallow reedy bays, hedges, scrub, woodland, marsh, grassland.

Key birds: *Winter*: Wildfowl and thrushes, breeding warblers/waterfowl. *Summer*: Lesser Whitethroat, Sedge and Grasshopper Warblers, Little and Great Crested Grebes, Tawny Owl, Barn Owl, Buzzard. *Winter*: Whooper Swan, Goldeneye, Hen Harrier, Short-eared Owl, Redwing, Fieldfare, Peregrine, Raven. *All year*: Bullfinch, Siskin, Redpoll, Goldfinch, Stonechat. *Passage waders*: Ruff, Spotted Redshank, Curlew Sandpiper, Green Sandpiper.

Other notable flora and fauna: Bee and northern marsh orchid, royal fern, skullcap, needle spikerush. Migrant hawker, hairy, four-spotted chaser dragonflies, banded demoiselle, wall

brown, gatekeeper, clouded yellow and orange tip butterflies. Brown hare, water vole.
Contact: The Warden, 01407 730 762.

6. LLYN CEFNI

Welsh Water/Forestry Commission/United Utilities.
Location: Entrance at Bodffordd SH 433 775 and Rhosmeirch SH 451 783. A reservoir located two miles NW of Llangefni, in central Anglesey. Follow B5111 or B5109 from the village.
Access: Open at all times. Dogs allowed except in sanctuary area. Good footpath (wheelchair accessible) for most of the site, bridges over streams.
Facilities: Two picnic sites, good footpath, coach parking at Rhosmeirch car prk SH451 783.
Public transport: Bus 32, 4 (44 Sun only, 52 Thu only). Tel 0871 200 2233 for information.
Habitat: Large area of open water, reedy bays, coniferous woodland, scrub, carr.
Key birds: *Summer:* Sedge and Grasshopper Warblers, Whitethroat, Buzzard, Tawny Owl, Little Grebe, Gadwall, Shoveler, Kingfisher. *Winter:* Waterfowl (Whooper Swan, Goldeneye), Crossbill, Redpoll, Siskin, Redwing. *All year:* Stonechat, Treecreeper, Song Thrush.
Other notable flora and fauna: Northern marsh orchid, rustyback fern, needle spikerush. Banded demoiselle, migrant hawker, golden ringed dragonfly, emerald damselfly. Ringlet, gatekeeper, clouded yellow and wall butterflies. Bloody nose beetle.
Contact: The Warden, 01407 730 762.

7. MAWDDACH VALLEY

RSPB (North Wales Office).
Location: Coed Garth Gell (SH 688 192), a woodland and heathland reserve, is adjacent to the main Dolgellau to Barmouth road (A496) near Taicynhaeaf. Use lay-bys close to the reserve's entrances. Arthog Bog (SH630138) is off the main Dolgellau to Tywyn road (A493) west of Arthog. Parking is available near by at the Morfa Mawddach station.
Access: Nature trails are open at all times.
Facilities: Nature trails at both sites and information boards.
Public transport: A regular bus service runs between Dolgellau and Barmouth and stops close to the reserve entrance at Coed Garth Gell. The Arthog Bog part of the reserve is served by the Dolgallau to Tywyn bus services which stops close by. The Arthog Bog reserve can be visited on the train by stopping at adjacent Morfa Mawddach Station.
Habitat: Oak woodland, bracken and heathland at Coed Garth Gell. Willow and alder scrub and raised bog at Arthog Bog.
Key birds: *At Coed Garth Gell:* Buzzard, Sparrowhawk, Peregrine, Raven, Lesser Spotted Woodpecker, Grey Wagtail, Dipper and Hawfinch are joined in the summer by Pied Flycatcher, Spotted Flycatcher, Wood Warbler, Redstart, Tree Pipit and Cuckoo. *At Arthog Bog:* Buzzard, Sparrowhawk, Peregrine, Raven are resident. Summer migrants include Tree Pipit, Grasshopper Warbler and Cuckoo.

In winter flocks of Redpoll and Siskin are common and Red-breasted Merganser, Pintail and Little Egret are on the nearby estuary.
Other notable flora and fauna: Coed Garth Gell has Tunbridge filmy and beech ferns and a wide variety of butterflies. Golden-ringed dragonflies are regular.
Contact: Coed Garth Gell, Mawddach Valley Reserve, 01654 700 222; e-mail: mawddach@rspb.org.uk

8. MORFA HARLECH NNR

CCW (North West Area), managed by Snowdonia NP Authority.
Location: SH 574 317, W of Harlech. On the A496 Harlech road. Minor road leads to a pay-and-display car park, then a short footpath leads to the beach.
Access: Open all year.
Facilities: Car park. Disabled parking bays and three coach parking spaces.
Public transport: The site is served by both bus and train. Train stations are at Harlech and Ty Gwyn (Ty Gwyn is near the saltmarsh wintering birds.) Contact Traveline Cymru 08712 002 233.
Habitat: Shingle (no shingle at Harlech), coast, marsh, dunes. Also forestry plantation, grassland, swamp.
Key birds: *Spring/summer:* Whitethroat, Spotted Flycatcher, Grasshopper Warbler, migrants. *Passage:* Waders, Manx Shearwater, ducks. *Winter:* Divers, Whooper Swan, Wigeon, Teal, Pintail, Scaup, Common Scoter, Hen Harrier, Merlin, Peregrine, Short-eared Owl, Little Egret, Water Pipit, Snow Bunting, Twite. *All year/breeding:* Redshank, Lapwing, Ringed Plover, Snipe, Curlew, Shelduck, Oystercatcher, Stonechat, Whinchat, Wheatear, Linnet, Reed Bunting, Sedge Warbler. Also Red-breasted Merganser, Kestrel, gulls.
Other notable fauna: Sand lizard, otter, water vole.
Contact: CCW; 0845 1306 229;
e-mail: enquiries@ccw.gov.uk
Snodonia National Park Authority, 01776 770 274;
e-mail:parc@snowdonia-npa.gov.uk
www.eryri-npa.gov.uk

9. SOUTH STACK CLIFFS

RSPB (North Wales Office).
Location: RSPB Car Park and Visitor Centre SH 208 820, Ellins Tower information centre SH 206 820. Follow A55 to W end in Holyhead, proceed straight on at roundabout, continue straight on through traffic lights. After another half mile turn L and follow the Brown Tourist signs for RSPB South Stack.
Access: RSPB car park with disabled parking, 'Access for all' track leading to a viewing area overlooking the lighthouse adjacent to Ellins Tower Visitor centre. Access to Ellins Tower gained via staircase. Reserve covered by an extensive network of paths, some of which are not accessible via wheelchair.
Facilities: Free access to Visitor Centre and Ellins Tower which has windows overlooking main auk colony open daily (10am-5.30pm Easter-Sep).
Public transport: Mainline station Holyhead (3 miles).
Habitat: Sea cliffs, maritime grassland, maritime heath, lowland heath.

Key birds: Peregrine, Chough, Fulmar, Puffin, Guillemot, Razorbill, Rock Pipit, Skylark, Stonechat, Linnet, Shag, migrant warblers and passage seabirds.
Other notable flora and fauna: Spathulate Fleawort, endemic to South Stack, adders, lizards, porpoise.
Contact: South Stack Visitor Centre, 01407 762 100; e-mail: south.stack@rspb.org.uk
www.rspb.org.uk/southstackcliffs

10. SPINNIES ABER OGWEN

North Wales Wildlife Trust.
Location: SH 613 721. From Bangor follow the Tal-y-Bont road from roundabout on A5122 near Penrhyn Castle entrance. Road to reserve is signposted on L after 1km. Reserve can also be approached from aroad at J 12 off A55. Minor road leads to car park where reserve entrance is signposted.
Access: Open all year. Dogs on leads. Keep to the paths. Wheelchair accessible to the main hide.
Facilities: Two hides clearly signposted from the car park, main hide is wheelchair accessible and offers views of Traeth Lafan sands and the Spinnies lagoon. There is a drop-off point at the main entrance. Footpaths are good throughout.
Public transport: Take the 5 or 5X bus from Bangor or Llandudno.
Habitat: Woodland, scrub, grassland, shingle beach mudflats, reed swamp and open water.
Key birds: Autumn/*winter*: Large numbers of wintering wildfowl and waders such as Redshank, Greenshank, Wigeon and Teal. Kingfisher can be seen from Sep-Mar. *Spring/summer*: Mergansers, feeding Sandwich Terns, large numbers of Mute Swans, Little Grebe, Blackcap and Sedge Warbler.
Other notable flora and fauna: Broad-leaved helleborine, snowdrops, dog's mercury, bluebells.

Red admiral, Speckled wood, holly blue, orange tip and small copper butterflies.
Contact: Chris Wynne, Conservation Officer, 01248 351 541. E-mail: ChrisWynne@wildlifetrustswales.org
www.wildlifetrust.org.uk/northwales

11. TRAETH LAFAN

Gwynedd Council.
Location: NE of Bangor, stretching to Llanfairfechan.
1) Minor road from old A55 near Tal-y-Bont (SH 610 710) to Aber Ogwen car park by coast (SH 614 723).
2) Also access from minor road from Abergwyngregyn village to Morfa Aber Reserve (SH 646 731).
3) Access on foot to Morfa Madryn Reserve 1 mile W from Llanfairfechan promenade (SH 679 754).
Access: Open access from 1, 2, and 3. All sites are wheelchair accessible.
Facilities: Public paths. 1) Car park, hides 200m away at Spinnies Reserve. 2) Car park and hide. 3) Car and coach park with toilets and café, hides at reserve.
Public transport: For local bus and train timetables call 0870 60 82 608 or log on to www.gwynedd.gov.uk
Habitat: Intertidal sands and mudflats, wetlands, streams. SPA SAC SSSI and LNR.
Key birds: Third most important area in Wales for wintering waders; of national importance for moulting Great Crested Grebe and Red-breasted Merganser; internationally important for Oystercatcher and Curlew; passage waders; winter concentrations of Goldeneye and Greenshank, and of regional significance for wintering populations of Black-throated, Red-throated and Great Northern Divers and Black-necked and Slavonian Grebes and breeding Lapwings at Morfa Madryn.
Contact: Countryside and Access Unit, 01286) 679827.

Southern Wales

Glamorgan, Gower, Gwent

SUMMER along the Gower coastline will produce breeding seabirds, Peregrines and thousands of Manx Shearwaters offshore. Cardiff Bay is good for passage and wintering waders. The best wetlands are Kenfig Pools — half way between and Cardiff and Swansea — and the Newport Wetlands Reserve. Both are worth visiting at any time of year.

1. CWM CLYDACH

RSPB Wales
Location: SN 684 026. N of Swansea. Three miles N of J45 on M4, through the village of Clydach on B4291, follow the signs for Craig Cefn Parc, the car park is close to the New Inn pub.
Access: Open at all times along public footpaths and

waymarked trails. Not suitable for wheelchairs. Coach parking not available.
Facilities: Two nature trails, car park, information boards.
Public transport: Hourly buses from Swansea stop at reserve entrance. Nearest railway station is in Swansea.
Habitat: Oak woodland on steep slopes lining the banks of the fast-flowing Lower Clydach River.
Key birds: Red Kite, Sparrowhawk, Buzzard, Raven, Green Woodpecker, Dipper and Grey Wagtail are joined in the summer by Spotted Flycatcher, Garden Warbler, Wood Warbler and Cuckoo. In winter Siskin, Lesser Redpoll and Woodcock are regular.
Other notable flora and fauna: Wood sorrel, silver-

washed fritillary and speckled wood butterflies. Good range of fungi.
Contact: Reserve warden, 029 2035 3000;
e-mail: cymru@rspb.org.uk

2. CWM COL-HUW

The Wildlife Trust of South and West Wales.
Location: SS 957 674. SE from Bridgend, site includes Iron Age fort, overlooking Bristol Channel. From Bridgend take B4265 S to Llanwit Major. Follow beach road from village.
Access: Park in seafront car park. Climb steps. Open all year.
Facilities: All year toilets and café. Information boards.
Public transport: None.
Habitat: Unimproved grassland, woodland, scrub and Jurassic blue lias cliff.
Key birds: Cliff-nesting House Martin colony, breeding Fulmar, Grasshopper Warbler. Large autumn passerine passage. Peregrine. Seawatching vantage point. Occasional Chough.
Contact: Trust HQ, 01656 724 100.
e-mail:info@welshwildlife.org
www.welshwildlife.org

3. KENFIG NNR

Bridgend County Borough Council.
Location: SS 802 811. Seven miles W of Bridgend. From J37 on M4, drive towards Porthcawl, then North Cornelly, then follow signs.
Access: Open at all times. Unsurfaced sandy paths, not suitable for wheelchairs. Flooding possible in winter and spring. Coach parking available.
Facilities: Toilets, hides, free car parking and sign-posted paths. Visitor centre open weekends and holidays (10am-4.30pm), weekdays (2pm-4.30pm).
Public transport: Local bus service: contact reserve for details.
Habitat: 1,300 acre sand dune system, freshwater lake with reeds, numerous wet dune slacks, sandy coastline with some rocky outcrops.
Key birds: *Summer*: Warblers including Cetti's, Grasshopper, Sedge, Reed and Willow Warbler, Blackcap and Whitethroat. *Winter*: Wildfowl, Water Rail, Bittern, grebes.
Other notable flora and fauna: 16 species of orchid, hairy dragonfly, red-veined and

ruddy darters, small blue, dark green fritillary, grayling, brown argus butterflies.
Contact: David Carrington, Ton Kenfig, Bridgend, CF33 4PT. 01656 743 386.
e-mail:david.carrington@bridgend.gov.uk

4. MAGOR MARSH

Gwent Wildlife Trust.
Location: ST 428 866. Magor can be reached from junctions 23 and 23A of the M4 motorway. Reserve lies to S of Magor. Leave M4 at exit 23, turning R onto B4245. Follow signs for Redwick in Magor village. Take first L after railway bridge. Reserve entrance is half mile further on R.
Access: Open all year. Keep to path. Wheelchair access to bird hide. No dogs please.
Facilities: Hide. Car park, footpaths and boardwalks.
Public transport: Bus service to Magor village. Reserve is approx 10 mins walk along Redwick road.
Habitat: Sedge fen, reedswamp, willow carr, damp hay meadows and open water.
Key birds: Important for wetland birds. *Spring*: Reed, Sedge and Grasshopper Warblers, occasional Garganey and Green Sandpiper on passage, Hobby. *Winter*: Teal, Peregrine, Jack Snipe, Snipe, occasional Shoveler and Gadwall, Bittern records in two recent years. *All year*: Little Egret, Little Grebe, Reed Bunting, Cetti's Warbler and Water Rail.
Contact: Gwent Wildlife Trust, 01600 740 358;
e-mail:info@gwentwildlife.co.uk
www.gwentwildlife.org

5. NEWPORT WETLANDS NNR

CCW/ RSPB/ Newport City Council.
Location: ST 334 834. SW of Newport. Reserve car park on West Nash Road, just before entrance to Uskmouth power station. From M4 J 24 take the A48 to Newport Retail Park, turn towards steelworks and follow brown 'duck' signs to the reserve car park.
Access: Free entry 9am to 5pm each day apart from Dec 25. Six disabled parking bays. All nature trails are accessible by wheelchair. Dogs only on perimeter footpath.
Facilities: Information centre, tea-rooms, shop, toilets (inc disabled), viewing screens.
Public transport: The 63 service runs from Newport Bus Station to the reserve daily (exc bank hols) 07.30, 09.00, 11.00, 13.00, 15.00, 16.50 and 18.00 hours.
Habitat: 438 hectares of wet meadows, saline lagoons, reedbed, scrub and mudflats on Severn estuary.
Key birds: *Spring/ summer*: Breeding

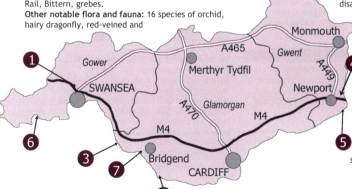
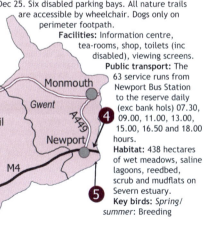

waders such as Lapwing and Oystercatcher, Bearded Tit, Cetti's Warbler, Cuckoo and regular migrants on passage. *Autumn*: Large numbers of migrating wildfowl and waders arrive at the reserve — regulars include Curlew, Dunlin, Ringed Plover, Shoveler. *Winter*: Massive Starling roost (up to 50,000 birds). Bittern, nationally important numbers of Black-tailed Godwit, Shoveler and Dunlin.
Other notable flora and fauna: Badger, wood mouse, otter. Great crested newt. Orchids in spring, 16 species of dragonfly, 23 species of butterfly and around 200 species of moth.
Contact: Newport Wetlands Reserve, CCW, 0845 1306 229.
RSPB visitor centre - 01633 636 363;
e-mail: newport-wetlands@rspb.org.uk

6. OXWICH
CCW (Swansea Office).
Location: SS 872 773. 12 miles from Swansea, off A4118.
Access: NNR open at all times. No permit required for access to foreshore, dunes, woodlands and facilities.
Facilities: Private car park, summer only. Toilets summer only. Marsh boardwalk and marsh lookout. No visitor centre, no facilities for disabled visitors.
Public transport: Bus service Swansea/Oxwich. First Cymru, tel 01792 580 580.
Habitat: Freshwater marsh, saltmarsh, foreshore, dunes, woodlands.
Key birds: *Summer*: Breeding Reed, Sedge and Cetti's

Warblers, Treecreeper, Nuthatch, woodpeckers. *Winter*: Wildfowl.
Contact: Countryside Council for Wales, 0845 1306 229; e-mail:enquiries@ccw.gov.uk www.ccw.gov.uk

7. PARC SLIP NATURE PARK
The Wildlife Trust of South and West Wales.
Location: SS 880 840. 1km W of Aberkenfig. Tourist signposts show the route from J36 of the M4.
Access: Open dawn to dusk. Space for coach parking.
Facilities: Four hides, nature trail, interpretation centre. Car park off Fountain Road. Access for wheelchairs.
Public transport: On Route No 4 of the National Cycle Network. Bus No 63 from Bridgend bus station stops outside the Fountain Inn at the bottom of Fountain Road. Train station at Tondu.
Habitat: Restored opencast mining site, wader scrape, lagoons, grassland, woodland.
Key birds: *Summer*: Breeding Tufted Duck, Lapwing, Skylark. Migrant waders (inc. Little Ringed Plover, Green Sandpiper), Little Gull. Kingfisher, Green Woodpecker. *Winter*: Snipe, Water Rail, Red-breasted Merganser.
Other notable flora and fauna: Twenty species of dragonfly have been recorded, inc emperor and scarce blue-tailed damselfly. Seven species of orchid, southern marsh, twayblade and broad-leaved helleborine.
Contact: Trust HQ, 01656 724 100.
e-mail:info@welshwildlife.org www.welshwildlife.org

Western Wales
Carmarthenshire, Ceredigion, Pembrokeshire

A SUMMER boat trip to either Skomer or Skokholm to see the huge seabird colonies, is a must-do outing in summer. Inland, steep wooded valleys are good for Redstarts, Pied Flycatchers, Wood Warblers and Red Kites. The National Wetland Centre for Wales is at Llanelli. Ynys-hir, north of Aberystwyth, hosted the BBC's *Springwatch* programme in 2012.

1. CASTLE WOODS
The Wildlife Trust of South and West Wales.
Location: SN 615 217. About 60 acres of woodland overlooking River Tywi, W of Llandeilo town centre.
Access: Open all year by footpath from Tywi Bridge, Llandeilo (SN 627 221).
Facilities: Call for advice.
Public transport: None.
Habitat: Old mixed deciduous woodlands.
Key birds: All three woodpeckers, Buzzard, Raven, Sparrowhawk. *Summer*: Pied and Spotted Flycatchers,

Redstart, Wood Warbler. *Winter*: On water meadows look for Teal, Wigeon, Goosander, Shoveler, Tufted Duck and Pochard.
Contact: Welsh Wildlife Centre, 01239 621 600;
e-mail: info@welshwildlife.org
www.welshwildlife.org

2. CORS CARON
CCW (West Wales Area).
Location: SN 692 625/SY25 6JF (car park). On B4343 two miles N of Tregaron.
Access: Open access from car park along Old Railway Walk S to boardwalk on SE bog (both wheelchair accessible), N for 3 miles overlooking reserve. Circular 4 mile open access Riverside Walk, shut at times due to flooding/management requirements. Dogs under control on Old Railway Walk, on leads on boardwalk, not allowed on Riverside Walk.
Facilities: Coach accessible car park with toilets and picnic space. Bird hide on boardwalk, 2nd hide on Old

Railway Walk 1.5 miles from car park.
Public transport: None.
Habitat: Raised bog, river, fen, wet grassland, willow woodland, reedbed.
Key birds: *Summer:* Lapwing, Redshank, Curlew, Red Kite, Hobby, Grasshopper Warbler, Whinchat, Redpoll, Reed Bunting. *Winter:* Teal, Wigeon, Whooper Swan, Hen Harrier, Red Kite.
Other notable flora and fauna: Small red damselfy among the abundant dragonflies which can be seen from boardwalk. Also adder and common lizard.
Contact: CCW, 0845 1306 229; www.ccw.gov.uk

3. DYFI

CCW (West Wales Area).
Location: SN 610 942. Large estuary area W of Machynlleth. Public footpaths off A493 E of Aberdyfi, and off B4353 (S of river); minor road from B4353 at Ynyslas to dunes and parking area.
Access: Ynyslas dunes and the estuary have unrestricted access. No access to Cors Fochno (raised bog) for casual birdwatching; permit required for study and research purposes. Good views over the bog and Aberleri marshes from W bank of Afon Leri.
Facilities: Public hide overlooking marshes beside footpath at SN 611 911.
Public transport: None.
Habitat: Sandflats, mudflats, saltmarsh, creeks, dunes, raised bog, grazing marsh.
Key birds: *Winter:* Greenland White-fronted Goose, wildfowl, waders and raptors. *Summer:* Breeding wildfowl and waders (inc. Teal, Shoveler, Merganser, Lapwing, Curlew, Redshank).
Contact: CCW, 0845 1306 229; www.ccw.gov.uk

4. GWENFFRWD - DINAS

RSPB Wales
Location: SN 788 471. North of Llandovery.From A483 take B road signposted to Llyn Brianne Reservoir.
Access: Public nature trail at Dinas open at all times.
Facilities: Nature trail including a board walk. Other parts of the trail are rugged. Car park and information board at start of trail. Coach parking can be arranged.
Public transport: Nearest train station at Llandovery, 10 miles away.
Habitat: Hillside oak woods, streams and bracken slopes. Spectacular upland scenery.
Key birds: Upland species such as Red Kite, Buzzard, Peregrine, Raven, Goosander, Dipper and Grey Wagtail are joined in the summer by Pied Flycatcher, Spotted Flycatcher, Wood Warbler, Redstart, Tree Pipit, Common Sandpiper and Cuckoo. Marsh Tit and all three woodpecker species are present.
Other notable flora and fauna: Golden-ringed dragonfly, purple hairstreak, silver-washed fritillary and Wilson's filmy fern.
Contact: Reserve Warden, 01654 700 222; e-mail: gwenffrwd.dinas@rspb.org.uk

5. NATIONAL WETLANDS CENTRE WALES

The Wildfowl & Wetlands Trust.
Location: SS 533 984. Overlooks the Burry Inlet near Llanelli. Leave M4 at junction 48. Signposted from A484, E of Llanelli.
Access: Open daily 9.30am-5pm, except Christmas Eve and Christmas Day. Grounds are open until 6pm in summer. The centre is fully accessible with disabled toilets. Mobility scooters and wheelchairs are free to hire.
Facilities: Visitor centre with toilets, hides, restaurant, shop, education facilities, free car and coach parking. The centre has level access and hard-surfaced paths.
Public transport: Bus from Llanelli to Lllwydhendy, approx 1 mile from the centre. Telephone Traveline Cymru 0871 200 2233 (7am-10pm daily).
Habitat: Inter-tidal mudflats, reedbeds, pools, marsh, waterfowl collection.
Key birds: Large flocks of Curlew, Oystercatcher, Redshank on saltmarsh. *Winter:* Pintail, Wigeon, Teal. Also Little Egret, Short-eared Owl, Peregrine.
Other notable flora and fauna: Bee and southern marsh orchids, yellow bartisa. Damselflies and dragonflies, water voles and otters.
Contact: Centre Manager, WWT National Wetlands Centre Wales, 01554 741 087; www.wwt.org.uk e-mail:info.llanelli@wwt.org.uk

6. RAMSEY ISLAND

RSPB Wales
Location: SM 706 237. One mile offshore from St Justinians lifeboat station. Two miles west of St Davids, Pembrokeshire.
Access: Open every day, weather permitting, April-Oct (1st-31st). No wheelchair access. Coach and car parking available at St Justinians. For boat bookings Contact: Thousand Island Expeditions, 01437 721 721; e-mail. sales@ thousandislands.co.uk
Facilities: Toilets, small RSPB shop selling snacks

and hot and cold drinks. Self-guiding trail with introduction from resident wardens. Guided walks are also available.

Public transport: Trains to Haverfordwest Station. Hourly buses to St Davids and then Celtic Coaster shuttle bus to boat embarkation point (Tel 01348 840 539).

Habitat: Acid grassland, maritime heath, seacliffs.

Key birds: *Spring/summer:* Cliff-nesting auks (Guillemot, Razorbill), Kittiwake, Fulmar, Lesser, Great Black-backed and Herring Gulls, Shag, Wheatear, Stonechat. Skylark, Linnet, Lapwing. *All year:* Peregrine, Raven, Chough.

Other notable fauna: Largest grey seal colony is southern Britain, red deer, harbour porpoise.

Contact: The Warden, 07836 535 733; e-mail: ramsey.island@rspb.org.uk www.rspb.org.uk/ramseyisland

7. SKOKHOLM ISLAND

The Wildlife Trust of South and West Wales.
Location: SM 735 050. Island lying S of Skomer.
Access: Occasional day visits, also 3 or 4 night stays available. Weekly accomm. Apr-Sep, tel 01239 621 212 for details and booking.
Facilities: Call for details.
Public transport: None.
Habitat: Cliffs, bays and inlets.
Key birds: *Summer:* Large colonies of Razorbill, Puffin, Guillemot, Manx Shearwater, Storm Petrel, Lesser Black-backed Gull. Migrants inc. rare species.
Other notable fauna: Grey seals, harbour porpoise, occasional common, bottlenose and risso's dolphins.
Contact: 01239 621 212; e-mail: info@welshwildlife.org www.welshwildlife.org

8. SKOMER ISLAND

The Wildlife Trust of South and West Wales.
Location: SM 725 095. Fifteen miles from Haverfordwest. Take B4327 turn-off for Marloes, embarkation point at Martin's Haven, two miles past village.
Access: Apr 1-Oct 31. Boats sail at 10am, 11am and noon every day except Mon (Bank Holidays excluded). Check (www.welshwildlife.org/2011/access-to-skomer-island) for more details. Closed four days beginning of June for seabird counts. Not suitable for infirm (steep landing steps and rough ground).
Facilities: Information centre, toilets, two hides, wardens, booklets, guides, nature trails.
Public transport: None.
Habitat: Maritime cliff, heathland, freshwater ponds.
Key birds: Largest colony of Manx Shearwater in the world (overnight). Puffin, Guillemot, Razorbill (Apr-end Jul). Kittiwake (until end Aug), Fulmar (absent Oct), Short-eared Owl (during day Jun and Jul), Chough, Peregrine, Buzzard (all year), migrants.
Contact: Reserve Warden, 07971 114 302.
e-mail: skomer@wtww.co.uk www.welshwildlife.org

9. WELSH WILDLIFE CENTRE

The Wildlife Trust of South and West Wales.
Location: SN 188 451. Two miles SE of Cardigan. River Teifi is N boundary. Sign-posted from Cardigan to Fishguard road.
Access: Open 10.30am-5pm all year. Free parking for WTSWW members, £3 non-members. Dogs on leads welcome. Disabled access to visitor centre, paths, four hides.
Facilities: Visitor centre, restaurant, network of paths and seven hides.
Public transport: Train station, Haverfordwest (23 miles). Bus station in Cardigan. Access on foot from Cardigan centre, ten mins.
Habitat: Wetlands, marsh, swamp, reedbed, open water, creek (tidal), river, saltmarsh, woodland.
Key birds: Cetti's Warbler, Kingfisher, Water Rail, Greater Spotted Woodpecker, Dipper, gulls, Marsh Harrier, Sand Martin, Hobby, Redstart, occasional Bittern and Red Kite.
Contact: Welsh Wildlife Centre, 01239 621 600; e-mail: info@welshwildlife.org www.welshwildlife.org

10. YNYS-HIR

RSPB Wales.
Location: SN 68 29 63. Off A487 Aberystwyth - Machynlleth road in Eglwys-fach village. Six miles SW of Machynlleth.
Access: Open every day (9am-9pm or dusk if earlier) except Christmas Day. Visitor centre open daily Apr-Oct (10am-5pm), Wed-Sun Nov-Mar (10am-4pm). Coaches welcome but please call for parking information. Sorry, no dogs allowed.
Facilities: Visitor centre and toilets. Numerous trails, six hides, drinks machine.
Public transport: Bus service to Eglwys-fach from either Machynlleth or Aberystwyth, tel. 01970 617 951. Rail service to Machynlleth.
Habitat: Estuary, freshwater pools, woodland and wet grassland.
Key birds: Large numbers of wintering waders, wildfowl and birds of prey on the estuary are replaced with breeding woodland birds in spring and summer. *All year:* Red Kite, Buzzard, Little Egret, Lapwing, Teal. *Spring:* Wood Warbler, Redstart, Pied Flycatcher, nine species of warbler. *Winter:* Greenland White-fronted Goose, Barnacle Goose, Wigeon, Hen Harrier.
Other notable flora and fauna: Sixteen species of dragonfly and damselfly include small red damselfly and golden-ringed dragonfly. Butterflies include dark green fritillary, brimstone and speckled wood. Otters and brown hares are resident though the former are rarely seen.
Contact: RSPB Ynys-Hir Reserve, 01654 700 222. e-mail:ynyshir@rspb.org.uk

COUNTY DIRECTORY

David Cromack

Animal hospitals exist in many counties to tend sick or injured birds such as Barn Owls, which are often victims of collisions with vehicles.

ENGLAND

THE INFORMATION in the directory has been obtained either from the persons listed or from the appropriate national or other bodies. In some cases, where it has not proved possible to verify the details directly, alternative responsible sources have been relied upon. When no satisfactory record was available, previously included entries have sometimes had to be deleted. Readers are requested to advise the editor of any errors or omissions.

AVON
See Somerset.

BEDFORDSHIRE

Bird Atlas/Avifauna
An Atlas of the Breeding Birds of Bedfordshire 1988-92 by R A Dazley and P Trodd (Bedfordshire Natural History Society, 1994).

Bird Recorders
Steve Blain, 9 Devon Drive, Biggleswade, Bedfordshire SG18 0FJ. 07979 606 300;
E-mail: recorder@bedsbirdclub.org.uk

Bird Report
BEDFORDSHIRE BIRD REPORT (1946-), from Mary Sheridan, 28 Chestnut Hill, Linslade, Leighton Buzzard, Beds LU7 2TR. 01525 378 245;
E-mail: membership@bnhs.org.uk

BTO Regional Representative
RR. Nigel Willits, Orchard Cottage, 68 High Street, Wilden, Beds MK44 2QD. 01234 771 948;
E-mail: btoinbeds@gmail.com

Club
BEDFORDSHIRE BIRD CLUB. (1992; 300). Miss Sheila Alliez, Flat 61 Adamson Court, Adamson Walk, Kempston, Bedford MK42 8QZ.
E-mail: alliezsec@peewit.freeserve.co.uk
www.bedsbirdclub.org.uk
Meetings: 8.00pm, last Tuesday of the month (Sep-Mar), Maulden Village Hall, Maulden, Beds.

Ringing Groups
IVEL RG. Graham Buss, 11 Northall Close, Eaton Bray, Dunstable, LU6 2EB. 01525 221 023;
E-mail: g1j2buss@yahoo.co.uk

RSPB. WB Kirby. The Lodge, Sandy, BedfordshireSG19 2DL.01767 680 551. E-mail: will.kirby@rspb.org.uk

RSPB Local Groups
BEDFORD. (1970; 80). Bob Montgomery, 36 Princes Road, Bromham, Beds MK43 8QD. 01234 822 035;
e-mail: montgomery547@btinternet.com
www.rspb.org.uk/groups/bedford/
Meetings: 7.30pm, 3rd Thursday of the month, A.R.A. Manton Lane, Bedford.

LUTON AND SOUTH BEDFORDSHIRE. (1973; 120+). Mick Price. 01582 871 047;
E-mail: mickprice1964@hotmail.co.uk
www.rspb.org.uk/groups/luton

Meetings: 7.45pm, 2nd Wednesday of the month, Houghton Regis Social Centre, Parkside Drive, Houghton Regis, LU5 5QN.

Wetland Bird Survey Organiser
BEDFORDSHIRE. Mr R I Bashford, 6 Brook Road, St Neots, Cambridgeshire PE19 7AX.
E-mail: richard.bashford@rspb.org.uk

Wildlife Trust
See Cambridgeshire.

BERKSHIRE

Bird Atlas/Avifauna
The Birds of Berkshire by P E Standley et al (Berkshire Atlas Group/Reading Ornithological Club, 1996).

Bird Recorder
RECORDER (Records Committee and rarity records). Chris DR Heard, 3 Waterside Lodge, Ray Mead Road, Maidenhead, Berkshire SL6 8NP. 01628 633 828;
e-mail: chris.heard@virgin.net

Bird Reports
BERKSHIRE BIRD BULLETIN (Monthly, 1986-), from Brian Clews, 118 Broomhill, Cookham, Berks SL6 9LQ. 01628 525314; e-mail: brian.clews@btconnect.com

THE BIRDS OF BERKSHIRE (1974-), from Secretary of the Berkshire Ornithological Club.
E-mail: mike.turton@berksoc.org.uk
www.berksoc.org.uk

BIRDS OF THE THEALE AREA (1988-), from Secretary, Theale Area Bird Conservation Group.

NEWBURY DISTRICT BIRD REPORT (1959-) - covering West Berkshire (approx 12 miles from centre of Newbury), plus parts of north Hants, south Oxon, from Secretary, Newbury District Ornithological Club.

BTO Regional Representatives
RR. Sarah Priest and Kent White. 01635 268 442;
e-mail: btoberks.ken.sarah@googlemail.com

Clubs
BERKSHIRE BIRD BULLETIN GROUP. (1986; 100). Berkshire Bird Bulletin Group, PO Box 680, Maidenhead, Berks, SL6 9ST. 01628 525 314;
E-mail: brian.clews@btconnect.com

NEWBURY DISTRICT ORNITHOLOGICAL CLUB. (1959; 110). John L Swallow, Yew Tree House, High Street, Kintbury, Hungerford, Berkshire RG17 9TN. 07795

027 490; e-mail: info1@ndoc.org.uk
www.ndoc.org.uk
Meetings: Indoor lectures from October to March
and regular bird watching days around Newbury,
throughout the summer and winter. Please see
website for details.

BERKSHIRE ORNITHOLOGICAL CLUB. (1947; 320). Mike
Turton, 7, Fawcett Crescent, Woodley, Reading, RG5
3HX. 07815 644 385; www.berksoc.org.uk
E-mail: mike.turton@berksoc.org.uk
Meetings: 8pm, alternate Wednesdays (Oct-Mar).
University of Reading.

THEALE AREA BIRD CONSERVATION GROUP. (1988;
75). Catherine McEwan, Secretary. 01189 415 792;
e-mail: catherine_j_mcewan@fsmail.net
www.freewebs.com/tabcg/index.htm
Meetings: 8pm, 1st Tuesday of the month, Englefield
Social Club.

Ringing Groups
NEWBURY RG. D Lond, 6 St Marks Close, Thatcham,
Berks RG19 3SZ. E-mail: duncanflong@aol.com
www.newburyrg.co.uk

RUNNYMEDE RG. D G Harris, 22 Blossom Waye,
Hounslow, TW5 9HD. www.rmxrg.org.uk
E-mail: daveharris@tinyonline.co.uk

RSPB Local Groups
EAST BERKSHIRE. (1974; 200). Gerry Studd, 5 Cherry
Grove, Holmer Green, High Wycombe, Bucks HP15
6RG. 01494 715 609; e-mail: gerrystudd@aol.com
www.eastberksrspb.org.uk
Meetings: 7.30pm, Thursdays (Sept-April), Methodist
Church Hall, King Street, Maidenhead, SL6 1EA

READING. (1986; 130). Carl Feltham. 0118 941 1713;
e-mail: carl.feltham@virginmedia.com
www.reading-rspb.org.uk;
Meetings: 8.00Pm, 2nd Tuesday of the month (Sep-
Jun), Pangbourne Village Hall, Pangbourne.

WOKINGHAM & BRACKNELL. (1979; 200). Les Blundell,
Folly Cottage, Buckle Lane, Warfield, RG42 5SB.
01344 861964; e-mail: lesblundell@ymail.com
www.rspb.org.uk/groups/wokinghamandbracknell
Meetings: 8.00pm, 2nd Tuesday of the month (Sep-
Jun), Finchampstead Memorial Hall, Wokingham,
RG40 4JU.

Wetland Bird Survey Organiser
BERKSHIRE. Mr & Mrs White, Yonder Cottage, Ashford
Hill, Thatcham, Berkshire RG19 8AX. 07831 697 371;
e-mail: white.zoothera@gmail.com

Wildlife Hospitals
LIFELINE. Wendy Hermon, Treatment Centre Co-
ordinator, Swan Treatment Centre, Cuckoo Weir
Island, South Meadow Lane, Eton, Windsor, Berks SL4
6SS. 01753 859 397 (fax) 01753 622 709;
e-mail: wendyhermon@swanlifeline.org.uk
www.swanlifeline.org.uk Registered charity. Thames
Valley 24-hour swan rescue and treatment service.

Veterinary support and hospital unit. Operates
membership scheme.

Wildlife Trust
Director, See Oxfordshire,

BUCKINGHAMSHIRE

Bird Atlas/Avifauna
The Birds of Buckinghamshire ed by P Lack and D
Ferguson (Buckinghamshire Bird Club, 1993). Now out
of print.

Bird Recorder
Andy Harding, 93 Deanshanger Lane, Old Stratford,
Milton Keynes MK19 6AX. 01908 565 896;
e-mail: andyh444@sky.com

Bird Reports
*AMERSHAM BIRDWATCHING CLUB ANNUAL REPORT
(1975-)*, from Secretary.

BUCKINGHAMSHIRE BIRD REPORT (1980-) - only some
reports since 1990 are available, from John Gearing,
Valentines, Dinton, Aylesbury, Bucks, HP17 8UW.
E-mail: john_gearing@hotmail.com

NORTH BUCKS BIRD REPORT (12 pa), from John
Gearing. 01296 748 245;
e-mail: clubrecorder@bucksbirdclub.co.uk

BTO Regional Representatives
RR. Roger Warren. 01491 638 691;
e-mail: rcwarren@btinternet.com

BTO Garden BirdWatch Ambassador
Stephanie Plaster;
e-mail: steph.plaster@googlemail.com

Clubs
BUCKINGHAMSHIRE BIRD CLUB.
(1981; 340). Rob Andrew;
e-mail: Secretary@bucksbirdclub.co.uk
www.bucksbirdclub.co.uk

NORTH BUCKS BIRDERS. (1977; N/A). Ted Reed,
c/o AACS, The Open University, Walton Hall, Milton
Keynes MK7 6AA. 01908 653 517 (work);
e-mail: ted.reed@open.ac.uk
Meetings: No meetings. Contact is via North Bucks
email group. To join contact the Group Administrator,
Simon Nichols (si.nich@yahoo.com)

RSPB Local Groups
See also Herts: Chorleywood.

AYLESBURY. (1981; 220). Brian Fisher. 01844 215 924;
e-mail: brian.fisher45@yahoo.co.uk
www.rspb.org.uk/groups/aylesburyPrebendal Farm
Community Centre, Fowler Road, Aylesbury HP19
7QW.

NORTH BUCKINGHAMSHIRE. (1976; 440). Chris Ward,
41 William Smith Close, Woolstone, Milton Keynes,
MK15 0AN. 01908 669 448;

e-mail: northbucksrspb@hotmail.com
www.rspb.org.uk/groups/northbucks
Meetings: 7.45pm, 2nd Thursday of the month, Cruck Barn, City Discovery Centre, Bradwell Abbey, MK13 9AP.

Wetland Bird Survey Organiser
BUCKINGHAMSHIRE. Graeme Taylor, Field House, 54 Halton Lane, Wendover, Aylesbury, Buckinghamshire HP22 6AU. 01296 625 796.

Wildlife Hospitals
WILDLIFE HOSPITAL TRUST. St Tiggywinkles, Aston Road, Haddenham, Aylesbury, Bucks, HP17 8AF. 01844 292 292 (24hr helpline);
www.sttiggywinkles.org.uk
E-mail: mail@sttiggywinkles.org.uk
Registered charity. All British species. Veterinary referrals and helpline for vets and others on wild bird treatments. Full veterinary unit and staff. Pub: *Bright Eyes* (free to members - sae).

Wildlife Trust
Director, See Oxfordshire,

CAMBRIDGESHIRE

Bird Atlas/Avifauna
An Atlas of the Breeding Birds of Cambridgeshire (VC 29) P M M Bircham et al (Cambridge Bird Club, 1994).

The Birds of Cambridgeshire: checklist 2000 (Cambridge Bird Club)

Bird Recorders
CAMBRIDGESHIRE. Mike Foley,
E-mail: recorder@cambridgebirdclub.org.uk

Bird Reports
CAMBRIDGESHIRE BIRD REPORT (1925-), from Bruce Martin, 178 Nuns Way, Cambridge, CB4 2NS. (H)01223 700 656; e-mail: bruce.s.martin@btinternet.com

PETERBOROUGH BIRD CLUB REPORT (1999-), from Secretary, Peterborough Bird Club.

BTO Regional Representatives
CAMBRIDGESHIRE RR. Mark Welch.
E-mail: m.welch@nhm.ac.uk

HUNTINGDON & PETERBOROUGH. Derek Langslow. 01733 232 153;
E-mail: derek.langslow@btinternet.com

Clubs
CAMBRIDGESHIRE BIRD CLUB. (1925; 350). Michael Holdsworth, 4a Cavendish Avenue, Cambridge, Cambs CB1 7US. E-mail: secretary@cambridgebirdclub.org.uk
www.cambridgebirdclub.org.uk
Meetings: 2nd Friday of the month, St John's Church Hall, Hills Road, Cambridge/Cottenham Village College.

PETERBOROUGH BIRD CLUB. (1999; 210)
Hilary Cromack, 55 Thorpe Park Road, Peterborough

PE3 6LJ. 01733 566 815;
E-mail: h.cromack@btinternet.com
www.peterboroughbirdclub.co.uk
Meetings: Indoor last Tuesday of each month from Sep-Apr inclusive at 7.30pm at PO Social Club, Bourges Boulevard, Peterborough. Outdoor meeting monthly throughout most of year.

Ringing Group
WICKEN FEN RG. Dr C J R Thorne, 17 The Footpath, Coton, Cambs CB23 7PX. 01954 2105 66;
E-mail: cjrt@cam.ac.uk

RSPB Local Groups
CAMBRIDGE. (1977; 150). Melvyn Smith. 01954 202 354; e-mail: mel_brensmith@hotmail.co.uk
www.RSPB.org.uk/groups/cambridge
Meetings: 3rd Wednesday of every month Jan-May and Sept-Dec 8pm. The Wilkinson Room, St John's the Evangelist, Hills Road, Cambridge, CB2 8RN

HUNTINGDONSHIRE. (1982; 180). Pam Peacock. 01487 840 615; e-mail: pam.evan@btinternet.com
www.rspb.org.uk/groups/huntingdonshire
Meetings: 7.30pm, last Wednesday of the month (Sep-Apr), Free Church, St Ives.

Wetland Bird Survey Organisers
CAMBRIDGESHIRE (including Huntingdonshire). Bruce Martin, 178 Nuns Way, Cambridge, Cambs CB4 2NS. (H)01223 700 656;
E-mail: bruce.s.martin@ntlworld.com

NENE WASHES. Charlie Kitchin, RSPB Nene Washes, 21a East Delph, Whittlesey, Cambs PE7 1RH. 01733 205 140; e-mail: Charlie.kitchin@rspb.org.uk

OUSE WASHES. Paul Harrngton, Ouse Washes RSPB Reserve, Welches Dam, Manea, March PE15 0NF.
E-mail: paul.harrington@rspb.org.uk

SOUTH LINCOLNSHIRE/PETERBOROUGH (inland). Bob Titman. 01733 583 254; e-mail: titman@nildram.co.uk

Wildlife Trust
THE WILDLIFE TRUST FOR BEDFORDSHIRE, CAMBRIDGESHIRE, NORTHAMPTONSHIRE AND PETERBOROUGH. (1990; 36, 000). The Manor House, Broad Street, Great Cambourne, Cambridgeshire CB23 6DH. 01954 713 500 (fax) 01954 710 051;
E-mail: cambridgeshire@wildlifebcnp.org
www.wildlifebcnp.org

CHESHIRE & WIRRAL

BirdAtlas/Avifauna
Birds in Cheshire and Wirral - A Breeding and Wintering Atlas 2004-2007 by Professor David Norman, Liverpool University Press, Autumn 2008.

The Birds of Sandbach Flashes 1935-1999 by Andrew Goodwin and Colin Lythgoe (The Printing House, Crewe, 2000).

Bird Recorder (inc Wirral)
CHESHIRE & WIRRAL. Hugh Pulsford, 6 Buttermere Drive, Great Warford, Alderley Edge, Cheshire SK9 7WA. 01565 880 171;
E-mail: countyrec@cawos.org

Bird Report
CHESHIRE & WIRRAL BIRD REPORT (1969-), from Andrew Duncalf, 25 Monarch Drive, Northwich, Cheshire CW9 8UN. 07771 774 5210; e-mail: andrewduncalf@cawos.org www.cawos.org

SOUTH EAST CHESHIRE ORNITHOLOGICAL SOCIETY BIRD REPORT (1985-), from Secretary, South East Cheshire Ornithol Soc., 01270 582 642.

BTO Regional Representatives
MID CHESHIRE. Paul Miller. 01928 787 535;
E-mail: paulandhilarymiller@live.co.uk

NORTH & EAST CHESHIRE. Mark Eddowes, 59 Westfield Drive, Knutsford, Cheshire WA16 0BH. 01565 621 683; e-mail: mark.eddowes@esrtechnology.com

SOUTH RR & RDO. Charles Hull, Edleston Cottage, Edleston Hall Lane, Nantwich, Cheshire CW5 8PL. 01270 628 194; e-mail: edleston@yahoo.co.uk

BTO Garden BirdWatch Ambassador
George Pilkington;
e-mail: nurturing-nature@virginmedia.com

Clubs
CHESHIRE & WIRRAL ORNITHOLOGICAL SOCIETY. (2012; 311). Dr Ted Lock, 2 Bourne Street, Wilmslow, Cheshire SK9 5HD. 01625 540 466; www.cawos.org
E-mail: secretary@cawos.org
Meetings: 7.45pm, 1st Friday of the month, St Vincent's Church Hall, Tatton Street, Knutsford.

CHESTER & DISTRICT ORNITHOLOGICAL SOCIETY. (1967; 50). David King, 13 Bennett Close, Willaston, South Wirral, CH64 2XF. 0151 327 7212.
Meetings: 7.30pm, 1st Thursday of the month (Oct-Mar), Caldy Valley Community Centre.

KNUTSFORD ORNITHOLOGICAL SOCIETY. (1974; 55). Derek A Pike, 2 Lilac Avenue, Knutsford, Cheshire WA16 0AZ. 01565 653 811;
E-mail: tony@mobberley.eu www.10X50.com
Meetings: 7.30pm, 4th Friday of the month (not Dec), Jubilee Hall, Stanley Road, Knutsford.

LANCASHIRE & CHESHIRE FAUNA SOCIETY. (1914; 140). Dave Bickerton, 64 Petre Crescent, Rishton, Blackburn, Lancs BB1 4RB. 01254 886 257;
E-mail: bickertond@aol.com www.lacfs.org.uk

LYMM ORNITHOLOGY GROUP. (1975; 60). Anne Ledden. 01514 240 441;
E-mail: secretary-log@tiscali.co.uk
www.users.zetnet.co.uk/lymmog/
Meetings: 8.00pm, last Friday of the month (Aug-May), Lymm Village Hall.

MID-CHESHIRE ORNITHOLOGICAL SOCIETY. (1963; 80). John Drake, 17 Wisenholme Close, Beechwood West, Runcorn, Cheshire WA7 2RU. 01928 561 133; E-mail: contact@midcheshireos.co.uk www.midcheshireos.co.uk
Meetings: 7: 30pm, 2nd Friday of the month (Oct-Mar), Cuddington and Sandiway Village Hall.

SOUTH EAST CHESHIRE ORNITHOLOGICAL SOCIETY. (1964; 140). Derek Owen (Chairman), E-mail: derek_owen07@tiscali.co.uk www.secos.org.uk
Meetings: 2nd Friday (Sept-Apr), 7.30pm, Ettiley Heath Church Community Centre, Sandbach.

WILMSLOW GUILD BIRDWATCHING GROUP. (1965; 67). Tom Gibbons, Chestnut Cottage, 37 Strawberry Lane, Wilmslow, Cheshire SK9 6AQ. 01625 520 317. http://wgbw.wikidot.com
Meetings: 7.30pm last Friday of the month, Wilmslow Guild, Bourne St, Wilmslow.

Ringing Groups
CHESHIRE SWAN RINGING GROUP. David Cookson. 01270 567 526; e-mail: Cheshireswans@aol.com http://www.record-lrc.co.uk/c1.aspx?Mod=Ar ticle&ArticleID=G0012001 Blog for Swan news, weather records, bird reports and photos at http://cheshireswanringing.blogspot.co.uk/

MERSEYSIDE RG. Bob Harris, 3 Mossleigh, Whixalll, Whitchurch, Shropshire SY13 2SA;
E-mail: harris@liv.ac.uk

SOUTH MANCHESTER RG. Mr N.B. Powell, e-mail: neville.powell@tiscali.co.uk

RSPB Local Groups
CHESTER. (1988; 220). Norman Sadler. 01244 335 670; e-mail: chester1RSPB@btinternet.com www.rspb.org.uk/groups/chester
Meetings: 7.30pm, 3rd Wednesday of the month (Sep-Apr), St Mary's Centre, Chester.

MACCLESFIELD. (1979; 250). Anne Bennett. 01260 271 231; e-mail: secretary@macclesfieldrspb.org.uk www.macclesfieldrspb.org.uk
Meetings: 7.45pm, 2nd Tuesday of the month (Sept-May), Senior Citizens Hall, Duke Street, MACCLESFIELD, Cheshire, SK11 6UR.

NORTH CHESHIRE. (1976; 100). Paul Grimmett. 01925 268 770; e-mail: paulwtwitcher@hotmail.com www.rspb.org.uk/groups/north_cheshire
Meetings: 7.45pm, 3rd Friday (Jan-April and Sept-Nov), Appleton Parish Hall, Dudlow Green Road, Appleton, Warrington.

Wetland Bird Survey Organiser
CHESHIRE SOUTH. David Cookson. 01270 567 526; e-mail: cheshireswans@aol.com

ENGLAND

Wildlife Hospitals
RSPCA STAPELEY GRANGE WILDLIFE CENTRE. London Road, Stapeley, Nantwich, Cheshire, CW5 7JW. 0300 123 0722. All wild birds. Oiled bird wash facilities and pools. Veterinary support.

Wildlife Trust
CHESHIRE WILDLIFE TRUST. (1962; 13, 100). Bickley Hall Farm, Bickley, Malpas, Cheshire SY14 8EF. 01948 820 728 (fax) 0709 2888 469;
E-mail: info@cheshirewt.org.uk
www.cheshirewildlifetrust.co.uk

CLEVELAND and Co. DURHAM

Bird Atlas/Avifauna
A Summer Atlas of Breeding Birds of County Durham by Stephen Westerberg/Kieth Bowey. (Durham Bird Club, 2000).

The Birds of Durham by Keith Bowey and Mark Newsome. (Durham Bird Club 2012)

The Breeding Birds of Cleveland. Teesmouth Bird Club, 2008.

Bird Recorder
CLEVELAND. Tom Francis.
E-mail: mot.francis@ntlworld.com

DURHAM. Mark Newsome, 69 Cedar Drive, Jarrow, NE32 4BF. 07834 978 255;
E-mail: mvnewsome@hotmail.com

Bird Report
BIRDS IN DURHAM (1971-), from D Sowerbutts, 9 Prebends Fields, Gilesgate, Durham, DH1 1HH. 0191 386 7201; e-mail: d16lst@tiscali.co.uk

CLEVELAND BIRD REPORT (1974-), from Mr J Fletcher, 43 Glaisdale Avenue, Middlesbrough TS5 7PF. 01642 818 825.

BTO Regional Representatives
CLEVELAND RR. Vic Fairbrother, 8, Whitby Avenue, Guisborough, Cleveland, TS14 7AP. 01287 633 744; e-mail: vic.fairbrother@ntlworld.com

DURHAM RR. David L Sowerbutts, 9 Prebends Field, Gilesgate Moor, Durham, DH1 1HH. 0191 386 7201; e-mail: david.sowerbutts@dunelm.org.uk

Club
DURHAM BIRD CLUB. (1975; 320). Paul Anderson, Chairman, 2 Hawsker Close, Tunstall Village, Sunderland SR3 2YD. E-mail: paulandcath29@aol.com
www.durhambirdclub.org
Meetings: Monthly indoor meetings (Sept-Apr), Durham Wildlife Trust HQ at Rainton Meadows, Houghton le Spring.

TEESMOUTH BIRD CLUB. (1960; 425). Chris Sharp (Hon Sec.), 45 Endeavour Close, Seaton Carew, Hartlepool

TS25 1EY. 01429 865 163; www.teesmouthbc.com
Meetings: 7.30pm, 1st Monday of the month (Sep-Apr), Stockton Library, Church Road, Stockton.

Ringing Groups
DURHAM DALES RG. J R Hawes, Fairways, 5 Raby Terrace, Willington, Crook, Durham DL15 0HR.

NORTHUMBRIA RG. Richard Barnes, 12 Thorp Cottages, Bar Moor, Ryton, Tyne & Wear NE40 3AU. 0191 413 3846.

TEES RG. E Wood, Southfields, 16 Marton Moor Road, Nunthorpe, Middlesbrough, Cleveland TS7 0BH. 01642 323 563.

SOUTH CLEVELAND RG. W Norman, 2 Station Cottages, Grosmont, Whitby, N Yorks YO22 5PB. 01947 895 226; e-mail: wilfgros@btinternet.com

RSPB Local Group
CLEVELAND. (1974; 150). Terry Reeve.
E-mail: ClevelandRSPB@googlemail.com
www.rspb.org.uk/groups/cleveland
Meetings: 7.00 for 7.30pm, 2nd Monday of each month (Sep-Apr), Nature's World, Ladgate Lane, Middlesbrough, Cleveland

DARLINGTON. (2005). Clifford Evans. 01325 466 471; e-mail: cgevans@talktalk.net
www.communigate.co.uk/ne/darlingtonrspbgroup/index.phtml
Meetings: 1st Thursday of the month (Sept-July), Cockerton Methodist Church, Cockerton Green, Darlington.

DURHAM. (1974; 125). Richard Cowen. 0191 377 2061; e-mail: richardcowen2002@yahoo.co.uk
www.durham-rspb.org.uk
Meetings: 7.30pm, 2nd Tuesday of the month (Oct-Mar), Room CG83, adjacent to Scarborough Lecture Theatre, University Science Site, Stockton Road entrance.

Wetland Bird Survey Organisers
DURHAM. Vacant.

TEES ESTUARY. Mike Leakey, c/o Natural England, British Energy, Tees Road, Hartlepool TS25 2BZ. 01429 853 325 / 0300 060 1729;
e-mail: mike.leakey@naturalengland.org.uk

Wildlife Trust
DURHAM WILDLIFE TRUST. (1971; 4, 000). Rainton Meadows, Chilton Moor, Houghton-le-Spring, Tyne & Wear, DH4 6PU. 0191 584 3112 (fax) 0191 584 3934; e-mail: mail@durhamwt.co.uk www.durhamwt.co.uk

TEES VALLEY WILDLIFE TRUST. (1979; 5, 000). Margrove Heritage Centre, Margrove Park, Boosbeck, Saltburn-by-the-Sea, TS12 3BZ. 01287 636 382 (fax) 01287 636 383; e-mail: info@teeswildlife.org
www.teeswildlife.org

CORNWALL AND ISLES OF SCILLY

Bird Atlas/Avifauna
The Essential Guide to Birds of The Isles of Scilly 2007 by RL Flood, N Hudson and B Thomas, published by authors.

Bird Recorders
CORNWALL. Darrell Clegg, 55 Lower Fore Street, Saltash, Cornwall PL12 6JQ.
E-mail: recorder@cbwps.org.uk

ISLES OF SCILLY. Will Wagstaff, 42 Sally Port, St Mary's, Isles of Scilly TR21 0JE. 01720 422 212;
e-mail: will@islandwildlifetours.co.uk
www.carnithen.co.uk

Bird Reports
BIRDS IN CORNWALL (1931-), from the secretary, CBWPS. E-mail: secretary@cbwps.org.uk
www.cbwps.org.uk

ISLES OF SCILLY BIRD REPORT and NATURAL HISTORY REVIEW 2000 (1969-), from see website;
www.scilly-birding.co.uk

BTO Regional Representatives
CORNWALL. Stephen Jackson, 2, Trelawney Cottages, Falmouth, Cornwall TR11 3NY. 01326 313 533;
E-mail: stephen.f.jackson@btinternet.com

ISLES OF SCILLY RR & RDO. Will Wagstaff, 42 Sally Port, St Mary's, Isles of Scilly TR21 0JE. 01720 422 212; e-mail: will@islandwildlifetours.co.uk

Clubs
CORNWALL BIRDWATCHING & PRESERVATION SOCIETY. (1931; 762). Cait Hutchings, 24 Kernick Road, Penryn, Cornwall TR10 8NT. 01326 375 593; (M)07896 353 601;
e-mail: secretary@cbwps.org.uk
www.cbwps.org.uk

CORNWALL WILDLIFE TRUST PHOTOGRAPHIC GROUP. (40). David Chapman, 41 Bosence Road, Townshend, Nr Hayle, Cornwall TR27 6AL. 01736 850 287;
e-mail: david@ruralimages.freeserve.co.uk
www.ruralimages.freeserve.co.uk
Meetings: Mixture of indoor and outdoor meetings, please phone for details.

ISLES OF SCILLY BIRD GROUP. (2000; 510). Membership Secretary. 32 Sallyport, St Mary's, Isles of Scilly TR21 0JE;
E-mail: isbgmembership@btinternet.com
www.scilly-birding.co.uk

Ringing Group
SCILLONIA SEABIRD GROUP. Peter Robinson, Secretary, 19 Pine Park Road, Honiton, Devon EX14 2HR. (Tel/fax) 01404 549 873 (M)07768 538 132;
e-mail: pjrobinson2@aol.com
www.birdexpertuk.com

RSPB Local Group
CORNWALL. (1972; 420). Roger Hooper. 01209 820 610; e-mail: rogerwhooper@btinternet.com
www.rspb.org.uk/groups/cornwall
Meetings: Indoor meetings (Oct-Apr), outdoor throughout the year.

Wetland Bird Survey Organisers
CORNWALL (excl. Tamar Complex). Simon Taylor, 42 Pendarves Street, Troon, Camborne, Cornwall TR14 9EG; e-mail: simon.taylor@ap-group.co.uk

TAMAR COMPLEX. Gladys Grant, 18 Orchard Crescent, Oreston, Plymouth, Devon PL9 7NF.
E-mail: gladysgrant@talktalk.net

Wildlife Hospital
MOUSEHOLE WILD BIRD HOSPITAL & SANCTUARY ASSOCIATION LTD. Raginnis Hill, Mousehole, Penzance, Cornwall, TR19 6SR. 01736 731 386. All species. No ringing.

Wildlife Trust
CORNWALL WILDLIFE TRUST. (1962; 14, 000). Five Acres, Allet, Truro, Cornwall, TR4 9DJ. 01872 273 939 (fax) 01872 225 476;
E-mail: info@cornwallwildlifetrust.org.uk
www.cornwallwildlifetrust.org.uk

THE ISLES OF SCILLY WILDLIFE TRUST. (1984: 324) Carn Thomas, Hugh Town, St Marys, Isles of Scilly TR21 0PT.01720 422 153 (fax) 01720 422 153;
E-mail: enquiries@ios-wildlifetrust.org.uk
www.ios-wildlifetrust.org.uk

CUMBRIA

BirdAtlas/Avifauna
*The Breeding Birds of Cumbria*by Stott, Callion, Kinley, Raven and Roberts (Cumbria Bird Club, 2002).

Bird Recorders
CUMBRIA. Colin Raven, 18 Seathwaite Road, Barrow-in-Furness, Cumbria, LA14 4LX.
E-mail: colin@walneyobs.fsnet.co.uk

NORTH EAST. Chris Hind,
E-mail: chris.m.hind@gmail.com

NORTH WEST (Allerdale & Copeland). Derek McAlone, 88 Whinlatter Road, Mirehouse, Whitehaven, Cumbria CA28 8DQ. 01946 691 370;
E-mail: derekmcalone@hotmail.co.uk

SOUTH (South Lakeland & Furness). Ronnie Irving. 24 Birchwood Close, Vicarage Park, Kendal, Cumbria LA9 5BJ. E-mail: ronnie@fenella.fslife.co.uk

Bird Reports
BIRDS AND WILDLIFE IN CUMBRIA (1970-), from Dave Piercy, Secretary, Derwentwater Youth Hostel, Borrowdale, Keswick CA12 5UR. 01768 777 909;
e-mail: daveandkathypiercy@tiscali.co.uk
www.cumbriabirdclub.org.uk

239

WALNEY BIRD OBSERVATORY REPORT, from Warden, see Reserves.

BTO Regional Representative
CUMBRIA. Clive Hartley, Undercragg, Charney Well La, Grange Over Sands, LA11 6DB. 01539 536 824; e-mail: clive.hartley304@btinternet.com

Clubs
ARNSIDE & DISTRICT NATURAL HISTORY SOCIETY. (1967; 221). Roger Spooner. 01524 701 619. www.arnsidesilverdaleaonb.org.uk
Meetings: 7.30pm, 2nd Tuesday of the month (Sept-Apr). WI Hall, Arnside. (Also summer walks).

CUMBRIA BIRD CLUB. (1989; 330). Dave Piercy, Secretary, Derwentwater Youth Hostel, Borrowdale, Keswick CA12 5UR. 01768 777 246; E-mail: daveandkathypiercy@tiscali.co.uk www.cumbriabirdclub.org.uk
Meetings: Various evenings and venues (Oct-Mar) check on website for further details.

Ringing Groups
EDEN RG. G Longrigg, 1 Spring Cottage, Heights, Appleby-in-Westmorland, Cumbria CA16 6EP.

MORECAMBE BAY WADER RG. J Sheldon, 140 Oxford Street, Barrow-in-Furness, Cumbria LA14 5PJ.

WALNEY BIRD OBSERVATORY. K Parkes, 176 Harrogate Street, Barrow-in-Furness, Cumbria, LA14 5NA. 01229 824 219.

RSPB Local Groups
CARLISLE. (1974; 400). Richard Dixon, 01697 473 544; e-mail: sunzeco@hotmail.co.uk www.rspb.org.uk/groups/carlisle
Meetings: 7.30pm, Wednesday monthly (Sep-Mar), Tithe Barn, (Behind Marks And Spencer's), West Walls, Carlisle CA3. Also monthly field trips except August.

SOUTH LAKELAND. (1973; 305). Richard Evans, 01539 722 221; e-mail: revansinkendal@gmail.com www.rspb.org.uk/groups/southlakeland/
Meetings: Contact above.

WEST CUMBRIA. (1986; 270). Marjorie Hutchin, 3 Camerton Road, Gt Broughton, Cockermouth, Cumbria CA13 0YR. 01900 825 231; E-mail: majorie.hutchin@btinternet.com www.rspb.org.uk/groups/westcumbria
Meetings: 7.30pm, 1st Tuesday (Sept-Apr), United Reformed Church, Main St, Cockermouth

Wetland Bird Survey Organisers
CUMBRIA OUTER SOUTH. Dave Shackleton. E-mail: d.shackleton@btinternet.com

DUDDON ESTUARY. Rosalyn & Colin Gay. 01842 750 050; e-mail: webs@bto.org

IRT/MITE/ESK ESTUARY. Peter Jones, 01842 750 050 E-mail: webs@bto.org

SOLWAY ESTUARY INNER SOUTH. Norman Holton. E-mail: norman.holton@rspb.org.uk

SOLWAY ESTUARY NORTH. Andy Riches. 07792 713 693; e-mail: slioch69@aol.com

Wildlife Trust
CUMBRIA WILDLIFE TRUST. (1962; 15, 000). Plumgarths, Crook Road, Kendal, Cumbria LA8 8LX. 01539 816 300 (fax) 01539 816 301; E-mail: mail@cumbriawildlifetrust.org.uk www.cumbriawildlifetrust.org.uk

DERBYSHIRE

Bird Atlas/Avifauna
The Birds of Derbyshire, ed. RA Frost (in preparation)

Bird Recorders
1. JOINT RECORDER. Roy A Frost, 66 St Lawrence Road, North Wingfield, Chesterfield, Derbyshire S42 5LL. 01246 850 037; e-mail: frostra66@btinternet.com

2. Records Committee & rarity records. Rodney W Key, 3 Farningham Close, Spondon, Derby, Derbyshire DE21 7DZ. 01332 678 571; E-mail: r_key@sky.com

3. JOINT RECORDER. Richard M R James, 10 Eastbrae Road, Littleover, Derby, DerbyshireDE23 1WA. 01332 771 787; e-mail: rmrjames@yahoo.co.uk

Bird Reports
CARSINGTON BIRD CLUB ANNUAL REPORT, from The Secretary.

DERBYSHIRE BIRD REPORT (1954- 2010). 2010 will become 2011 in mid-Nov 2012, from Bryan Barnacle, Mays, Malthouse Lane, Froggatt, Hope Valley, Derbyshire S32 3ZA. 01433 630 726; E-mail: barney@mays1.demon.co.uk

OGSTON BIRD CLUB REPORT (1970-), from contact for Ogston Bird Club below.

BTO Regional Representatives
NORTH RR. Dave Budworth, 121 Wood Lane, Newhall, Swadlincote, Derbys DE11 0LX. 01283 215 188; E-mail: dbud01@aol.com

SOUTH RR. Dave Budworth, 121 Wood Lane, Newhall, Swadlincote, Derbys DE11 0LX. 01283 215 188; E-mail: dbud01@aol.com

Clubs
BAKEWELL BIRD STUDY GROUP. (1987; 80).Ken Rome, View Cottage, Wensley, Matlock, Derbys DE4 2LH. E-mail: viewcottage@lineone.net www.bakewellbirdstudygroup.co.uk
Meetings: 7.30pm, 2nd Monday of the month, Friends Meeting House, Bakewell.

BUXTON FIELD CLUB. (1946; 68). B Aries, 1 Horsefair Avenue, Chapel-en-le-Frith, High Peak, Derbys SK23

9SQ. 01298 815 291;
E-mail: brian.aries@btinternet.com
Meetings: 7.30pm, Saturdays fortnightly (Oct-Mar),
Methodist Church Hall, Buxton.

CARSINGTON BIRD CLUB. (1992; 257). Paul Hicking
(Secretary), 12 Beaurepaire Crescent, Belper,
DerbyshireDE5 1HR. 01773 827 727;
E-mail: membership@carsingtonbirdclub.co.uk
www.carsingtonbirdclub.co.uk
Meetings: 3rd Tuesday of the month (Sep-Mar),
Hognaston Village Hall, (Apr-Aug), outdoors.

DERBYSHIRE ORNITHOLOGICAL SOCIETY. (1954;
550). Steve Shaw, 84 Moorland View Road, Walton,
Chesterfield, Derbys S40 3DF. 01246 236090;
E-mail: steveshaw84mvr@btinternet.com -
www.derbyshireOS.org.uk
Meetings: 7.30pm, last Friday of the winter months,
various venues.

OGSTON BIRD CLUB. (1969; 1, 126). Peter Birley, 35
Rosemary Drive, Alvaston, Derby, DE24 0TA. 01332
753 078; e-mail: peter.birley@sky.com
www.ogstonbirdclub.co.uk

SOUTH PEAK RAPTOR STUDY GROUP. (1998; 12). M E
Taylor, 76 Hawksley Avenue, Newbold, Chesterfield,
Derbys S40 4TL. 01246 277749.

Ringing Groups
DARK PEAK RG. W M Underwood, Ivy Cottage, 15
Broadbottom Road, Mottram-in-Longdendale, Hyde,
Cheshire SK14 6JB.
E-mail: w.m.underwood@talk21.com

SORBY-BRECK RG. Dr Geoff P Mawson, Moonpenny
Farm, Farwater Lane, Dronfield, Sheffield S18 1RA.
E-mail: moonpenny@talktalk.net
www.sorbybreckringinggroup.co.uk

SOUDER RG. Dave Budworth, 121 Wood Lane,
Newhall, Swadlincote, Derbys DE11 0LX.
E-mail: dbud01@aol.com

RSPB Local Groups
CHESTERFIELD. (1987; 274). Alan Goddard. 01246 230
244; (M)07764 895 657;
E-mail: alandgoddard10@btinternet.com
www.rspb.org.uk/groups/chesterfield
Meetings: 7.15pm, usually 3rd Monday of the month,
Winding Wheel, New Exhibition Centre, 13 Holywell
Street, Chesterfield.

DERBY LOCAL GROUP. (1973; 500). Ray Worthy, 01332
232 748; e-mail: worthyrm@yahoo.co.uk
www.rspb.org.uk/groups/derby
Meetings: 7.30pm, 2nd Wednesday of the month
(Sep-Apr), Broughton Suite, Grange Banqueting Suite,
457 Burton Road, Littleover, Derby DE23 6FL.

HIGH PEAK. (1974; 110). Jim Jeffery. 0161 494 5367;
e-mail: henrygordon@live.co.uk
www.rspb.org.uk/groups/highpeak
Meetings: 7.30pm, 3rd Monday of the month (Sep-
May), Marple Senior Citizens Hall, Memorial Park,
Marple, Stockport SK6 6BA.

Wildlife Trust
DERBYSHIRE WILDLIFE TRUST. (1962; 14, 000). East
Mill, Bridge Foot, Belper, Derbyshire DE56 1XH. 01773
881 188 (fax) 01773 821 826;
E-mail: enquiries@derbyshirewt.co.uk
www.derbyshirewildlifetrust.org.uk

DEVON

Bird Atlas/Avifauna
Birds Of Devon by Michael Tyler (Devon Birdwatching
& Preservation Society, 2010).

Tetrad Atlas of Breeding Birds of Devon by H P Sitters
(Devon Birdwatching & Preservation Society, 1988).

The Birds of Lundy by Tim Davis and Tim Jones 2007.
Available from R M Young (Bookseller) on 01769 573
350 (see www.birdsoflundy.org.uk for further details).

Bird Recorder
Steve Waite, 38 Durley Road, Seaton, Devon EX12
2HW. 01297 20326. E-mail: recorder@devonbirds.org -
www.devonbirds.org/

Bird Reports
DEVON BIRD REPORT (1971). See contact for Devon
Birdwatching and Preservation Society.
www.devonbirds.org

LUNDY FIELD SOCIETY ANNUAL REPORT (1946-). £3
each inc postage, check website for availability, from
Frances Stuart, 3 Lower Linden Road, Clevedon, North
Somerset BS21 7SU. E-mail: lfssec@hotmail.co.uk

BTO Regional Representative
RR. Stella Beavan. 07710 879 277;
E-mail: stella@treedown.eclipse.co.uk

BTO Garden BirdWatch Ambassador
DEVON (north). David Gayton;
e-mail: gayton881@btinternet.com

Clubs
DEVON BIRD WATCHING &
PRESERVATION SOCIETY.
(1928; 1200). Mr Mike Daniels,
1 Babbs Cottage, Princetown,
Yelverton, Devon PL20 6QJ.
01822 890 899;
e-mail: nellmegfly@btinternet.com
www.devonbirds.org

KINGSBRIDGE & DISTRICT NATURAL HISTORY SOCIETY.
(1989; 130). Martin Catt, Migrants Rest, East Prawle,
Kingsbridge, Devon TQ7 2DB. 01548 511 443;
E-mail: martin.catt@btinternet.com www.knhs.org.uk
Meeting: 4th Monday of Sept-Apr, 7.30pm phone for
venue.

LUNDY FIELD SOCIETY. (1946; 450). Mr Michael
Williams, 5 School Place, , Oxford, Oxon OX1 4RG.
E-mail: lfssec@hotmail.co.uk www.lundy.org.uk
Meeting: AGM 1st Saturday in March, Exeter.

ENGLAND

TOPSHAM BIRDWATCHING & NATURALISTS' SOCIETY. (1969; 140). Keith Chester (Membership Secretary). 01392 877 817; e-mail: tbnsociety@hotmail.com http://topshambns.blogspot.com
Meetings: 7.30pm, 2nd Friday of the month (Sep-May), Matthews Hall, Topsham.

Ringing Groups
AXE ESTUARY RINGING GROUP. Mike Tyler, The Acorn, Shute Road, Kilmington, Axminster EX13 7ST. 01297 349 58; e-mail: mwtyler2@googlemail.com axeestuaryringinggroup.blogspot.co.uk

DEVON & CORNWALL WADER RG. R C Swinfen, 72 Dunraven Drive, Derriford, Plymouth, PL6 6AT. 01752 704 184.

LUNDY FIELD SOCIETY. A M Taylor, 26 High Street, Spetisbury, Blandford, Dorset DT11 9DJ. 01258 857 336; e-mail: ammataylor@yahoo.co.uk

SLAPTON BIRD OBSERVATORY. R C Swinfen, 72 Dunraven Drive, Derriford, Plymouth, PL6 6AT. 01752 704 184.

RSPB Local Groups
EXETER & DISTRICT. (1974; 400). Roger Tucker. 01392 860518; e-mail: parrog@aol.com
www.exeter-rspb.org.uk
Meetings: 7.30p, various evenings, Southernhay United Reformed Church Rooms, Dix's Field, Exeter.

PLYMOUTH. (1974; 600). Mrs Eileen Willey, 11 Beverstone Way, Roborough, Plymouth, PL6 7DY. 01752 208 996; e-mail: edward.willey@sky.com

TORBAY AND SOUTH DEVON TEAM. John Allan. 01626 821 344; e-mail: john@morsey.f2s.com
www.rspb.org.uk/groups/torbayandsouthdevon

Wetland Bird Survey Organiser
DEVON other sites. Peter Reay, Crooked Fir, Moorland Park, South Brent, Devon TQ10 9AS. 01364 73293; e-mail: peter.p.j.reay@btinternet.com

TAMAR COMPLEX. Gladys Grant, 18 Orchard Crescent, Oreston, Plymouth, PL9 7NF. 01752 406 287; e-mail: gladysgrant@talktalk.net

TAW/TORRIDGE ESTUARY. Terry Chaplin. 01271 342 590; e-mail: terry@chaplin.eclipse.co.uk

Wildlife Hospitals
BIRD OF PREY CASUALTY CENTRE. Mrs J E L Vinson, Crooked Meadow, Stidston Lane, South Brent, Devon, TQ10 9JS. 01364 72174. Birds of prey, with emergency advice on other species. Aviaries, rehabilitation facilities. Veterinary support.

Wildlife Trust
DEVON WILDLIFE TRUST. (1962; 33, 000). Cricklepit, Commercial Road, Exeter, EX2 4AB. 01392 279 244; E-mail: contactus@devonwildlifetrust.org
www.devonwildlifetrust.org

DORSET

Bird Atlas/Avifauna
The Birds of Dorset by Dr George Green (Christopher Helm 2004).

Bird Recorder
Kevin Lane. E-mail: kevin@broadstoneheath.co.uk

Bird Reports
DORSET BIRDS (1977-), from Neil Gartshore, Moor Edge, 2 Bere Road, Wareham, Dorset BH20 4DD. 01929 552 560; e-mail: enquiries@callunabooks.co.uk

THE BIRDS OF CHRISTCHURCH HARBOUR (1956-), from Ian Southworth, 1 Bodowen Road, Burton, Christchurch, Dorset BH23 7JL.
E-mail: ianbirder@aol.com

PORTLAND BIRD OBSERVATORY REPORT, from Warden, see Reserves,

BTO Regional Representatives
DORSET. Ieuan Evans (temporary). 01842 750 050; e-mail: ieuan.evans@bto.org

Clubs
CHRISTCHURCH HARBOUR ORNITHOLOGICAL GROUP. (1956; 275). Mr. I.H. Southworth, Membership Secretary, 1 Bodowen Road, Burton, Christchurch, Dorset BH23 7JL. 01202 478 093. www.chog.org.uk

DORSET BIRD CLUB. (1987; 525). Mrs Diana Dyer, The Cedars, 30 Osmay Road, Swanage, Dorset BH19 2JQ. 01929 421 402; www.dorsetbirds.org.uk
E-mail: membership@dorsetbirds.org.uk

DORSET NATURAL HISTORY & ARCHAEOLOGICAL SOCIETY. (1845; 2188). Dorset County Museum. High West Street, Dorchester, Dorset DT1 1XA. 01305 262 735; e-mail: secretary@dorsetcountymuseum.org
www.dorsetcountymuseum.org

Ringing Groups
CHRISTCHURCH HARBOUR RS. E C Brett, 3 Whitfield Park, St Ives, Ringwood, Hants, BH24 2DX; E-mail: ed_brett@lineone.net

PORTLAND BIRD OBSERVATORY. Martin Cade, Old Lower Light, Portland Bill, Dorset, DT5 2JT. 01305 820 553; e-mail: obs@btinternet.com
www.portlandbirdobs.org.uk

STOUR RG. R Gifford, 62 Beacon Park Road, Upton, Poole, Dorset BH16 5PE.

RSPB Local Groups
BLACKMOOR VALE. (1981; 130). Alison Rymell, Group Leader. 01985 844 819;
E-mail: alisonrymell@yahoo.co.uk
www.rspb.org.uk/groups/blackmoorvale
Meetings: 7.30pm, 3rd Friday in the month, Gillingham Primary School.

ENGLAND

EAST DORSET. (1974; 435). Hugh Clark. 01202 532 595; e-mail: hugh.clark@hotmail.co.uk www.rspb.org.uk/groups/eastdorset
Meetings: 7.30pm, 2nd Wednesday of the month, St Mark's Church Hall, Talbot Village, Wallisdown, Bournemouth.

POOLE. (1982; 305). Pam Hunt, 01929 553 338; e-mail: pam.hunt@talktalk.net www.rspb.org.uk/groups/poole
Meetings: 7.30pm, Upton Community Centre, Poole Road, Upton.

SOUTH DORSET. (1976; 422). Andrew Parsons. 01305 772 678; e-mail: andrew_parsons_141@yahoo.co.uk www.rspb.org.uk/groups/southdorset
Meetings: 3rd Thursday of each month (Sep-April), St. Georges Church Hall, Fordington, Dorchester, Dorset, DT1 1LB.

Wetland Bird Survey Organisers
DORSET (excl estuaries). John Jones, 14 Church Lane, Sutton Waldron, Nr Blandford, Dorset DT11 8PA.01747 811 490; e-mail: blackbirdcott@tiscali.co.uk

THE FLEET & PORTLAND HARBOUR. Steve Groves, Abbotsbury Swannery, New Barn Road, Abbotsbury, Dorset DT3 4JG. (W)01305 871 684; E-mail: swannery@gotadsl.co.uk

POOLE HARBOUR. Paul Morton. E-mail: paulolua@yahoo.co.uk

RADIPOLE & LODMOOR. Toby Branston, RSPB Weymouth Reserves.

Wildlife Hospital
SWAN RESCUE SANCTUARY. Ken and Judy Merriman, The Wigeon, Crooked Withies, Holt, Wimborne, Dorset BH21 7LB. 01202 828 166.www.swan. jowebdesign.co.uk 24 hr rescue service for swans. Large sanctuary of 40 ponds and lakes. Hospital and intensive care. Veterinary support. Free advice and help line. Three fully equipped rescue ambulances. Rescue water craft for all emergencies. Viewing by appointment only.

Wildlife Trust
DORSET WILDLIFE TRUST. (1961; 25, 000). Brooklands Farm, Forston, Dorchester, Dorset, DT2 7AA. 01305 264 620; E-mail: enquiries@dorsetwildlifetrust.org.uk www.dorsetwildlife.org.uk

DURHAM
See Cleveland and Co. Durham.

ESSEX

Bird Atlas/Avifauna
The Birds of Essex by Simon Wood (A&C Black, August 2007).

The Breeding Birds of Essex by M K Dennis (Essex Birdwatching Society, 1996).

Bird Recorder
RECORDER. Les Steward, 6 Creek View, Basildon, Essex SS16 4RU. 01268 551 464, e-mail: les.steward@btinternet.com

Bird Report
ESSEX BIRD REPORT (inc Bradwell Bird Obs records) (1950-), from Peter Dwyer, Sales Officer, 48 Churchill Avenue, Halstead, Essex, CO9 2BE. Tel/(fax) 01787 476524; e-mail: petedwyer@petedwyer.plus.com

BTO Regional Representatives
NORTH-EAST RR. Position vacant. 01842 750 050. E-mail: info@bto.org

NORTH-WEST RR. Graham Smith. 01277 354 034; e-mail: silaum.silaus@tiscali.co.uk

SOUTH RR. Position vacant. 01842 750 050. E-mail: info@bto.org

Club
ESSEX BIRDWATCHING SOCIETY. (1949; 700). John and Louise Sykes, Joint General Secretary, 14 Acres End, Chelmsford, Essex CM7 2PL. 01245 355 132; E-mail: john.sykes@btinternet.com www.ebws.org.uk
Meetings: 1st Friday of the month (Oct-Mar), Friends' Meeting House, Rainsford Road, Chelmsford.

Ringing Groups
ABBERTON RG. C P Harris, Wyandotte, Seamer Road, Southminster, Essex, CM0 7BX.

BRADWELL BIRD OBSERVATORY. C P Harris, Wyandotte, Seamer Road, Southminster CM0 7BX.

RSPB Local Groups
CHELMSFORD AND CENTRAL ESSEX. (1976; 1200). Graham Webster. 01621 843 799; E-mail: gjwebster123@aol.com www.rspb.org.uk/groups/chelmsford
Meetings: 8pm, Thursdays, eight times a year. The Cramphorn Theatre, Chelmsford.

COLCHESTER. (1981; 220). Mr Russell Leavett, 10 Grove Road, Brantham, Manningtree, Essex CO11 1TX. 01206 399 059; e-mail: rleavett@btinternet.com www.rspb.org.uk/groups/colchester
Meetings: 7.45pm, 2nd Thursday of the month (Sep-Apr), Shrub End Community Hall, Shrub End Road, Colchester. Regular coach and car trips to local birding sites and those further afield.

SOUTH EAST ESSEX. (1983; 200). Graham Mee, 34 Park View Drive, Leigh on Sea, Essex SS9 4TU. 01702 525 152; e-mail: grahamm@southendrspb.co.uk www.southeastrspb.org.uk
Meetings: 7.30pm, usually 1st Tuesday of the month (Sep-May), Belfairs School Hall, School Way, Leigh-on-Sea SS9 4HX.

Wetland Bird Survey Organiser
CROUCH/ROACH ESTUARY and SOUTH DENGIE. Canon Peter Mason, 32 Providence, Burnham on Crouch, Essex CM0 8JU. E-mail: Petermason32@waitrose.com

ENGLAND

HAMFORD WATER. Julian Novorol. 01255 880 552.

LEE VALLEY. Cath Patrick. Myddelton House, Bulls Cross, Enfield, Herts EN2 9HG. 01992 79 882; E-mail: cpatrick@leevalleypark.org.uk

NORTH BLACKWATER. John Thorogood. 01206 768 771.

SOUTH BLACKWATER AND NORTH DENGIE. Anthony Harbott. 01992 575 213; E-mail: anthonyharbott@talktalk.net

STOUR ESTUARY. Rick Vonk, RSPB, Unit 13 Court Farm, 3 Stutton Road, Brantham Suffolk CO11 1PW. (D)01473 328 006; e-mail: rick.vonk@rspb.org.uk

THAMES ESTUARY. Foulness. Chris Lewis. E-mail: cpm.lewis@ukonline.co.uk

Wildlife Trust
ESSEX WILDLIFE TRUST. (1959; 36, 000). The Joan Elliot Visitor Centre, Abbots Hall Farm, Great Wigborough, Colchester, CO5 7RZ. 01621 862 960 (fax) 01621 862 990; e-mail: admin@essexwt.org.uk www.essexwt.org.uk

GLOUCESTERSHIRE

Bird Atlas/Avifauna
Atlas of Breeding Birds of the North Cotswolds. (North Cotswold Ornithological Society, 1990).

Birds of Gloucestershire CM Swaine (Alan Sutton 1982 - now out of print).

Birds of The Cotswolds (Liverpool University Press 2009).

Bird Recorder
GLOUCESTERSHIRE EXCLUDING S.GLOS (AVON). Richard Baatsen. E-mail: baatsen@surfbirder.com

Bird Reports
CHELTENHAM BIRD CLUB BIRD REPORT (1998-2001) - no longer published, from Secretary.

GLOUCESTERSHIRE BIRD REPORT (1953-). £7.50 including postage, from David Cramp, 2 Ellenor Drive, Alderton, Tewkesbury, GL20 8NZ. E-mail: djcramp@btinternet.com

NORTH COTSWOLD ORNITHOLOGICAL SOCIETY ANNUAL REPORT (1983-), from T Hutton, 15 Green Close, Childswickham, Broadway, Worcs WR12 7JJ. 01386 858 511.

BTO Regional Representative
Mike Smart, 143 Cheltenham Road, Gloucester, GL2 0JH. 01452 421 131; E-mail: smartmike@btinternet.com

Clubs
CHELTENHAM BIRD CLUB. (1976; 94). Membership Secretary. 01451 850 385. www.cheltenhambirdclub.org.uk

Meetings: 7.15pm, Mondays (Oct-Mar), Bournside School, Warden Hill Road, Cheltenham.

DURSLEY BIRDWATCHING & PRESERVATION SOCIETY. (1953; 350). The Secretary; E-mail: dbwps@yahoo.com http://dursleybirdwatchers.btck.co.uk/ **Meetings:** 7.45pm, 2nd and 4th Monday (Sept-Mar), Dursley Community Centre.

GLOUCESTERSHIRE NATURALISTS' SOCIETY. (1948; 500). Mike Smart, 143 Cheltenham Road, Gloucester, GL2 0JH. 01452 421 131; www.glosnats.org E-mail: smartmike@btinternet.com

NORTH COTSWOLD ORNITHOLOGICAL SOCIETY. (1982; 70). T Hutton, 15 Green Close, Childswickham, Broadway, Worcs WR12 7JJ. 01386 858 511. E-mail: info@ncosbirds.org.uk www.ncosbirds.org.uk **Meetings:** Monthly field meetings, usually Sunday 9.30pm.

Ringing Groups
COTSWOLD WATER PARK RG. John Wells, 25 Pipers Grove, Highnam, Glos, GL2 8NJ. E-mail: john.wells2@btinternet.com

SEVERN ESTUARY GULL GROUP. M E Durham, 6 Glebe Close, Frampton-on-Severn, Glos GL2 7EL. 01452 741 312.

WILDFOWL & WETLANDS TRUST. Richard Hearn, Wildfowl & Wetlands Trust, Slimbridge, Glos, GL2 7BT. E-mail: richard.hearn@wwt.org.uk

RSPB Local Group
GLOUCESTERSHIRE. (1972; 600). David Cramp, 2 Ellenor Drive, Alderton, Tewkesbury, GL20 8NZ. 01242 620 281; e-mail: djcramp@btinternet.com www.rspb.org.uk/groups/gloucestershire **Meetings:** 7.30pm, 3rd Tuesday of the month, Gala Club, Longford, Gloucester GL2 9EB.

Wildlife Hospital
VALE WILDLIFE RESCUE - WILDLIFE HOSPITAL + REHABILITATION CENTRE. Any staff member, Station Road, Beckford, Tewkesbury, Glos GL20 7AN. 01386 882 288; e-mail: info@valewildlife.org.uk www.valewildlife.org.uk All wild birds. Intensive care. Registered charity. Veterinary support.

Wetland Bird Survey Organisers
GLOUCESTERSHIRE. Mike Smart, 143 Cheltenham Road, Gloucester, GlosGL2 0JH. 01452 421 131; e-mail: smartmike@btinternet.com

COTSWOLD WATER PARK. Gareth Harris, Cotswold Water Park Society, Cotswold House, Manor Farm, Down Ampney Estate, Cirencester, Glos GL7 5QF. 01793 752 413 or 01793 752 730; E-mail: gareth.harris@waterpark.org www.waterpark.org

ENGLAND

Wildlife Trust
GLOUCESTERSHIRE WILDLIFE TRUST. (1961; 26, 500). Conservation Centre, Robinswood Hill Country Park, Reservoir Road, Gloucester, GL4 6SX. 01452 383 333; e-mail: info@gloucestershirewildlifetrust.co.uk
www.gloucestershirewildlifetrust.co.uk

HAMPSHIRE

Bird Atlas/Avifauna
Birds of Hampshire by J M Clark and J A Eyre (Hampshire Ornithological Society, 1993).

Bird Recorder
RECORDER. Keith Betton, 8 Dukes Close, Folly Hill, Farnham, Surrey GU9 0DR. 01252 724 068; E-mail: keithbetton@hotmail.com

Bird Reports
HAMPSHIRE BIRD REPORT (1955-). 2010 now available. (Check for the 2011 edition which may be available at the end of 2012). From Mr Bryan Coates, 8 Gardner Way, Chandler's Ford, Eastleigh, Hants SO53 1JL. 023 80 252 960; e-mail: sandyandbryan@tiscali.co.uk www.hos.org.uk

BTO Regional Representatives
RR. Glynne C Evans, Waverley, Station Road, Chilbolton, Stockbridge, Hants SO20 6AL. 01264 860 697; e-mail: hantsbto@hotmail.com

BTO Garden BirdWatch Ambassador
Alick Jones; e-mail: gbwhants@btinternet.com

Clubs
HAMPSHIRE ORNITHOLOGICAL SOCIETY. (1979; 1, 500). John Shillitoe, Honarary Secretary, Westerly, Hundred Acres Road, Wickham, Hampshire PO17 6HY. 01329 833 086; e-mail: john@shillitoe.freeserve.co.uk www.hos.org.uk

Ringing Groups
FARLINGTON RG. D A Bell, 38 Holly Grove, Fareham, Hants, PO16 7UP.

ITCHEN RG. W F Simcox, 10 Holdaway Close, Kingsworthy, Winchester, SO23 7QH. E-mail: wilfsimcox@gmx.com

RSPB Local Groups
BASINGSTOKE. (1979; 90). Peter Hutchins, 35 Woodlands, Overton, Whitchurch, RG25 3HN. 01256 770 831; (M)07895 388 378; E-mail: fieldfare@jaybry.gotadsl.co.uk www.rspb.org.uk/groups/basingstoke
Meetings: 7.30pm 3rd Wednesday of the month (Sept-May), The Barn, Church Cottage, St Michael's Church, Church Square, Basingstoke.

NEW FOREST. Dane Thomas. 01452 615 171; E-mail: RSPB@newmilton.org www.rspb.org.uk/groups/newforest
Meetings: 7.30pm 2nd Wednesday of the month (Sept-June) Lyndhurst Community Centre, High Street, Lyndhurst SO43 7NY.

NORTH EAST HAMPSHIRE. (1976; 215). Sue Radbourne. 01276 29 434; www.northeasthantsrspb.org.uk E-mail: Mailto@northeasthantsRSPB.org.uk
Meetings: See website.

PORTSMOUTH. (1974; 210). Gordon Humby, 19 Charlesworth Gardens, Waterlooville, Hants, PO7 6AU. 02392 353 949; E-mail: PortsmouthRSPB@googlemail.com www.rspb.org.uk/groups/portsmouth
Meetings: 7.30pm, 4th Saturday of every month. St Andrews Church Hall, Havant Road, Farlington, Portsmouth, PO6 1AA.

WINCHESTER & DISTRICT LOCAL GROUP. (1974; 100). Pam Symes, 29A Maytree Close, Badger Farm, Winchester, SO22 4JE. 01962 851 821; E-mail: psymes033@gmail.com www.rspb.org.uk/groups/winchester
Meetings: 7.30pm, 1st Wednesday of the month (not Jan or Aug), Shawford Parish Hall, Pearson Lane, Shawford.

Wetland Bird Survey Organisers
AVON VALLEY. John Clark, 4 Cygnet Court, Old Cove Road, Fleet, Hants GU51 2RL. 01252 623 397; E-mail: johnclark50@sky.com

HAMPSHIRE (estuaries/coastal). John Shillitoe. E-mail: john@shillitoe.freeserve.co.uk

HAMPSHIRE (Inland - excluding Avon Valley). Keith Wills, 51 Peabody Road, Farnborough, Hants GU14 6EB. E-mail: keithb.wills@ukgateway.net

ISLE OF WIGHT. Jim Baldwin. 01983 202 223; E-mail: jimr.baldwin@tiscali.co.uk

Wildlife Trust
HAMPSHIRE & ISLE OF WIGHT WILDLIFE TRUST. (1960; 28, 000). Beechcroft House, Vicarage Lane, Curdridge, Hampshire SO32 2DP. 01489 774 400 (fax) 01489 774 401; e-mail: feedback@hwt.org.uk www.hiwwt.org.uk

HEREFORDSHIRE

Bird Recorder
Steve Coney, 5 Springfield Road, Withington, Hereford, HR1 3RU. 01432 850 068; E-mail: coney@bluecarrots.com

Bird Report
THE BIRDS OF HEREFORDSHIRE (2008 -), from Mr WJ Marler, Cherry Tree House, Walford, Leintwardine, Craven Arms, Shropshire SY7 0JT.

THE YELLOWHAMMER - Herefordshire Ornithological Club annual report, (1951-), from Mr I Evans, 12 Brockington Drive, Tupsley, Hereford, HR1 1TA. 01432 265 509; e-mail: iforelanine@tiscali.co.uk

BTO Regional Representative
Chris Robinson, 01981 510 360; e-mail: herefordbtorep@btinternet.com

ENGLAND

Club
HEREFORDSHIRE ORNITHOLOGICAL CLUB. (1950; 439).
TM Weale, Foxholes, Bringsty Common, Worcester,
WR6 5UN. 01886 821 368; www.herefordshirebirds.org
E-mail: weale@tinyworld.co.uk
Meetings: 7.30pm, 2nd Thursday of the month
(Autumn/winter), Holmer Parish Centre, Holmer,
Hereford.

Ringing Group
LLANCILLO RG. Dr G R Geen, Little Langthorns, High
Cross Lane, Little Canfield, Dunmow, Essex CM6 1TD.
01371 878 095; e-mail: grahamgeen@btinternet.com

Wetland Bird Survey Organiser
HEREFORDSHIRE. Chris Robinson, Rock Cottage,
Newton St Margarets, Hereford, HR2 0QW. 01981 510
360; e-mail: herefordbtorep.btinternet.com

Wildlife Trust
HEREFORDSHIRE NATURE TRUST. (1962; 2, 535).
Lower House Farm, Ledbury Road, Tupsley, Hereford,
HR1 1UT. 01432 356 872;
E-mail: enquiries@herefordshirewt.co.uk
www.herefordshirewt.org

HERTFORDSHIRE

Bird Atlas/Avifauna
Birds at Tring Reservoirs by R Young et al
(Hertfordshire Natural History Society, 1996).

Mammals, Amphibians and Reptiles of Hertfordshire
by Hertfordshire NHS in association with Training
Publications Ltd, 3 Finway Court, Whippendell Road,
Watford WD18 7EN, (2001).

The Breeding Birds of Hertfordshire by K W Smith et
al (Herts NHS, 1993). Purchase from HNHS at £5 plus
postage. E-mail: herts.naturalhistorysociety@aol.com

Bird Recorder
Ken Smith (Acting Recorder). 24 Mandeville Road,
Welwyn Garden City, Herts AL8 7JU. 01707 330 405.
E-mail: birdrecorder@hnhs.org   www.hnhs.org/birds

Bird Report
HERTFORDSHIRE BIRD REPORT 2009 (from 1908-2009),
from Linda Smith, 24 Mandeville Road, Welwyn
Garden City, Herts AL8 7JU. 01707 330 405;
E-mail: secretary@hnhs.org www.hnhs.org

BTO Regional Representative
Chris Dee, 26 Broadleaf Avenue, Thorley Park,
Bishop's Stortford, Herts, CM23 4JY. 01279 755 637;
e-mail: hertsbto@hotmail.com
website: http://hertsbto.blogspot.com

BTO Garden BirdWatch Ambassadors
Jean Crystal; e-mail: jeanlcrystal@aol.com

Simon Jones; e-mail: simon.l.jones@ntlworld.com

Myra Campbell;
e-mail: myra42campbell@googlemail.com

Clubs
FRIENDS OF TRING RESERVOIRS. (1993; 400).
Membership Secretary, PO Box 1083, Tring HP23 5WU.
01442 822 471; e-mail: keith@fotr.org.uk
www.fotr.org.uk
Meetings: See website.

HERTFORDSHIRE BIRD CLUB.
(1971; 352) Part of Hertfordshire
Natural History Society. Linda
Smith, 24 Mandeville
Rise, Welwyn Garden
City, Herts AL8 7JU.
01707 330 405; e-mail: secretary@hnhs.org
www.hnhs.org/birds

HERTFORDSHIRE NATURAL HISTORY SOCIETY AND
HERTS BIRD CLUB. (1875; 320) Linda Smith, 24
Mandeville Rise, Welwyn Garden City, Herts AL8 7JU.
01707 330 405; e-mail: secretary@hnhs.org
www.hnhs.org and www.hertsbirdclub.org.uk
Meetings: Saturday afternoon, Nov and Mar (date and
venue varies).

Ringing Groups
MAPLE CROSS RG. P Delaloye.
E-mail: pdelaloye@tiscali.co.uk

RYE MEADS RG. Chris Dee, 26 Broadleaf Avenue,
Thorley Park, Bishop's Stortford, Herts CM23 4JY.
01279 755 637; e-mail: ringingsecretary@rmrg.org.uk
www.rmrg.org.uk

TRING RG. Mick A'Court, 6 Chalkshire Cottages,
Chalkshire road, Butlers Cross, Bucks HP17 0TW.
01296 623 610; e-mail: mick_acourt@o2.co.uk

RSPB Local Groups
CHORLEYWOOD & DISTRICT. (1977; 142). Carol Smith,
24 Beacon Way, Rickmansworth, Herts WD3 7PE.
01923 897 885; e-mail: carolsmithuk@hotmail.com
www.rspb.org.uk/groups/chorleywood
Meetings: 8pm, 3rd Thursday of the month (Sept-
Nov, Jan-May), 2nd Thursday (Dec), Russell School,
Brushwood Drive, Chorleywood.

HARPENDEN. (1974; 1000). Geoff Horn, 41 Ridgewood
Drive, Harpenden, Herts AL5 3LJ. 01582 765 443;
e-mail: geoffrhorn@yahoo.co.uk
www.rspb.org.uk/groups/harpenden
Meetings: 8pm, 2nd Thursday of the month (Sept-
June), All Saint's Church Hall, Station Road,
Harpenden.

HEMEL HEMPSTEAD. (1972; 150). Ian Wilson, 15
Seymour Crescent, Hemel Hempstead, Herts, HP2
5DS. 01442 265 022; www.hemelrspb.org.uk
E-mail: ian.aeronautics@gmail.com
Meetings: 8pm, 1st Monday of the month (Sep-
Jun), The Cavendish School, Warners End, Hemel
Hempstead.

HITCHIN & LETCHWORTH. (1972; 111). Dr Martin
Johnson, 1 Cartwright Road, Royston, Herts SG8 9ET.
01763 249 459; e-mail: martinrjspc@hotmail.com

www.rspb.org.uk/groups/hitchinandletchworth
Meetings: 7.30pm, 1st Friday of the month, The
Settlement, Nevells Road, Letchworth SG6 4UB.

POTTERS BAR & BARNET. (1977; 1400). Lesley
Causton, 57 Lakeside Crescent, East Barnet, Herts
EN4 8QH. 0208 440 2038; www.pottersbar-rspb.org.uk
e-mail: lesleycauston@talktalk.net
Meetings: 2.00pm, 2nd Wednesday of the month,
St Johns URC Hall, Mowbray Road, Barnet. Evening
meetings, 3rd Friday of the month (not Jul, Aug or
Dec) 7.45pm, Potters Bar United Reform Church,
Tilbury Hall, Darkes Lane, Potters Bar, EN6 1BZ.

ST ALBANS. (1979; 1550 in catchment area). Peter
Antram, 6 Yule Close, Bricket Wood, St Albans AL2
3XZ. 01923 678 534;
e-mail: st-albans-rspb@hotmail.co.uk
www.rspb.org.uk/groups/stalbans
Meetings: 7.30pm, 2nd Tuesday of the month (Sep-
May), St Saviours Church Hall, Sandpit Lane, St
Albans.

SOUTH EAST HERTS. (1971; 2, 400 in catchment
area). Terry Smith, 31 Marle Gardens, Waltham
Abbey, Essex, EN9 2DZ. 01992 715634;
e-mail: se_herts_rspb@yahoo.co.uk
www.rspb.org.uk/groups/southeasthertfordshire
Meetings: 7.30pm, usually last Tuesday of the month
(Sept-June), URC Church Hall, Mill Lane, Broxbourne
EN10 7BQ.

STEVENAGE. (1982; 1300 in the catchment area). Mrs
Ann Collis, 16 Stevenage Road, Walkern, Herts, 01483
861 547; e-mail: p.collis672@btinternet.com
www.rspb.org.uk/groups/stevenage
Meetings: 7.30pm, 3rd Tuesday of the month, Friends
Meeting House, Cuttys Lane, Stevenage.

WATFORD. (1974; 590). Janet Reynolds. 01923 249
647; e-mail: janet.reynolds@whht.nhs.uk
www.rspb.org.uk/groups/watford
Meetings: 7.30pm, 2nd Wednesday of the month
(Sep-Jun), Stanborough Centre, St Albans Rd,
Watford.

Wetland Bird Survey Organiser
HERTFORDSHIRE (excl. Lee Valley). Jim Terry.
E-mail: jimjoypaddy@virginmedia.com

LEE VALLEY. Cath Patrick. Myddelton House, Bulls
Cross, Enfield, Herts EN2 9HG. 01992 717 711;
E-mail: cpatrick@leevalleypark.org.uk

Wildlife Trust
HERTS & MIDDLESEX WILDLIFE TRUST. (1964; 18, 500).
Grebe House, St Michael's Street, St Albans, Herts,
AL3 4SN. 01727 858 901; e-mail: info@hmwt.org
www.wildlifetrust.org.uk/herts/

ISLE OF WIGHT

Bird Recorder
Robin Attrill, 17 Waterhouse Moor, Harlow, Essex
CM18 6BA. E-mail: robin@rpattrill.freeserve.co.uk

Bird Reports
*ISLE OF WIGHT BIRD REPORT (1986-) (Pre-1986 not
available),* from Mr DJ Hunnybun, 40 Churchill Road,
Cowes, Isle of Wight, PO31 8HH. 01983 292 880;
e-mail: davehunnybun@hotmail.com

BTO Regional Representative
James C Gloyn, 3 School Close, Newchurch, Isle of
Wight, PO36 0NL. 01983 865 567;
E-mail: gloynjc@yahoo.com

Clubs
ISLE OF WIGHT NATURAL HISTORY &
ARCHAEOLOGICAL SOCIETY. (1919; 500). The
Secretary, Unit 16, Prospect Business Centre,
Prospect Business Centre, West Cowes, Isle of Wight
PO31 7HD. E-mail: iwnhas@btconnect.com
www.iwnhas.org

ISLE OF WIGHT ORNITHOLOGICAL GROUP. (1986; 155).
Mr DJ Hunnybun, 40 Churchill Road, Cowes, Isle of
Wight, PO31 8HH. 01983 292 880;
E-mail: davehunnybun@hotmail.com
http://iowbirds.awardspace.com/IWOG.htm

Wildlife Trust
Director, See Hampshire,

KENT

Bird Atlas/Avifauna
Birding in Kent by D W Taylor et al 1996. Pica Press

Bird Recorder
Barry Wright, 6 Hatton Close, Northfleet, Kent DA11
8SD. 01474 320 918 (M)07789 710 555;
e-mail: barrybirding@tiscali.co.uk

Bird Reports
DUNGENESS BIRD OBSERVATORY REPORT (1989-), from
Warden, see Reserves.

KENT BIRD REPORT (1952-), from Chris Roome,
Rowland House, Station Road, Staplehurst, KentTN12
0PY. 01580 891 686;
e-mail: chris.roome@zulogic.co.uk

SANDWICH BAY BIRD OBSERVATORY REPORT, from
Warden, see Reserves,

BTO Regional Representatives
RR. Geoff Orton, 07788 102 238;
e-mail: geofforton@hotmail.com

Club
KENT ORNITHOLOGICAL SOCIETY. (1952; 650). Mr
Martin Coath, 14A Mount Harry Road, Sevenoaks, Kent
TN13 3JH. 01732 460 710;
E-mail: crag_martin2000@yahoo.co.uk
www.kentos.org.uk
Meetings: Indoor: October-April at various venues;
the AGM in April is at Grove Green community Hall,
Grovewood Drive, Maidstone ME14 5TQ. See website
for details: www.kentos.org.uk

ENGLAND

Ringing Groups
DARTFORD RG. R Taylor.
E-mail: dreolin@btopenworld.com

DUNGENESS BIRD OBSERVATORY. David Walker,
Dungeness Bird Observatory, Dungeness, Romney
Marsh, Kent TN29 9NA. 01797 321 309;
E-mail: dungeness.obs@tinyonline.co.uk
www.dungenessbirdobs.org.uk

RECULVER RG. Chris Hindle, 42 Glenbervie Drive,
Herne Bay, Kent, CT6 6QL. 01227 373 070;
E-mail: christopherhindle@hotmail.com

SANDWICH BAY BIRD OBSERVATORY. Mr KB Ellis, 6
Alderney Gardens, St Peters, Broadstairs, Kent CT10
2TN. 01304 617 341; e-mail: keithjulie@talktalk.net

SWALE WADER GROUP. Rod Smith, 67 York Avenue,
Chatham, Kent, ME5 9ES. 01634 865 836.
www.swalewaders.co.uk

RSPB Local Groups
CANTERBURY. (1973; 216). Wendy Kennett. 01227 477
113; e-mail: wendywiffles@yahoo.co.uk
www.rspb.org.uk/groups/canterbury
Meetings: 8.00pm, 2nd Tuesday of the month
(Sept-Apr), Chaucer Social Club, Off Chaucer Drive,
Canterbury, CT1 1YW.

GRAVESEND. (1977; 250).
Jeffrey Kirk, 01474 365 757;
E-mail: jeffandwendy28@btopenworld.com
www.rspbgravesend.org.uk
Meetings: 7.45pm, 2nd Wednesday of the month
(Sep-May), St Botolph's Hall, Northfleet, Gravesend
DA11 9EX. 2.00pm 4th Tuesday of the month (Nov,
Jan-Mar), Kent Room, Woodville Halls, Gravesend
DA12 1AU.

MAIDSTONE. (1973; 250). Dick Marchese, 11 Bathurst
Road, Staplehurst, Tonbridge, Kent TN12 0LG. 01580
892 458; e-mail: marchese8@aol.com
http://maidstone.localrspb.org.uk/
Meetings: 7.30pm 4th Thursday of the month, Grove
Green Community Hall, Penhurst Close, Grove Green,
opposite Tesco's.

MEDWAY. (1974; 230). Marie Tilley. 01634 387 431;
e-mail: marie.tilley@btinternet.com
www.medway-rspb.pwp.blueyonder.co.uk
Meetings: 7.45pm 3rd Tuesday of the month (except
Aug), Parkwood Community Centre, Parkwood Green,
Gillingham ME8 9PN.

SEVENOAKS. (1974; 265). Anne Chapman. 01732 456
459; e-mail: anneanddave.chapman@virgin.net
www.rspb.org.uk/groups/sevenoaks
Meetings: 7.45pm 1st Thursday of the month, Otford
Memorial Hall.

THANET. (1975; 119). Peter Radclyffe, Cottage of St
John, Caterbury Road, Sarre, Kent CT7 0JY. 01843
847 345; e-mail: Hazel.johnson1@sky.com
www.rspb.org.uk/groups/thanet

Meetings: 7.30pm last Tuesday of the month (Jan-
Nov), Portland Centre.

TONBRIDGE. (1975; 150 reg attendees/1700 in
catchment). Gabrielle Sutcliffe. 01732 365 583;
e-mail: martin@ellismp.plus.com
www.rspb.org.uk/groups/tonbridge
Meetings: 7.45pm 3rd Wednesday of the month (Sept-
Apr), St Phillips Church, Salisbury Road.

Wetland Bird Survey Organisers
DUNGENESS AREA. David Walker, Dungeness Bird
Observatory, Dungeness, Romney Marsh, Kent TN29
9NA. E-mail: dungeness.obs@tinyonline.co.uk
www.dungenessbirdobs.org.uk

EAST KENT. Ken Lodge, 14 Gallwey Avenue,
Birchington, Kent CT7 9PA. 01843 843 105;
E-mail: lodge9pa@btinternet.com

NORTH KENT ESTUARIES. Vacant.

PEGWELL BAY. Pete Findley;
E-mail: pwjfindley@hotmail.com

Wildlife Hospital
RAPTOR CENTRE. Eddie Hare, Ivy Cottage,
Groombridge Place, Groombridge, Tunbridge Wells,
Kent TN3 9QG. 01892 861 175;
E-mail: raptorcentre@btconnect.com
www.raptorcentre.co.uk Birds of prey. Veterinary
support. 24hr rescue service for sick and injured birds
of prey that covers the South-East.

Wildlife Trust
KENT WILDLIFE TRUST. (1958; 10500). Tyland Barn,
Sandling, Maidstone, Kent, ME14 3BD. 01622 662 012
E-mail: info@kentwildlife.org.uk
www.kentwildlifetrust.org.uk

LANCASHIRE

Bird Atlas/Avifauna
An Atlas of Breeding Birds of Lancaster and District
by Ken Harrison (Lancaster & District Birdwatching
Society, 1995).

Birds of Lancashire and North Merseyside by White,
McCarthy and Jones (Hobby Publications 2008).

Breeding Birds of Lancashire and North Merseyside
(2001), sponsored by North West Water. Contact:
Bob Pyefinch, 12 Bannistre Court, Tarleton, Preston
PR4 6HA.

Bird Recorder
(See also Manchester).

Inc North Merseyside. Steve White, 102 Minster Court,
Crown Street, Liverpool, L7 3QD. 0151 707 2744;
e-mail: stevewhite102@btinternet.com

Bird Reports
BIRDS OF LANCASTER & DISTRICT (1959-), from RSPB
Leighton Moss shop and Lambert's, Rosemary Lane,

Lancaster (£8), The Bramblings, 1 Washington Drive, Warton LA5 9RA. E-mail: ldbws@yahoo.co.uk www.lancasterbirdwatching.org.uk

EAST LANCASHIRE ORNITHOLOGISTS' CLUB BIRD REPORT (1982-) Members £2.50, Non-members £5.50, from Tony Cooper, 28 Peel Park Ave, Clitheroe BB7 1ET; www.eastlancashireornithologists.org.uk

CHORLEY AND DISTRICT NATURAL HISTORY SOCIETY ANNUAL REPORT (1979 -), published on website www.chorleynats.org.uk

BLACKBURN & DISTRICT BIRD CLUB ANNUAL REPORT (1992-), from Doreen Bonner, 6 Winston Road, Blackburn, BB1 8BJ. 01254 261 480; E-mail: webmaster@blackburnbirdclub.co.uk www.blackburnbirdclub.co.uk

FYLDE BIRD REPORT (1983-), from Paul Ellis, 18 Staining Rise, Blackpool, FY3 0BU. www.fyldebirdclub.org

LANCASHIRE BIRD REPORT (1914-), from Dave Bickerton, 64 Petre Crescent, Rishton, Blackburn, Lancs BB1 4RB. 01254 886 257; E-mail: bickertond@aol.com

ROSSENDALE ORNITHOLOGISTS' CLUB BIRD REPORT (1977-).from Secretary, Rossendale Ornithologists Club, 25 Church St, Newchurch, Rossendale, Lancs BB4 9EX. E-mail: info@rossendalebird.freeuk.com www.rossendalebird.freeuk.com

BTO Regional Representatives
EAST RR. Tony Cooper, 28 Peel Park Avenue, Clitheroe, Lancs, BB7 1ET. 01200 424 577; E-mail: anthony.cooper34@btinternet.com

NORTH & WEST RR. Jean Roberts. 01524 770 295; e-mail: JeanRbrts6@aol.com

SOUTH RR. Stuart Piner, 01524 751 987; E-mail: stuartpiner@hotmail.com

Clubs
BLACKBURN & DISTRICT BIRD CLUB. (1991; 134). Jim Bonner, 6 Winston Road, Blackburn, BB1 8BJ. 01254 261 480; e-mail: webmaster@ blackburnbirdclub.co.uk www.blackburnbirdclub.co.uk
Meetings: Normally 7.30pm, 1st Monday of the month, (Sept-Apr), Church Hall, Preston New Road. Check website for all indoor and outdoor meetings.

CHORLEY & DISTRICT NATURAL HISTORY SOCIETY. (1979; 170). Phil Kirk, Millend, Dawbers Lane, Euxton, Chorley, Lancs PR7 6EB. 01257 266783; E-mail: secretary@chorleynats.org.uk www.chorleynats.org.uk
Meetings: 7.30pm, 3rd Thursday of the month (Sept-Apr), St Mary's Parish Centre, Chorley

EAST LANCASHIRE ORNITHOLOGISTS' CLUB. (1955; 45). Dr J Plackett, 71 Walton Lane, Nelson, Lancs BB9

8BG. 01282 612 870; E-mail: j.plackett@eastlancsornithologists.org.uk www.eastlancsornithologists.org.uk
Meetings: 7.30pm, 1st Monday of the month (Check website or local press), St Anne's Church Hall, Fence, Nr Burnley.

FYLDE BIRD CLUB (Registered charity number 1102961). (1982; 110). Paul Ellis, 18 Staining Rise, Blackpool, FY3 0BU. 01253 891281; e-mail: paul. ellis24@btopenworld.com or KBeaver@uclan.ac.uk www.fyldebirdclub.org
Meetings: 7.45pm, 4th Tuesday of the month, River Wyre Hotel, Breck Road, Poulton le Fylde.

FYLDE NATURALISTS' SOCIETY. (1946; 140). Julie Clarke, 7 Cedar Avenue, Poulton-le-Fylde, Blackpool, FY6 8DQ. 01253 883 785; E-mail: secretary@fyldenaturalists.co.uk www.fyldenaturalists.co.uk
Meetings: 7.30pm, fortnightly (Sep-Mar), Fylde Coast Alive, Church Hall, Raikes Parade, Blackpool unless otherwise stated in the Programme.

LANCASHIRE & CHESHIRE FAUNA SOCIETY. (1914; 150). Dave Bickerton, 64 Petre Crescent, Rishton, Lancs, BB1 4RB. 01254 886 257; E-mail: bickertond@aol.com www.lacfs.org.uk

LANCASTER & DISTRICT BIRD WATCHING SOCIETY. (1959; 200). Peter Cook (Secretary), 21 Threshfield Avenue, Heysham, Morecambe LA3 2DU. 01524 851 454; (M) 07880 541 798; E-mail: peter.cook33@btinternet.com www.lancasterbirdwatching.org.uk
Meetings: 7.30pm, last Monday of the month (Sep-Nov, Feb-Mar), Bare Methodist Church Hall, St Margarets Road, Morecambe; (Jan and Apr) the Hornby Institute, Hornby.

PRESTON BIRD WATCHING & NATURAL HISTORY SOCIETY. (1876 as the Preston Scientific Society; 140). Stephen R. Halliwell, 3 Baillie Street, Williams Lane, Fulwood Park, Preston. 01772 705 468; E-mail: stephen.halliwell@prestonsociety.co.uk www.prestonsociety.co.uk
Meetings: Check website for details.

ROSSENDALE ORNITHOLOGISTS' CLUB. (1976; 35). Ian Brady, 25 Church St, Newchurch, Rossendale, Lancs BB4 9EX. 01706 222 120; http://roc.wikispaces.com
Meetings: 7.30pm, 3rd Monday of the month, Weavers Cottage, Bacup Road, Rawtenstall.

Ringing Groups
FYLDE RG. G Barnes, 17 Lomond Avenue, Marton, Blackpool, FY3 9QL.

NORTH LANCS RG. John Wilson BEM, 40 Church Hill Avenue, Warton, Carnforth, Lancs LA5 9NU. E-mail: johnwilson711@btinternet.com

SOUTH WEST LANCASHIRE RG. I H Wolfenden, 35 Hartdale Road, Thornton, Liverpool, Merseyside L23 1TA. 01519 311 232.

ENGLAND

RSPB Local Groups

BLACKPOOL. (1983; 170). Alan Stamford, 6 Kensington Road, Cleveleys, FY5 1ER. 01253 859 662; E-mail: alanstamford140@msn.com
Meetings: 7.30pm, 2nd Friday of the month (Sept-June), Cleveleys Community Centre, Beach Road, Cleveleys.

LANCASTER. (1972; 176). Michael Gardner. 01524 65 211; e-mail: RSPBlancaster@gmail.com
www.rspb.org.uk/localgroups/lancaster

Wetland Bird Survey Organisers

MORECAMBE BAY NORTH. Clive Hartley. 01539 536 824; e-mail: clive.hartley304@btinternet.com

MORECAMBE BAY SOUTH. Jean Roberts. 01546 770 295; e-mail: Jeanrbrts6@aol.com

NORTH LANCASHIRE (Inland). Mr Pete Marsh.01842 750 050; e-mail: webs@bto.org

RIBBLE ESTUARY. Ken Abram.
E-mail: k.abram@btinternet.com

RIVER LUNE. Jean Roberts. 07815 979 856;
E-mail: Jeanrbrts6@aol.com

WEST LANCASHIRE (INLAND)Tom Clare.
E-mail: Tom.Clare@www.org.uk

Wildlife Trust

THE WILDLIFE TRUST FOR LANCASHIRE, MANCHESTER AND NORTH MERSEYSIDE. (1962; 18, 000). Communications Officer, The Barn, Berkeley Drive, Bamber Bridge, Preston PR5 6BY. 01772 324 129; E-mail: info@lancswt.org.uk www.lancswt.org.uk

LEICESTERSHIRE & RUTLAND

The Birds of Leicestershire and Rutland by Rob Fray et al. (A&C Black, due August 2009)

Bird Recorder

Steve Lister, 6 Albert Promenade, Loughborough, Leicestershire LE11 1RE. 01509 829 495; E-mail: stevelister@surfbirder.com

Bird Reports

LEICESTERSHIRE & RUTLAND BIRD REPORT (1941-), from Mrs S Graham, 5 Lychgate Close, Cropston, Leicestershire LE7 7HU. 0116 236 6474; E-mail: JSGraham83@aol.com
www.lros.org.uk

RUTLAND NAT HIST SOC ANNUAL REPORT (1965-), from Secretary. 01572 747302.

BTO Regional Representative

LEICESTER & RUTLAND RR. David Wright, 01530 231 102; e-mail: wrig361@aol.com

Clubs

BIRSTALL BIRDWATCHING CLUB. (1976; 50). Mr KJ Goodrich, 6 Riversdale Close, Birstall, Leicester, LE4 4EH. 0116 267 4813; e-mail: kjgood1532@aol.com

Meetings: 7.30pm, 2nd Tuesday of the month (Oct-Apr), The Rothley Centre, Mountsorrel Lane, Rothley, Leics LE7 7PR.

LEICESTERSHIRE & RUTLAND ORNITHOLOGICAL SOCIETY. (1941; 580). Jennifer Thompson, 36 Burnside Road, Leicester, LE12 6QD. 0116 233 0320; e-mail: jennythompson1301@gmail.com
www.lros.org.uk
Meetings: 7.30pm, 1st Friday of the month (Oct-May), Oadby Methodist Church, off Central Car Park, alternating with The Rothley Centre, Mountsorrel Lane, Rothley. Additional meeting at Rutland Water Birdwatching Cntr.

SOUTH LEICESTER BIRDWATCHERS. (2006; 60). Paul Seaton, 76 Roehampton Drive, Wigston, Leics, LE18 1HU. 07973 156 060;
E-mail: paul.lseaton@ntlworld.com
Meetings: 7.30 pm, 2nd Wednesday of the month (Sep-Jun), County Scout Centre, Winchester Road, Blaby, Leicester LE8 4HN.

RUTLAND NATURAL HISTORY SOCIETY. (1964; 256). Mrs L Worrall, 6 Redland Close, Barrowden, Oakham, Rutland, LE15 8ES. 01572 747 302.; e-mail: contactrnhs@btinternet.com www.rnhs.org.uk
Meetings: 7.30pm, 1st Tuesday of the month (Oct-Apr), Oakham CofE School, Burley Road, Oakham.

Ringing Groups

RUTLAND WATER RG. Tim Appleton, Reserve Manager, Egleton, Oakham, Rutland LE15 8BT; E-mail: awbc@rutland water.org.uk

STANFORD RG. John Cranfield, 41 Main Street, Fleckney, Leicester, LE8 8AP. 0116 240 4385; E-mail: JacanaJohn@talktalk.net
www.stanfordrg.org.uk

RSPB Local Groups

LEICESTER. (1969; 1600 in catchment area). Graham Heninghem, 0116 616 098; e-mail: grahamheninghem@waitrose.com
www.rspb.org.uk/groups/leicester
Meetings: 7.30pm, 3rd Friday of the month (Sep-May), Trinity Methodist Hall, Harborough Road, Oadby, Leicester, LE2 4LA

LOUGHBOROUGH. (1970; 300). Robert Orton. 01509 413 936; e-mail: Lboro.RSPB@virgin.net
www.rspb.org.uk/groups/loughborough
Meetings: Monthly Friday nights, Loughborough University.

Wetland Bird Survey Organisers

LEICESTERSHIRE & RUTLAND (excl Rutland Water). Brian Moore. E-mail: b_moore@ntlworld.com

RUTLAND WATER. Tim Appleton, Reserve Manager, Egleton, Oakham, Rutland LE15 8BT. 01572 770 651; e-mail: tim@rutlandwater.org.uk

Wildlife Trust
LEICESTERSHIRE & RUTLAND WILDLIFE TRUST. (1956; 14, 000). Brocks Hill Environment Centre, Washbrook Lane, Oadby, Leicestershire LE2 5JJ. 0116 272 0444 (fax) 0116 272 0404; e-mail: info@lrwt.org.uk
www.lrwt.org.uk

LINCOLNSHIRE

Bird Recorders
NORTH. John Clarkson.
E-mail: recorder_north@lincsbirdclub.co.uk

SOUTH. John Badley.
E-mail: recorder_south@lincsbirdclub.co.uk

Bird Reports
LINCOLNSHIRE BIRD REPORT (1979-), (years sold out 1979, 1981, 1987, 1989, 1990, 1992-1995). 2010 is the latest report, £16.75 including postage, from Bill Sterling, Newlyn, 5 Carlton Avenue, Healing, NE Lincs DN41 7PW. E-mail: wbsterling@hotmail.com

LINCOLNSHIRE RARE AND SCARCE BIRD REPORTS (1997-1999) & *(2000-2002)*, £13.75 each including postage, Bill Sterling, Newlyn, 5 Carlton Avenue, Healing, NE Lincs DN41 7PW.
E-mail: wbsterling@hotmail.com

SCUNTHORPE & NORTH WEST LINCOLNSHIRE BIRD REPORT (1973-), from Secretary, Scunthorpe Museum Society, Ornithological Section, (Day)01724 402 871 (Eve)01724 734 261.

BTO Regional Representatives
EAST RR. Philip Espin. 01507 605 448;
E-mail: philespin@live.co.uk

NORTH RR. Chris Gunn.
E-mail: donandchris@hotmail.co.uk

SOUTH RR. Hugh Dorrington. 01778 440 716;
E-mail: hdorrington@btconnect.com

WEST RR. Peter Overton, 01400 273 323;
E-mail: nyika@biosearch.org.uk
Sponsoring the Kestrel in the Bird Atlas through Biosearch Expeditions www.biosearch.org.uk

Club
LINCOLNSHIRE BIRD CLUB. (1979; 304). Robert Carr, 35 St Leonard's Close, Woodhall Spa, Lincs LN10 6SX.
E-mail: secretary@lincsbirdclub.co.uk
www.lincsbirdclub.co.uk
Meetings: Local groups hold winter evening meetings (contact Secretary for details).

SCUNTHORPE MUSEUM SOCIETY (Ornithological Section). (1973; 50). Keith Parker, 7 Ryedale Avenue, Winterton, Scunthorpe, Lincs DN15 9BJ.
Meetings: 7.15pm, 3rd Monday of the month (Sep-Apr), Scunthorpe Museum, Oswald Road.

Ringing Groups
GIBRALTAR POINT BIRD OBSERVATORY. Mr M.R. Briggs. E-mail: mbriggs@gibobs.fsworld.co.uk

MID LINCOLNSHIRE RG. J Mawer, 2 The Chestnuts, Owmby Road, Searby, Lincolnshire DN38 6EH. 01652 628 583.

WASH WADER RG. P L Ireland, 27 Hainfield Drive, Solihull, W Midlands, B91 2PL. 0121 704 1168;
E-mail: enquiries@wwrg.org.uk

RSPB Local Groups
GRIMSBY AND CLEETHORPES. (1986; 2200 in catchment area). Jenny Curtis. 01472 232 632;
e-mail: grimsbyRSPB@gmail.com
www.rspb.org.uk/groups/grimsby
Meetings: 7.30pm, 1st Monday of the month (Sept-May), Corpus Christi Church Hall, Grimsby Road, Cleethorpes, DN35 7LJ.

LINCOLN. (1974; 250). Peter Skelson, 26 Parksgate Avenue, Lincoln, LN6 7HP. 01522 695747;
E-mail: peter.skelson@lincolnrspb.org.uk
www.lincolnrspb.org.uk
Meetings: 7.30pm, 2nd Thursday of the month (not Jun, Jul, Aug, Dec), The Robert Hardy Centre, Bishop Grosseteste College, Longdales Road, Lincoln.

SOUTH LINCOLNSHIRE. (1987; 350). Adrian Slater. 01205 360 858; www.southlincsrspb.org.uk
E-mail: adrian.slater@btopenworld.com
Meetings: Contact group.

Wetland Bird Survey Organisers
HUMBER ESTUARY - Inner South. Keith Parker.
E-mail: Keith.Parker@corusgroup.com

HUMBER ESTUARY -Mid South. Harriet Billanie, 07912 855 305; e-mail: hdennison17@hotmail.com

HUMBER ESTUARY -North. Nick Cutts, 01842 750 050;
e-mail: webs@bto.org.uk

HUMBER ESTUARY - Outer South. John Walker. 01507 338 611.

SOUTH LINCOLNSHIRE/PETERBOROUGH (inland). Bob Titman. 01733 583 254; e-mail: titman@nildram.co.uk

Wildlife Trust
LINCOLNSHIRE WILDLIFE TRUST. (1948; 26, 000). Banovallum House, Manor House Street, Horncastle, Lincs, LN9 5HF. 01507 526 667; www.lincstrust.org.uk
e-mail: info@lincstrust.co.uk

LONDON, GREATER

Bird Atlas/Avifauna
The Breeding Birds Illustrated magazine of the London Area, 2002. ISBN 0901009 121 ed Jan Hewlett (London Natural History Society).

Two Centuries of Croydon's Birds by John Birkett (RSPB Croydon Local Group 2007). £10 plus p&p.

Bird Recorder (see also Surrey)
Andrew Self, 16 Harp Island Close, Neasden, London, NW10 0DF. 07889 761 828; e-mail: a-self@sky.com
http://londonbirders.wikia.com

ENGLAND

Bird Report

CROYDON BIRD SURVEY (1995), from Secretary, Croydon RSPB Group, 020 8640 4578; e-mail: johndavis.wine@care4free.net www.croydon-rspb.org.uk

LONDON BIRD REPORT (20-mile radius of St Paul's Cath) (1936-), from Catherine Schmitt, Publications Sales, London Natural History Society, 4 Falkland Avenue, London N3 1QR. 020 8346 4359.

BTO Regional Representatives

LONDON, NORTH. Ian Woodward, 245 Larkshall Road, Chingford, London, E4 9HY. 02085 298 964; E-mail: ianw_bto_nlon@hotmail.co.uk

LONDON, SOUTH. Richard Arnold. 0208 224 1135; e-mail: bto@thomsonecology.com

Clubs

THE LONDON BIRD CLUB (formerly the Ornithological Section of the London Natural History Society). (1858; 1000). Mrs Angela Linnell, 20 Eleven Acre Rise, Loughton, Essex, IG10 1AN. 020 8508 2932; www.lnhs.org.uk
E-mail: angela.linnell@phonecoop.coop
Meetings: See website.

MARYLEBONE BIRDWATCHING SOCIETY. (1981; 110). Marion Hill, 20 Howitt Close, Howitt Road, London NW3 4LX. E-mail: birdsmbs@yahoo.com www.birdsmbs.org.uk
Meeting: 2nd Friday of month (Sept-May), 7.15pm Gospel Oak Methodist Church, Lisburne Road, London NW3 2NT. Also programme of Saturday local and coach outings and weekly walks on Hampstead Heath.

Ringing Groups

LONDON GULL STUDY GROUP - (SE including Hampshire, Surrey, Susex, Berkshire and Oxfordshire). This group is no longer active but still receiving sightings/recoveries of ringed birds. (Also includes Hampshire, Surrey, Sussex, Berkshire and Oxfordshire). No longer in operation but able to give information on gulls. Mark Fletcher, 24 The Gowans, Sutton-on-the-Forest, York, YO61 1DJ. E-mail: m.fletcher48@btinternet.com

RUNNYMEDE RG. D G Harris, 22 Blossom Waye, Hounslow, TW5 9HD; http://rmxrg.org.uk e-mail: daveharris@tinyonline.co.uk

RSPB Local Groups

BEXLEY. -1979. Tony Banks, 15 Boundary Road, Sidcup, Kent DA15 8SS. 020 8859 3518; E-mail: tonybanks@fsmail.net www.bexleyrspb.org.uk
Meetings: 7.30pm, 3rd Friday of the month, Hurstmere School Hall, Hurst Road, Sidcup.

BROMLEY. (1972; 285). Val Bryant, 11 Hastings Road, Bromley, Kent BR2 8NZ. 0208 462 6330; E-mail: valbryant5@gmail.com

www.rspb.org.uk/groups/bromley
Meetings: 2nd Wednesday of the month (Sep-Jun), 4th floor, Central Library Building, Bromley High Street.

CENTRAL LONDON. (1974; 250). Margaret Blackburn. 0208 866 5853; e-mail: mblackburn@tesco.net www.janja.dircon.co.uk/rspb
Meetings: (Indoor) 2nd Thursday of the month (Sep-May), St Columba's Church Hall, Pont St, London SW1. See website for details of field meetings.

CROYDON. (1973; 4000 in catchment area). John Davis, 9 Cricket Green, Mitcham, CR4 4LB. 020 8640 4578; e-mail: johndavis.wine@care4free.net www.croydon-rspb.org.uk
Meetings: 2nd Monday of each month at 2pm-4pm and again at 8pm-10pm at Old Whitgiftian Clubhouse, Croham Manor Road, South Croydon.

ENFIELD. (1971; 2700). Norman G Hudson, 125 Morley Hill, Enfield, Middx, EN2 0BQ. 020 8363 1431 (daytime); e-mail: dorandnor@tiscali.co.uk www.rspb.org.uk/groups/enfield
Meetings: 8pm, 1st Thursday of the month, St Andrews Hall, Enfield Town.

HAVERING. (1972; 270). Martin Runchman. 01767 690 093; e-mail: mrunchman@yahoo.com www.rspb.org.uk/groups/havering/
Meetings: 8pm, 2nd Friday of the month, Hornchurch Library, North Street, Hornchurch.

NORTH EAST LONDON. David Littlejohns. 0208 989 4746; e-mail: NelondonRSPB@yahoo.co.uk www.rspb.org.uk/groups/northeastlondon
Meetings: 7.30pm, 2nd Tuesday of every month, Snaresbrook Primary School, Meadow Walk, South Woodford, LONDON, E18 2EN.

NW LONDON. (1983; 2000 in catchment area). Bob Husband, The Firs, 49 Carson Road, Cockfosters, Barnet, Herts EN4 9EN. 020 8441 8742; e-mail: bobhusband@hotmail.co.uk www.rspb.org.uk/groups/nwlondon. A full programme of events can be downloaded from the site.
Meetings: 8pm, Usually last Tuesday of the month, (Sep-Mar), Wilberforce Centre, St Paul's Church, The Ridgeway, Mill Hill, London, NW7 1QU.

PINNER & DISTRICT. (1972; 300). Ian Jackson, 5 Oakfield Avenue, Kenton, Harrow, Middx HA3 8TH. 020 8907 3513; e-mail: imnme@btinternet.com www.rspb.org.uk/groups/pinner/
Meetings: 8pm, 2nd Thursday of the month (Sept-May), Church Hall, St John The Baptist Parish Church, Pinner HA5 3AS.

RICHMOND & TWICKENHAM. (1979; 241). Roger Theobald. 0208 977 6343; E-mail: RichmondRSPB@yahoo.co.uk www.rspb.org.uk/groups/richmond
Meetings: 8.00pm, 1st Wednesday of the month and 2pm 2nd Tuesday of the month, both meetings held York House, Twickenham.

ENGLAND

Wetland Bird Survey Organiser
GREATER LONDON (excl. Thames Estuary). Helen Baker, 60 Townfield, Rickmansworth, Herts WD3 7DD. 01923 772 441; e-mail: helen.baker60@tiscali.co.uk

LEE VALLEY. Cath Patrick. Myddelton House, Bulls Cross, Enfield, Herts EN2 9HG. 01992 717 711; e-mail: cpatrick@leevalleypark.org.uk

Wildlife Trust
LONDON WILDLIFE TRUST. (1981; 7500). Skyline House, 200 Union Street, London, SE1 0LX. 0207 261 0447; e-mail: enquiries@wildlondon.org.uk www.wildlondon.org.uk

MANCHESTER, GREATER

Bird Atlas/Avifauna
Breeding Birds in Greater Manchester by Philip Holland et al (1984).

Bird Recorder
RECORDER. Ian McKerchar, 42 Green Ave, Astley, Manchester, M29 7EH. 01942 701 758; E-mail: ianmckerchar1@gmail.com www.manchesterbirding.com

Bird Reports
BIRDS IN GREATER MANCHESTER (1976-). 2006 sold out. Year 2001 onwards from County Recorder.

LEIGH ORNITHOLOGICAL SOCIETY BIRD REPORT (1971-), from Mr D Shallcross, 28 Surrey Avenue, Leigh, Lancs, WN7 2NN.
E-mail: chairman@leighos.org.uk www.leighos.org.uk

BTO Regional Representatives
MANCHESTER. Steve Suttill, 94 Manchester Road, Mossley, Ashton-under-Lyne, Lancashire OL5 9AY. 01457 836 360; e-mail: suttill.parkinson@virgin.net www.manchesterbirding.com

Clubs
ALTRINGHAM AND DISTRICT NATURAL HISTORY SOCIETY. Claire Joures (Secretary). 0161 928 4513. **Meetings:** 7: 30pm, Tuesdays, Hale Methodist Church Hall, Oak Road, off Hale Road, Hale. 50p charge includes refreshments.

GREATER MANCHESTER BIRD RECORDING GROUP. (2002; 40) Restricted to contributors of the county bird report. Ian McKerchar.
E-mail: ianmckerchar1@gmail.com www.manchesterbirding.com

LEIGH ORNITHOLOGICAL SOCIETY. (1971; 118). Mr D Shallcross, 28 Surrey Avenue, Leigh, Lancs, WN7 2NN. E-mail: chairman@leighos.org.uk www.leighos.org.uk
Meetings: 7.15pm, Fridays, Leigh Library (check website for details).

ROCHDALE FIELD NATURALISTS' SOCIETY. (1970; 90). Mrs D Francis, 20 Hillside Avenue, Shaw, Oldham OL2 8HR. 01706 843 685; e-mail: secretary@

rochdalefieldnaturalistssociety.co.uk
www.rochdalefieldnaturalistssociety.co.uk
Meetings: 7.30pm (Sept-Apr) at Cutgate Baptist Church, Edenfield Rd, Rochdale. Yearly syllabus (out after AGM in Sept) states dates of lectures and outings.

STOCKPORT BIRDWATCHING SOCIETY. (1972; 80). Dave Evans, 36 Tatton Road South, Stockport, Cheshire, SK4 4LU. 0161 432 9513; E-mail: windhover@ntlworld.com
Meetings: 7.30pm, last Wednesday of the month (Sep-Apr), The Heatons Sports Club, Heaton Moor Stockport.

Ringing Groups
LEIGH RG. A J Gramauskas, 21 Elliot Avenue, Golborne, Warrington, WA3 3DU. 0151 929 215.

SOUTH MANCHESTER RG. Mr N.B. Powell.
E-mail: neville.powell@tiscali.co.uk

RSPB Local Groups
BOLTON. (1978; 320). Barrie Shore.
E-mail: b.shore@sky.com
http://boltonrspb.users.btopenworld.com
Meetings: 7.30pm, Thursdays (dates vary), Canon Slade School, Bradshaw Brow, BOLTON, BL2 3BP.

MANCHESTER. (1972;3600 in catchment area). Peter Wolstenholme, 31 South Park Road, Gatley, Cheshire, SK8 4AL. 0161 428 2175;
e-mail: Conservation@RSPBmanchester.org.uk
http://johnfair.brinkster.net/rspb/default.asp
Meetings: 7.30 pm, St James Parish Hall, Gatley Green, Church Road, Gatley, Cheadle.

STOCKPORT LOCAL GROUP. (1979; 120). Gay Crossley, 5 Broadhill Close, Bramhall, Stockport, Cheshire SK7 3BY. 0161 439 3210.; e-mail: StockportRSPB@googlemail.com www.rspb.org.uk/groups/stockport
Meetings: 7.30pm, 2nd Monday of the month (Sep-Apr), Stockport College of Technology, Lecture Theatre B.

WIGAN. (1973; 80). Neil Martin. 01695 624 860; e-mail: neimaz07@yahoo.co.uk
www.rspb.org.uk/groups/wigan
Meetings: 7.45pm. St Anne's Parish Hall, Church Lane, Shevington, Wigan, Lancashire, WN6 8BD.

Wetland Bird Survey Organiser
GREATER MANCHESTER. Adrian Dancy. 0161 234 3537; e-mail: a.dancy@ntlworld.com

Wildlife Trust
Mr James Ellaby, Communications Officer, See Lancashire,

MERSEYSIDE & WIRRAL

Bird Atlas see Cheshire

Bird Recorders see Cheshire; Lancashire

ENGLAND

HILBRE BIRD OBSERVATORY REPORT, from Warden,
see Reserves.

BTO Regional Representatives
MERSEYSIDE RR and RDO. Bob Harris, 3 Mossleigh,
Whixall, Whitchurch, Shropshire SY13 2SA. 01948 880
112; e-mail: harris@liv.ac.uk

WIRRAL RR. Paul Miller. 01928 787 535;
E-mail: paulandhilarymiller@live.co.uk

BTO Garden BirdWatch Ambassador
Miss J Grant. E-mail: janet.grant1967@tiscali.co.uk

Clubs
MERSEYSIDE NATURALISTS' ASSOCIATION. (1938; 150).
David Bryant, Chairman, 13, Strafford Drive, Bootle,
Merseyside L20 9JN. 0151 523 5240;
E-mail: chairman@mnapage.info
www.mnapage.info
Meetings: 2-4pm, Saturday afternoons (Feb, Oct and
Nov), Bootle Cricket Club, check website for details.
7-8 coach outings per year.

WIRRAL BIRD CLUB. (1977; 150). The Secretary.
E-mail: wirralbirdclub@gmail.com
www.wirralbirdclub.com

Ringing Groups
MERSEYSIDE RG. Bob Harris, 3 Mossleigh, Whixalll,
Whitchurch, Shropshire SY13 2SA. Work 0151 706
4311; e-mail: harris@liv.ac.uk

SOUTH WEST LANCASHIRE RG. I H Wolfenden, 35
Hartdale Road, Thornton, Liverpool, Merseyside L23
1TA. 01519 311 232.

RSPB Local Groups
LIVERPOOL. (1966; 162). Chris Tynan, 10 Barker
Close, Huyton, Liverpool, L36 0XU. 0151 480 7938
(M)07831 352 870; e-mail: christtynan@aol.com
www.rspbliverpool.org.uk
Meetings: Indoor meetings, 7 for 7.30pm, 3rd Monday
of the month (Sep-Apr), Mossley Hill Parish Church,
Junc. Rose Lane and Elmswood Rd. Outdoor meetings
visiting sites across the north west.

SOUTHPORT. (1974; 300). Alan Toms. 01704 871 540;
e-mail: tomsrspb@talktalk.net
www.rspb.org.uk/groups/southport
Meetings: 7.45pm, 3rd Friday of the month, Lord
Street West Church Hall, Duke Street, Southport.

WIRRAL. (1982; 120). Jeremy Bradshaw. 0151 632
2364; e-mail: Info@wirralRSPB.org.uk
www.rspb.org.uk/groups/wirral
Meetings: 7.30pm, 1st Thursday of the month,
Bromborough Civic Centre, 2 Bromborough Village
Road, Wirral.

Wetland Bird Survey Organiser
ALT ESTUARY. Steve White;
e-mail: stevewhite102@btinterncom

DEE ESTUARY. Colin Wells;
e-mail: colin.wells@rspb.org.uk

MERSEY ESTUARY. Graham Thomason. 01842 750 050;
e-mail: webs@bto.org

MERSEYSIDE (inland). Vacant.

Wildlife Trust
Mr James Ellaby, Communications Officer, See
Lancashire.

NORFOLK

Bird Atlas/Avifauna
The Birds of Norfolk by Moss Taylor, Michael Seago,
Peter Allard & Don Dorling (Pica Press, 1999).

Bird Recorder
JOINT COUNTY RECORDERS. Dave and Jacquie
Bridges, 27 Swann Close, Hempstead Road, Holt,
Norfolk NR25 6DP. 01263 713 249;
e-mail: dnjnorfolkrec@aol.com

Bird Reports
CLEY BIRD CLUB 10-KM SQUARE BIRD REPORT (1987-),
from Peter Gooden, 45 Charles Road, Holt, Norfolk,
NR25 6DA. 01263 712368.

*NAR VALLEY
ORNITHOLOGICAL SOCIETY
ANNUAL REPORT (1976-),*
from The Chairman, Ian
Black.

*NORFOLK BIRD & MAMMAL
REPORT (1953-),* from DL Paull, 8 Lindford Drive,
Eaton, Norwich NR4 6LT. E-mail: info@nnns.org.uk
www.NNNS.org.uk

*NORFOLK ORNITHOLOGISTS' ASSOCN ANNUAL REPORT
(1961-),* from Holme Bird Observatory, 01485 525
406, or NOA, Broadwater Road, Holme Next the Sea,
Hunstanton, Norfolk, PE36 6LQ.
E-mail: info@noa.org.uk

WENSUM VALLEY BIRDWATCHING SOCIETY (2003-),
from; e-mail: admin@wvbs.co.uk
www.wvbs.co.uk

BTO Regional Representatives
NORTH-EAST RR. Chris Hudson, Cornerstones, 5
Ringland Road, Taverham, Norwich, NR8 6TG. 01603
868 805 (M)07771 635 844;
e-mail: Chris697@btinternet.com

NORTH-WEST RR. Bob Osborne. 01553 670 430;
e-mail: rtoclass40@yahoo.co.uk

SOUTH-EAST RR. Rachel Warren. 01603 593 912;
e-mail: campephilus@btinternet.com

SOUTH-WEST RR. Vince Matthews, Rose's Cottage,
The Green, Merton, Thetford, Norfolk IP25 6QU.
01953 884 125;
e-mail: norfolksouthwest@tiscali.co.uk

ENGLAND

Clubs

CLEY BIRD CLUB. (1986; 500). Peter Gooden, 45 Charles Road, Holt, Norfolk, NR25 6DA. 01263 712 368.
Meetings: 8.00pm, Wednesdays, monthly (Dec-Feb), White Horse Hotel, Blakeney.

GREAT YARMOUTH BIRD CLUB. (1989; 30). Keith R Dye, 104 Wolseley Road, Great Yarmouth, Norfolk, NR31 0EJ. 01493 600 705.www.gybc.org.uk
Meetings: 7.45pm, 4th Monday of the month, Rumbold Arms, Southtown Road.

NAR VALLEY ORNITHOLOGICAL SOCIETY. (1976; 125). Ian Black, Three Chimneys, Tumbler Hill, Swaffham, Norfolk, PE37 7JG. 01760 724 092; e-mail: ian_a_black@hotmail.com
Meetings: 7.30pm, last Tuesday of the month (Jul-Nov and Jan-May), Barn Theatre, Convent of The Sacred Heart, Mangate Street, Swaffham, PE37 7QW.

NORFOLK & NORWICH NATURALISTS' SOCIETY. (1869; 630). The Secretary, Woodhouse, Free Lane, Ditchingham, Bungay NR35 2DW. www.NNNS.org.uk
Meetings: 7.30pm, 3rd Tuesday of the month (Oct-Mar), St Andrew's Church Hall, Church Lane, Norwich

NORFOLK ORNITHOLOGISTS' ASSOCIATION. (1962; 1100). Sophie Barker, Broadwater Road, Holme-next-Sea, Hunstanton, Norfolk PE36 6LQ. 01485 525 406; e-mail: info@noa.org.uk www.noa.org.uk

WENSUM VALLEY BIRDWATCHING SOCIETY. (2003; 125). Colin Wright, 7 Hinshalwood Way, Old Costessey, Norwich, Norfolk NR8 5BN. 01603 740 548; e-mail: admin@wvbs.co.uk www.wvbs.co.uk
Meetings: 7.30pm, 3rd Thursday of the month, Weston Longville village hall.

Ringing Groups

BTO NUNNERY RG. Kate Risely, c/o BTO, The Nunnery, Thetford, Norfolk IP24 2PU.
E-mail: kate.risely@bto.org

HOLME BIRD OBSERVATORY. Miss SA Barker.
E-mail: info@noa.org.uk

NORTH NORFOLK FARMLAND STUDY & RINGING GROUP. Keith Herber, Laleham, 60 Dale End, Brancaster Staithe, Kings PE31 8DA. 01485 210 980; e-mail: keith.herber@btinternet.com

NORTH WEST NORFOLK RG. Mr J L Middleton, 8 Back Lane, Burnham Market, Norfolk PE31 8EY.
E-mail: johnmiddleton@bmarket.freeserve.co.uk

SHERINGHAM RG. D Sadler, 26 Abbey Road, Sheringham, Norfolk, NR26 8NN. 01263 821 904.

WASH WADER RG. P L Ireland, 27 Hainfield Drive, Solihull, W Midlands, B91 2PL. 0121 704 1168; e-mail: pli@blueyonder.co.uk

RSPB Local Groups

NORWICH. (1971; 360). David Porter. 01603 745 310;

e-mail: RSPBnorwichgroup@virginmedia.com
www.rspb.org.uk/groups/norwich
Meetings: 7.30pm, 2nd Monday of the month (except Aug), Hellesdon Community Centre, Middletons Lane, Hellesdon, Norwich (entrance of Woodview Road).

WEST NORFOLK. (1977; 176). Neil Stephenson. 01553 828 752; e-mail: neilstephenson@onetel.com
www.rspb.org.uk/groups/westnorfolk/
Meetings: 7.15pm, 3rd Wednesday of the month (Sep-Apr), South Wootton Village Hall, Church Lane, South Wootton, King's Lynn.

Wetland Bird Survey Organisers

BREYDON WATER. Jim Rowe, 01842 750 050;
E-mail: webs@bto.org.uk

NORTH NORFOLK COAST. Michael Rooney.
E-mail: michael.rooney@naturalengland.org.uk

NORFOLK (excl. estuaries). Tim Strudwick, RSPB Strumpshaw Fen, Staithe Cottage, Low Road, Strumpshaw Norfolk NR13 4HS.
E-mail: tim.strudwick@rspb.org.uk

THE WASH. Jim Scott. 01485 545 261;
e-mail: jim.scott@rspb.org.uk

Wildlife Trust

NORFOLK WILDLIFE TRUST. (1926; 35, 000). Bewick House, 22 Thorpe Road, Norwich, Norfolk NR1 1RY. 01603 625 540 (fax) 01603 598 300;
e-mail: info@norfolkwildlifetrust.org.uk
www.norfolkwildlifetrust.org.uk

NORTHAMPTONSHIRE

Bird Recorder

Position vacant, Enquiries to Mike Alibone, 25 Harrier Park, East Hunsbury, Northants NN4 0QG.
E-mail: northantsbirds@ntlworld.com

Bird Report

NORTHAMPTONSHIRE BIRD REPORT (1969-), from Mr John Coleman, 2 Marsons Drive, Crick, Northants NN6 7TD. 01788 822 905.
http://northamptonshirebirdclub.ning.com

BTO Regional Representatives

RR. Barrie Galpin. 01780 444 351;
e-mail: barrie.galpin@zen.co.uk

BTO Garden BirdWatch Ambassador

Mr J A & Mrs L Tyler.
E-mail: linda.john_gbw@yahoo.co.uk

Clubs

NORTHAMPTONSHIRE BIRD CLUB. (1973; 100).
http://sites.google.com/site/northantsbirdclub/
Meetings: 7.30pm, 1st Wednesday of the month.
Moulton Community Sports Centre, Pound Lane, Moulton, Northants.

Ringing Group
NORTHANTS RG. D M Francis, 2 Brittons Drive, Billing Lane, Northampton, NN3 5DP.

STANFORD RG. John Cranfield, 41 Main Street, Fleckney, Leicester, LE8 8AP. 0116 240 4385; e-mail: JacanaJohn@talktalk.net

RSPB Local Groups
MID NENE. (1975; 350). Hilary Guy. 01536 516 422; e-mail: hilary@snowdrop.demon.co.uk
www.rspb.org.uk/groups/midnene
Meetings: 7.30pm, 2nd or 3rd Thursday of the month (Sep-Apr), The Saxon Hall, Thorpe Street/Brook Street, Raunds.

NORTHAMPTON. (1978; 3000). Liz Wicks, 6 Waypost Court, Lings, Northampton, NN3 8LN. 01604 513 991; e-mail: lizydrip@ntlworld.com
Meetings: 7.30pm, 2nd Thursday of the month, Northants County Council staff sports and social club (Wootton Hall Pavilion), Wootton Hall Park, Wootton NN4 0JA.

Wetland Bird Survey Organiser
Jim Williams, Langsend, Newnham, Nr Daventry, Northants NN11 3HQ. 01203 402 121; e-mail: jim.williams4@btinternet.com

Wildlife Trust
Director, See Cambridgeshire.

NORTHUMBERLAND (inc Tyne & Wear)

Bird Atlas/Avifauna
The Atlas of Breeding Birds in Northumbria edited by J C Day et al (Northumberland and Tyneside Bird Club, 1995).

Bird Recorder
Tim Dean, 2 Knocklaw Park, Rothbury, Northumberland NE65 7PW. 01669 621460 (M)07766 263167; e-mail: t.r.dean@btinternet.com

Bird Reports
BIRDS IN NORTHUMBRIA (1970-), from Trevor Blake, 6 Glenside, Ellington, Morpeth, Northumberland NE61 5LS. 01670 862 635; e-mail: trevor.1958@live.co.uk

BIRDS ON THE FARNE ISLANDS (1971-), from Secretary, Natural History Society of Northumbria. 0191 2326386; e-mail: nhsn@ncl.ac.uk
www.nhsn.ncl.ac.uk

BTO Regional Representative & Regional Development Officer
RR. Tom Cadwallender, 22 South View, Lesbury, Alnwick, Northumberland NE66 3PZ. 01665 830 884; e-mail: tomandmurielcadwallender@hotmail.com

RDO. Muriel Cadwallender, 22 South View, Lesbury, Alnwick, Northumberland NE66 3PZ. 01665 830 884; e-mail: tomandmurielcadwallender@hotmail.com

BTO Garden BirdWatch Ambassador
Val Tuck; e-mail: V.L.Tuck@newcastle.ac.uk

Clubs
NATURAL HISTORY SOCIETY OF NORTHUMBRIA. (1829; 900). The Natural History Society of Northumbria, Great North Museum: Hancock, Newcastle upon Tyne, NE2 4PT. 0191 232 6386; e-mail: nhsn@ncl.ac.uk
www.NHSN.ncl.ac.uk
Meetings: Weekly indoor and outdoor meetings throughout the year, details can be found at www.nhsn.ncl.ac.uk

NORTH NORTHUMBERLAND BIRD CLUB. (1984; 210). Richard Narraway, Workshop Cottage, The Friary, Bamburgh, NE69 7AE. 01668 214 759; e-mail: ringouzel@ northnorthumberlandbirdclub.co.uk
www.northnorthumberlandbirdclub.co.uk
Meetings: 7.30pm, 1st Friday of the month(Sept), 2nd Friday (Oct-Jun), Bamburgh Pavilion (below castle).

NORTHUMBERLAND & TYNESIDE BIRD CLUB. (1958; 270). Alan Tilmouth, 12 Stowe Gardens, Pegsworth, Morpeth, NE61 6TH. 01670 512 013; e-mail: ntbcorg@gmail.com www.ntbc.org.uk
Meetings: 7.00pm, 2nd Thursday of the month (Sep-Apr), Newcastle Falcons Rugby Club, Brunton Road, Kenton Bank Foot, Newcastle upon Tyne NE13 8AF.

NATURAL HISTORY SOCIETY OF NORTHUMBRIA. (1829; about 950). John Littlewood, Natural History Society of Northumbria, Great North Museum: Hancock, Barras Bridge, Newcastle upon Tyne NE2 4PT. 0191 232 6386; e-mail: nhsn@ncl.ac.uk
www.nhsn.ncl.ac.uk
Meetings: Weekly indoor and outdoor meetings throughout the year, details can be found at www.nhsn.ncl.ac.uk

Ringing Groups
NORTHUMBRIA RG. Secretary. B Galloway, 34 West Meadows, Stamfordham Road, Westerhope, Newcastle upon Tyne NE5 1LS. 0191 286 4850.

RSPB Local Group
NEWCASTLE UPON TYNE. (1969; 250). Marie Ollerenshaw. E-mail: NewcastleRSPBgroup@gmail.com
www.rspb.org.uk/groups/newcastle
Meetings: 7pm, (Mar, Jun, Sep, Nov), Northumbria University, Ellison Place, Newcastle upon Tyne.

Wetland Bird Survey Organisers
LINDISFARNE. Andrew Craggs, Lindisfarne NNR, Beal Station, Beal, Berwick Upon Tweed TD15 2SP. 01289 381 470;
E-mail: andrew.craggs@naturalengland.org.uk

NORTHUMBERLAND COAST. Daniel Turner, 9 Haswell Gardens, North Shields, Tyne & Wear NE3 2DY. 01912 576 680; E-mail: Dan.M.Turner@btopenworld.com

NORTHUMBERLAND (Inland). Steve Holliday, 2 Larriston Place, Cramlington, Northumberland NE23 8ER. E-mail: steveholliday@hotmail.co.uk

ENGLAND

Wildlife Hospitals
BERWICK SWAN & WILDLIFE TRUST. The Honorary
Secretary, Windmill Way East, Ramparts Business
Park, Berwick-upon-Tweed TD15 1TU. 01289 302882;
e-mail: swan-trust@hotmail.co.uk
www.swan-trust.org Registered charity. All categories
of wildlife. Pools for swans and other waterfowl.
Veterinary support.

Wildlife Trust
NORTHUMBERLAND WILDLIFE TRUST. (1962; 13, 000).
The Garden House, St Nicholas Park, Jubilee Road,
Gosforth, Newcastle upon Tyne, NE3 3XT. 0191 284
6884 (fax) 0191 284 6794;
e-mail: mail@northwt.org.uk www.nwt.org.uk

NOTTINGHAMSHIRE

Bird Recorders
Andy Hall. E-mail: andy.h11@ntlworld.com

Bird Reports
LOUND BIRD REPORT (1990-) latest 2007 report £4,
from Gary Hobson, 18 Barnes Avenue, Wrenthorpe,
Wakefield, WF1 2BH. 01924 384 419;
e-mail: gary.lbc1@tiscali.co.uk

BIRDS OF NOTTINGHAMSHIRE (1943-) - £8 for 2010,
£3 for previous issues, plus p&p, from Ms Jenny
Swindells, 21 Chaworth Road, West Bridgford,
Nottingham NG2 7AE. 0115 9812 432;
e-mail: j.swindells@btinternet.com
www.nottsbirders.net

*NETHERFIELD WILDLIFE GROUP ANNUAL REPORT
(1990-)*. £5 inc postage, from Mr N Matthews, 4
Shelburne Close, Heronridge, Nottingham, NG5 9LL.
www.netherfieldwildlife.org.uk

BTO Regional Representatives
RR. Mrs Lynda Milner, 6 Kirton Park, Kirton, Newark,
Notts NG22 9LR. 01623 862 025;
e-mail: milner.lynda@googlemail.com

BTO Garden BirdWatch Ambassadors
Angela Rymell; e-mail: angela.rymell@live.com

Jean Parrott; e-mail: candjparrott@btinternet.com

Chris du Feu; e-mail: chris@chrisdufeu.force9.co.uk

Jane Carruthers;
e-mail: paul.carruthers93@ntlworld.com

Morag Whitworth;
e-mail: morag.whitworth@gmail.com

Clubs
LOUND BIRD CLUB. (1991; 90).
Gary Hobson, 18 Barnes Avenue,
Wrenthorpe, Wakefield, WF1
2BH. 01924 384 419; e-mail:
loundbirdclub@btinternet.com
www.loundbirdclub.com
Meetings: Various walks and talks
throughout the year, see website for
details.

NETHERFIELD WILDLIFE GROUP. (1999; 130). Philip
Burnham, 57 Tilford Road, Newstead Village,
Nottingham, NG15 0BU. 01623 401 980 (M)07765 369
590; e-mail: philb50@fastmail.fm
www.netherfieldwildlife.org.uk

NOTTINGHAMSHIRE BIRDWATCHERS. (1935; 320). Ms
Jenny Swindells, 21 Chaworth Road, West Bridgford,
Nottingham, NG2 7AE. 0115 9812 432;
e-mail: j.swindells@btinternet.com
www.nottsbirders.net
Meetings and events: Please see website for details.

WOLLATON NATURAL HISTORY SOCIETY. (1976; 86).
Graham Birkett, 07528 753 470.
Meetings: 7.30pm, 3rd Wednesday of the month, St
Leonards Community Centre, Wollaton Village, HG8
2ND.

Integrated Population Monitoring Group
TRESWELL WOOD INTEGRATED POPULATION
MONITORING GROUP. Chris du Feu, 66 High Street,
Beckingham, Notts, DN10 4PF.
E-mail: chris@chrisdufeu.force9.co.uk

Ringing Groups
BIRKLANDS RG. A Ashley, 39 Winkburn Road,
Mansfield, Notts NG19 6SJ. 07794 179 494;
e-mail: alowe@nottswt.co.uk

NORTH NOTTS RG. Adrian Blackburn, Willows End, 27
Palmer Road, Retford, Notts DN22 6SS. 01777 706516
(M)07718 766 873; e-mail: adrian.blackburn@sky.com

SOUTH NOTTINGHAMSHIRE RG. K J Hemsley, 8 Grange
Farm Close, Toton, Beeston, Notts NG9 6EB.
E-mail: k.hemsley@ntlworld.com

RSPB Local Groups
MANSFIELD LOCAL GROUP. (1986; 200). John Barlow,
240 Southwell Road West, Mansfield, Notts NG18 4LB.
01623 626 647;
e-mail: Terri-Cumberland@supanet.com
www.rspb.org.uk/groups/mansfield
Meetings: 7pm, 1st Wednesday of the month (Sep-
Jun), Bridge St Methodist Church, Rock Valley,
Mansfield.

NOTTINGHAM. (1974; 290). Penny Cross, 93 Hilton
Road, Nottingham, NG3 6AQ. 0115 960 4205;
e-mail: pennyguilbert@hotmail.com
www.notts-rspb.org.uk
Meetings: 7.30pm, 1st Wed of month (Sept -
May). Nottingham Mechanics, North Sherwood St.
Nottingham, NG1 4EZ.

Wetland Bird Survey Organiser
Gary Hobson, 18 Barnes Avenue, Wrenthorpe,
Wakefield, WF1 2BH. 01924 384 419 (eve);
e-mail: gary.lbc1@tiscali.co.uk

Wildlife Trust
NOTTINGHAMSHIRE WILDLIFE TRUST. (1963; 4, 300).
The Old Ragged School, Brook Street, Nottingham,
NG1 1EA. 0115 958 8242; e-mail: info@nottswt.co.uk
www.nottinghamshirewildlife.org.uk

ENGLAND

OXFORDSHIRE

Bird Atlas/Avifauna
Birds of Oxfordshire by J W Brucker et al (Oxford, Pisces, 1992).

The New Birds of the Banbury Area by T G Easterbrook (Banbury Ornithological Society, 1995).

Bird Recorder
Ian Lewington, 119 Brasenose Road, Didcot, Oxon, OX11 7BP. 01235 819 792;
e-mail: lewbirder@btinternet.com

Bird Reports
BIRDS OF OXFORDSHIRE (1921-), from Barry Hudson, Pinfold, 4 Bushy Row, Bampton, Oxon OX18 2JU. 01865 775632.

BANBURY ORNITHOLOGICAL SOCIETY ANNUAL REPORT (1952-). £5 each including postage, from MJ Lewis, Old Mill Cottage, Avon Dassett, Southam, Warwickshire, CV47 2AE. 01295 690 643;
e-mail: mikelewisad@hotmail.com

BTO Regional Representatives
NORTH. Frances Buckel, Witts End, Radbones Hill, Over Norton, Chipping Norton, Oxon OX7 5RA. 01608 644 425; e-mail: fran.buckel@btinternet.com

SOUTH RR. Mr John Melling, 17 Lime Grove, Southmoor, Nr Abingdon, Oxon OX13 5DN. 01865 820 867; e-mail: bto-rep@oos.org.uk

Clubs
BANBURY ORNITHOLOGICAL SOCIETY (includes parts of Northamptonshire, Oxfordshire and Warwickshire). (1952; 100). Frances Buckel, Witts End, Radbones Hill, Over Norton, Chipping Norton, Oxon OX7 5RA. 01608 644 425; e-mail: fran.buckel@btinternet.com
www.banburyornithologicalsociety.org.uk
Meetings: 7.30pm, 2nd Monday of the month, The Banbury Cricket Club, White Post Road, Bodicote OX15 4BN.

OXFORD ORNITHOLOGICAL SOCIETY. (1921; 330). Barry Hudson, Pinfold, 4 Bushy Row, Bampton, Oxon OX18 2JU. 01993 852 028;
e-mail: secretary@oos.org.uk
www.oos.org.uk
Meetings: 7.45pm, various dates, Stratfield Brake, Kidlington.

Ringing Group
EDWARD GREY INSTITUTE. Dr A G Gosler, c/o Edward Grey Institute, Department of Zoology, South Parks Road, Oxford OX1 3PS. 01865 271 158;
e-mail: andrew.gosler@zoo.ox.ac.uk

RSPB Local Groups
OXFORD. (1977; 100). Roy Grant, 23 St Christopher's Place, Cowley, Oxford OX4 2HS. 01865 774 659;
e-mail: roy.otters@hotmail.co.uk
www.rspb-oxford.org.uk

Meetings: 7.45pm, normally 1st Thursday of the month, Sandhills Primary School, Terret Avenue, Headington, Oxford (opposite Thornhill park and ride).

VALE OF WHITE HORSE. (1977; 330). Jane Rudd. 01235 771 716; e-mail: henry.rudd@sky.com
www.rspb-vwh.org.uk
Meetings: 7.45pm, 3rd Monday of the month (Sep-May). Steventon Village Hall, The Green, Steventon, Abingdon OX13 3RR

Wetland Bird Survey Organiser
OXFORDSHIRE (North). Sandra Bletchly.
E-mail: sandra.banornsoc@btinternet.com

OXFORDSHIRE (South). Ian Lees. 01865 256 370;
e-mail: ianlees@me.com

Wildlife Trust
BBOWT. (1959; 24, 000). The Lodge, 1 Armstrong Road, Littlemore, Oxford, OX4 4XT. 01865 775 476 (fax) 01865 711 301; e-mail: info@bbowt.org.uk
www.bbowt.org.uk

SHROPSHIRE

Bird Atlas/Avifauna
Atlas of the Breeding Birds of Shropshire (Shropshire Ornithological Society, 1995).

Bird Recorder
Geoff Holmes, 22 Tenbury Drive, Telford Estate, Shrewsbury, SY2 5YF. 01743 364 621;
e-mail: geoff.holmes.4@btinternet.com

Bird Report
SHROPSHIRE BIRD REPORT (1956-) Annual, from Helen Griffiths (Hon Secretary), 104 Noel Hill Road, Cross Houses, Shrewsbury SY5 6LD. 01743 761507;
e-mail: helen.griffiths@naturalengland.org.uk
www.shropshirebirds.com

BTO Regional Representative
Allan Dawes. 01691 654 245;
e-mail: allandawes@btinternet.com

Club
SHROPSHIRE ORNITHOLOGICAL SOCIETY. (1955; 800). Helen Griffiths, 104 Noel Hill Road, Cross Houses, Shrewsbury, SY5 6LD. 01743 761 507;
e-mail: hjgriffiths104@btinternet.com
www.shropshirebirds.com
Meetings: 7.15pm, 1st Thursday of month (Oct-Apr), Shirehall, Shrewsbury.

RSPB Local Groups
SHROPSHIRE. (1992; 320). Brenda Faulconbridge. 01295 253 330; e-mail: bfaulconbridge@aol.com
www.rspb.org.uk/groups/shropshire
Meetings: 7.30pm, 4th Wednesday of the month (Sep-Apr), Council Chamber, Shirehall, Shrewsbury. Also field trip year round. 3rd Wednesday in the month (Oct-March) Secret Hills Centre Craven Arms.

SOUTH SHROPSHIRE Sub Group - CRAVEN ARMS. (2004; c100). Alvin Botting. 01547 540 176; e-mail: alvinbotting@btinternet.com www.rspbsouthshropshire.co.uk **Meetings:** 7.30pm, 2nd Tuesday of the month (Sep-Apr), Culmington Village Hall, Culmington, Ludlow SY8 2DA.

Wetland Bird Survey Organiser
SHROPSHIRE. Michael Wallace. 01743 369 035; e-mail: michaelwallace47@gmail.com

Wildlife Trust
SHROPSHIRE WILDLIFE TRUST. (1962; 10, 000). 193 Abbey Foregate, Shrewsbury, Shropshire SY2 6AH. 01743 284 280 (fax) 01743 284 281; e-mail: enquiries@shropshirewildlifetrust.org.uk www.shropshirewildlifetrust.org.uk

SOMERSET & BRISTOL

Bird Atlas/Avifauna
Atlas of Breeding Birds in Avon 1988-91 by R L Bland and John Tully (John Tully, 6 Falcondale Walk, Westbury-on-Trym, Bristol BS9 3JG, 1992).

Bristol Ornithology no. 29 by Robin Prythock (Bristol Ornithological Club 2008).

The Birds of Exmoor and the Quantocks by DK Ballance and BD Gibbs. (Isabelline Books, 2 Highbury House, 8 Woodland Crescent, Falmouth TR11 4QS. 2003).

Bird Recorders
Brian D Gibbs, 23 Lyngford Road, Taunton, Somerset, TA2 7EE. 01823 274 887; www.somersetbirds.net e-mail: brian.gibbs@virgin.net

BRISTOL, S GLOUCESTERSHIRE, BATH AND NE SOMERSET, NORTH SOMERSET. John Martin, 34 Cranmoor Green, Pilning, Bristol BS35 4QF. 01454 633 040; (M)07767 867 341; www.boc-bristol.org.uk e-mail: avonbirdrecorder@googlemail.com

Bird Reports
AVON BIRD REPORT (1977-), £9 plus postage, from Harvey Rose, Arncliffe, Walton Way, Clevedon BS21 7AS.

EXMOOR NATURALIST (1974-), from Secretary, Exmoor Natural History Society. E-mail: carol.enhs@virgin.net

SOMERSET BIRDS (1912-) £7.50 inc p&p, , from Somerset Ornithological Society, c/o Flat 2, Dunboyne, Bratton Lane, Minehead, Somerset TA24 8SQ. 01643 706 820.

BTO Regional Representatives
AVON RR. Gordon Youdale, 01454 881 690; e-mail: gordon.youdale@blueyonder.co.uk

SOMERSET RR. Eve Tigwell, Hawthorne Cottage, 3 Friggle Street, Frome, Somerset BA11 5LP. 01373 451 630; e-mail: eve.tigwell@zen.co.uk

Clubs
BRISTOL NATURALISTS' SOCIETY (Ornithological Section). (1862; 550). Hon. Secretary, Bristol Naturalists' Society, C/O City Museum & Art Gallery, Bristol BS8 1RL. 01179 243 352; e-mail: info@bristolnats.org.uk www.bristolnats.org.uk **Meetings:** 7.30pm, 2nd Wednesday in the month (check for dates, Oct-Mar), Westmorland Hall, Westmorland Road, Bristol

BRISTOL ORNITHOLOGICAL CLUB. (1966; 620). Mrs Judy Copeland, 19 St George's Hill, Easton-in-Gordano, North Somerset, BS20 0PS. 01275 373 554; e-mail: judy.copeland@tiscali.co.uk www.bristolornithologicalclub.co.uk **Meetings:** 7.30pm, 3rd Thursday of the month, Newman Hall, Grange Court Road, Westbury-on-Trym.

CAM VALLEY WILDLIFE GROUP. (1994: 356). André Fournier, 1 Boomfield Lane, Paulton, Bristol BS39 7QU. 01761 418 153; e-mail: enquiries@cvwg.org.uk www.somersetmade.co.uk/cvwg/

EXMOOR NATURAL HISTORY SOCIETY. (1974; 480). The Secretary, 12 King George Road, Minehead, Somerset, TA24 5JD. 01643 707 624; e-mail: carol.enhs@talktalk.net www.enhs.org.uk **Meetings:** 7.30pm, 1st Wednesday of the month (Oct-Mar), Methodist Church Hall, The Avenue, Minehead.

SOMERSET ORNITHOLOGICAL SOCIETY. (1974; 440). Mr JA Hazell, Membership Secretary, 9 Hooper Road, Street, Somerset BA16 0NP. 01458 443 780; e-mail: jeff.hazell@somersetbirds.net www.somersetbirds.net **Meetings:** Indoor meetings, with guest speaker, various Thursdays Oct to Apr; and Field meetings, with leader, on 10 to 12 dates throughout the year.

Ringing Groups
CHEW VALLEY RS. Mr A Ashman. E-mail: alan.ashman@talktalk.net

GORDANO VALLEY RG. Lyndon Roberts, 20 Glebe Road, Long Ashton, Bristol, BS41 9LH. 01275 392 722; e-mail: mail@lyndonroberts.com

RSPCA. Mr K Leighton. E-mail: kev.leighton@O2.co.uk

STEEP HOLM RS. A J Parsons, Barnfield, Tower Hill Road, Crewkerne, Somerset, TA18 8BJ. 01460 73640.

RSPB Local Groups
BATH AND DISTRICT. (1969; 220). Alan Barrett. 01225 310 905; e-mail: alan_w_h_barrett@yahoo.co.uk www.rspb.org.uk/groups/bath **Meetings:** 7.30pm, 3rd Wednesday of the month (Sep-Apr), First Floor, Green Park Station, BATH, BA1 2DR.

SOUTH SOMERSET. (1979; 300). Denise Chamings, Daniels Farm, Lower Stratton, South Petherton, Somerset TA13 5LP. 01460 240 740; e-mail: denise.chamings@talktalk.net

www.rspb.org.uk/groups/southsomerset
Meetings: 7.30pm, 3rd Thursday of the month (Sep-May), The Millennium Hall, Seavington St. Mary, Ilminster, TA19 0QH.

TAUNTON. (1975; 148). Eric Luxton. 01823 283 033; e-mail: eric.luxton@btinternet.com
www.rspb.org.uk/groups/taunton
Meetings: 7.30pm, last Friday of the month, Trull Memorial Hall, Church Road, Trull, TAUNTON TA3 7JZ

WESTON-SUPER-MARE (N SOMERSET). (1976; 215). Eric Allcock. 01934 418 162; e-mail: ericallcock50@yahoo.com
www.rspb.org.uk/groups/westonsupermare
Meetings: 7.45pm, 1st Thursday of the month (Sep-Apr), St Pauls Church Hall, Walliscote Road, Weston-Super-Mare.

Wetland Bird Survey Organisers
SEVERN ESTUARY - SOUTHERN COAST. Harvey Rose, Arncliffe, Walton Bay, Clevdeon. 01179 681 638; e-mail: H.E.Rose@bristol.ac.uk

SOMERSET (other sites). Eve Tigwell.01373 451 630;E-mail: eve.tigwell@zen.co.uk

SOMERSET LEVELS. Steve Meen, RSPB West Sedgemoor, Dewlands Farm, Redhill, Curry Rivel, Langport Somerset TA10 0PH. 01458 252 805; e-mail: steve.meen@rspb.org.uk

Wildlife Trusts
AVON WILDLIFE TRUST. (1980; 17, 000). 32 Jacobs Wells Road, Bristol, BS8 1DR. 0117 917 7270 (fax) 0117 929 7273; e-mail: mail@avonwildlifetrust.org.uk
www.avonwildlifetrust.org.uk

SOMERSET WILDLIFE TRUST. (1964; 21, 000). Tonedale Mill, Tonedale, Wellington, Somerset TA21 0AW. 01823 652 400 (fax) 01823 652 411; e-mail: enquiries@somersetwildlife.org
www.somersetwildlife.org

STAFFORDSHIRE

Bird Recorder
Nick Pomiankowski, 22 The Villas, West End, Stoke ST4 5AQ. 01782 849 682; e-mail: staffs-recorder@westmidlandbirdclub.com

Bird Report See West Midlands

BTO Regional Representatives
NORTH EAST. Martin Godfrey. 01785 229 713; e-mail: martinandrosie@aol.com

SOUTH & CENTRAL. Martin Godfrey. 01785 229 713; e-mail: martinandrosie@aol.com

WEST. Martin Godfrey. 01785 229 713; e-mail: martinandrosie@aol.com

Clubs
SOUTH PEAK RAPTOR STUDY GROUP. (1998; 12). M E

Taylor, 76 Hawksley Avenue, Newbold, Chesterfield, Derbys S40 4TL. 01246 277 749.

WEST MIDLAND BIRD CLUB (STAFFORD BRANCH). Scott Petrek (Branch Secretary).
E-mail: stafford-secretary@westmidlandbirdclub.com
www.westmidlandbirdclub.com/stafford
Meetings: 7.30pm, 2nd Friday of the month (Oct-Mar), at Perkins Engines Sports & Social Club, Tixall Road, Stafford.

WEST MIDLAND BIRD CLUB (TAMWORTH BRANCH). (1992). Barbara Stubbs, 19 Alfred Street, Tamworth, Staffs, B79 7RL. 01827 57865;
e-mail: tamworth@westmidlandbirdclub.com
www.westmidlandbirdclub.com/tamworth
Meetings: 7.30pm, 3rd Friday of the month (Sep-Apr), Phil Dix Centre, Corporation Street, Tamworth.

RSPB Local Groups
BURTON-ON-TRENT AND SOUTH DERBYSHIRE. (1973; 50). Dave Lummis, 121 Wilmot Road, Swadlincote, Derbys, DE11 9BN. 01283 219 902; e-mail: davelummis@hotmail.co.uk
www.basd-rspb.co.uk
Meetings: 7.30pm 1st Wednesday of the month, All Saint's Church, Branston Road, Burton.

LICHFIELD & DISTRICT. (1977; 1150). Bob Russon, 108 Walsall Road, Lichfield, Staffs, WS13 8AF. 01543 252 547; e-mail: LichfieldRSPB@hotmail.co.uk
www.rspb.org.uk/groups/lichfield
Meetings: 7.30pm, 2nd Tuesday of the month (Jan-May, Sept-Dec), St Mary's Centre, Lichfield.

NORTH STAFFS. (1982; 208). John Booth, 32 St Margaret Drive, Sneyd Green, Stoke-on-Trent, ST1 6EW. 01782 262 082; e-mail: daylateuk@yahoo.co.uk
www.rspb.org.uk/groups/northstaffordshire
Meetings: 7.30pm, normally 3rd Wednesday of the month, North Staffs Conference Centre (Medical Institute).

SOUTH WEST STAFFORDSHIRE. (1972; 165). Mrs Theresa Dorrance, 39 Wilkes Road, Codsall, Wolverhampton, WV8 1RZ. 01902 847 041; e-mail: stevedorrance@googlemail.com
Meetings: 8.00pm, 2nd Tuesday of the month (Sep-May), Codsall Village Hall.

Wetland Bird Survey Organisers
STAFFORDSHIRE. Steven Turner.
E-mail: sjturner76@btinternet.com

Wildlife Hospitals
BRITISH WILDLIFE RESCUE CENTRE. Alfred Hardy, Amerton Working Farm, Stowe-by-Chartley, Stafford, ST18 0LA. 01889 271 308; e-mail: joyce.hardy351@ntlworld.com
www.britishwildliferescue.co.uk On A518 Stafford/Uttoxeter road. All species, including imprints and

permanently injured. Hospital, large aviaries and caging. Open to the public every day. Veterinary support.

GENTLESHAW BIRD OF PREY HOSPITAL. Jenny Smith, Gentleshaw Wildlife Centre, Fletcher's Country Garden Centre, Stone Road, Eccleshall, Staffs ST21 6JY. 01785 850 379;
e-mail: info@gentleshawwildlife.co.uk
www.gentleshawwildlife.co.uk Registered charity. All birds of prey (inc. owls). Hospital cages and aviaries; release sites. Veterinary support. Also GENTLESHAW BIRD OF PREY AND WILDLIFE CENTRE, Fletchers Country Garden Centre, Stone Road, Eccleshall, Stafford. 01785 850379 (1000-1700).

Wildlife Trust
STAFFORDSHIRE WILDLIFE TRUST. (1969; 14, 000). The Wolseley Centre, Wolseley Bridge, Stafford, ST17 0WT. 01889 880 100 (fax) 01889 880 101;
e-mail: info@staffs-wildlife.org.uk
www.staffs-wildlife.org.uk

SUFFOLK

Bird Atlas/Avifauna
Birds of Suffolk by S H Piotrowski (February 2003) Quatermelon.

Bird Recorders
NORTH EAST. Andrew Green,
E-mail: andrew@waveney1.fsnet.co.uk

SOUTH EAST (inc. coastal region from Slaughden Quay southwards). Scott Mason.
E-mail: smsuffolkbirder@gmail.com

WEST (whole of Suffolk W of Stowmarket, inc. Breckland). Colin Jakes, 7 Maltward Avenue, Bury St Edmunds, Suffolk IP33 3XN. 01284 702 215;
e-mail: colin@jakes.myzen.co.uk

Bird Report
SUFFOLK BIRDS (inc Landguard Bird Observatory Report) (1950-), from Ipswich Museum, High Street, Ipswich, Suffolk.

BTO Regional Representative
Mick T Wright, 15 Avondale Road, Ipswich, IP3 9JT. 01473 710 032; e-mail: micktwright@btinternet.com

BTO Garden BirdWatch Ambassador
Carl Powell. E-mail: carlann.powell@tiscali.co.uk

Clubs

LAVENHAM BIRD CLUB. (1972; 54). Mr G Pattrick, Brights Farmhouse, Brights Lane, Lavenham, Suffolk CO10 9PH. 01787 248 128.
Meetings: 7.30pm, normally 3rd Saturday (Sep-Mar, except Dec), Lavenham Guildlhall.

SUFFOLK ORNITHOLOGISTS' GROUP. (1973; 650). Phil Whittaker, Oak Barn, Pipps Ford, Needham Market, Ipswich, Suffolk IP6 8LJ. 01449 76 0353;
e-mail: info@sogonline.org.uk www.sogonline.org.uk
Meetings: Last Thursday of month (Jan-Mar, Oct-Nov), London Road Holiday Inn (IP2 0UA) on SW side of Ipswich near the A14/A12 Copdock roundabout.

Ringing Groups
DINGLE BIRD CLUB. Dr D Pearson, 4 Lupin Close, Reydon, Southwold, Suffolk IP18 6NW. 01502 722 348.

LACKFORD RG. Dr Peter Lack, 11 Holden Road, Lackford, Bury St Edmunds, Suffolk IP28 6HZ.
E-mail: bee.eaters@btinternet.com

LANDGUARD RG. Landguard Ringing Group, Landguard Bird Observatory, View Point Road, Felixstowe, Suffolk, IP11 3TW. 01394 673 782;
e-mail: landguardbo@yahoo.co.uk www.lbo.co.uk

LITTLE OUSE RG (formerly MARKET WESTON RG). Dr R H W Langston, Walnut Tree Farm, Thorpe Street, Hinderclay, Diss, Norfolk IP22 1HT.
E-mail: rlangston@wntfarm.demon.co.uk

RSPB Local Groups
BURY ST EDMUNDS. (1982; 150). Dan Brawn. 0845 393 2011; e-mail: danbrawn@mathematics.fsnet.co.uk
www.rspb.org.uk/groups/burystedmunds
Meetings: 7.30pm, 3rd Tuesday of the month (Sep-May), County Upper School, Beetons Way, Bury St Edmunds.

IPSWICH. (1975; 230). Mr Chris Courtney, St Elmo, 19 Marlborough Road, Ipswich, Suffolk IP4 5AT. 01473 423 213; e-mail: chrisc.courtney@yahoo.co.uk
www.rspb.org.uk/groups/ipswich
Meetings: 7.30pm, 2nd Thursday of the month (Sep-Apr), Sidegate Lane Primary School, Sidegate Lane, Ipswich.

LOWESTOFT & DISTRICT. (1976; 130). Charles Goddard. 01502 731 846;
e-mail: charles.goddard@sky.com
www.rspb.org.uk/groups/lowestoft
Meetings: 7.15pm 1st Monday in the month, St Marks Church Centre, Oulton Broad.

WOODBRIDGE. (1987; 390). Malcolm Key, Riverside, Parham, Suffolk, IP13 9LZ. 01728 723 155;
e-mail: malcolm.key@btopenworld.com
Meetings: 7.30pm, 1st Thursday of the month (Oct-May), Woodbridge Community Hall.

Wetland Bird Survey Organisers
ALDE COMPLEX. Mr I Castle. (Day) 01394 450 188, evening (fax) 01394 450 181;
e-mail: ian@castle-hamlett.co.uk

ALTON WATER. Mr J A Glazebrook;
e-mai: johnglazebrooke@btopenworld.com

ORWELL ESTUARY. Mick T Wright, 15 Avondale Road, Ipswich, SuffolkIP3 9JT. 01473 710 032;
e-mail: micktwright@btinternet.com

DEBEN ESTUARY. Nick Mason, The Decoy, 8 Mallard Way, Hollesley, Nr Woodbridge, Ipswich IP12 3QJ. 01394 411 150 or 07876 086 039; e-mail: nick.mason4@btinternet.com

STOUR ESTUARY. Rick Vonk, RSPB, Unit 13 Court Farm, 3 Stutton Road, Brantham Suffolk CO11 1PW. (D)01473 328 006; e-mail: rick.vonk@rspb.org.uk

SUFFOLK (other sites). Alan Miller, Suffolk Wildlife Trust, Moonrakers, Back Lane, Wenhaston, Halesworth, Suffolk, IP19 9DY. E-mail: alan.miller@suffolkwildlifetrust.org

Wildlife Trust
SUFFOLK WILDLIFE TRUST. (1961; 25, 000). Brooke House, The Green, Ashbocking, Ipswich, IP6 9JY. 01473 890 089 (fax) 01473 890 165; e-mail: info@suffolkwildlifetrust.org www.suffolkwildlifetrust.org

SURREY

Bird Atlas/Avifauna
Birds of Surrey by Jeffery Wheatley (Surrey Bird Club 2007).

Bird Recorder (inc London S of Thames & E to Surrey Docks)
SURREY (includes Greater London south of the Thames and east to the Surrey Docks, excludes Spellthorne). Eric Soden, Ceres, Moushill Lane, Milford, Surrey GU8 5BQ. 01483 429 799; e-mail: eric.soden@talktalk.net

Bird Report
SURBITON AND DISTRICT BIRD WATCHING SOCIETY (1972-), from Thelma Caine, 21 More Lane, Esher, Surrey KT10 8AJ. E-mail: sdbws@encief.co.uk www.encief.co.uk/sdbws

SURREY BIRD REPORT (1952-), from J Gates, 5 Hillside Road, Weybourne, Farnham, Surrey GU9 9DW. 01252 315 047; e-mail: jeremygates@live.com

BTO Regional Representative
RR. Penny Williams, Bournbrook House, Sandpit Hall Lane, Chobham Surrey GU24 8HA. 01276 857 736; e-mail: penny@waxwing.plus.com

Clubs
SURBITON & DISTRICT BIRDWATCHING SOCIETY. (1954; 140). Gary Caine, 21 More Lane, Esher, Surrey, KT10 8AJ. 01372 468 432; e-mail: gary.caine@royalmail.co.uk www.encief.co.uk/sdbws
Meetings: 7.30pm, 3rd Tuesday of the month, Surbiton Library Annex.

SURREY BIRD CLUB. (1957; 340). Penny Williams, Bournbrook House, Sandpit Hall Lane, Chobham Surrey GU24 8HA. 01276 857 736;

e-mail: penny@waxwing.plus.com www.surreybirdclub.org.uk
Meetings: See website for details.

Ringing Groups
HERSHAM RG. A J Beasley, 29 Selbourne Avenue, New Haw, Weybridge, Surrey KT15 3RB. E-mail: abeasley00@hotmail.com

RUNNYMEDE RG. D G Harris, 22 Blossom Waye, Hounslow, TW5 9HD. E-mail: daveharris@tinyonline. co.ukhttp://rmxrg.org.uk

RSPB Local Groups
DORKING & DISTRICT. (1982; 230). John Burge, Broughton Norrels Drive, East Horsley, Leatherhead, KT24 5DR. 01483 283 803; e-mail: burgejs@gmail.com www.rspb.org.uk/groups/dorkinganddistrict
Meetings: 8.00pm, Fridays once a month (Sep-Apr), Christian Centre, next to St Martin's Church, Dorking.

EAST SURREY. (1984; 2800 plus in catchment area). John Lawrence, 123 Chaldon Way, Coulsdon, Surrey CR5 1DN. 01737 553 316; www.eastsurreyrspb.co.uk e-mail: jfjlawrence@gmail.com
Meetings: 8.00pm, 2nd Wednesday of the month (except August), White Hart Barn, Godstone, RH9 8DT.

EPSOM & EWELL. (1974; 102). Janet Gilbert, 78 Fairfax Avenue, Ewell, Epsom, Surrey KT17 2QQ. 0208 394 0405; e-mail: janetegilbert@btinternet.com www.rspb.org.uk/groups/epsom
Meetings: 7.45pm, 2nd Friday of the month, All Saints Church Hall, Fulford Road, West Ewell.

GUILDFORD AND DISTRICT. (1974; 550). Michael Grimshaw. 01483 467 074; e-mail: michaelgrimshaw@btinternet.com www.rspb.org.uk/groups/guildford
Meetings: 2.15pm 2nd Thursday and 7.45pm 4th Wednesday (Oct-Apr), Onslow Village Hall, Guildford.

NORTH WEST SURREY. (1973; 150). Dave Braddock, 20 Meadway Drive, New Haw, Surrey, KT15 2DT. 01932 858 692; e-mail: dave.braddock@btinternet.com www.rspb.org.uk/groups/nwsurrey
Meetings: 7.45pm, 4th Wednesday of the month (not Dec, Jul, Aug), Sir William Perkin's School, Chertsey KT16 9BN.

Wetland Bird Survey Organiser
SURREY (includes Greater London south of the Thames and east to the Surrey Docks, excludes Spellthorne). Penny Williams. E-mail: penny@waxwing.plus.com

Wildlife Hospitals
THE SWAN SANCTUARY. See National Directory.

THE WILDLIFE AID FOUNDATION. Randalls FarmHouse, Randalls Road, Leatherhead, Surrey, KT22 0AL. 01372 377 332, 24-hr emergency line 09061 800 132 (50p/min) (fax) 01372 375 183; e-mail: mail@wildlifeaid.org.uk www.wildlifeaid.org.uk Registered charity. Wildlife hospital and rehabilitation centre helping all native British species. Special housing for birds of prey. Membership scheme and fund raising activities. Veterinary support.

Wildlife Trust
SURREY WILDLIFE TRUST. (1959; 25, 700). School Lane, Pirbright, Woking, Surrey, GU24 0JN. 01483 795 440 (fax) 01483 486 505;
e-mail: info@surreywt.org.uk
www.surreywildlifetrust.org

SUSSEX

Bird Atlas/Avifauna
The Birds of Selsey Bill and the Selsey Peninsular (a checklist to year 2000) From: Mr O Mitchell, 21 Trundle View Close, Barnham, Bognor Regis, PO22 0JZ.

Birds of Sussex ed by Paul James (Sussex Ornithological Society, 1996). www.eastsurreyrspb.co.uk

Fifty Years of Birdwatching, a celebration of the acheivements of the Shoreham District OS from 1953 onwards. £5 + P&P at current rates. Mrs Sue Miles, SDOS Hon.Secretary, 24 Chancellors Park, Hassocks, West Sussex BN6 8EZ. e-mail: secretary@sdos.org or through website www.sdos.org

Henfield Birdwatcher Reports 2000 and 2005 ed Mike Russell et al, Henfield Birdwatch.

Bird Recorder
Mr David Howey, 2 Portobello Cottages, South Coast Road, Telscombe Cliffs, East Sussex BN10 7BD. 01273 300 906; e-mail: recorder@sos.orgwww.sos.org

Bird Reports
BIRDS OF RYE HARBOUR NR ANNUAL REPORT (1977- no longer printed, but available on www.WildRye.info), from Dr Barry Yates, see Clubs.

PAGHAM HARBOUR LOCAL NATURE RESERVE ANNUAL REPORT, from Warden, see Reserves,

SHOREHAM DISTRICT ORNITHOLOGICAL SOCIETY ANNUAL REPORT (1952-) - back issues available at £3.50 + P&P at current rates, from Mrs Sue Miles, 24 Chancellors Park, Hassocks, West Sussex BN6 8EZ. E-mail: secretary@sdos.orgor through website - www.sdos.org

SUSSEX BIRD REPORT (1963-), from J E Trowell, Lorrimer, Main Road, Icklesham, Winchelsea, E Sussex, TN36 4BS. E-mail: membership@sos.org.uk www.sos.org.uk

BTO Regional Representative
Dr Helen Crabtree. 01444 441 687;
e-mail: hcrabtree@gmail.com

Clubs
FRIENDS OF RYE HARBOUR NATURE RESERVE. (1973; 1900). Friends of Rye Harbour, 2 Watch Cottages,

Nook Beach, Winchelsea, E Sussex TN36 4LU. 01797 223 862; e-mail: rhnroffice@sussex.org.uk
www.wildrye.info www.RXwildlife.org.uk
www.RyeHarbour.net
Meetings: Monthly talks in winter, monthly walks all year.

HENFIELD BIRDWATCH. (1999; 135). Mike Russell, 31 Downsview, Small Dole, Henfield, West Sussex BN5 9YB. 01273 494 311;
e-mail: mikerussell@sussexwt.org.uk

SHOREHAM DISTRICT
ORNITHOLOGICAL SOCIETY.
(1953; 200). Mrs Sue
Miles (Hon. Secretary), 24
Chancellors Park, Hassocks,
West Sussex BN6 8EZ.
E-mail: secretary@sdos.
orgmembership@sdos.org
or through website - www.sdos.org
Meetings: 7.30pm, 2nd Tuesday of the month (Oct-Apr), St Peter's Church Hall, Shoreham-by-Sea. (7 indoor meetings, 18+ field outings).

SUSSEX ORNITHOLOGICAL SOCIETY. (1962; 1700). Val Bentley, Chetsford, London Road, Henfield, West Sussex BN5 9JJ. 01273 494 723;
e-mail: secretary@sos.org.uk www.sos.org.uk
Meetings: Annual conference in January (Haywards Heath), AGM in April, field outings throughout year.

Ringing Groups
BEACHY HEAD RS. R D M Edgar, 32 Hartfield Road, Seaford, E Sussex BN25 4PW.

CUCKMERE RG. Tim Parmenter, 18 Chapel Road, Plumpton Green, East Sussex, BN7 3DD. 01273 891 881.

RYE BAY RG. P Jones, Elms Farm, Pett Lane, Icklesham, Winchelsea, E Sussex TN36 4AH. 01797 226374; e-mail: philjones@beamingbroadband.com

STEYNING RINGING GROUP. B R Clay, Meghana, Honeysuckle Lane, High Salvington, Worthing, West Sussex BN13 3BT. E-mail: brian.clay@ntlworld.com

RSPB Local Groups
BATTLE. (1973; 80). David Yates. 01424 773 826;
e-mail: familyatbattle@yahoo.co.uk
www.battlerspb.org.uk
Meetings: 7.30pm, 4th Tuesday of the month, Battle and Langton Primary School, Battle.

BRIGHTON & DISTRICT. (1974; 260). Mark Weston. 07802 293 417; e-mail: mark.weston@rspb.org.uk
www.rspb.org.uk/groups/brighton
Meetings: 7.30pm, 4th Thursday of the month, All Saints Church Hall, Eaton Road, Hove. Anyone is welcome, non-members should phone first as dates can vary.

CHICHESTER & SW SUSSEX. (1979; 245). Kerry Jackson. 01243 265 783;
e-mail: chichesterrspb@aol.com

ENGLAND

www.rspb.org.uk/groups/chichester
Meetings: 7.30 pm 2nd Thursday of each month, Newell Centre, Newell Centre, Tozer Way, St Pancras, Chichester from Sept to May. Three monthly walks all year.

CRAWLEY & HORSHAM. (1978; 148). Andrea Saxton, 104 Heath Way, Horsham, W Sussex, RH12 5XS. 01403 242 218; e-mail: Andrea.saxton@sky.com
www.rspb.org.uk/groups/crawley
Meetings: 8.00pm, 3rd Wednesday of the month (Sept-Apr), The Friary Hall, Crawley.

EAST GRINSTEAD. (1998; 185). Nick Walker, 14 York Avenue, East Grinstead, W Sussex RH19 4TL. 01342 315 825; e-mail: nickwalker55@btinternet.com
www.rspb.org.uk/groups/egrinstead
Meetings: 8.00pm, last Wednesday of the month, Large Parish Hall, De La Warr Road, East Grinstead.

EASTBOURNE & DISTRICT. (1993; 320). Ian Muldoon. 01273 476 852; e-mail: ian1muldoon@yahoo.co.uk
www.rspb.org.uk/groups/eastbourne
Meetings: 2.15 pm and 7.30 pm, 1st Wednesday of the month (Sep-Jun), St. Wilfrid's Church Hall, Eastbourne Road, Pevensey Bay.

HASTINGS & ST LEONARDS. (1983; 110). Richard Prebble, 01424 751 790;
e-mail: Lynn.jenkins98@gmail.com
www.rspb.org.uk/groups/hastings
Meetings: 7.30pm, 3rd Friday of the month, Taplin Centre, Upper Maze Hill.

Wetland Bird Survey Organiser
CHICHESTER HARBOUR. Mr E Rowsell. Conservation Officer, Chichester Harbour Conservancy, Harbour Office, Itchenor, Chichester, W Sussex PO20 7AW. 01243 510 985; e-mail: edward@conservancy.co.uk

OTHER SITES. Richard Bown.
E-mail: hr.bown@btinternet.com

Wildlife Hospital
BRENT LODGE BIRD & WILDLIFE TRUST. Penny Cooper, Brent Lodge, Cow Lane, Sidlesham, Chichester, West Sussex, PO20 7LN. 01243 641 672 (emergency number).
www.brentlodge.org All species of wild birds and small mammals. Full surgical and medical facilities (inc. X-ray) in conjunction with veterinary support. Purpose-built oiled bird washing unit. Veterinary support.

Wildlife Trust
SUSSEX WILDLIFE TRUST. (1961; 33, 000). Woods Mill, Shoreham Road, Henfield, W Sussex, BN5 9SD. 01273 492630 (fax) 01273 494500;
e-mail: enquiries@sussexwt.org.uk
www.sussexwildlifetrust.org.uk

Tyne & Wear
See Northumberland.

WARWICKSHIRE

Bird Recorder
Jonathan Bowley, 17 Meadow Way, Fenny Compton, Southam, Warks, CV47 2WD. 01295 770 069;
e-mail: warks-recorder@westmidlandbirdclub.com

Bird Report See West Midlands.

BTO Regional Representatives
WARWICKSHIRE. Mark Smith. 01926 735 398;
e-mail: mark.smith36@ntlworld.com

Clubs
NUNEATON & DISTRICT BIRDWATCHERS' CLUB. (1950; 78). Alvin K Burton, 23 Redruth Close, Horeston Grange, Nuneaton, Warwicks CV11 6FG. 024 7664 1591.
http://ndbwc.webs.com/

Meetings: 7.30pm, 3rd Thursday of the month (Sep-Jun), Hatters Space Community Centre, Upper Abbey Street, Nuneaton.

Ringing Groups
ARDEN RG. Roger J Juckes, 24 Croft Lane, Temple Grafton, Alcester, Warks B49 6PA. 01789 778748.

BRANDON RG. David Stone, Overbury, Wolverton, Stratford-on-Avon, Warks CV37 0HG. 01789 731488.

RSPB Local Group
See West Midlands.

Wetland Bird Survey Organiser
WARWICKSHIRE. Matthew Griffiths. 01564 826 685;
E-mail: matt_avesmaster@hotmail.com

Wildlife Trust
WARWICKSHIRE WILDLIFE TRUST. (1970; 13, 000). Brandon Marsh Nature Centre, Brandon Lane, Coventry, CV3 3GW. 024 7630 2912 (fax) 024 7663 9556; e-mail: enquiries@wkwt.org.uk
www.warwickshire-wildlife-trust.org.uk

WEST MIDLANDS

Bird Atlas/Avifauna
The New Birds of the West Midlands edited by Graham and Janet Harrison (West Midland Bird Club, 2005). Available from 147 Worlds End Lane, Quinton, birmingham B32 1JX.

Bird Recorder
Kevin Clements, 26 Hambrook Close, Dunstall Park, Wolverhampton, West Midlands WV6 0XA. 01902 568 997; e-mail: west-mids-recorder@westmidlandbirdclub.com

Bird Reports
THE BIRDS OF SMESTOW VALLEY AND DUNSTALL PARK (1988-), from Secretary, Smestow Valley Bird Group.

ENGLAND

WEST MIDLAND BIRD REPORT (inc Staffs, Warks, Worcs and W Midlands) (1934-), from Barbara Oakley, 147 Worlds End, Quinton, Birmingham B32 1JX. E-mail: secretary@westmidlandbirdclub.com - www.westmidlandbirdclub.com

BTO Regional Representative
BIRMINGHAM & WEST MIDLANDS. Steve Davies. 01562 885 789; e-mail: stevedaviesbtorep@hotmail.co.uk

Clubs
SMESTOW VALLEY BIRD GROUP. (1988; 46). Frank Dickson, 11 Bow Street, Bilston, Wolverhampton, WV14 7NB. 01902 493 733.

WEST MIDLAND BIRD CLUB - serving Ornithologists in Staffs, Warks, Worcs and the West Midlands County. (1929; 2000). Barbara Oakley.
E-mail: secretary@westmidlandbirdclub.com
www.westmidlandbirdclub.com
Meetings: Check website for details of the different branches and their events.

WEST MIDLAND BIRD CLUB (BIRMINGHAM BRANCH). (1995; 800). Andy Mabbett.
E-mail: birmingham@westmidlandbirdclub.com
www.westmidlandbirdclub.com/birmingham
Meetings: 7.30pm, usually last Tuesday (Oct-Apr), Unitarian New Meeting, 31 Ryland Street, Ladywood, Birmingham B16 8BL.

WEST MIDLAND BIRD CLUB (SOLIHULL BRANCH). (1973). Raymond Brown, The Spinney, 63 Grange Road, Dorridge, Solihull B93 8QS. 01564 772 550; e-mail: solihull@westmidlandbirdclub
www.westmidlandbirdclub.com/solihull
Meetings: 7.30 pm, Fridays (usually 1st of month), Guild House, Knowle, Solihull B93 0LN.

Ringing Groups
MERCIAN RG (Sutton Coldfield). Mr DJ Clifton. 59 Daisybank Crescent, Walsall, WS5 3BH. 01922 628 572.

RSPB Local Groups
BIRMINGHAM. (1975; 100). John Bailey, 52 Gresham Road, Hall Green, Birmingham, B28 0HY. 0121 777 4389; e-mail: jvbailey@btinternet.com www.rspb-birmingham.org.uk
Meetings: 7.30pm, 3rd Thursday of the month (Sep-Jun), Salvation Army Citadel, St Chads, Queensway, Birmingham.

COVENTRY & WARWICKSHIRE. (1969; 130). Ron Speddings.01926 428 365;
e-mail: Ron@speddings.spacomputers.com
www.rspb.org.uk/groups/coventryandwarwickshire
Meetings: 7.30pm, 4th Friday of the month, (Sep-May unless otherwise stated), Warwick Arts Centre And Baginton Village Hall.

SOLIHULL. (1983; 2600). John Roberts, 115 Dovehouse Lane, Solihull, West Midlands, B91 2EQ. 0121 707 3101; e-mail: johnbirder@care4free.net
www.rspb.org.uk/groups/solihull
Meetings: 7.30pm, usually 2nd Tuesday of the month (Sep-Apr), Oliver Bird Hall, Church Hill Road, Solihull.

STOURBRIDGE. (1978; 150). David Ackland. 01384 293 090; e-mail: davidackland@blueyonder.co.uk
www.rspb.org.uk/groups/stourbridge
Meetings: 2nd Wednesday of the month (Sep-May), Wollaston Suite, Stourbridge Town Hall, Crown Centre, STOURBRIDGE, West Midlands, DY8 1YE

SUTTON COLDFIELD. (1986; 250). Martin Fisher. 0121 308 4400; e-mail: martinjfisher@care4free.net
www.rspb.org.uk/groups/suttoncoldfield
Meetings: 7.30pm, 1st Monday of the month, Bishop Vesey's Grammer School.

WALSALL. (1970). Mike Pittaway, 2 Kedleston Close, Bloxwich, Walsall, WS3 3TW. 01922 710 568;
e-mail: michaelp@kedclose.freeserve.co.uk
www.rspb-walsall.org.uk
Meetings: 7.30pm, 3rd Wednesday of the month, St Marys School, Jesson Road, Walsall.

WOLVERHAMPTON. (1974; 100). Barry Proffitt. 01902 751 835; e-mail: RSPBwolverhampton@hotmail.co.uk
www.rspb.org.uk/groups/wolverhampton
Meetings: 7.30pm, 2nd Wednesday of the month (Sept-Apr), The Newman Centre, Haywood Drive, Tettenhall, Wolverhampton. Also monthly field-trips (Sep-Jun).

Wetland Birds Survey Organiser
WESTMIDLANDS. Nick Lewis.
E-mail: nick.r.lewis@btinternet.com

Wildlife Trust
THE WILDLIFE TRUST FOR BIRMINGHAM AND THE BLACK COUNTRY. (1980; 5, 500). 28 Harborne Road, Edgbaston, Birmingham, B15 3AA. 0121 454 1199 (fax) 0121 454 6556; e-mail: info@bbcwildlife.org.uk
www.bbcwildlife.org.uk

WILTSHIRE

Bird Atlas/Avifauna
Birds of Wiltshireby James Ferguson-Lees 2007, Wiltshire Ornithological Society

Bird Recorder
Rob Turner, 14 Ethendun, Bratton, Westbury, Wilts, BA13 4RX. 01380 830 862;
e-mail: robt14@btopenworld.com

Bird Report
HOBBY (journal of the Wiltshire OS) (1975-), from John Osborne, 4 Fairdown Avenue, Westbury, Wiltshire BA13 3HS. 01373 8645 98;
e-mail: josb@talktalk.net
www.wiltshirebirds.co.uk

265

ENGLAND

BTO Regional Representatives
NORTH. Bill Quantrill. 01225 866 245;
e-mail: william.quantrill@btinternet.com

SOUTH. Bill Quantrill. 01225 866 245;
e-mail: william.quantrill@btinternet.com

Clubs
SALISBURY & DISTRICT NATURAL
HISTORY SOCIETY. (1952; 146).
Elisabeth Richmond, 15 Chantry
Road, Wilton, Salisbury, SP2
0LT. 01722 742 755; e-mail:
erichmond@madasafish.com
www.salisburynaturalhistory.com
Meetings: 7.30pm, 3rd Thursday
of the month (Sept-Apr),
Salisbury Baptist Church, Brown Street, Salisbury.

WILTSHIRE ORNITHOLOGICAL SOCIETY. (1974; 500).
Phil Deacon, 12 Rawston Close, Nythe, Swindon, Wilts
SN3 3PW. 01793 528 930;
e-mail: phil.deacon@ntlworld.com
www.wiltshirebirds.co.uk
Meetings: See website for details.

Ringing Group
COTSWOLD WATER PARK RG. John Wells, 25 Pipers
Grove, Highnam, Glos, GL2 8NJ.
E-mail: john.wells2@btinternet.com

WEST WILTSHIRE RG. Mr M.J. Hamzij, 13 Halfway
Close, Trowbridge, Wilts BA14 7HQ.
E-mail: m.hamzij@btinternet.com

RSPB Local Groups
SOUTH WILTSHIRE. (1986; 720). Tony Goddard, 3
Forestry House, Livery Road, Farley, Salisbury, SP5
1AG. 01722 712 713;
e-mail: goddard543@hotmail.com
www.rspb.org.uk/groups/southwiltshire
Meetings: 7.30pm, Tuesday evenings (monthly),
Salisbury Arts Centre, Salisbury.

Wetland Birds Survey Organiser
COTSWOLD WATER PARK. Gareth Harris, Keynes
Country Park, Spratsgate Lane, Shorncote, Glos GL7
6DF. 01793 752 413 or 01793 752 730;
e-mail: gareth.harris@waterpark.org
www.waterpark.org

WILTSHIRE. Julian Rolls, c/o WeBS Office, BTO, The
Nunnery, Thetford, Norfolk IP24 2PU.

Wildlife Trust
WILTSHIRE WILDLIFE TRUST. (1962; 18, 500). Elm
Tree Court, Long Street, Devizes, Wilts, SN10 1NJ.
01380 725 670 (fax) 01380 729 017;
e-mail: info@wiltshirewildlife.org
www.wiltshirewildlife.org

WORCESTERSHIRE

Bird Recorder
Steven Payne, 6 Norbury Close, Redditch B98 8RP.
01527 60169;
e-mail: worcs-recorder@westmidlandbirdclub.com
www.westmidlandbirdclub.com

Bird Report See West Midlands.

BTO Regional Representative
G Harry Green MBE, Windy Ridge, Pershore Road,
Little Comberton, Pershore, Worcs, WR10 3EW. 01386
710 377; e-mail: zen130501@zen.co.uk

Ringing Group
WYCHAVON RG. J R Hodson, 15 High Green, Severn
Stoke, Worcester, WR8 9JS. 01905 371 333;
e-mail: hodson77@btinternet.com

Club
WEST MIDLAND BIRD CLUB (KIDDERMINSTER BRANCH).
Celia Barton, 28A Albert Street, Wall Heath,
Kingswinford, DY6 0NA. 01384 839 838;
e-mail: kidderminster@westmidlandbirdclub.com
www.westmidlandbirdclub.com
Meetings: 7.30pm, 4th Wednesday of the month
(Sep-Apr), St Oswalds Church Centre, Broadwaters,
Kidderminster.

RSPB Local Group
WORCESTER & MALVERN. (1980; 300). Frances Evans,
120 Bath Road, Worcester WR5 3EP. 01905 359 132;
e-mail: francesevans@gmail.com
www.rspb.org.uk/groups/worcester
Meetings: 7.30pm, 2nd Wednesday in month (Sept-
May), Powick Village Hall.

Wetland Birds Survey Organiser
WORCESTERSHIRE. Andrew Warr, 14 Bromsgrove
Street, Barbourne, Worcester WR3 8AR.
E-mail: andrew.warr3@btopenworld.com

Wildlife Hospital
VALE WILDLIFE RESCUE - WILDLIFE HOSPITAL +
REHABILITATION CENTRE. Any staff member, Station
Road, Beckford, Tewkesbury, Glos GL20 7AN. 01386
882 288; e-mail: info@valewildlife.org.uk
www.valewildlife.org.uk All wild birds. Intensive
care. Registered charity. Veterinary support.

Wildlife Trust
WORCESTERSHIRE WILDLIFE TRUST. (1968; 9, 000).
Lower Smite Farm, Smite Hill, Hindlip, Worcester,
WR3 8SZ. 01905 754 919 (fax) 01905 755868;
e-mail: enquiries@worcestershirewildlifetrust.org
www.worcswildlifetrust.co.uk
Charity no. 256618.

YORKSHIRE

Bird Atlas/Avifauna
Atlas of Breeding Birds in the Leeds Area 1987-1991

by Richard Fuller et al (Leeds Birdwatchers' Club, 1994).

The Birds of Halifax by Nick Dawtrey (only 20 left), 14 Moorend Gardens, Pellon, Halifax, W Yorks, HX2 0SD.

The Birds of Yorkshire by John Mather (Croom Helm, 1986).

An Atlas of the Breeding Birds of the Huddersfield Area, 1987-1992. by Brian Armitage et al (2000) - very few copies left.

Birds of Barnsley by Nick Addey (Pub by author, 114 Everill Gate Lane, Broomhill, Barnsley S73 0YJ, 1998).

Birds of The Huddersfield Area by Paul and Betty Bray (Huddersfield Birdwatchers Club 2008).

Breeding Bird Atlas for Barnsley in preparation.

County Bird Recorders
Craig Thomas, Sunnybank, Church Lane, Flamborough YO15 1PG. 01262 851 677; e-mail: craigcthomas@yahoo.co.uk

Vice County Bird Recorders
VC61 (Yorkshire Naturalists' Union, Bird Section - East Yorkshire). Geoff Dobbs, 1 Priory Road, Beverley, East Yorkshire HU17 0EG. 07778 559 763; e-mail: geoffdobbs@aol.com

VC62 (West Yorkshire)/HARROGATE & CRAVEN. Phil Bone, 11 Dorrington Close, Pocklington, York, YO42 2GS. 0788 084 6905; e-mail: philsarab@aol.co.uk

VC63 (South & West Yorkshire). Covering all bird study groups and South and West Yorkshire and three reserves - Fairburn Ings, Old Moor (both RSPB) and Potteric Carr (Yorkshire Wildlife Trust), John Wint, 9 Yew Tree Park, Whitley, Goole, East Yorkshire DN14 0NZ. 01977 662 826; e-mail: j.wint114@btinternet.com

VC64 (Mid-West Yorkshire). Ian Court, 2 Burley Mews, Steeton, Keighley BT20 6TX. 01535 658 582; e-mail: ian.court@mypostoffice.co.uk

VC65 (North Yorkshire West). Steve Worwood, 18 Coltsgate Hill, Ripon, HG4 2AB; e-mail: steve@worwood.entadsl.com

Bird Reports
BARNSLEY & DISTRICT BIRD STUDY GROUP REPORT (1971-), from Waxwing Books, Sunnybank Cottage, Ruston Parva, Driffield YO25 4DG.

YORK ORNITHOLOGICAL CLUB REPORT (1966 -). 2010 report is scheduled for publication in Nov 2012. Latest report can be ordered and paid for through the club website, from Jenny Dixon, Carver's Cottage, Main Street, Askham Bryan, York YO23 3QU. 01904 703 505; e-mail: j.dixon023@btinternet.com www.yorkbirding.org.uk

YORKSHIRE NATURALISTS' UNION: BIRD REPORT (1940-). 2010 edition £12 including postage, from Jill Warwick, Sharow Grange, Sharow, Ripon, HG4 5BN. 01765 602 832; e-mail: jill@swland.co.uk

BRADFORD NATURALISTS' SOCIETY ANNUAL REPORT, from Mr I Hogg, 23 St Matthews Road, Bankfoot, Bradford, BD5 9AB. 01274 727902.

BRADFORD ORNITHOLOGICAL GROUP REPORT (1987-) - after the 2008 issue, this report will only be available to paid up members of the group., from Jenny Barker, 3 Chapel Fold, Slack Lane, Oakworth, Keighley, BD22 0RQ.

DONCASTER BIRD REPORT (1955-), from Mr M Roberts, 8 Sandbeck court, Rossington, Doncaster, DN11 0FN. 01302 326 265.

FILEY BRIGG BIRD REPORT (1976-), from Colin and Rose Court. 01723 515 925; e-mail: recorder@fbog.co.uk www.fbog.co.uk

HARROGATE & DISTRICT NATURALISTS' SOCIETY BIRD REPORT (1996-) 2011 edition £6 including postage, from Jill Warwick, Sharow Grange, Sharow, Ripon, HG4 5BN. 01765 602 832; e-mail: jill@swland.co.uk

HULL VALLEY WILDLIFE GROUP REPORT (2000-) covering Hull Valley. from Roy Lyon, 670 Hotham Road South, Hull, HU5 5LE. 07754 439 496. www.hullvalleywildlifegroup.co.uk

BIRDS IN HUDDERSFIELD (1966-), from Mr M Wainman, 2 Bankfield Avenue, Taylor Hill, Huddersfield HD4 7QY. 01484 305 054; e-mail: brian.armitage@ntlworld.com

LEEDS BIRDWATCHERS' CLUB ANNUAL REPORT (1949-), from Peter Murphy, 12 West End Lane, Horsforth, Leeds LS18 5JP.

BIRDS OF ROTHERHAM (1975-) - cost £2.50 inc p&p, cheque payable to R.D.O.S., from The Secretary, Rotherham & District Bird Club. rdos@hotmail.co.uk www.rotherhambirds.co.uk

BIRDS IN THE SHEFFIELD AREA (1973-), from Richard Hill, Honorary Secretary, 22 Ansell Road, Sheffield, South Yorkshire S11 7PE. E-mail: Secretary@sbsg.org www.sbsg.org

THE BIRDS OF SK58 (1993-), from Secretary, SK58 Birders. E-mail: recorder@sk58birders.com www.sk58birders.com

SORBY RECORD (1962-), from Ken Dorning, Sorby NHSoc, c/o Room C12i, Dainton Building, Brook Hill, Sheffield S3 7HF.

SPURN BIRD OBSERVATORY ANNUAL REPORT, from Warden, see Reserves.

ENGLAND

SWILLINGTON INGS BIRD GROUP - ANNUAL REPORT AND TWENTY YEAR REVIEW - 2008, from Chris Robinson, 43 Northfield Road, Sprotbrough, Doncaster, DN5 8AY. 07534 271 254; e-mail: GBFShrike@hotmail.com http://sibg1.wordpress.com

WINTERSETT AREA ANNUAL REPORT (1988-), from Steve Denny, 13 Rutland Drive, Crofton, Wakefield, WF4 1SA. 01924 864487.

BTO Regional Representatives & Regional Development Officers
NORTH-EAST RR. Mick Carroll. 10 Crofts Avenue, Pickering, North Yorkshire YO18 7HP. 01751 476 550.

NORTH-WEST RR. Gerald Light. 01756 753 720; e-mail: gerald@uwlig.plus.com

SOUTH-EAST AND SOUTH-WEST RR. Position vacant. 01842 750 050. E-mail: info@bto.org

EAST RR. Position vacant. 01842 750 050. E-mail: info@bto.org

BRADFORD RR & RDO. Mike L Denton, 77 Hawthorne Terrace, Crosland Moor, Huddersfield, HD4 5RP. 01484 646 990.

YORKSHIRE (HARROGATE) RR. Mike Brown, 48 Pannal Ash Drive, Harrogate, N Yorks, HG2 0HU. 01423 567 382; e-mail: mikebtorep@gmail.com

HULL RR. Geoff Dobbs, 1 Priory Road, Beverley, East Yorkshire HU17 0EG. 07778 559 763; e-mail: geoffdobbs@aol.com

LEEDS & WAKEFIELD RR & RDO. Position vacant. 01842 750 050; e-mail: info@bto.org

RICHMOND RR. John Edwards, 7 Church Garth, Great Smeaton, Northallerton, N Yorks DL6 2HW. 01609 881 476; e-mail: john@jhedwards.plus.com

YORK RR. Rob Chapman, 12 Moorland Road, York, YO10 4HF. 01904 633 558; e-mail: robert.chapman@tinyworld.co.uk

BTO Garden BirdWatch Ambassadors
John Preston; e-mail: johnpreston64@tiscali.co.uk

Liz Clinton; e-mail: liztomclinton@aol.com

Tim Godson; e-mail: tim.godson@btinternet.com

John Kirkman; e-mail: suekirkman.uk@gmail.com

Kevin Coy; e-mail: kjcoy79@waitrose.com

Mike Gray; e-mail: sdmike.gray@btinternet.com

Pippa Jones; e-mail: pippajones@ntlworld.com

Clubs
BARNSLEY BIRD STUDY GROUP. (1970; 35). Graham Speight, 58 Locke Avenue, Barnsley, South Yorkshire S70 1QH. 01226 321 300.
Meetings: 7.15pm, 1st Thursday in the month (Nov-Mar), RSPB Old Moor, Barnsley.

BRADFORD ORNITHOLOGICAL GROUP. (1987; 160). Shaun Radcliffe, 8 Longwood Avenue, Bingley, W Yorks, BD16 2RX. 01274 770 960.
www.bradfordbirding.org
Meetings: 1st Tuesday of the month - see website for details.

CASTLEFORD & DISTRICT NATURALISTS' SOCIETY. (1956; 16). Michael J Warrington, 31 Mount Avenue, Hemsworth, Pontefract, W Yorks WF9 4QE. 01977 614 954; e-mail: michaelwarrington@talktalk.net
Meetings: 7.30pm, Tuesdays monthly (Sep-Mar), SkillsXchange Campus, Castleford. Check contact name for dates.

DONCASTER & DISTRICT ORNITHOLOGICAL SOCIETY. (1955; 40). Dave Ward, Membership Secretary, 11 Newstead Road, Scawthorpe, Doncaster DN5 9JS. www.birdingdoncaster.org.uk
Meetings: 7.15pm, last Thursday of the month (Jan-May and Sep-Nov), Parklands Sports and social club, Wheatley Hall Road.

FILEY BRIGG ORNITHOLOGICAL GROUP. (1977; 100). Dr Sue Hull, 32 West Road, Filey, N Yorkshire YO14 9LP. 01723 515 042; e-mail: secretary@fbog.co.uk www.fbog.co.uk

HARROGATE & DISTRICT NATURALISTS' SOCIETY. (1947; 350). Ms Sue Coldwell, General Secretary, 4 Abbotts Way, Knaresborough, North Yorkshire HG5 8EU.
E-mail: gensec@hdns.org.uk www.hdns.org.uk
Meetings: 7.30pm, St. Roberts Centre, 2/3 Robert Street, Harrogate. The programme of meetings is sent out to members in September.

HORNSEA BIRD CLUB. (1967; 35). John Eldret, 44 Rolston Road, Hornsea, HU18 1UH. 01964 532 854.
Meetings: 7.30pm, 3rd Friday of the month (Sep-Mar), Hornsea Library. Monthly visits to local bird reserves.

HUDDERSFIELD BIRDWATCHERS' CLUB. (1966; 90). Chris Abell, 57 Butterley Lane, New Mill, Holmfirth, HD9 7EZ. 01484 681 499; e-mail: cdabell@gmail.com www.huddersfieldbirdwatchersclub.co.uk
Meetings: 7.30pm, Tuesday's fortnightly (Sep-May), The Old Court Room, Town Hall, Ramsden St, Huddersfield HD1 2TA.

HULL VALLEY WILDLIFE GROUP. (1997; 175). The Secretary, 29 Beech View, Cranswick, East Yorkshire YO25 9QQ. 01377 270 957. 01377 270 957. www.hullvalleywildlifegroup.co.uk

LEEDS BIRDWATCHERS' CLUB. (1949; 60). Peter Murphy, 12 West End lane, Horsforth, Leeds, LS18 5JP. 0113 293 0188; e-mail: pandbmurphy@ntlworld.com
Meetings: 7.15pm Monday fortnightly, Quaker Meeting House, Woodhouse Lane, Leeds.

ENGLAND

ROTHERHAM & DISTRICT ORNITHOLOGICAL SOCIETY. (1974; 80). Malcolm Taylor, 18 Maple Place, Chapeltown, Sheffield, S35 1QW. 0114 246 1848; e-mail: rdos@hotmail.co.uk
www.rotherhambirds.co.uk
Meetings: 7.30pm, 2nd Friday of the month, United Reform church hall, Herringthorpe.

SCARBOROUGH BIRDERS. (1993; 38). Steve Wignell, Flat 3, 101 Castle Road, Scarborough, N Yorkshire YO11 1HX.
07859 435 592.
www.scarboroughbirding.co.uk
Meetings: 3rd Thursday of the month (Sep-Nov) and (Jan -Apr). Check website for details.

SHEFFIELD BIRD STUDY GROUP. (1972; 160). Richard Hill, Honorary Secretary, 22 Ansell Road, Sheffield, South Yorkshire S11 7PE.
E-mail: Secretary@sbsg.org www.sbsg.org
Meetings: 7.15pm, 2nd Wednesday of the month (Sep-May), Lecture Theatre 5, Sheffield University Arts Tower.

SK58 BIRDERS. (1993; 66). Andy Hirst, 15 Hunters Drive, Dinnington, Sheffield, S25 2TG. 07947 068 125; e-mail: contact@sk58birders.com
www.sk58birders.com
Chair: Mick Clay, 2 High St, S.Anston, Sheffield. 01909 566 000.
Meetings: 7.30pm, last Wednesday of the month (except July, Aug & Dec (Christmas social)), Upstairs Room, Loyal Trooper pub, South Anston.

SORBY NHS (ORNITHOLOGICAL SECTION). (1918; 400). The Secretary, c/o 159 Bell Hagg Road, Sheffield S6 5DA, E-mail: secretary@sorby.org.uk
www.sorby.org.uk
Meetings: Indoor and field meetings held regularly as advertised on the website and in the newsletter.

SOUTH PEAK RAPTOR STUDY GROUP. (1998; 12). M E Taylor, 76 Hawksley Avenue, Newbold, Chesterfield, Derbys S40 4TL. 01246 277749.

SOUTH RYEDALE AND EAST YORKSHIRE RAPTOR GROUP. Mick Carroll. 10 Crofts Avenue, Pickering, North Yorkshire YO18 7HP. 01751 476 550.

SWILLINGTON INGS BIRD GROUP. (1989; 83). Chris Robinson, 43 Northfield Road, Sprotbrough, Doncaster, DN5 8AY. 07534 271 254.
http://sibg1.wordpress.com
Meetings: 7.30pm, 1st Thursday of even months with informal social evenings 1st Thursday of odd months (please phone for details of venue).

WAKEFIELD NATURALISTS' SOCIETY. (1851; 32). Michael Warrington, 31 Mount Avenue, Hemsworth, Pontefract, W Yorks WF9 4QE. 01977 614 954; e-mail: michaelwarrington@talktalk.net

Meetings: 7.30pm, 2nd Tuesday of the month (Sep-Apr), Friends Meeting House, Thornhill Street, Wakefield.

YORK ORNITHOLOGICAL CLUB. (1967; 80). Linda Newton, 5 Fairfields Drive, Skelton, York YO30 1YP, 01904 471 446; e-mail: secretary@yorkbirding.org.uk
www.yorkbirding.org.uk
Meetings: 7.30pm, 1st Tuesday of the month, St Olaves Church Hall, Marygate Lane, Marygate, YORK YO30 7BJ.

YORKSHIRE NATURALISTS' UNION (Bird Section). (1875; 500). Mr John Wint (Vice Chairman). 01977 662 826; e-mail: j.wint114@btinternet.com
www.ynu.org.uk

Ringing Groups
BARNSLEY RG. M C Wells, 715 Manchester Road, Stocksbridge, Sheffield, S36 1DQ. 0114 288 4211; e-mail: barnsleybsg.plus.com

DONCASTER RG. D Hazard, 41 Jossey Lane, Scawthorpe, Doncaster, S Yorks DN5 9DB. 01302 788 044; e-mail: dave.hazard@tiscali.co.uk

EAST DALES RG. P. Bone, 11 Dorrington Close, Pocklington, York, YO42 2GS.
E-mail: philsarab@aol.co.uk

EAST YORKS RG. Peter J Dunn, 43 West Garth Gardens, Cayton, Scarborough, N Yorks YO11 3SF. 01723 583149; e-mail: pjd@fbog.co.uk
www.eyrg.co.uk

SORBY-BRECK RG. Geoff P Mawson, Moonpenny Farm, Farwater Lane, Dronfield, Sheffield S18 1RA.
E-mail: moonpenny@talktalk.net

SPURN BIRD OBSERVATORY. Paul Collins, Kew Villa, Seaside Road, Kilnsea, Hull HU12 0UB. 01964 650 479; e-mail: pcnfa@hotmail.com

WINTERSETT RG. P Smith, 16 Templar Street, Wakefield, W Yorks, WF1 5HB. 01924 375 082.

RSPB Local Groups
AIREDALE AND BRADFORD. (1972; 3500 in catchment area). Paul Barrett. 01274 582 078;
e-mail: AbRSPB@blueyonder.co.uk
www.rspb.org.uk/groups/airedaleandbradford
Meetings: 7.30pm, monthly on Fridays, Room 3, Shipley Library.

WAKEFIELD. (1987; 130). Duncan Stokoe, 12 New Road, Horbury, Wakefield, West Yorkshire WF4 5LR.
E-mail: duncanstokoe@gmail.com
www.rspb.org.uk/groups/wakefield
Meetings: 7.30pm, 4th Thursday of the month (Sep-Apr), Ossett War Memorial Community Centre, Prospect Road, Ossett, WF5 8AN.
YORK. (1972; 600). Chris Lloyd, 7 School Lane, Upper Poppleton, York YO26 6JS. 01904 794 865; e-mail: rspb.calyork@btinternet.com
www.yorkrspb.org.uk

Meetings: 7.30pm, Tues, Wed or Thurs, Temple Hall, York St John University, Lord Mayors Walk, York.

CRAVEN & PENDLE. (1986; 300). Colin Straker. 01756 751 888; e-mail: colin.straker@btinternet.com
www.cravenandpendlerspb.org
Meetings: 7.30pm 2nd Wednesday of the month (Sep-May), St Andrews Church Hall, Newmarket Street, Skipton.

DONCASTER. (1984; 105). Trevor Bonham, Willowford, Melton Mill Lane, High Lane, Doncaster, DN5 7TE. 01709 585 677; e-mail: trevorbonham@yahoo.co.uk
www.rspb.org.uk/groups/doncaster
Meetings: 7.30pm Castle Park Rugby Club, Armthorpe Road, Doncaster, DN2 5QB on the second Wed of the month, beginning on 12th Sept 2012.

EAST YORKSHIRE. (1986;120). Paul Leyland, 61 Muston Road, Hunmanby, North Yorkshire, YO14 0JY. 01723 891507; e-mail: eastyorksrspb@yahoo.co.uk
www.rspb.org.uk/groups/eastyorkshire
Meetings: 7.30pm, North Bridlington Library, Martongate, BRIDLINGTON (check website for details).

HARROGATE DISTRICT. (2005). Bill Sturman. 01423 870 883; e-mail: pam-bill@sturmanw.fsnet.co.uk
www.harrogaterspb.com
Meetings: 7.50pm, 3rd Monday of the month (Oct-Mar). Christ Church Parish Centre, The Stray, Harrogate HG1 4SW.

HUDDERSFIELD & HALIFAX. (1981; 120). David Hemingway, 267 Long Lane, Dalton, Huddersfield, HD5 9SH. 01484 301 920;
e-mail: d.hemingway@ntlworld.com
www.rspb.org.uk/groups/huddersfieldand halifax
Meetings: 7.30pm, Huddersfield Methodist Mission, 3-13 Lord Street, Huddersfield, HD1 1QA.

HULL & DISTRICT. (1983; 334). Betty Hilton. 01482 849 503; e-mail: betty9hilton@gmail.com
www.rspb.org.uk/groups/hull
Meetings: 7.30pm, Tuesdays (Sept-Apr), Christchurch United Reformed Church, South Ella Way, Kirk Ella, HULL. (£2 for Local Group Members and £2.50 for Non Members).

LEEDS. (1974; 560). Ian Willoughby. 0113 258 6555. E-mail: RSPBleeds@googlemail.com
www.rspb.org.uk/groups/leeds
Meetings: 7.30pm, 3rd Wednesday of the month (Sep-Apr), Friends Meeting House, 188 Woodhouse Lane, Leeds, Yorkshire, LS2 9DX.

RICHMONDSHIRE & HAMBLETON. (2005). Jim Brettell. 01748 850 272; e-mail: jgb@barneyschool.org.uk
www.rspb.org.uk/groups/richmondshireandhambleton
Meetings: Check website.

SHEFFIELD. (1981; 500). Susan Bradshaw. 0114 239 9072; E-mail: s.bradshaw@sheffield.ac.uk
www.rspb-sheffield.org.uk
Meetings: 7.30pm 1st Thursday of the month (Sept-May), Central United Reformed Church, Norfolk St, Sheffield.

Wetland Bird Survey Organisers
EAST YORKSHIRE AND SCARBOROUGH (excl. Humber). Mrs S Pashby, 10 Ambrey Close, Hunmanby, Filey, North Yorks YO14 0LZ. 01723 891 377.

HARROGATE AND YORKSHIRE DALES. Mr W G Haines. 07870 8289 788; e-mail: bill.haines@tiscali.co.uk

LEEDS AREA. Paul Morris. E-mail: pmorris@wyjs.org.uk

Wildlife Hospital
ANIMAL HOUSE WILDLIFE WELFARE. Mrs C Buckroyd, 14 Victoria Street, Scarborough, YO12 7SS. 01723 371 256 (please leave a message on the answer machine and callers will be contacted as soon as possible); e-mail: cynthiabuckroyd@talktalk.net or cindybuckroyd@hotmail.com All species of wild birds. Oiled birds given treatment before forwarding to cleaning stations. Incubators, hospital cages, heat pads, release sites. Birds ringed before release. Prior telephone call requested. Collection if required. Veterinary support. Charity shop at 127 Victoria Road.

Wildlife Trusts
THE WILDLIFE TRUST FOR SHEFFIELD AND ROTHERHAM. (1985; 5, 613). 37 Stafford Road, Sheffield, S2 2SF. 0114 263 4335 (fax) 0114 263 4345; e-mail: mail@wildsheffield.com
www.wildsheffield.com

YORKSHIRE WILDLIFE TRUST. (1946; 21, 500). 1 St George's Place, Tadcaster Road, YorkYO24 1GN. 01904 659 570 (fax) 01904 613 467;
e-mail: info@ywt.org.uk
www.ywt.org.uk

SCOTLAND

Bird Report
SCOTTISH BIRD REPORT from: The
SOC, The Scottish Birdwatching
Resource Centre, Waterston House,
Aberlady, East Lothian, EH32 0PY

Club
See Scottish Ornithologists' Club in
National Directory.

ANGUS & DUNDEE

Bird Recorder
ANGUS & DUNDEE. Jon Cook, 76 Torridon Road,
Broughty Ferry, Dundee, DD5 3JH. 01382 738 495;
e-mail: 1301midget@tiscali.co.uk

Bird Report
ANGUS & DUNDEE BIRD REPORT (1974-), from the
County Recorder, 01382 738 495;
e-mail: 1301midget@tiscali.co.uk

**BTO Regional Representatives & Regional
Development Officer**
ANGUS RR & RDO. Bruce Lynch, 01382 737 528;
e-mail: b_lynch1@sky.com

Clubs
ANGUS & DUNDEE BIRD CLUB.
(1997; 230). Dorothy Fyffe,
33 Ireland Street, Carnoustie,
Angus DD7 6AS. 01241 853
053. www.angusbirding.com
Meetings: 7.30pm, Tuesdays,
Panbride Church Hall,
Carnoustie, Angus.

SOC TAYSIDE BRANCH. (145).
Brian Boag, Birch Brae, Knapp, Inchture, Perthshire
PH14 9SW. 01828 686 669
www.the-soc.org.uk

Ringing Group
TAY RG. Ms S Millar, Edenvale Cottage, 1 Lydox
Cottages, Dairsie, Fife, KY15 4RN;
e-mail: shirley@edenecology.co.uk

RSPB Members' Groups
DUNDEE. (1972;110). Graham Smith, 01382 532 461;
e-mail: grahamnjen@hotmail.com
www.RSPB.org.uk/groups/dundee
Meetings: 7.30 pm, monthly on a Wednesday
(Sep-Mar), Methodist Church, 20, West Marketgait,
DUNDEE. Admission £1.00 for all, including
refreshments. outdoor meetings on Sunday leaving
Crichton Street, Dundee at 9am.

Wetland Bird Survey Organisers
ANGUS (excl Montrose Basin). Dr BM Lynch 01382 737
528; e-mail: b_lynch1@sky.com

MONTROSE BASIN. Anna Cheshier, Scottish Wildlife
Trust, Montrose Basin Wildlife Centre, Rossie Braes,
Montrose, Angus DD10 9TA;
e-mail: acheshier@swt.org.uk

ARGYLL

Birds of Argyll (Argyll Bird Club 2007, £45 inc
postage), available from Bob Furness, The Cnoc,
Tarbert, Arrochar, Dunbartonshire G83 7DG. 01301
702 603

Bird Recorder
ARGYLL. Paul Daw, Tigh-na-Tulloch, Tullochgorm,
Minard, Argyll, PA32 8YQ. 01546 886 260;
e-mail: monedula@globalnet.co.uk

Bird Reports
ARGYLL BIRD REPORT (1984-), From Dr Bob Furness,
The Cnoc, Tarbet, Dunbartonshire G83 7DG. 01301
702 603; e-mail: r.furness@bio.gla.ac.uk

ISLE OF MULL BIRD REPORT (2011), From Mr Alan
Spellman, Maridon, Lochdon, Isle of Mull, Argyll PA64
6AP. 01680 812 448;
e-mail: mullbirds@btinternet.com
www.mullbirds.com

MACHRIHANISH SEABIRD OBSERVATORY REPORT
(1992-), from the Observatory, see reserves section.

BTO Regional Representatives
ARGYLL (MULL, COLL, TIREE AND MORVERN). Arthur
Brown/Rod Little, 01688 400 415/01688 400 315;
e-mail: pamartbrown@btinternet.com/rltt@aol.com

ARGYLL MAINLAND, BUTE AND GIGHA. Position
vacant, 01842 750 050 ; e-mail: info@bto.org

ISLAY, JURA, COLONSAY RR. John S Armitage, Airigh
Sgallaidh, Portnahaven, Isle of Islay, PA47 7SZ. 01496
860 396; e-mail: jsa@ornquest.plus.com
www.birdingodyssey.blogspot.com

Club
ARGYLL BIRD CLUB. (1983;270). Katie Pendreigh, The
Whins, Farry Road, Tayinloan, Argyll PA37 1PT. 01631
710 630. www.argyllbirdclub.org
Meetings: All-day Indoor Meetings are held on a
Saturday in early March and early November each
year, see website for details.

ISLE OF MULL BIRD CLUB.
(2001;160), Mrs Janet T Hall,
Membership Secretary, Druim Mhor,
Craignure, Isle of Mull, Argyll PA65
6AY. 01680 812 441;
e-mail: oystercatcher@dee-emm.co.uk
www.mullbirdclub.org.uk
Meetings: 7 for 7.30pm start, 3rd Friday of the month
(Oct-Apr), Craignure Village Hall.

SCOTLAND

Ringing Group
TRESHNISH ISLES AUK RG. Robin Ward, 25 Fairfield Road, Tadcaster, N Yorkshire LS24 9SD; e-mail: robin.ward2@virginmedia.com

RSPB Local Group
HELENSBURGH. (1975; 62). John Clark, 01436 821 178; e-mail: johnclark@jcmc.demon.co.uk
Meetings: The Guide Halls, Lower John Street, Helensburgh.

Wildlife Hospital
WINGS OVER MULL. Richard and Sue Dewar, Auchnacroish House, Torosay, Craignure, Isle of Mull PA65 6AY. Tel/fax: 01680 812 594; e-mail:dewars@wingsovermull.com www.wingsovermull.com

Wetland Bird Survey Organisers
ARGYLL MAINLAND. Paul Daw, Tigh-na-Tulloch, Minard, Inveraray, Argyll PA32 8YQ. 01546 886 260; e-mail: monedula@globalnet.co.uk

MULL. Paul Daw, Tigh-na-Tulloch, Minard, Inveraray, Argyll PA32 8YQ. 01546 886 260; e-mail: monedula@globalnet.co.uk

TIREE & COLL. John Bowler, e-mail: john.bowler@rspb.org.uk

AYRSHIRE

Bird Recorder
AYRSHIRE. Fraser Simpson, 4 Inchmurrin Drive, Kilmarnock, Ayrshire KA3 2JD. e-mail: recorder@ayrshire-birding.org.uk www.ayrshire-birding.org.uk

Bird Reports
AYRSHIRE BIRD REPORT (1976-), From Dr RG Vernon, 29 Knoll Park, Ayr KA7 4RH. 01292 442 195; e-mail: rgv_mcv@tiscali.co.uk

BTO Regional Representative
AYRSHIRE RR. Brian Broadley, 01290 424 241; e-mail: brianbroadley@onegreendoor.com

Club
SOC AYRSHIRE. (1962; 154). Anne Dick, Rowanmyle House,Tarbolton, Mauchline KA5 5LU. 01292 541 981. www.ayrshire-birding.org.uk www.the-soc.org.uk
Meetings: 7.30pm, Tuesdays monthly, Monkton Community Church, Monkton by Prestwick.

RSPB Local Groups
CENTRAL AYRSHIRE LOCAL GROUP. (1978; 85). Ronnie Coombes (Group Leader), 01292 265 891; e-mail: ronnie.coombes@tesco.net www.ayrshire-birding.org.uk
Meetings: 7.30pm 3rd Monday of the month (Sep-Apr), Newton Wallacetown Church Hall, 60 Main Street, Ayr.

NORTH AYRSHIRE. (1976; 180). John Tedd, 01294 823 434; e-mail: john.tedd@virgin.net

www.narspb.org.uk
Meetings: 7.30pm, various Fridays (Sep-Apr), Argyll Centre, Donaldson Avenue, Saltcoats, Ayrshire, KA21 5AG.

Wetland Bird Survey Organisers
AYRSHIRE. Mr David Grant, e-mail: david.grant@sac.ac.uk

ARRAN. Jim Cassels, Kilpatrick Kennels, Kilpatrick, Blackwaterfoot, Isle of Arran KA27 8EY; e-mail: james.cassels@virgin.net

Wildlife Hospital
HESSILHEAD WILDLIFE RESCUE CENTRE. Gay & Andy Christie, Gateside, Beith, Ayrshire, KA15 1HT. 01505 502 415; e-mail: info@hessilhead.org.uk www.hessilhead.org.uk All species. Releasing aviaries. Veterinary support. Visits only on open days please.

THE SCOTTISH BORDERS

Bird Atlas/Avifauna
The Breeding Birds of South-east Scotland, a tetrad atlas 1988-1994 by R D Murray et al. (Scottish Ornithologists' Club, 1998).

Bird Recorder
Ray Murray, 4 Bellfield Crescent, Eddleston, Peebles, EH45 8RQ. 01721 730 677; e-mail: raymurray1@tiscali.co.uk

Bird Report
BORDERS BIRD REPORT (1979-), From Malcolm Ross, Westfield Cottage, Smailholm, Kelso TD5 7PN.01573 460 699; e-mail: eliseandmalcolm@btinternet.com

BTO Regional Representative
RR. Graham Pyatt, The Schoolhouse, Manor, Peebles EH45 9JN. 01721 740 319; e-mail: d.g.pyatt@btinternet.com

Club
SOC BORDERS BRANCH. (100). Graham Pyatt, The Schoolhouse, Manor, Peebles EH45 9JN. 01721 740 319; www.the-soc.org.uk
Meetings: 7.30pm, 2nd Monday of the month, George & Abbotsford Hotel, Melrose.

Ringing Group
BORDERS RG. (1991; 10). Dr T W Dougall, 38 Leamington Terrace, Edinburgh, EH10 4JL. (Office) 0131 344 2600

RSPB Members' Group
BORDERS. (1995; 94). John Marshall, 01896 850 564; e-mail: ncmandjrm@btinternet.com
Meetings: 7.30pm, 3rd Wednesday of the month, The Corn Exchange, Market Square, Melrose.

Wetland Bird Survey Organisers
BORDERS. Andrew Bramhall, 2 Abbotsferry Road, Tweedbank, Galashiels, Scottish Borders TD1 3RX; e-mail: andrew@atbramhall.go-plus.net

CAITHNESS

Bird Recorders
CAITHNESS. Sinclair Manson,
e-mail: sinclairmanson@btinternet.com

Bird Report
CAITHNESS BIRD REPORT (1983-97). Now incorporated
into *The Highland Bird Report,* from Mrs Lynda
Graham, 9 Burn Brae Terrace, Westhill, Inverness IV2
5HD. 01463 791 292.

BTO Regional Representative
CAITHNESS. Donald Omand, 9 Skiall, Shebster,
Thurso, Caithness KW14 7YD. 01847 811 403;
e-mail: achreamie@yahoo.co.uk

Club
SOC CAITHNESS BRANCH. (51). Angus McBay,
Schoolhouse, Weydale, Thurso, Caithness, KY14 8YJ.
01847 894 663; e-mail: angus.mcbay@btinternet.com
www.the-soc.org.uk

CLYDE

Bird Atlas/Avifauna
*A Guide to Birdwatching in the Clyde Area (2001)*by
Cliff Baister and Marin Osler (Scottish Ornithologists'
Club, Clyde branch).

Clyde Breeding Bird Atlas (working title). In
preparation.

Bird Recorder
CLYDE. Iain P Gibson, 8 Kenmure View, Howwood,
Johnstone, Renfrewshire, PA9 1DR. 01505 705 874;
e-mail: iaingibson.soc@btinternet.com

Bird Reports
CLYDE ISLANDS (ARRAN, BUTE & CUMBRAES). Bernard
Zonfrillo, 28 Brodie Road, Glasgow G21 3SB;
e-mail: b.zonfrillo@bio.gla.ac.uk

CLYDE BIRDS (1973-2005), From
Valerie Wilson, Flat 2/1, 12
Rawcliffe Gardens, Glasgow, G41
3DA.
e-mail: wilsonval@btinternet.com

Clyde Birds

Clyde Bird Report 2005
Clyde Islands Bird Report 2005

BTO Regional Representatives
LANARK, RENFREW, DUMBARTON.
Andy Winnington, 010475 528 841;
e-mail: andy.winnington@yahoo.com

Club
SOC CLYDE BRANCH. (300). Hayley Douglas, Top
Right, 35 Church Street, Lochwinnoch PA12 4AE.
07715 634 079. www.the-soc.org.uk

Ringing Groups
CLYDE RG. (1976; 22)I Livingstone, 57 Strathview
Road, Bellshill, Lanarkshire, ML4 2UY. 01698 749 844;
e-mail: iainlivcrg@googlemail.com

RSPB Members' Groups
GLASGOW. (1972;141). Alan Hill. 01389 730 696;
e-mail: alankarenhill@btinternet.com
www.rspb.org.uk/groups/glasgow
Meetings: 7.30pm, monthly on a Thursday (Sep-Apr),
Adelaides, 209 Bath Street, Glasgow G2 4HZ.

HAMILTON. (1976;90). Jim Lynch, 0141 583 1044;
e-mail: birder45a@yahoo.co.uk
www.baronshaugh.co.uk
Meetings: 7.30pm, 3rd Thursday of the month
(Sept-May), Watersports Centre, Motherwell (next to
Strathclyde Loch).

RENFREWSHIRE. (1986; 200). Iain Smeaton,
e-mail: RenfrewRSPB@hotmail.co.uk
www.rspb.org.uk/groups/renfrewshire
Meetings: 1st Friday of the month (Sep-Apr), The
McMaster Centre, 2a Donaldson Drive, Renfrew.

Wetland Bird Survey Organisers
CLYDE ESTUARY. John Clark, Laighfield, Station Road,
Shandon, Helensburgh G84 8NX;
e-mail: johnclark@jcmc.demon.co.uk

GLASGOW/RENFREWSHIRE/LANARKSHIRE/
DUNBARTONSHIRE. John Clark, Laighfield, Station
Road, Shandon, Helensburgh G84 8NX;
e-mail: johnclark@jcmc.demon.co.uk

BUTE. Ian Hopkins, 2 Eden Place, 179 High Street,
Rothesay, Isle of Bute PA20 9BS. 01700 504 042;
e-mail: ian@hopkins0079.freeserve.co.uk

DUMFRIES & GALLOWAY

Bird Recorders
DUMFRIES & GALLOWAY. Paul Collin, Gairland, Old
Edinburgh Road, Minnigaff, Newton Stewart, DG8 6PL.
01671 402 861; e-mail: pncollin@live.co.uk

Bird Report
DUMFRIES & GALLOWAY REGION BIRD REPORT (1985-),
From Peter Swan, 3 Castle View, Castle Douglas, DG7
1BG. 01556 502 144.

BTO Regional Representatives
DUMFRIES RR. Edmund Fellowes, 01387 262 094;
e-mail: edmundfellowes@aol.com

KIRKCUDBRIGHT RR and Atlas Co-ordinator. Andrew
Bielinski, 41 Main Street, St Johns Town of Dalry,
Castle Douglas, Kirkcudbright, DG7 3UP. 01644 430
418 (evening); e-mail: andrewb@bielinski.fsnet.co.uk

WIGTOWN RR. Geoff Sheppard, The Roddens,
Leswalt, Stranraer, Wigtownshire, DG9 0QR. 01776
870 685; e-mail: geoff.roddens@btinternet.com

Clubs
SOC DUMFRIES BRANCH. (1961; 105). Mrs Pat Abery,
East Daylesford, Colvend, Dalbeattie, Dumfries, DG5
4QA. 01556 630 483. www.the-soc.org.uk
Meetings: 7.30pm, 2nd Wednesday of the month
(Sept-Apr), Cumberland St Day Centre.

SCOTLAND

SOC STEWARTRY BRANCH. (1976; 80). Miss Joan Howie, 60 Main Street, St Johns Town of Dalry, Castle Douglas, Kirkcudbrightshire, DG7 3UW. 01644 430 226 www.the-soc.org.uk
Meetings: 7.30pm, usually 2nd Thursday of the month (Sep-Apr), Kells School, New Galloway.

SOC WEST GALLOWAY BRANCH. (1975; 50). Geoff Sheppard, The Roddens, Leswalt, Stranraer, Wigtownshire, DG9 0QR. 01776 870 685; e-mail: geoff.roddens@btinternet.com www.the-soc.org.uk
Meetings: 7.30pm, 2nd Tuesday of the month (Oct-Mar), Stranraer Library.

Ringing Group
NORTH SOLWAY RG. Geoff Sheppard, The Roddens, Leswalt, Stranraer, Wigtownshire, DG9 0QR. 01776 870 685; e-mail: geoff.roddens@btinternet.com

RSPB Members' Group
GALLOWAY. (1985;150). Cynthia Douglas, Midpark, Balmaclellan, Castle Douglas, DG7 3PX. 01644 420 605; e-mail: cynthia@cdouglas.plus.com www.rspb.org.uk/groups/galloway
Meetings: 7.30pm 3rd Tuesday in the month (Sep-Apr inc),Parish Church Hall, Queen Street, Castle Douglas.

Wetland Bird Survey Organisers
AUCHENCAIRN AND ORCHARDTON BAYS. Euan MacAlpine, Auchenshore, Auchencairn, Castle Douglas, Galloway DG7 1QZ. 01556 640 244; e-mail: js.eamm@sky.com

FLEET BAY. David Hawker. 01557 814 249; e-mail: hawker398@btinternet.com

LOCH RYAN. Paul Collin, Gairland, Old Edinburgh Road, Minnigaff, Newton Stewart DG8 6PL. 01671 402 861; e-mail: pncollin@live.co.uk

ROUGH FIRTH. Judy Baxter, Saltflats Cottage, Rockcliffe, Dalbeattie, DG5 4QQ. 01556 630 262; e-mail: Jbaxter@nts.org.uk

WIGTOWN BAY. Paul Collin, Gairland, Old Edinburgh Road, Minnigaff, Newton Stewart, DG8 6PL. 01671 402 861; e-mail: pncollin@live.co.uk

DUMFRIES AND GALLOWAY (other sites). Andy Riches, 07792 142 446; e-mail: slioch69@aol.com

SOLWAY ESTUARY - NORTH. Andy Riches, 07792 142 446; e-mail: slioch69@aol.com

FIFE

Bird Atlas/Avifauna
The Fife Bird Atlas 2003 by Norman Elkins, Jim Reid, Allan Brown, Derek Robertson & Anne-Marie Smout. Available from Allan W. Brown (FOAG), 61 Watts Gardens, Cupar, Fife KY15 4UG, 01334 656 804, e-mail: swans@allanwbrown.co.uk

Bird Recorders
FIFE REGION INC OFFSHORE ISLANDS (NORTH FORTH). Mr Malcolm Ware, 15a King Street, Inverkeithing, Fife, KY11 1NB; e-mail: malcolm.ware12@talktalk.net

ISLE OF MAY BIRD OBSERVATORY. Iain English, 19 Nethan Gate, Hamilton, S Lanarks, ML3 8NH; e-mail: i.english@talk21.com

Bird Reports
FIFE BIRD REPORT (1988-) (FIFE & KINROSS BR 1980-87), From Mr Malcolm Ware, 15a King Street, Inverkeithing, Fife, KY11 1NB; e-mail: malcolm.ware12@talktalk.net

ISLE OF MAY BIRD OBSERVATORY REPORT (1985-), From Iain English, 19 Nethan Gate, Hamilton, S Lanarks, ML3 8NH; e-mail: i.english@talk21.com

BTO Regional Representative
FIFE & KINROSS RR. Norman Elkins, 18 Scotstarvit View, Cupar, Fife, KY15 5DX. 01334 654 348; e-mail: jandnelkins@btinternet.com

Clubs
FIFE BIRD CLUB. (1985; 200). Mr Drew Crosbie (Membership Secretary), 14 Dunvegan Drive, Falkirk, Central Scotland FK2 7UG; www.fifebirdclub.org
Meetings: 7.30pm, (various evenings), Dean Park Hotel, Chapel Level, Kirkcaldy.

LOTHIANS AND FIFE SWAN & GOOSE STUDY GROUP. (1978; 12)Allan & Lyndesay Brown, 61 Watts Gardens, Cupar, Fife, KY15 4UG; e-mail: swans@allanwbrown.co.uk

SOC FIFE BRANCH. (1950;170). Karen Dick,South Lodge, St Michaels, St Andrews KY16 0DU. 01334 848 278; (M)7825 786 165; e-mail: fifesoc@sky.com www.the-soc.org.uk
Meetings: 7.30pm, 2nd Wednesday of the month (Sep-Apr), Venue details available at www.the-soc.org.uk/branch-meetings.htm#fife

Ringing Groups
ISLE OF MAY BIRD OBSERVATORY. David Grieve, 50 Main Street, Symington, Biggar, South Lanarkshire ML12 6LJ. 01899 309 176

TAY RG. Ms S Millar, Edenvale Cottage, 1 Lydox Cottages, Dairsie, Fife, KY15 4RN; e-mail: shirley@edenecology.co.uk

Wetland Bird Survey Organisers
FIFE (excluding estuaries). Grey Goose count organiser for Fife, Lothians and Borders. Allan Brown, 61 Watts Gardens, Cupar, Fife KY15 4UG; e-mail: swans@allanwbrown.co.uk

FORTH ESTUARY (North). Alastair Inglis, 5 Crowhill Road, Dalgety Bay, Fife KY11 5LJ; e-mail: aandjinglis@hotmail.com

SCOTLAND

EDEN ESTUARY. Norman Elkins, 18 Scotstarvit View, Cupar, Fife KY15 5DX. 01334 654 348; e-mail: jandnelkins@btinternet.com

TAY AND EDEN ESTUARIES. Norman Elkins, 18 Scotstarvit View, Cupar, Fife KY15 5DX. 01334 654 348; e-mail: jandnelkins@btinternet.com

Wildlife Hospital
SCOTTISH SPCA WILD LIFE REHABILITATION CENTRE. Middlebank Farm, Masterton Road, Dunfermline, Fife, KY11 8QN. 01383 412 520 All species. Open to visitors, groups and school parties. Illustrated talk on oiled bird cleaning and other aspects of wildlife rehabilitation available. Veterinary support.

FORTH

Bird Recorder
UPPER FORTH (Does not include parts of Stirling in Loch Lomondside/Clyde Basin). Chris Pendlebury, 3 Sinclair Street, Dunblane, FK5 0AH. 07798 711 134; e-mail: chrispendlebury@gmail.com

Bird Report
FORTH AREA BIRD REPORT (1975-) - enlarged report published annually in The Forth Naturalist and Historian, University of Stirling. From Dr Roy Sexton, Asst. Editor, Forth Naturalist and Historian, 22 Alexander Drive, Bridge of Allan, FK9 4QB.01786 833 409; e-mail: RoyGravedigger@AOL.com www.fnh.stir.ac.uk

BTO Regional Representative
CENTRAL RR. Neil Bielby, 56 Ochiltree, Dunblane, Perthshire, FK15 0DF. 01786 823 830; e-mail: n.bielby@sky.com

Club
SOC CENTRAL SCOTLAND BRANCH. (1968; 101). Mr RL Gooch, The Red House, Dollarfield, Dollar, Clacks FK14 7LX. 01259 742 326; www.the-soc.org.uk
Meetings: 7.30pm, 1st Thursday of the month (Sep-Apr), The Smith Art Gallery and Museum, Dumbarton Road, Stirling.

RSPB Members' Group
CENTRAL, FORTH VALLEY. (1995; 111). Jenni Fulton, 0790 153 8078; e-mail: jennifultonRSPB@yahoo.co.uk www.rspb.org.uk/groups/forthvalley
Meetings: 7.30pm, 3rd Thursday of the month (Sept-Apr), Hillpark Centre, Stirling.

Wetland Bird Survey Organiser
CENTRAL (excl Forth Estuary). Neil Bielby, 56 Ochiltree, Dunblane, Perthshire FK15 0DF. 01786 823 830; e-mail: n.bielby@sky.com

FORTH ESTUARY (Inner). Michael Bell, 48 Newton Crescent, Dunblane, Perthshire FK15 0DZ. 01786 822 153; e-mail: mvbell34@tiscali.co.uk

Coordinator for the Icelandic breeding goose counts (Pinkfeet & Greylag) for inner Forth, Forth Valley & Perthshire. Michael Bell, 48 Newton Crescent,

Dunblane, Perthshire FK15 0DZ. 01786 822 153; e-mail: mvbell34@tiscali.co.uk

HIGHLAND

Bird Atlas/Avifauna
The Birds of Sutherland by Alan Vittery (Colin Baxter Photography Ltd, 1997).

Birds of Skye by Andrew Currie. In preparation.

Bird Recorders
ROSS-Shire, INVERNESS-SHIRE, SUTHERLAND, BADENOCH & STRATHSPEY, LOCHABER, LOCHALSH and SKYE. Hugh Insley, 1 Drummond Place, Inverness,IV2 4JT. 01463 230 652; (M)07831 479 804; e-mail: hugh.insley@btinternet.com

Bird Reports
HIGHLAND BIRD REPORT (1991-). 2008 edition £9.50 inc p&p, from Alistair F McNee, Liathach, 4 Balnafettack Place, Inverness, IV3 8TQ01463 220 493; e-mail: aj.mcnee@care4free.net

BTO Regional Representatives & Regional Development Officers
INVERNESS & SPEYSIDE RR & RDO. Hugh Insley, 1 Drummond Place, Inverness,IV2 4JT. 01463 230 652; e-mail: hugh.insley@btinternet.com

RUM, EIGG, CANNA & MUCK RR & RDO. Bob Swann, 14 St Vincent Road, Tain, Ross-shire, IV19 1JR. 01862 894 329; e-mail: robert.swann@homecall.co.uk

ROSS-SHIRE RR. Simon Cohen, e-mail: saraandsimon@hotmail.com

SUTHERLAND. Position vacant.

SKYE. Position vacant.

Clubs
EAST SUTHERLAND BIRD GROUP. (1976; 120). Tony Mainwood, 13 Ben Bhraggie Drive, Golspie, Sutherland KW10 6SX. 01408 633 247; e-mail: tony.mainwood@btinternet.com
Meetings: 7.30pm, Last Monday of the month (Oct, Nov, Jan, Feb, Mar), Golspie Community Centre.

SOC HIGHLAND BRANCH. (1955; 151). Kathy Bonniface, Alt Dubh, North End, Tomatin, IV13 7YP. 01808 511 740; e-mail: kathybonniface@aol.com www.the-soc.org.uk
Meetings: 7.45pm, 1st Tuesday of the month (Sep-Mar), Culloden Library.

Ringing Groups
HIGHLAND RG. Bob Swann, 14 St Vincent Road, Tain, Ross-shire, IV19 1JR; e-mail: robert.swann@homecall.co.uk

RSPB Members' Group
HIGHLAND. (1987; 214). Doreen Manson, Muirton

275

SCOTLAND

Lodge, Urray, Muir of Ord, Ross-shire IV6. 01997 433 283; e-mail: john@jmanson2.wanadoo.co.uk
www.rspb.org.uk/groups/highland
Meetings: 7.30pm, last Thursday of the month (Sep-Apr), Kingsmill Hotel, Culcabock Road, Inverness.

Wetland Bird Survey Organisers
BADENOCH AND STRATHSPEY. Keith Duncan 01842 750 050; e-mail: webs@bto.org

LOCHABER. John Dye, e-mail: john.dye@virgin.net

SKYE & LOCHALSH. Bob McMillan, 11 Elgol, Nr Broadford, Isle of Skye IV49 9BL;
e-mail: bob@skye-birds.com

LOTHIAN

Bird Atlas/Avifauna
The Breeding Birds of South-east Scotland, a tetrad atlas 1988-1994 by R D Murray et al. (Scottish Ornithologists' Club, 1998).

Bird Recorder
Stephen Welch, 25 Douglas Road, Longniddry EH32 0LQ; 01875 852 802;(M) 07931 524 963;
e-mail: lothianrecorder@the-soc.org.uk

Bird Report
LOTHIAN BIRD REPORT (1979-), from the Lothian SOC Branch Secretary.

BTO Regional Representative
Alan Heavisides, 9 Addiston Crescent, Balerno, Edinburgh, EH14 7DB. 0131 449 3816;
e-mail: alanheavisides@yahoo.com

BTO Garden BirdWatch Ambassador
John Wilson; e-mail: jib4wilson@o2.co.uk

Clubs
EDINBURGH NATURAL HISTORY SOCIETY. (1869; 200). The Secretary, e-mail: enquiries@ edinburghnaturalhistorysociety.org.uk
www.edinburghnaturalhistorysociety.org.uk
Meetings: 7.30pm, 4th Wednesday of the month The Guide Hall, 33 Melville Street, Edinburgh.

LOTHIANS AND FIFE SWAN AND GOOSE STUDY GROUP. (1978; 12). Allan & Lyndesay Brown, 61 Watts Gardens, Cupar, Fife, KY15 4UG;
e-mail: swans@allanwbrown.co.uk

LOTHIAN SOC. (1936; 570). Doreen Main; Seatoller, Gullane, East Lothian EH31 2DH. 01620 844 532;
e-mail: doreen.main@yahoo.com www.the-soc.org.uk
Meetings: 7.30pm, 2nd Tuesday (Sep-Dec and Jan-Apr), Lounge 2, Meadowbank Sports Stadium - Oct & Mar), Waterston House, Aberlady.

Ringing Group
LOTHIAN RG. Mr M Cubitt, 12 Burgh Mills Lane, Linlithgow,West Lothian EH49 7TA.

RSPB Members' Group
EDINBURGH. (1974;480). Rosie Filipiak;
e-mail: rosie.birds1@gmail.com
www.rspb.org.uk/groups/edinburgh/
Meetings: 7.30pm, 3rd Tuesday or Wednesday of the month (Sep-Apr), Napier University, Craiglockhart Campus, Edinburgh. Outdoor meetings held year round (check group website for details).

Wetland Bird Survey Organisers
FORTH ESTUARY (Outer South). Duncan Priddle, 19c High Street, Haddington, East Lothian EH41 3ES. 01620 827 459; e-mail: dpriddle@eastlothian.gov.uk

LOTHIAN (excl estuaries). Joan Wilcox, 18 Howdenhall Gardens, Edinburgh, Midlothian EH16 6UN. 0131 6648 893; e-mail: webs@bto.org

TYNINGHAME ESTUARY. Mr R Anderson, John Muir Country Park, East Lothian Countryside Ranger Service, Block C, Brewery Park, Haddington EH41 3HA. 01620 827 318;
e-mail: randerson@eastlothian.gov.uk

MORAY & NAIRN

Bird Atlas/Avifauna
The Birds of Moray and Nairn by Martin Cook (Mercat Press, 1992.

Bird Recorder
NAIRN. Martin J H Cook, Rowanbrae, Clochan, Buckie, Banffshire, AB56 5EQ. 01542 850 296;
e-mail: martin.cook99@btinternet.com

MORAY. Martin J H Cook, Rowanbrae, Clochan, Buckie, Banffshire, AB56 5EQ. 01542 850 296;
e-mail: martin.cook99@btinternet.com

Bird Reports
BIRDS IN MORAY AND NAIRN (1988-), From the Moray & Nairn Recorder, 01542 850 296;
e-mail: martin.cook99@btinternet.com

MORAY & NAIRN BIRD REPORT (1985-1998), From The Moray & Nairn Recorder, 01542 850 296;
 e-mail: martin.cook99@btinternet.com

BTO Regional Representatives
NAIRN RR. Bob Proctor, 78 Marleon Field, Elgin, Moray, IV30 4GE;
e-mail: bobandlouise@proctor8246.fsnet.co.uk

MORAY RR. Bob Proctor, 78 Marleon Field, Elgin, Moray, IV30 4GE;
e-mail: bobandlouise@proctor8246.fsnet.co.uk

Wetland Bird Survey Organisers
LOSSIE ESTUARY. Bob Proctor, 78 Marleon Field, Silvercrest, Bishopmill, Elgin, IV30 4GE;
e-mail: bobandlouise@proctor8246.fsnet.co.uk

MORAY & NAIRN (Inland). David Law,
e-mail: jdavidlaw@btinternet.com

276

MORAY BASIN COAST. Bob Swann, 14 St Vincent Road, Tain, Ross-Shire IV19 1JR.
e-mail: robert.swann@homecall.co.uk

NORTH EAST SCOTLAND

Bird Atlas/Avifauna
The Birds of North East Scotland by S T Buckland, M V Bell & N Picozzi (North East Scotland Bird Club, 1990).

The Breeding Birds of North-East Scotland: Including part of the Cairngorms National Park, by Ian Francis and Martin Cook (SOC, 2011).

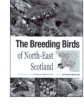

The Breeding Birds of North-East Scotland

Bird Recorder
NORTH-EAST SCOTLAND. Hywel Maggs, 4 Merlin Terrace, Newburgh, Ellon, Aberdeenshire AB41 6FA. 01358 788 106; e-mail: hywelmaggs@hotmail.com

Bird Reports
NORTH-EAST SCOTLAND BIRD REPORT (1974-), from Dave Gill, Drakemyre Croft, Cairnorrie, Methlick, Aberdeenshire, AB41 7JN. 01651 806 252; e-mail: david@gilldavid1.orangehome.co.uk

NORTH SEA BIRD CLUB ANNUAL REPORT (1979-), From Andrew Thorpe, Ocean Laboratory and Centre for Ecology, Aberdeen University, Newburgh, Ellon, Aberdeenshire AB41 6AA. 01224 274 428; e-mail: nsbc@abdn.ac.uk

BTO Regional Representatives
ABERDEEN. Paul Doyle, 01358 751 384; e-mail: paul@wildlifeweb.co.uk

KINCARDINE & DEESIDE. Graham Cooper, Westbank, Beltie Road, Torphins, Banchory, Aberdeen, AB31 4JT. 01339 882 706; e-mail: grm.cooper@btinternet.com

Clubs
SOC GRAMPIAN BRANCH. (1956; 110). Hugh Addlesee, 31 Ashtree Road, Banchory, Aberdeen, AB31 5JB. 01330 829 949; www.the-soc.org.uk
e-mail: grampian.secretary@the-soc.org.uk
Meetings: 7.30pm, usually 1st Monday of the month (Sep-Apr), Sportsmans's Club, 11 Queens Road, Aberdeen.

Ringing Groups
GRAMPIAN RG. R Duncan, 86 Broadfold Drive, Bridge of Don, Aberdeen, AB23 8PP;
e-mail: Raymond@waxwing.fsnet.co.uk

RSPB Members' Group
ABERDEEN & DISTRICT. (1975; 210). Mark Sullivan, 29 Earlswells Rd, Cults,AB15 9NY. 01224 861 446; e-mail: geolbird_abz@btinternet.com
www.rspb.org.uk/groups/aberdeen

Meetings: 7.30pm, monthly in the winter, Lecture Theatre, Zoology Dept, Tillydrone Av, Aberdeen. Two birding trips monthly throughout the year.

Wildlife Hospital
GRAMPIAN WILDLIFE REHABILITATION TRUST. 40 High Street, New Deer, Turriff, Aberdeenshire, AB53 6SX. 01771 644 489; (M)07803 235 383; e-mail: laurence.brain@btconnect.com
Veterinary surgeon. Access to full practice facilities. Will care for all species of birds.

ORKNEY

Bird Atlas/Avifauna
The Birds of Orkney by CJ Booth et al (The Orkney Press, 1984).

Bird Recorder
Mr EJ Williams, Fairholm, Finstown, Orkney, KW17 2EQ; e-mail: jim@geniefea.freeserve.co.uk

Bird Report
ORKNEY BIRD REPORT (inc North Ronaldsay Bird Report) (1974-), from Mr EJ Williams, Fairholm, Finstown, Orkney, KW17 2EQ;
e-mail: jim@geniefea.freeserve.co.uk

BTO Regional Representative
Colin Corse, Garrisdale, Lynn Park, Kirkwall, Orkney, KW15 1SL. 01856 874 484;
e-mail: ccorse@btinternet.com

Club
SOC ORKNEY BRANCH. (1993; 15). Colin Corse, Garrisdale, Lynnpark Road, Kirkwall, Orkney, KW15 1SL. 01856 874 484; www.the-soc.org.uk

Ringing Groups
NORTH RONALDSAY BIRD OBSERVATORY. Ms A E Duncan, Twingness, North Ronaldsay, Orkney KW17 2BE. e-mail: alison@nrbo.prestel.co.uk
www.nrbo.co.uk

ORKNEY RG. Colin Corse, Garrisdale, Lynn Park, Kirkwall, Orkney, KW15 1SL. 01856 874 484; e-mail: ccorse@btinternet.com

SULE SKERRY RG. Dave Budworth, 121 Wood Lane, Newhall, Swadlincote, Derbys, DE11 0LX. 01283 215 188.

RSPB Members' Group
ORKNEY. (1985;300 in catchment area). Dick Matson 01856 751 426; e-mail: p.wilson410@btinternet.com
Meetings: Meetings advertised in newsletter and local press, held at St Magnus Centre, Kirkwall.

Wetland Bird Survey Organiser
ORKNEY. Eric Meek, Smyril, Stenness, Stromness, Orkney KW16 3JX. 01856 850 176;
e-mail: eric.meek@rspb.org.uk

SCOTLAND

OUTER HEBRIDES

Bird Recorder
OUTER HEBRIDES AND WESTERN ISLES. Brian Rabbits, 6 Carinish, Isle of North Uist HS6 5HL. 01876 580 328; e-mail: rabbitts@hebrides.net

Bird Report
OUTER HEBRIDES BIRD REPORT (1989-91 and 1997-2007), From The Recorder. 6 Carinish, Isle of North Uist HS6 5HL. 01876 580 328; e-mail: rabbitts@hebrides.net

BTO Regional Representatives & Regional Development Officer
BENBECULA & THE UISTS RR & RDO. Yvonne Benting, 07501 332 803; e-mail: uistbto@gmail.com

LEWIS & HARRIS RR. Chris Reynolds, 11 Reef, Isle of Lewis, HS2 9HU. 01851 672 376; e-mail: cmreynolds@btinternet.com

Ringing Group
SHIANTS AUK RG. Mr J.J. Lennon, The Dovecote,Main Street,Flintham,Newark NG23 5LA. 01636 525 963. Group Secretary, Jim Lennon, The Dovecote, Main Street, Flintham, Newark NG23 5LA. 01636 525 963.

Wetland Bird Survey Organiser
UISTS AND BENBECULA. Yvonne Benting, Suthainn, Askernish,Isle of South Uist HS8 5SY07501 332 803e-mail: uistbto@gmail.com

ISLAY, JURA AND COLONSAY. John Armitage, Airigh Sgallaidh, Portnahaven, Isle of Islay PA47 7SZ01496 860 396; e-mail: jsa@ornquest.plus.com www.islaybirder.blogspot.com/

PERTH & KINROSS

Bird Recorder
PERTH & KINROSS. Scott Paterson, 12 Ochil View, Kinross, KY13 8TN. 01577 864 248, e-mail: scottpaterson12@yahoo.co.uk

Bird Report
PERTH & KINROSS BIRD REPORT (1974-) - 2009 and 2010 report in preparation, from the Recorder. 12 Ochil View, Kinross, KY13 8TN. 01577 864 248, e-mail: scottpaterson12@yahoo.co.uk

BTO Regional Representative
PERTHSHIRE RR. Richard Paul. 01882 632 212; e-mail: richard@rannoch.net

Clubs
PERTHSHIRE SOCIETY OF NATURAL SCIENCE (Ornithological Section). (1964; 25). Miss Esther Taylor, 23 Verena Terrace, Perth PH2 0BZ. 01738 621 986; e-mail: birdsatpsns@btinternet.com www.psns.org.uk
Meetings: 7.30pm, Wednesdays monthly (Oct-Mar), Perth Museum. Summer outings.

Wetland Bird Survey Organiser
LOCH LEVEN. Jeremy Squire, c/o Scottish Natural Heritage, The Pier, Kinross, KY13 8UF; e-mail: jeremy.squire@snh.gov.uk

PERTH AND KINROSS (INLAND). Michael Bell; e-mail: mvbell34@tiscali.co.uk

PERTHSHIRE. Ron Youngman, Blairchroisk Cottage, Ballinluig, Pitlochry, Perthshire PH9 0NE; e-mail: blairchroisk@aol.com

TAY AND EDEN ESTUARIES. Norman Elkins, 18 Scotstarvit View, Cupar, Fife KY15 5DX. 01334 654 348; e-mail: jandnelkins@btinternet.com

SHETLAND

Bird Recorders
FAIR ISLE. David Parnaby, e-mail: fibo@btconnect.com

SHETLAND. Mark Chapman, 55 Leaside, Firth, Mossbank, ShetlandZE2 9TF. 01806 242 401; e-mail: msc.1@btinternet.com

Bird Reports
FAIR ISLE BIRD OBSERVATORY REPORT (1949-), From Scottish Ornithologists' Club, 21 Regent Terrace, Edinburgh, EH7 5BT. 0131 556 6042

SHETLAND BIRD REPORT (1969-) £10 inc p&p, no pre 1973 available, From Rob Fray, Shetland Bird Club, Sunnydell, Virkie, Shetland ZE3 9JS; e-mail: robfray@btinternet.com £10 plus P&P.

BTO Regional Representative
RR and RDO. Dave Okill, Heilinabretta, Trondra, Shetland, ZE1 0XL. 01595 880 450; e-mail: david@auroradesign.plus.com

Club
SHETLAND BIRD CLUB. (1973; 200). Helen Moncrieff, Scholland, Virkie, Shetland ZE3 9JL. 01950 460 249; e-mail: helen. moncrieff@btinternet.com www.nature-shetland.co.uk

Ringing Groups
FAIR ISLE BIRD OBSERVATORY. Deryk Shaw, Bird Observatory, Fair Isle, Shetland, ZE2 9JU; e-mail: fairisle.birdobs@zetnet.com

SHETLAND RG. Dave Okill, Heilinabretta, Trondra, Shetland, ZE1 0XL. 01595 880 450.

Wetland Bird Survey Organiser
SHETLAND. Paul Harvey, Shetland Biological Records Centre, Shetland Amenity Trust, Garthspool, Lerwick, Shetland, ZE1 0NY. (Day)01595 694 688; e-mail: sbrc@shetlandamenity.org

WALES

Bird Report
See Welsh Ornithological Society in National Directory

BTO Honorary Wales Officer
BTO WALES OFFICER. John Lloyd, Cynghordy Hall, Cynghordy, Llandovery, Carms SA20 0LN; e-mail: the_lloyds@dsl.pipex.com

Club
See Welsh Ornithological Society in National Directory.

EAST WALES

Bird Atlas/Avifauna
The Birds of Gwent by Venables et al, published by Helm on behalf of Gwent Ornithological Society.

The Birds of Radnorshire in preparation, due 2012

The Gwent Atlas of Breeding Birds by Tyler, Lewis, Venables & Walton (Gwent Ornithological Society, 1987).

Bird Recorders
BRECONSHIRE. Andrew King, Heddfan, Pennorth, Brecon, Powys LD3 7EX. 01874 658 351; e-mail: andrew.king53@virgin.net

GWENT. Chris Jones, 22 Walnut Drive, Caerleon, Newport, South Wales NP18 3SB; e-mail: countyrecorder@gwentbirds.org.uk

MONTGOMERYSHIRE. Paul Leafe; e-mail: paul_leafe@hotmail.co.uk

RADNORSHIRE (VC43). Pete Jennings, Park View, Staunton-on-Arrow, Leominster HR6 9HT. 01544 388 905; e-mail: radnorshirebirds@hotmail.com

Bird Reports
BRECONSHIRE BIRDS (1962-), from Brecknock Wildlife Trust.

GWENT BIRD REPORT (1964-), from Jerry Lewis, Y Bwthyn Gwyn, Coldbrook, Abergavenny, Monmouthshire NP7 9TD. (H)01873 855 091; (W)01633 644 856.

MONTGOMERYSHIRE BIRD REPORT (1981-82-), from Montgomeryshire Wildlife Trust.

BTO Regional Representatives
BRECKNOCK RR. John Lloyd, Cynghordy Hall, Cynghordy, Llandovery, Carms, SA20 0LN. 01550 750 202; e-mail: the_lloyds@dsl.pipex.com

GWENT RR. Jerry Lewis, Y Bwthyn Gwyn, Coldbrook, Abergavenny, Monmouthshire NP7 9TD. 01873 855 091; e-mail: jerryLewis@monmouthshire.gov.uk

MONTGOMERY RR. Jane Kelsall, 01970 832 625; e-mail: janekelsall@phonecoop.coop

RADNORSHIRE RR. Carlton Parry, 01597 824 050; e-mail: cj.parry@tiscali.co.uk

Clubs
THE GWENT ORNITHOLOGICAL SOCIETY. Year formed and number of members: (1964; 420). T J Russell. 01600 716 266; e-mail: secretary@ GwentBirds.org.uk
www.gwentbirds.org.uk
Meetings: 7.30pm, alternate Saturdays (Sept-Apr), Goytre Village Hall.

MONTGOMERYSHIRE WILDLIFE TRUST BIRD GROUP. Year formed and number of members: (1997; 110). A M Puzey, Four Seasons, Arddleen, Llanymynech, Powys SY22 6RU. 01938 590 578.
www.montwt.co.uk/bird_group.html
Meetings: 7.30pm, 3rd Wednesday of the month (Jan-Mar) and (Sep-Dec), Welshpool Methodist Hall.

RADNORSHIRE BIRD GROUP. Year formed and number of members: Pete Jennings, Park View, Staunton-on-Arrow, Leominster HR6 9HT. 01544 388 905; e-mail: radnorshirebirds@hotmail.com
Co-ordinates bird recording and surveys in the county through the county recorder

Ringing Groups
GOLDCLIFF RG. Mr Richard M Clarke. e-mail: chykembro2@aol.com

LLANGORSE RG. (1987; 15). Jerry Lewis, Y Bwthyn Gwyn, Coldbrook, Abergavenny, Monmouthshire NP7 9TD. H:01873 855 091; W:01633 644 856.

Wetland Bird Survey Organisers
RADNORSHIRE. Pete Jennings, Park View, Staunton-on-Arrow, Leominster HR6 9HT. 01544 388 905; e-mail: radnorshirebirds@hotmail.com

BRECONSHIRE. Andrew King, Heddfan, Pennorth, Brecon LD3 7EX. e-mail: andrew.king53@virgin.net

MONTGOMERYSHIRE. Jane Kelsall. 01970 872 019; e-mail:janekelsall@phonecoop.coop

Wildlife Trusts
BRECKNOCK WILDLIFE TRUST. Year formed and number of members: (1963; 650). Lion House, Bethel Square, Brecon, Powys LD3 7AY. 01874 625 708; e-mail: enquiries@brecknockwildlifetrust.org.uk
www.brecknockwildlifetrust.org.uk

GWENT WILDLIFE TRUST. Year formed and number of members: (1963; 9,950). Seddon House, Dingestow, Monmouth, NP25 4DY. 01600 740 600; e-mail: info@gwentwildlife.org
www.gwentwildlife.org

WALES

MONTGOMERYSHIRE WILDLIFE TRUST. Year formed and number of members: (1982; 1000). 42 Broad Street, Welshpool, Powys, SY21 7RR. 01938 555 654; e-mail: info@montwt.co.uk www.montwt.co.uk

RADNORSHIRE WILDLIFE TRUST. Year formed and number of members: (1987; 878). Warwick House, High Street, Llandrindod Wells, Powys LD1 6AG. 01597 823 298; e-mail:info@rwtwales.org www.radnorshirewildlifetrust.org.uk

NORTH WALES

Bird Atlas/Avifauna
The Birds of Caernarfonshire by John Barnes (1998, from Lionel Pilling, 51 Brighton Close, Rhyl LL18 3HL).

Bird Recorders
ANGLESEY. Stephen Culley, 22 Cae Derwydd, Cemaes Bay, Anglesey, LL67 0LP. 01407 710 542; e-mail: SteCul10@aol.com

CAERNARFONSHIRE. John Barnes, Fach Goch, Waunfawr, Caernarfon, LL55 4YS. 01286 650 362.

DENBIGHSHIRE & FLINTSHIRE. Ian Spence, 43 Blackbrook, Sychdyn, Mold, Flintshire CH7 6LT. 01352 750118; e-mail: ianspence.cr@btinternet.com www.cbrg.org.uk

MEIRIONNYDD. Jim Dustow, Lake Vyrnwy/ Llyn Efyrnwy RSPB, Oswestry, Shropshire SY10 OLZ; e-mail: Jim.Dustow@rspb.org.uk

Bird Reports
BARDSEY BIRD OBSERVATORY ANNUAL REPORT, from the Warden, see Reserves.

CAMBRIAN BIRD REPORT (sometime Gwynedd Bird Report) (1953-), from Geoff Gibbs. 01248 681 936; e-mail: geoffkate.gibbs@care4free.net www.welshos.org.uk/cambrian/

NORTH-EAST WALES BIRD REPORT (2004-), formerly CLWYD BIRD REPORT (2002-2003), from Ian M Spence, 43 Blackbrook, Sychdyn, Mold, Flintshire CH7 6LT. 01352 750 118; e-mail: ianspence.cr@btinternet.com www.cbrg.org.uk

MEIRIONNYDD BIRD REPORT Published in Cambrian Bird Report (above).

WREXHAM BIRDWATCHERS' SOCIETY ANNUAL REPORT (1982-), from the Secretary, Wrexham Birdwatchers' Society.

BTO Regional Representatives
ANGLESEY RR. Tony White. 01407 710 137; e-mail: wylfor@treg5360.freeserve.co.uk

CAERNARFON RR. Geoff Gibbs. 01248 681 936; e-mail: geoffkate.gibbs@care4free.net

CLWYD EAST RR. Dr Anne Brenchley, Ty'r Fawnog, 43

Black Brook, Sychdyn, Mold, Flints CH7 6LT. 01352 750 118; e-mail: anne.brenchley@btinternet.com

CLWYD WEST RR. Mel ab Owain, 31 Coed Bedw, Abergele, Conwy, LL22 7EH. 01745 826 528; e-mail: melabowain@btinternet.com

MEIRIONNYDD RR. David Anning. 01654 761 481; e-mail: anning.ecology@tiscali.co.uk

BTO Garden BirdWatch Ambassadors
David Lee; e-mail: oldfield51@btinternet.com

Clubs
BANGOR BIRD GROUP. Year formed and number of members: (1947; 100). Jane Prosser, 15 Victoria Street, Bangor, Gwynedd LL57 2HD. 01248 364 632. **Meetings:** 7.30pm every Wednesday, Semester terms, Bramble Building, University of Bangor.

CAMBRIAN ORNITHOLOGICAL SOCIETY. Year formed and number of members: (1952; 190). Barry Jones, Hon. Secretary, 24 Tan y Bryn Road, Llandudno LL30 1UU. 01492 868 467; e-mail: barrypaneuro@aol.co.uk www.welshos.org.uk/cambrian/ **Meetings:** 7.30pm, 1st Friday of the month, Pensychnant Centre, Sychnant Pass.

CLWYD BIRD RECORDING GROUP (committee that produces the Bird Report). Julie Rogers, Hon. Secretary, e-mail: julierogers123@gmail.com www.cbrg.org.uk

CLWYD ORNITHOLOGICAL SOCIETY. Year formed and number of members: (1956; 45). Ms J Irving, 45, Plas Uchaf Avenue, Prestatyn LL19 9NR, 01745 854 132; e-mail: jacqui970irving@btinternet.com **Meetings:** 7.30pm (Sep-Apr), Farmers Arms, Waen, St. Asaph.

DEE ESTUARY CONSERVATION GROUP. Year formed and number of members: (1973; 25 grps). Richard Smith, Secretary, e-mail: decg@deeestuary.co.uk www.deeestuary.co.uk/decg.htm

DEESIDE NATURALISTS' SOCIETY. Year formed and number of members: (1973; 1,000). The Secretary, e-mail: secretary@deesidenaturalists.org.uk www.deesidenaturalists.org.uk

WREXHAM BIRDWATCHERS' SOCIETY. Year formed and number of members: (1974; 90). Miss Marian Williams, 10 Lake View, Gresford, Wrexham, Clwyd LL12 8PU. 01978 854 633. **Meetings:** 7.30pm, 1st Friday of the month (Sep-Apr), Gresford Memorial Hall, Gresford.

Ringing Groups
BARDSEY BIRD OBSERVATORY. Steven Stansfield, Bardsey Island, off Aberdaron, Pwllheli, Gwynedd LL53 8DE. 07855 264 151; e-mail: warden@bbfo.org.uk

WALES

CHESHIRE SWAN GROUP. David Cookson, 01270 567 526; e-mail:Cheshireswans@aol.com www.record-lrc.co.uk (then follow link to Cheshire Swans Group).
MERSEYSIDE RG. Bob Harris, 3 Mossleigh, Whixall, Whitchurch, Shropshire SY13 2SA. Work 0151 706 4311; e-mail: harris@liv.ac.uk

SCAN RG. Dr D. Moss. e-mail: dorian@dorianmoss.com

RSPB Local Group
NORTH WALES. Year formed and number of members: (1986; 80). John Beagan, 01492 531 409 (answerphone); e-mail: colwynbooks@waitrose.com www.rspb.org.uk/groups/northwales
Meetings: 7.30pm, 3rd Friday of the month (Sep-Apr), St Davids Church Hall, Penrhyn Bay, Llandudno, Gwynedd, LL30 3EJ.

Wetland Bird Survey Organisers
ANGLESEY (other sites). Ian Sims, RSPB Malltraeth Marsh, Tai'r Gors, Pentre Berw, Gaerwen, Anglesey, LL60 6LB; e-mail: ian.sims@rspb.org.uk

CAERNARFONSHIRE. Rhion Pritchard, Pant Afonig, Hafod Lane, Bangor, Gwynedd LL57 4BU; e-mail: rhion678pritchard@btinternet.com

CLWYD (Coastal and inland). Position vacant.

ARTRO/MAWDDACH/TRAETH BACH/DYSYNNI ESTUARY. Jim Dustow, Lake Vyrnwy/ Llyn Efyrnwy RSPB, Oswestry, Shropshire SY10 OLZ; e-mail: Jim.Dustow@rspb.org.uk

MEIRIONNYDD (other sites). Trefor Owen. 01842 750 050; e-mail: info@bto.org

DEE ESTUARY. Colin Wells, Burton Point Farm, Station Road, Burton, Nr Neston, South Wirral CH64 5SB. 0151 336 7681.

FORYD BAY. Simon Hugheston-Roberts; e-mail: sm.roberts@ccw.gov.uk

Wildlife Trust
NORTH WALES WILDLIFE TRUST. Year formed and number of members: (1963; 6,450). 376 High Street, Bangor, Gwynedd, LL57 1YE. 01248 351 541; e-mail: nwwt@wildlifetrustswales.org www.northwaleswildlifetrust.org.uk

SOUTH WALES

Bird Atlas/Avifauna
An Atlas of Breeding Birds in West Glamorgan by David M Hanford et al (Gower Ornithological Society, 1992).

Birds of Glamorgan by Clive Hurford and Peter Lansdown (Published by the authors, c/o National Museum of Wales, Cardiff, 1995)

Bird Recorders
GLAMORGAN (EAST). David RW Gilmore, 116, Donald Street, Roath, Cardiff, Glamorgan CF24 4TN. 7779 176

766; e-mail: d.gilmore2@ntlworld.com

GOWER (WEST GLAMORGAN). Robert Taylor, 285 Llangyfelach Road, Brynhyfryd, Swansea, SA5 9LB. 01792 464 780; (M) 07970 567 007; e-mail: rob@birding.freeserve.co.uk

Bird Reports
EAST GLAMORGAN BIRD REPORT (title varies 1963-95) 1996-2010. 2011 should be published by end of 2012, from Mr John D Wilson, 122 Westbourne Road, Penarth, Vale of Glamorgan, CF64 3HH. 029 2033 9424; e-mail: john.wilson@glamorganbirds.org.uk www.glamorganbirds.org.uk

GOWER BIRDS (1965-) - covers Swansea, Neath and Port Talbot counties, from Barry Stewart, 36 Pencaecrwn Road, Gorseinon, Swansea SA4 4FU; e-mail: gowerbirdsf@hotmail.co.uk www.gowerbirds.org.uk

BTO Regional Representatives
EAST GLAMORGAN (former Mid & South Glam) RR. Wayne Morris, 8 Hughes Street, Penygraig, Tonypandy, Rhondda Cynon Taf CF40 1LX. 01443 430 284; e-mail: eastglambto@gmail.com http://eastglambto.wordpress.com

GLAMORGAN (WEST) RR. Alistair Flannagan, 27 Llys Dol, Morriston, Swansea SA6 6LD. 01792 537 439 ; e-mail: alastair.flannagan@ntlworld.com

BTO Garden BirdWatch Ambassadors
Mick Bailey; e-mail: mick@mickbailey.fsnet.co.uk
Amanda Skull; e-mail: gbw@hiafi.co.uk

Clubs
CARDIFF NATURALISTS' SOCIETY. Year formed and number of members: (1867; 200). Stephen R Howe, National Museum Wales, Cathays Park,CardiffCF10 3NP. 02920 573 363; www.cardiffnaturalists.org.uk e-mail: steve.howe@museumwales.ac.uk
Meetings: 7.30pm, various evenings, Cardiff Metropolitan University, Llandaff Campus, Western Avenue, Cardiff.

GLAMORGAN BIRD CLUB. Year formed and number of members: (1990; 300). Alan Rosney, 10 Parc-y-Nant, Nantgarw, CF15 7TJ. 01443 841 555; e-mail: alan.rosney@glamorganbirds.org.uk www.glamorganbirds.org.uk
Meetings: 7.30pm, 2nd Tuesday of winter months, Kenfig Reserve Centre.

GOWER ORNITHOLOGICAL SOCIETY. Year formed and number of members: (1956; 120). Peter Douglas-Jones, 28 Brynfield Road, Langland, Swansea, SA3 4SX. 01792 360 287; e-mail: peter.douglas-jones@ glamorganbirds.org.uk www.glamorganbirds.org.uk
Meetings: 7.15pm, last Friday of the month (Sep-Mar), The Environment Centre, Pier Street, Swansea.

WALES

Ringing Groups

FLAT HOLM RG. Brian Bailey, Tamarisk House, Wards Court, Frampton-on-Severn, Glos, GL2 7DY; e-mail: brian.bailey@sandbservices.eclipse.co.uk

KENFIG RG. Mr D.G. Carrington, Kenfig NNR, Ton Kenfig, Bridgend, CF33 4PT. 01656 743 386; (M) 07779 978 738; e-mail: david.carrington@bridgend.gov.uk; kenfignnr.blogspot.com; www.bridgendcountryside.com

RSPB Local Groups

CARDIFF & DISTRICT. Year formed and number of members: (1973:). Huw Moody-Jones . 01446 760 757; e-mail: huwmoodyjones@hotmail.com www.RSPB.org.uk/groups/cardiff
Meetings: 7.30pm, various Fridays (Sept-May), Llandaff Parish Hall, Llandaff, Cardiff.

WEST GLAMORGAN. Year formed and number of members: (1985; 346). Maggie Cornelius. 01792 229 244; e-mail: RSPBwglamgrp@googlemail.com www.rspb.org.uk/groups/westglamorgan
Meetings: 7.30pm, Environment Centre, Pier Street, Swansea, SA1 1RY

Wetland Bird Survey Organisers

EAST GLAMORGAN . Daniel Jenkins-Jones, 18 St. Margarets Road, Whitchurch, Cardiff, South Glamorgan CF14 7AA. (H)0292 062 1394; e-mail: jenkinsjones@btinternet.com

SEVERN ESTUARY. Niall Burton, c/o BTO, The Nunnery, Thetford, Norfolk, IP24 2PU. 01842 750 050; e-mail: niall.burton@bto.org

WEST GLAMORGAN. Alistair Flannagan, 01792 459 287; 01792 537 439; e-mail: alastair.flannagan@ntlworld.com

Wildlife Hospital

GOWER BIRD HOSPITAL. Karen Kingsnorth and Simon Allen, Valetta, Sandy Lane, Pennard, Swansea, SA3 2EW. 01792 371 630;

e-mail: admin@ gowerbirdhospital.org.uk www.gowerbirdhospital.org.uk All species of wild birds, also hedgehogs and small mammals. Prior phone call essential. Gower Bird Hospital cares for sick, injured and orphaned wild birds and animals with the sole intention of returning them to the wild. Post release radio tracking projects, ringing scheme. Contact us for more information.

Wildlife Trust

WILDLIFE TRUST OF SOUTH AND WEST WALES. Year formed and number of members: (2002; 4,000). Nature Centre, Parc Slip, Fountain Road, Tondu, Bridgend CF32 0EH. 01656 724 100; fax 01656 726 980; e-mail: info@welshwildlife.org www.welshwildlife.org

WEST WALES

Bird Atlas/Avifauna

Birds of Ceredigion by Hywel Roderick and Peter Davis (2010).

The Birds of Carmarthenshire by John Lloyd (in preparation)

Birds of Pembrokeshire by Jack Donovan and Graham Rees (Dyfed Wildlife Trust, 1994).

Bird Recorders

CARMARTHENSHIRE. Owen Harris, 5 William Terrace, Burry Port, Carmarthenshire SA16 0PG; e-mail: Owenharris@aol.com

CEREDIGION. Russell Jones, Bron y Gan, Talybont, Ceredigion, SY24 5ER. 07753 774 891; e-mail: russell.jones@rspb.org.uk

PEMBROKESHIRE 2. Stephen Berry, Ty-Cameron,, Dwrbach, Jordanston, Fishguard, Pembrokeshire SA65 9RR. 01348 875 604; (M)07772 869 730; e-mail: stephen.berry16@btinternet.com

PEMBROKESHIRE 2. Jon Green, Crud Yr Awel, Bowls Road, Blaenporth, Ceredigion SA43 2AR. 01239 811 561; e-mail: jonrg@tiscali.co.uk

Bird Reports

CARMARTHENSHIRE BIRD REPORT (1982-) £6.80 by post or £6.30 online. Available online at www.carmarthenshirebirds.co.uk or from Wendell Thomas, 48 Glebe Road, Loughor, Swansea, SA4 6QD

CEREDIGION BIRD REPORT (biennial 1982-87; annual 1988-2010) - £7 inc postage, cheques payable to South and West Wildlife Trust, from John Davis, Pantllidiart, Tristant, ABERYSTWYTH, SY23 4RQ

PEMBROKESHIRE BIRD REPORT (1981-), from Ms Barbara Priest, The Pines, Templeton, Pembs, SA67 8RT. e-mail: bpriest175@btinternet.com

BTO Regional Representatives

CARDIGAN RR. Moira Convery, 41 Danycoed, Aberystwyth, SY23 2HD. 01970 612 998; e-mail: moira.convery@gmail.com

CARMARTHEN RR. Terry Wells, 01267 238 836; e-mail: bto@twells.me.uk

PEMBROKE RR. Bob and Annie, 1 Rushmoor, Martletwy, Narberth,Pembrokeshire SA67 8BB. 01834 891 667; e-mail: rushmoor1@tiscali.co.uk

Clubs

CARMARTHENSHIRE BIRD CLUB. Year formed and number of members: (2003; 120).Owen Harris, 5

WALES

William Terrace, Burry Port, Carmarthenshire SA16 0PG. e-mail: Owenharris@aol.com www.carmarthenshirebirds.co.uk
Meetings: Winter evenings at WWT Penclacwydd (check website for details).

PEMBROKESHIRE BIRD GROUP. Year formed and number of members: (1993; 60). Ms Barbara Priest, The Pines, Templeton, Pembs, SA67 8RT. 01834 860 175; http://pembrokeshirebirdgroup.blogspot.co.uk/
Meetings: 7.30pm, 1st Monday of the month (Oct-Apr), The Patch, Furzy Park, Haverfordwest.

Ringing Group
PEMBROKESHIRE RG. J Hayes, 3 Wades Close, Holyland Road, Pembroke, SA71 4BN. 01646 687 036; e-mail: hayes313@btinternet.com

Wetland Bird Survey Organisers
CARDIGAN (incl Dyfi Estuary). Dick Squires; e-mail: dick.squires@rspb.org.uk

CARMARTHEN, BAY AND INLAND. Ian Hainsworth, 23 Rhyd y Defaid Drive, Swansea, SA2 8AJ. 01792 205 693; e-mail: ian.hains@ntlworld.com

CARMARTHENSHIRE. Terry Wells; e-mail: bto@wells.me.uk

PEMBROKESHIRE. Annie Haycock; e-mail: rushmoor1@tiscali.co.uk

Wildlife Hospital
NEW QUAY BIRD HOSPITAL. Jean Bryant, Penfoel, Cross Inn, Llandysul, Ceredigion, SA44 6NR. 01545 560 462All species of birds. Fully equipped for cleansing oiled seabirds. Veterinary support.

Wildlife Trust
GWENT (excl. Severn Estuary). Chris Jones, 22 Walnut Drive, Caerleon, Newport, Gwent NP18 3SB; e-mail: chrisj22@talktalk.net

ISLE OF MAN

Manx Bird Atlas
An Atlas of Breeding and Wintering Birds on the Isle of Man
Principal Editor: Chris Sharpe

Bird Recorder
Chris Sharpe. E-mail:chris@manxbirdlife.im

Bird Reports
MANX BIRD REPORT (1947-), published in *Peregrine*. From Mrs A C Kaye, Cronk Ny Ollee, Glen Chass, Port St Mary, Isle of Man IM9 5PL. 01624 834 015.

CALF OF MAN BIRD OBSERVATORY ANNUAL REPORT, from Secretary, Manx National Heritage, Manx Museum, Douglas, Isle of Man, IM1 3LY.

Bird Atlas/Avifauna
Manx Bird Atlas. 5-yr BBS and Winter Atlas research completed. (Liverpool University Press, 2007). Contact: Chris Sharpe (see below, BTO)

BTO Regional Representatives
Dr Pat Cullen, as above. 01624 623 308; e-mail:bridgeen@mcb.net

Club
MANX ORNITHOLOGICAL SOCIETY. (1967; 150). Mrs A C Kaye, Cronk Ny Ollee, Glen Chass, Port St Mary, Isle of Man IM9 5PL. 01624 834 015. http://manxbirdlife.im/manx-ornithological-society
Meetings: 1st Tues in month, 7.30pm, Union Mills Hall.

Ringing Group
MANX RINGING GROUP. Mr Kevin Scott; e-mail: manxrg@gmail.com www.manxringer.blogspot.com

Wetland Bird Survey Organiser
Dr Pat Cullen, Troutbeck, Cronkbourne, Braddan, Isle of Man, IM4 4QA. Home: 01624 623308 Work 01624 676774; E-mail:bridgeen@mcb.net

Wildlife Trust
MANX WILDLIFE TRUST. (1973; 900). 7-8 Market Place, Peel, Isle of Man IM5 1AB. 01624 844 432; E-mail:enquiries@manxwt.org.uk www.manxwt.org.uk

CHANNEL ISLANDS

Wetland Bird Survey Organisers
CHANNEL ISLANDS (inland). Glyn Young. 01534 860
000; e-mail:glyn.young@durrell.org

ALDERNEY

Atlas/Avifauna
The Birds of Alderney, by JG Sanders. (The Press at
St Anne, 2007).

Bird Recorder
Mark Atkinson; e-mail:atkinson@cwgsy.net

Bird Report
*ALDERNEY SOCIETY AND COUNTY ORNITHOLOGICAL
REPORT (1992-)*, from Recorder;
e-mail: atkinson@cwgsy.net

BTO Regional Representative
Philip Alexander. 01481 726 173;
e-mail:alybru@cwgsy.net

Wetland Birds Survey Organiser
Trust Ecologist, Alderney Wildlife Trust Office, 51
Victoria Street, St Anne Alderney GY9 3TA. 01481 822
935; e-mail:info@alderneywildlife.org

Wildlife Trust
ALDERNEY WILDLIFE TRUST. (2002; 460). Alderney
Wildlife Trust Office, 51 Victoria Street, St Anne
Alderney GY9 3TA. 01481 822 935;
e-mail:info@alderneywildlife.org
www.alderneywildlife.org

GUERNSEY

Bird Atlas/Avifauna
*Birds of the Bailiwick: Guernsey, Alderney, Sark and
Herm* by Duncan Spencer & Paul Hillion, 2010, Jill
Vaudin Publishing.

Bird Recorder
Mark Lawlor; e-mail:mplawlor@cwgsy.net

Bird Report
*REPORT & TRANSACTIONS OF LA SOCIETE
GUERNESIAISE (1882-)*, from Recorder.

BTO Regional Representative
Philip Alexander. 01481 726 173;
e-mail:alybru@cwgsy.net

Clubs
LA SOCIÉTÉ GUERNESIAISE (Ornithological Section).
(1882; 1,400). Secretary, La Société Guernesiaise,
Candie Gardens, St Peter Port, Port Guernsey GY1
1UG. 01481 725 093; e-mail:societe@cwgsy.net
www.societe.org.gg
Meetings: First Thurs of month, 8pm, Candie Gardens
lecture theatre.

RSPB Local Group
GUERNSEY BAILIWICK. (1975; 350+). Donna Francis.
01481 232 632; e-mail:donna@cwgsy.net
www.rspbguernsey.co.uk
Meetings: 8pm, La Villette Hotel, St Martins,
Guernsey, GY4 6QG.

Wetland Bird Survey Organiser
GUERNSEY COAST. Mary Simmons, Les Maeures, Mont
d'Aval, Castel, Guernsey GY5 7UQ. 01481 256 016;
e-mail:msim@cwgsy.net

Wildlife Hospital
GUERNSEY. GSPCA ANIMAL
SHELTER. Mrs Jayne Le
Cras, Les Fiers Moutons,
St Andrews, Guernsey, Channel Islands GY6 8UD.
01481 257 261; (emergency number 07781 104 082);
e-mail:admin@gspca.org.gg
www.gspca.org.gg All species. Modern cleansing
unit for oiled seabirds. 24-hour emergency service.
Veterinary support.

JERSEY

Bird Recorder
Tony Paintin, Cavok, 16 Quennevais Gardens, St
Brelade, Jersey, Channel Islands, JE3 8FQ. 01534 741
928; e-mail:cavokjersey@hotmail.com

Bird Report
JERSEY BIRD REPORT (1991-), from La Société
Jersiaise, 7 Pier Road, St Helier, Jersey JE2 4XW;
e-mail:societe@societe-jersiaise.org

BTO Regional Representative
Tony Paintin, Cavok, 16 Quennevais Gardens, St
Brelade, Jersey, Channel Islands, JE3 8FQ. 01534 741
928; e-mail:cavokjersey@hotmail.com

Club
SOCIÉTIÉ JERSIAISE (Ornithological Section). (1948;
40). C/O La Société Jersiaise, 7 Pier Road, St Helier,
Jersey JE2 4XW. 01534 758 314;
e-mail:societe@societe-jersiaise.org
www.societe-jersiaise.org
Meetings: 8.00pm, alternate Thursdays throughout
the year, Museum in St.Helier.

Wetland Bird Survey Organiser
JERSEY COAST. Roger Noel.
e-mail:rogernoel1@googlemail.com

Wildlife Hospital
JERSEY. JSPCA ANIMALS' SHELTER. The Manager, 89
St Saviour's Road, St Helier, Jersey, JE2 4GJ. 01534
724 331; e-mail:info@jspca.org.je
www.jspca.org.je All species. Expert outside support
for owls and raptors. Oiled seabird unit. Veterinary
surgeon on site. Educational Centre.

NORTHERN IRELAND

Bird Recorder
George Gordon, 2 Brooklyn Avenue, Bangor, Co Down, BT20 5RB. 028 9145 5763; e-mail: gordon@ballyholme2.freeserve.co.uk

Bird Reports
NORTHERN IRELAND BIRD REPORT, from Secretary, Northern Ireland, Birdwatchers' Association (see National Directory).

IRISH BIRD REPORT, Included in Irish Birds, BirdWatch Ireland in National Directory.

COPELAND BIRD OBSERVATORY REPORT, from the Bookings Secretary: David Galbraith, 028 9338 2539 or 07885 834 398; e-mail: davidgalbraith903@btinternet.com

BTO Regional Representatives
BTO IRELAND OFFICER. Shane Wolsey. 028 9146 7947; e-mail:shane@swolsey.biz

ANTRIM & BELFAST. Adam McClure. 028 2827 1875; e-mail:a.d.mcclure84@hotmail.co.uk

ARMAGH. Stephen Hewitt; e-mail: sjameshewitt@hotmail.com

DOWN. Kerry Leonard. 028 9145 2602; e-mail:kerrysleonard@hotmail.com

FERMANAGH. Michael Stinson. 07890 358 239; e-mail:mick.stinston@hotmail.com

LONDONDERRY. Charles Stewart, Bravallen, 18 Duncrun Road, Bellarena, Limavady, Co Londonderry BT49 0JD. 028 7775 0468; e-mail:charles.stewart2@btinternet.com

TYRONE. Michael Stinson. 07890 358 239; E-mail:mick.stinston@hotmail.com

BTO Garden BirdWatch Ambassador
Pat Flowerday. E-mail: pflowerday@utvinternet.com

Clubs
NORTHERN IRELAND BIRDWATCHERS' ASSOCIATION See National Directory.

NORTHERN IRELAND ORNITHOLOGISTS' CLUB See National Directory.

CASTLE ESPIE BIRDWATCHING CLUB (COMBER). (1995; 60). Dot Blakely, 8 Rosemary Park, Bangor, Co Down, BT20 3EX. 028 9145 0784; e-mail: dotbirdblakely@gmail.com

Ringing Groups
COPELAND BIRD OBSERVATORY. C Chris Acheson; e-mail: CWA70@hotmail.com

NORTH DOWN RINGING GROUP. Mr D C Clarke. 07774 780 750; e-mail: declan.clarke@homecall.co.uk;

RSPB Local Groups
ANTRIM. (1977; 23). Brenda Campbell . 02893 323 657; e-mail:brendacampbell@supanet.com
www.rspb.org.uk/groups/antrim
Meetings: 8pm, 2nd Monday of the month, College of Agriculture Food & Rural Enterprise, 22 Greenmount Road, ANTRIM

BANGOR. (1973; 25). Fulton Somerville; e-mail: fultonsomerville@yahoo.co.uk
Meetings: Trinity Presbyterian Church Hall, Main Street, Bangor, County Down.

BELFAST. (1970; 130). Derek McLain. 028 9334 1488; e-mail: d.mclain@btinternet.com
Meetings: Cooke Centenary Church Hall, Park Road, Belfast BT7 2FW.

COLERAINE. (1978; 45). Peter Robinson, 34 Blackthorn Court, Coleraine, Co Londonderry, BT52 2EX. 028 7034 4361; e-mail: robinson493@btinternet.com
Meetings: 7.30pm, third Monday of the month (Sept-Apr), St Patricks Church, Minor Church Hall, Corner of Brook St and Circular Road, Coleraine

FERMANAGH. (1977; 28). Doreen Brown. 028 6632 2479; e-mail: dbrown498@btinternet.com
Meetings: 8pm, Cathedral Hall, Halls Lane, Enniskillen BT74 7DR.

LARNE. (1974; 35). Jimmy Christie, 314 Coast Road, Ballygally, Co Antrim, BT40 2QZ. 028 2858 3223; E-mail: candjchristie@btinternet.com
Meetings: 7.30pm, 1st Wednesday of the month, Larne Grammar School.

LISBURN. (1978; 30). Peter Galloway. 028 9266 1982; E-mail: pgalloway56@o2.co.uk
www.rspblisburn.com
Meetings: 7.30pm, 4th Monday of the month, Friends Meeting House, 4 Magheralave Road, LISBURN

Wetland Bird Survey Organisers
BANN ESTUARY. Hill Dick. 02870 329 720; e-mail: webs@bto.org

BELFAST LOUGH. Shane Wolsey, 25 Ballyholme Esplanade, Bangor, County Down, BT20 5LZ. 07831 697 371; e-mail:shane@swolsey.biz

DUNDRUM BAY. Malachy Martin, Murlough NNR, Keel Point, Dundrum, Co. Down BT33 0NQ. 028 4375 1467; e-mail: Malachy.Martin@nationaltrust.org.uk

LARNE LOUGH. Doreen Hilditch; E-mail: mail18brae@btinternet.com

LOUGH FOYLE. Matthew Tickner. 02890 491 547; e-mail:matthew.tickner@rspb.org.uk

REPUBLIC OF IRELAND

STRANGFORD LOUGH. Kerry Mackie, WWT Castle Espie; 78 Ballydrain Road, Co Down. 02891 874 146; e-mail: kerry.mackie@wwt.org.uk

Wildlife Hospital
TACT WILDLIFE CENTRE. Mrs Patricia Nevines, 2 Crumlin Road, Crumlin, Co Antrim, BT29 4AD. 028 9442 2900; e-mail: tactwildlife@btinternet.com www.tactwildlifecentre.org.uk All categories of birds treated and rehabilitated; released where

practicable, otherwise given a home. Visitors (inc. school groups and organisations) welcome by prior arrangement. Veterinary support.

Wildlife Trust
ULSTER WILDLIFE TRUST. (1978; 7.500). 3 New Line, Crossgar, Co Down, BT30 9EP. 028 4483 0282 (fax) 028 4483 0888; e-mail: info@ulsterwildlifetrust.org www.ulsterwildlifetrust.org

---

REPUBLIC OF IRELAND

BirdWatch Ireland, Unit 20, Block D, Bullford Business Campus, Kilcoole, Co. Wicklow, Ireland 353 (0)1 281 9878 E-mail: info@ birdwatchireland.ie www.birdwatchireland.ie

 BirdWatchIreland

Rarities. Paul Milne, 100 Dublin Road, Sutton, Dublin 13, +353 (0)1 832 5653; e-mail: paul.milne@oceanfree.net

CLARE. John Murphy, e-mail: jemurphy@esatclear.ie

CORK. Mark Shorten, e-mail: mshorten@indigo.ie

DONEGAL. Ralph Sheppard, e-mail: rsheppard@eircom.net

DUBLIN, LOUTH, MEATH AND WICKLOW. Declan Murphy & Dick Coombes, e-mail: dmurphy@birdwatchireland.ie or e-mail: rcoombes@birdwatchireland.ie

GALWAY. Chris Peppiatt, e-mail: chris.peppiatt@iol.ie

KERRY. Michael O'Clery & Jill Crosher, e-mail: moclery@tinet.ie

LIMERICK. Tony Mee, Ballyorgan, Kilfinane, Co. Limerick.

MAYO. Tony Murray, National Parks and Wildlife, Lagduff More, Ballycroy, Westport; e-mail: murraytony@hotmail.com

MID-SHANNON. Stephen Heery, e-mail: sheery@eircom.net

MONAGHAN. Joe Shannon, e-mail: joeshan@eircom.net

WATERFORD. Paul Walsh, 16 Castlepoint, Crosshaven, Co. Cork; e-mail: pmwalsh@waterfordbirds.com

WEXFORD. Tony Murray, Wexford Wildfowl Reserve, North Slob; e-mail: murraytony@hotmail.com

Bird Reports
IRISH BIRD REPORT, contact BirdWatch Ireland in National, Directory).

CAPE CLEAR BIRD OBSERVATORY ANNUAL REPORT, from the observatory.

CORK BIRD REPORT (1963-71; 1976-), Cork Bird Report Editorial Team, Long Strand, Castlefreke, Clonakilty, Co. Cork; e-mail: cbr@corkecology.net

EAST COAST BIRD REPORT (1980-), Contact BirdWatch Ireland.

BirdWatch Ireland Branches
Branches may be contacted in writing via BirdWatch Ireland HQ (see entry in National Directory).

Ringing Groups
CAPE CLEAR B.O, Steve Wing, e-mail: steve.ccbo@gmail.com

GREAT SALTEE RINGING STATION, Mr O J Merne, 20 Cuala Road, Bray, Co Wicklow, Ireland, e-mail: omerne@eircom.net

MUNSTER RG, Mr K.P.C. Collins, Ballygambon, Lisronagh, Clonmel, County Tipperary, e-mail: kcsk@eircom.net

NATIONAL DIRECTORY

David Cromack

Anyone wishing to develop their bird-carving skills should make contact with the British Decoy Wildfowl Carving Association, which exhibits members work at Rutland bird fair and its own championship in Bakewell, Derbyshire.

NATIONAL ORGANISATIONS

After the title of each organisation you will see (in brackets) the year the
group was founded and, where known, the current membership figure.

ARMY ORNITHOLOGICAL SOCIETY (1960; 200)

Open to serving and retired MoD employees who
have an interest in their local MoD estate. Activities
include field meetings, expeditions, the preparation
of checklists of birds on Ministry of Defence property,
conservation advice and an annual bird count. Annual
journal *Adjutant*.
Contact: Maj AJ Bray RLC, www.armybirdingng.com
e-mail: secretary@aos.org.uk

ASSOCIATION FOR THE PROTECTION OF RURAL SCOTLAND (1926)

Works to protect Scotland's countryside from
unnecessary or inappropriate development,
recognising the needs of those who live and work
there and the necessity of reconciling these with the
sometimes competing requirements of recreational
use.
Contact: Association for the Protection Rural
Scotland, Gladstone's Land, 3rd Floor, 483
Lawnmarket, Edinburgh EH1 2NT. 0131 225 7012;
e-mail: info@ruralscotland.org
www.ruralscotland.btck.com

ASSOCIATION OF COUNTY RECORDERS AND EDITORS (1993; 120)

The basic aim of ACRE is to promote best practice
in the business of producing county bird reports,
in the work of Recorders and in problems arising in
managing record systems and archives. Organises
periodic conferences and publishes *newsACRE*.
Contact: The Secretary; e-mail: countyrec@cawos.org

BARN OWL TRUST (1988)

A registered charity dedicated to conserving the Barn
Owl and its environment. It is the main source of
Barn Owl information in the UK. It carries out surveys
of old buildings, due for development, and advises
on Barn Owl mitigation measures. A booklet *Barn
Owls on Site*, a guide for developers and planners,
published by English Nature is widely used by local
authorities and other official bodies. Trust members
have erected more than 2,000 nestboxes and is
closely involved in habitat creation both on its own
land and through farm visits.
Contact: Barn Owl Trust, Waterleat, Ashburton,
Devon TQ13 7HU. 01364 653 026;
www.barnowltrust.org.uk
e-mail: info@barnowltrust.org.uk

BIRDING FOR ALL (formerly The Disabled Birder's Association) (2000; 750)

Birding For All is a registered
charity and international
movement, which aims to
promote access to reserves
and other birding places and
to a range of services, so

that people with different needs can follow the
birding obsession as freely as able-bodied people.
Membership is currently free and new members are
needed to help send a stronger message to those who
own and manage nature reserves to improve access
when they are planning and improving facilities.
DBA also seeks to influence those who provide
birdwatching services and equipment. The DBA also
runs overseas trips. Chairman, Bo Beolens.
Contact: Phil Gatley. Membership Secretary.
e-mail: BAnderson1550539@aol.com
www.birdingforall.com

BIRD OBSERVATORIES COUNCIL (1970)

Aims to provide a forum for establishing closer links
and co-operation between individual observatories
and to help co-ordinate the work carried out by
them. All accredited bird observatories affiliated
to the Council undertake a ringing programme and
provide ringing experience to those interested.
Most are also provide accommodation for visiting
birdwatchers.
Contact: Peter Howlett, Bird Observatories Council,
c/o Dept of BioSyB, National Museum Wales, Cardiff
CF10 3NP. 0292 057 3233;
e-mail: info@birdobscouncil.org.uk
www.birdobscouncil.org.uk

BIRD STAMP SOCIETY (1986; 170)

Quarterly journal *Flight*
contains philatelic and
ornithological articles. Lists
all new issues and identifies
species. Runs a quarterly
Postal Auction; number of
lots range from 400 to 800
per auction. UK subs £14 per
annum from 1st August.

Contact: Bob Wilks, Membership Secretary, 4 Curlew
Road, Porthcawl, Mid-Glamorgan CF36 3QA; 01656
785055; e-mail: bobwilks581@btinternet.com
www.birdstampsociety.org

BIRDWATCH IRELAND (1968; 14,000 with a network of 20 branches)

The largest independent conservation organisation in
Ireland. Its primary objective is the protection of wild
birds and their habitats in Ireland through the efforts
of its staff, members and volunteers alike. It carries
out extensive research and survey work, operates
applied conservation projects and manages a network
of reserves nationwide. It publishes *Wings* magazine
and an annual journal *Irish Birds*.
Contact: BirdWatch Ireland, Unit 20, Block D, Bullford
Business Campus, Kilcoole, Co. Wicklow, Ireland. +353
(0)1 2819 878 353 (0)1 281 9878; Fax: +353 (0)1 281
0997; e-mail: info@birdwatchireland.org
www.birdwatchireland.ie

NATIONAL ORGANISATIONS

BRITISH BIRDS RARITIES COMMITTEE (1959, 16)
The Committee adjudicates records of species of rare occurrence in Britain (marked `R' in the Log Charts) and publishes its annual report in B*ritish Birds*. The BBRC also assesses records from the Channel Islands. In the case of rarities trapped for ringing, records should be sent to the Ringing Office of the British Trust for Ornithology, who will in turn forward them to the BBRC.
Contact: The Hon Secretary, British Birds Rarities Committee, e-mail: secretary@bbrc.org.uk
www.bbrc.org.uk

BRITISH DECOY WILDFOWL CARVERS ASSOCIATION (1990)
The Association is a non-profitmaking organisation, run by carvers to promote all aspects of their art. Its aims are: to produce three annual *Wingspan* newsletters: to keep the members in touch with the art; to promote regional groups; to generate local interest; to organise competitions and exhibitions; and finally, to care generally for wildfowl carvers' interests. Each September the Association stages the Bakewell Festival of Bird Art in the Peak District, which includes the national carving championships.
Contact: Janet Nash (club secretary)
e-mail: janet.nash@talk21.com www.bdwca.org.uk

BRITISH DRAGONFLY SOCIETY (1983; 1,500)

The BDS aims to promote the conservation and study of dragonflies. Members receive two issues of *Dragonfly News* and *BDS Journal* each year. There are countrywide field trips, an annual members' day and training is available on aspects of dragonfly ecology. The BDS has published a booklet, *Dig a Pond for Dragonflies* containing advice on pond creation and maintenance to attract dragonflies. *Managing Habitats for Dragonflies* is aimed at countryside managers.
Contact: Mr H Curry, Hon Secretary, British Dragonfly Society, 23 Bowker Way, Whittlesey, Cambs PE7 1PY.
e-mail: bdssecretary@dragonflysoc.org.uk
www.dragonflysoc.org.uk

BRITISH FALCONERS' CLUB (1927; 1,200)
Largest falconry club in Europe, with regional branches. Its aim is to encourage responsible falconers and conserve birds of prey by breeding, holding educational meetings and providing facilities, guidance and advice to those wishing to take up the sport. Publishes *The Falconer* annually and newsletter twice yearly.
Contact: British Falconers' Club, Westfield, Meeting Hill, Worstead, North Walsham, Norfolk NR28 9LS. 01692 404 057; www.britishfalconersclub.co.uk
e-mail: admin@britishfalconersclub.co.uk

BRITISH LIBRARY SOUND ARCHIVE - WILDLIFE SOUNDS (Formerly BLOWS - British Library of Wildlife Sounds) (1969).
The most comprehensive collection of bird sound recordings in existence: over 150,000 recordings of more than 8,000 species of birds worldwide, available for free listening. Copies or sonograms of most recordings can be supplied for private study or research and, subject to copyright clearance, for commercial uses. Contribution of new material and enquiries on all aspects of wildlife sounds and recording techniques are welcome. Publishes *Bioacoustics journal*, CD guides to bird songs and other wildlife, including ambience titles. Comprehensive catalogue available on-line at http://cadensa.bl.uk/uhtbin/cgisirsi/x/x/0/49/
Contact: Cheryl Tipp, Curator, Wildlife Sounds, The British Library Sound Archive, 96 Euston Road, London NW1 2DB. 020 7412 7403; (Fax) 020 7412 7441; e-mail: wildlifesound@bl.uk
www.bl.uk/reshelp/findhelprestype/sound/wildsounds/wildlife.html

BRITISH NATURALISTS ASSOCIATION (1905)
The association was founded to promote the interests of nature lovers and bring them together. It encourages and supports schemes and legislation for the protection of the country`s natural resources. It organises meetings, field weeks, lectures and exhibitions to help popularise the study of nature. BNA publishes two magazines, *Countryside* (bi-annual) and *British Naturalist* (bi-annual).
Contact: General Secretary, BNA, BM 8129, London WC1N 3XX. 0844 892 1817; www.bna-naturalists.org
e-mail: info@bna-naturalists.org

BRITISH ORNITHOLOGISTS' CLUB (1892; 450)
The Club's objects are 'the promotion of scientific discussion between members of the BOU, and others interested in ornithology, and to facilitate the publication of scientific information in connection with ornithology'. The Club maintains a special interest in avian systematics, taxonomy and distribution. About eight dinner meetings are held each year. Publishes the *Bulletin of the British Ornithologists' Club* quarterly, and a continuing series of occasional publications.
Contact: BOC Office, British Ornithologists' Club, PO Box 417, Peterborough, PE7 3FX. (Tel/Fax) 01733 844 820; e-mail: boc.admin@bou.org.uk
www.boc-online.org

BRITISH ORNITHOLOGISTS' UNION (1858; 1,100)
The BOU is one of the world's oldest and most respected ornithological societies. It aims to promote ornithology within the scientific and birdwatching communities, both in Britain and around the world. This is largely achieved

NATIONAL ORGANISATIONS

by the publication of its quarterly international journal, *Ibis*, featuring work at the cutting edge of our understanding of the world's birdlife. It also publishes an on-going series of country/island group 'checklists' (see website for details) and operates an active programme of meetings, seminars and conferences.

Work being undertaken around the world can include research projects that have received financial assistance from the BOU's on-going programme of Ornithological Research Grants. The BOU Records Committee maintains the official British List (see below)

Contact: Steve Dudley, British Ornithologists' Union, PO Box 417, Peterborough, PE7 3FX. (Tel/Fax) 01733 844 820; e-mail: bou@bou.org.uk www.bou.org.uk and www.ibis.ac.uk

BRITISH ORNITHOLOGISTS' UNION RECORDS COMMITTEE (11)

A standing committee of the British Ornithologists' Union, the BOURC's function is to maintain the British List, the official list of birds recorded in Great Britain. The up-to-date list can be viewed on the BOU website. Where vagrants are involved it is concerned only with those which relate to potential additions to the British List (ie first records). In this it differs from the British Birds Rarities Committee (qv).

It also examines, where necessary, important pre-1950 records, monitors introduced species for possible admission to, or deletion from, the List, and reviews taxonomy and nomenclature relating to the List. BOURC reports are published in *Ibis* and are also available via the BOU website.

Contact: Steve Dudley, BOURC, PO Box 417, Peterborough, PE7 3FX. (Tel/Fax) 01733 844 820; e-mail: bourc@bou.org www.bou.org.uk

BRITISH TRUST FOR ORNITHOLOGY (1933; 13,200)

A registered charity governed by an elected Council, BTO enjoys the support of a large number of county and local birdwatching clubs and societies through the BTO/Bird Clubs Partnership. Its aims are: 'To promote and encourage the wider understanding, appreciation and conservation of birds through scientific studies using the combined skills and enthusiasm of its members, other birdwatchers and staff.'

Through the fieldwork of its members and other birdwatchers, the BTO is responsible for the majority of the monitoring of British birds, British bird population and their habitats. BTO surveys include the National Ringing Scheme, the Nest Record Scheme, the Breeding Bird Survey (in collaboration with JNCC and RSPB), and the Waterways Breeding Bird Survey, which all contribute to an integrated programme of population monitoring.

The BTO also runs projects on the birds of farmland and woodland, also (in collaboration with WWT, RSPB and JNCC) the Wetland Bird Survey, in particular Low Tide Counts. Garden BirdWatch, now has more than 14,000 participants. The Trust has 140 voluntary regional representatives (see County Directory) who organise fieldworkers for the BTO's programme of national surveys in which members participate. The results of these co-operative efforts are communicated to government departments, local authorities, industry and conservation bodies for effective action.

For details of current activities see National Projects. Members receive *BTO News* six times a year and have the option of subscribing to the thrice-yearly journal, *Bird Study* and twice yearly *Ringing & Migration*. Local meetings are held in conjunction with bird clubs and societies; there are regional and national birdwatchers' conferences, and specialist courses in bird identification and modern censusing techniques. Grants are made for research, and members have the use of a lending and reference library at Thetford and the Alexander Library at the Edward Grey Institute of Field Ornithology (qv)

Contact: British Trust for Ornithology, The Nunnery, Thetford, Norfolk IP24 2PU. 01842 750 050; (Fax) 01842 750 030; e-mail: info@bto.org www.bto.org

BTO SCOTLAND (2000; 989)

BTO Scotland's main functions are to promote the work of the Trust and develop wider coverage for surveys in Scotland, by encouraging greater participation in survey work. It also seeks to develop contract research income within Scotland. BTO Scotland ensures that the Trust's work is not just related to the priorities of the UK as a whole but is also focused on the priorities of Scotland, with a landscape and wildlife so different from the rest of the UK.

Contact: BTO Scotland, British Trust for Ornithology, Biological and Environmental Sciences, University of Stirling, Stirling FK9 4LA. 01786 466 560 (Fax) 01786 466 561; e-mail: scot.info@bto.org www.bto.org

BRITISH WATERFOWL ASSOCIATION

The BWA is an association of enthusiasts interested in keeping, breeding and conserving all types of waterfowl, including wildfowl and domestic ducks and geese. It is a registered charity, without trade affiliations, dedicated to educating the public about waterfowl and the need for conservation as well as to raising the standards of keeping and breeding ducks, geese and swans in captivity. Publishes *Waterfowl* magazine for members three times a year

Contact: Mrs Sue Schubert, British Waterfowl Association, PO Box 163, Oxted, RH8 0WP. 01732 867 987; e-mail: info@waterfowl.org.uk www.waterfowl.org.uk

NATIONAL ORGANISATIONS

BRITISH WILDLIFE REHABILITATION COUNCIL (1987)
Promoting the care and rehabilitation of wildlife casualties through the exchange of information between people such as rehabilitators, zoologists and veterinary surgeons who are active in this field. Organises an annual symposium or workshop. Publishes a regular newsletter. Supported by many national bodies including the Zoological Society of London, the British Veterinary Zoological Society, the RSPCA, the SSPCA, and the Vincent Wildlife Trust.
Contact: To make a contribution - Janet Peto, BWRC, PO Box 8686, Grantham, Lincolnshire NG31 0AG; e-mail: admin@bwrc.org.uk www.bwrc.org.uk

BTCV (formerly British Trust for Conservation Volunteers) (1959)
BTCV's mission is to create a more sustainable future by inspiring people and improving places. It aims to enrich the lives of people, through volunteering opportunities, employment, improved health, and life skills development; to improve the biodiversity and local environment of 20,000 places and to support active citizenship in 5,000 community-based groups. BTCV currently supports 140,000 volunteers to take practical action to improve their urban and rural environments. Publishes a quarterly magazine, *Roots*, a series of practical handbooks and a wide range of other publications.
Contact: TCV, Sedum House, Mallard Way, Potteric Carr, Doncaster DN4 8DB. 01302 388 883; e-mail: Information@tcv.org.uk www.tcv.org.uk

BTCV CYMRU
Contact: The Conservation Centre, BTCV Cymru, Forest Farm Road, Whitchurch, Cardiff, CF14 7JJ. 029 2052 0990; Fax: 029 2052 2181; e-mail: wales@ttcv.org.uk www.btcvcymru.org

BTCV SCOTLAND
Runs 7-14 day Action Breaks in Scotland during which participants undertake conservation projects; weekend training courses in environmental skills; midweek projects in Edinburgh, Glasgow, Aberdeen, Stirling and Inverness.
Contact: BTCV Scotland, Balallan House, 24 Allan Park, Stirling FK8 2QG. 01786 479 697; (Fax) 01786 465359; e-mail: scotland@tcv.org.uk www2.btcv.org.uk/display/btcv_scotland

BTCV NORTHERN IRELAND (1983)
Contact: Conservation Volunteers Northern Ireland, Beech House, 159 Ravenhill Road, Belfast BT6 0BP. 028 9064 5169; (Fax) 028 9064 4409; e-mail: CVNI@btcv.org.uk www.cvni.org

BUGLIFE – THE INVERTEBRATE CONSERVATION TRUST (2000)
The first organisation in Europe devoted to the conservation of all invertebrates, actively engaged in halting the extinction of Britain's rarest slugs, snails, bees, wasps, ants, spiders, beetles and many more. It works to achieve this through practical conservation projects; promoting the environmental importance of invertebrates and raising awareness about the challenges to their survival; assisting in the development of helpful legislation and policy and encouraging and supporting invertebrate conservation initiatives by other organisations in the UK, Europe and worldwide.

Contact: Buglife (ICT), 1st Floor, 90 Bridge Street, Peterborough PE1 1DY. 01733 201 210; e-mail: info@buglife.org.uk www.buglife.org.uk

CAMPAIGN FOR THE PROTECTION OF RURAL WALES (1928; 2,800)
Its aims are to help the conservation and enhancement of the landscape, environment and amenities of the countryside, towns and villages of rural Wales and to form and educate opinion to ensure the promotion of its objectives. It gives advice and information upon matters affecting protection, conservation and improvement of the visual environment.
Contact: Ty Gwyn, 31 High Street, Welshpool, Powys SY21 7YD. 01938 552 525 or 01938 556 212; e-mail: info@cprwmail.org.uk www.cprw.org.uk

CENTRE FOR ECOLOGY & HYDROLOGY (CEH)
The work of the CEH, a component body of the Natural Environment Research Council, includes a range of ornithological research, covering population studies, habitat management and work on the effects of pollution. The CEH has a long-term programme to monitor pesticide and pollutant residues in the corpses of predatory birds sent in by birdwatchers, and carries out detailed studies on affected species. The Biological Records Centre (BRC), which is part of the CEH, is responsible for the national biological data bank on plant and animal distributions (except birds).
Contact: Centre for Ecology & Hydrology, Maclean Building, Benson Lane, Crowmarsh Gifford, Wallingford, Oxfordshire OX10 8BB. 01491 692 371. E-mail: enquiries@ceh.ac.uk www.ceh.ac.uk

CONSERVATION FOUNDATION (1982)
Created by David Bellamy and David Shreeve, it provides a means for people in public, private and not-for-profit sectors to collaborate on environmental causes. Over the years its programme has included award schemes, conferences, promotions, special events, field studies, school programmes, media work, seminars and workshops etc. The Conservation Foundation has created and managed environmental award schemes of all kinds including the Ford European Awards, The Trust House Forte Community Chest, The PA Golden Leaf Awards, The Co-op Save Our Species Awards, the Pollution Abatement Technology Awards and many others. For information about how to apply for current award schemes visit the website.
Contact: Conservation Foundation, 1 Kensington

Gore, London SW7 2AR. 020 7591 3111;
e-mail: info@conservationfoundation.co.uk
www.conservationfoundation.co.uk

COUNTRY LAND AND BUSINESS ASSOCIATION (Formerly Country Landowners Association) (1907; 36,000).
The CLA is at the heart of rural life and is the voice of the countryside for England and Wales, campaigning on issues which directly affect those who live and work in rural communities. Its members, ranging from some of the largest landowners, with interests in forest, moorland, water and agriculture, to some with little more than a paddock or garden, together manage 50% of the countryside.
Contact: Country Land and Business Association, 16 Belgrave Square, London, SW1X 8PQ. 020 7235 0511; (Fax) 020 7235 4696; e-mail: mail@cla.org.uk www.cla.org.uk

COUNTRYSIDE COUNCIL FOR WALES
The Government's statutory adviser on wildlife, countryside and maritime conservation matters in Wales and the executive authority for the conservation of habitats and wildlife. CCW champions the environment and landscapes of Wales and its coastal waters as sources of natural and cultural riches, as a foundation for economic and social activity, and as a place for leisure and learning opportunities.
Contact: Countryside Council for Wales, Maes-y-Ffynnon, Penrhosgarnedd, Bangor, Gwynedd LL57 2DL, 0845 1306 229; e-mail: enquiries@ccw.gov.uk www.ccw.gov.uk

CPRE (formerly Council for the Protection of Rural England) (1926; 60,000)

Patron HM The Queen. CPRE now has 43 county branches and 200 local groups. It highlights threats to the countryside and promotes positive solutions. In-depth research supports active campaigning, and through reasoned argument and lobbying, CPRE seeks to influence public opinion and decision-makers at every level. Membership is open to all.
Contact: CPRE National Office, 5-11 Lavington Street, London SE1 0NZ. 020 7981 2800; (Fax) 020 7981 2899; e-mail: info@cpre.org.uk www.cpre.org.uk

DEPARTMENT OF THE ENVIRONMENT FOR NORTHERN IRELAND
Responsible for the declaration and management of National Nature Reserves, the declaration of Areas of Special Scientific Interest, the administration of Wildlife Refuges, the classification of Special Protection Areas under the EC Birds Directive, the designation of Special Areas of Conservation under the EC Habitats Directive and the designation of Ramsar sites under the Ramsar Convention. It administers the Nature Conservation and Amenity Lands (Northern Ireland) Order 1985, the Wildlife (Northern Ireland) Order 1985, the Game Acts and the

Conservation (Natural Habitats, etc) Regulations (NI) 1995 and the Environment (Northern Ireland) Order 2002.
Contact: Environment and Heritage Service, Klondyke Building, Cromac Avenue, Gasworks Business Park, Lower Ormeau Road, Belfast BT7 2JA. 0845 302 0008; (pollution hotline; 0800 807 060);
e-mail: nieainfo@doeni.gov.uk www.ehsni.gov.uk

EARTHWATCH INSTITUTE (1971)
Earthwatch developed the innovative idea of engaging the general public into the scientific process by bringing together individual volunteers and scientists on field research projects, thereby providing an alternative means of funding, as well as a dedicated labour force for field scientists. Last year, more than 3,500 volunteers had worked on Earthwatch projects, which have grown to 140 projects in more than 50 countries around the world.
Contact: Earthwatch Institute (Europe), Mayfield House, 256 Banbury Road, Oxford OX2 7DE. 01864 318 838; e-mail: info@earthwatch.co.uk www.earthwatch.org/europe

EDWARD GREY INSTITUTE OF FIELD ORNITHOLOGY (1938)
The EGI takes its name from Edward Grey, first Viscount Grey of Fallodon, a life-long lover of birds and former Chancellor of the University of Oxford. The Institute now has a permanent research staff of 12-15 research students, five or six senior visitors and post-doctoral research workers. Field research is carried out mainly in Wytham Woods near Oxford and on the island of Skomer in West Wales. In addition there are laboratory facilities and aviary space for experimental work.
The Institute houses the Alexander Library, one of the largest collections of 20th Century material on birds in the world, and which is supported by the British Ornithologists Union which provides much of the material. It also houses the British Falconers Club library. The Library is open to members of the BOU and Oxford Ornithological Society; other bona fide ornithologists may use the library by prior arrangement.
Contact: Claire Harvey, PA to Professor Sheldon, The EGI, Department of Zoology, South Parks Road, Oxford OX1 3PS; +44(0)1865 271 275; Fax: +44(0)1865 271 168.e-mail: claire.harvey@zoo.ox.ac.uk www.zoo.ox.ac.uk/egi/

ENVIRONMENT AGENCY
A non-departmental body which aims to protect and improve the environment and to contribute towards the delivery of sustainable development through the integrated management of air, land and water. Functions include pollution prevention and control, waste minimisation, management of water resources, flood defence, improvement of salmon and freshwater fisheries, conservation of aquatic species, navigation and use of inland and coastal waters for recreation. Sponsored by the Department of the Environment, Transport and the Regions, MAFF and

NATIONAL ORGANISATIONS

the Welsh Office.
Contact: Environment Agency, National Customer Contact Centre, PO Box 544, Rotherham S60 1BY. General enquiries; 08708 506 506 (Mon-Fri, 8am - 6pm); pollution hotline 0800 807 060; floodline 0845 988 1188; www.environment-agency.gov.uk e-mail: enquiries@environment-agency.gov.uk

FARMING AND WILDLIFE ADVISORY GROUP (FWAG) (1969 - 2012)
An independent UK-registered charity led by farmers and supported by government and leading countryside organisations — now in administration with individual groups setting up.

FIELD STUDIES COUNCIL (1943)
Manages Centres where students from schools, universities and colleges, as well as individuals of all ages, can stay to study various aspects of the environment under expert guidance. Courses include many for birdwatchers, providing opportunities to study birdlife on coasts, estuaries, mountains and islands. Others demonstrate bird ringing. Research workers and naturalists wishing to use the records and resources are welcome. There are centres in England, Scotland, Wales and Northern Ireland — see website for contacts and courses available.
Contact: Field Studies Council, Preston Montford, Montford Bridge, Shrewsbury SY4 1HW. 0845 345 4071; 01743 852 100; www.field-studies-council.org e-mail: enquiries@field-studies-council.org

FIELDFARE TRUST

Fieldfare works with people with disabilities and countryside managers to improve access to the countryside for everyone. It provides advice and training services to countryside management teams, supported by its research into national standards for accessibility under the BT Countryside for All Project. For members of the public, it runs projects which can enable them to take action locally, provide information on accessible places to visit and run events like the Fieldfare Kielder Challenge which encourages young people to get active in the countryside.
Contact: Fieldfare Trust, Volunteer House, 69 Crossgate, Cupar, Fife KY15 5AS. 01334 657 708; e-mail: info@fieldfare.org.uk www.fieldfare.org.uk

FORESTRY COMMISSION OF GREAT BRITAIN (1919)
The government department responsible for the protection and expansion of Britain's forests and woodlands, it runs from national offices in England, Wales and Scotland, working to targets set by Commissioners and Ministers in each of the three countries. Its objectives are to protect Britain's forests and resources, conserve and improve the biodiversity, landscape and cultural heritage of forests and woodlands, develop opportunities for woodland recreation and increase public understanding and community participation in forestry.
Contact: Forestry Commission England, England National Office, 620 Bristol Business Park, Coldharbour Lane, Bristol BS16 1EJ. 0117 906 6000: e-mail: fc.england@forestry.gsi.gov.uk

Forestry Commission Scotland, 231 Corstorphine Road, Edinburgh EH12 7AT. 0131 334 0303, (Fax) 0131 314 6152; e-mail: fcscotland@forestry.gsi.gov.uk

Forestry Commission Wales, Welsh Assembly Government, Rhodfa Padarn, Llanbadarn Fawr, Aberystwyth, Ceredigion SY23 3UR. 0300 068 0300: e-mail: fcwenquiries@forestry.gsi.gov.uk

FRIENDS OF THE EARTH (1971; 100,000)
The largest international network of environmental groups in the world, represented in 68 countries. In the UK it has a unique network of campaigning local groups, working in 200 communities in England, Wales and Northern Ireland. It is largely funded by supporters with more than 90% of income coming from individual donations, the rest from special fundraising events, grants and trading.
Contact: Friends of the Earth, 26-28 Underwood Street, London, N1 7JQ. 020 7490 1555; e-mail: info@foe.co.uk www.foe.co.uk

GAME AND WILDLIFE CONSERVATION TRUST (formerly Game Conservancy Trust) (1933; 22,000)
A registered charity which researches the conservation of game and other wildlife in the British countryside. More than 60 scientists are engaged in detailed work on insects, pesticides, birds (30 species inc. raptors) mammals (inc. foxes), and habitats. The results are used to advise government, landowners, farmers and conservationists on practical management techniques which will benefit game species, their habitats, and wildlife. Each June the *Annual Review* lists about 50 papers published in the peer-reviewed scientific press.
Contact: Game & Wildlife Conservation Trust, Burgate Manor, Fordingbridge, Hampshire, SP6 1EF. 01425 652 381; (Fax) 01425 655 848; e-mail: info@gwct.org.uk www.gwct.org.uk

GAY BIRDERS CLUB (1994; 350+)
A voluntary society for lesbian, gay and bisexual birdwatchers, their friends and supporters, over the age of consent, in the UK and worldwide. The club has a network of regional contacts and organises day trips, weekends and longer events at notable birding locations in the UK and abroad; about 200+ events in a year. Members receive a quarterly newsletter Out *Birding* with details of all events. There is a Grand Get-Together every 18 months. Membership £12 waged and £5 unwaged.
Contact: Gay Birders Club, GeeBeeCee, BCM-Mono, London WC1N 3XX. e-mail: contact@gbc-online.org.uk www.gbc-online.org.uk

NATIONAL ORGANISATIONS

HAWK AND OWL TRUST (1969)

Registered charity dedicated to the conservation and appreciation of wild birds of prey and their habitats. Publishes a newsletter members' magazine, *Peregrine* and educational materials for all ages. The Trust achieves its major aim of creating and enhancing nesting, roosting and feeding habitats for birds of prey through projects which involve practical research, creative conservation and education, both on its own reserves and in partnership with landowners, farmers and others. Members are invited to take part in fieldwork, population studies, surveys, etc. The Trust manages three main reserves: Sculthorpe Moor in Norfolk; Shapwick Moor on the Somerset Levels; and Fylingdales Moor conservation area in North Yorkshire. Its Sculthorpe reserve near Fakenham, Norfolk and National Conservation and Education Centre at Chiltern Open Air Museum near Chalfont St Giles, Buckinghamshire, offers schools and other groups cross-curricular environmental activities **Contact:** Hawk and Owl Trust, PO Box 100400, Bishops Lydeard, Taunton TA4 2WX3WH. Tel: 0844 984 2824; e-mail: enquiries@hawkandowl.org www.hawkandowl.org

HELPWILDLIFE.CO.UK (2005)

Helpwildlife.co.uk is maintained by a very small team of people involved in British wildlife rehabilitation to fully utilise the internet to help with wildlife issues. The site aims to provide informed, unbiased advice about caring for sick or injured birds and animals. Volunteers trawl the internet for details of those who might be able to help so that assistance can be offered quickly in an emergency. Visitors to the site are invited to provide feedback on the listings published to ensure they are kept as up to date as possible. E-mail: info@helpwildlife.co.uk

INTERNATIONAL CENTRE FOR BIRDS OF PREY (1967)

The ICBP works for the conservation of birds of prey and their habitats through public education, captive breeding, treatment and rehabilitation of wild injured birds of prey. Education is on-going to visitors and specific groups and parties, from first schools to universities, offering off-site lectures and teaching.

The Centre continues its captive breeding aims; to research species; maintain the Collection and provide birds for demonstrations.
The Centre also works with many other groups and facilities to continue to support worldwide field research projects and international conservation programmes. It accepts, treats and rehabilitates injured wild birds of prey. Open all year 10.30am-5.30pm (or dusk if earlier). Closed Christmas and Boxing Day.
Contact: International Birds of Prey Centre, Boulsdon House, Newent, Gloucestershire, GL18 1JJ. 01531 820 286 or 01531 821 581;
e-mail: jpj@icbp.org www.icbp.org

IRISH RARE BIRDS COMMITTEE (1985)

Assesses records of species of rare occurrence in the Republic of Ireland. Details of records accepted and rejected are incorporated in the *Irish Bird Report*, published annually in *Irish Birds*. In the case of rarities trapped for ringing, ringers in the Republic of Ireland are required to send their schedules initially to the National Parks and Wildlife Service, 51 St Stephen's Green, Dublin 2. A copy is then taken before the schedules are sent to the British Trust for Ornithology.
Contact: Secretary: Kieran Fahy, Silveracre, Yoletown, Tacumshin, County Wexford.
e-mail: secretary@irbc.ie www.irbc.ie

JOINT NATURE CONSERVATION COMMITTEE (1990)

A committee of the three country agencies (English Nature, Scottish Natural Heritage and the Countryside Council for Wales), together with independent members and representatives from Northern Ireland and the Countryside Agency. Supported by specialist staff, its statutory responsibilities include the establishment of common standards for monitoring; the analysis of information and research; advising Ministers on the development and implementation of policies for or affecting nature conservation; and the undertaking and commissioning of research relevant to these functions. JNCC additionally has the UK responsibility for relevant European and wider international matters. The Species Team, located at the HQ address is responsible for terrestrial bird conservation.
Contact: Joint Nature Conservation Committee, Monkstone House, City Road, Peterborough PE1 1JY. 01733 562 626; e-mail: comment@jncc.gov.uk www.jncc.gov.uk

LINNEAN SOCIETY OF LONDON (1788: 2,000)

Named after Carl Linnaeus, the 18th Century Swedish biologist, who created the modern system of scientific biological nomenclature, the Society promotes all aspects of pure and applied biology. It houses Linnaeus' collection of plants, insects and fishes, library and correspondence. The Society has a major reference library of some 100,000 volumes. Publishes the *Biological*, *Botanical* and *Zoological* Journals, and the *Synopses of the British Fauna*.
Contact: Linnean Society of London, Burlington House, Piccadilly, London W1J 0BF. 020 7434 4479; e-mail: info@linnean.org www.linnean.org

MAMMAL SOCIETY (1954; 2,500)

The Mammal Society is the only organisation solely dedicated to the study and conservation of all British mammals. It seeks to raise awareness of mammal ecology and conservation needs, to survey British

294

mammals and their habitats to identify the threats they face and to promote mammal studies in the UK and overseas.
Contact: The Mammal Society, 3 The Carronades, New Road, Southampton SO14 0AA. 0238 0237 874; e-mail: enquiries@mammal.org.uk
www.mammal.org.uk

MARINE CONSERVATION SOCIETY (1983)

MCS is the UK charity that campaigns for clean seas and beaches around the British coastline, sustainable fisheries, and protection for all marine life. MCS is consulted on a wide range of marine issues and provides advice primarily to government, but also to industry, on topics ranging from offshore wind, oil and gas, to marine strategies and fisheries reform. It provides advice to ensure that further action is taken to conserve our seas and reduce the effect of marine activities on marine habitats and species. It has an extensive programme for volunteers, ranging from fund-raising and an annual clean-up of UK beaches, to surveys of species such as basking shark.

Contact: Marine Conservation Society, Unit 3 Wolf Business Park, Alton Road, Ross-on-Wye, Herefordshire HR9 5NB. 01989 566 017
www.mcsuk.org

NATIONAL TRUST (1895; 3.5 Million)

Charity that works for the preservation of places of historic interest or natural beauty in England, Wales and Northern Ireland. It relies on 3.5 million members, 49,000 volunteers, 500,000 school children and millions of visitors, donors and supporters. The Trust protects and opens to the public more than 300 historic houses and gardens, 49 industrial monuments and mills, plus more than 617,500 acres of land and 700 miles of coast. About 10% of SSSIs and ASSIs in England, Wales and Northern Ireland are wholly or partially owned by the Trust, as are 63 NNRs, 33% of Ramsar sites and 45% of SPAs. Central Office: Heelis, Kemble Drive, Swindon, Wiltshire SN2 2NA. Tel: 01793 817 400; (Fax) 01793 817 401.
Contact: National Trust, PO Box 39, Warrington, WA5 7WD. 0844 800 1895;
e-mail: enquiries@thenationaltrust.org.uk

NATIONAL TRUST FOR SCOTLAND (1931; 310,000)

The conservation charity that protects and promotes Scotland's natural and cultural heritage for present and future generations to enjoy. Its 128 properties open to the public are described in its annual *Scotland For You* guide.
Contact: National Trust for Scotland, Hermiston Quay, 5 Cultins Road, Edinburgh, EH11 4DF. 0844 493 2100; e-mail: information@nts.org.uk www.nts.org.uk

NATURAL ENGLAND

Natural England has been formed by bringing together English Nature, the landscape, access and recreation elements of the Countryside Agency and the environmental land management functions of the Rural Development Service. Natural England is working towards the delivery of four strategic outcomes: 1) A healthy natural environment through conservation and enhancement. 2) Encouraging more people to enjoy, understand and act to improve the natural environment. 3) Ensure the use and management of the natural environment is more sustainable. 4) A secure environmental future.
Contact: Natural England, Head Office – Foundry House, 3 Millsands, Riverside Exchange, Sheffield S3 8NH. 0845 600 3078;
e-mail: enquiries@naturalengland.org.uk
www.naturalengland.org.uk

NATURAL HISTORY MUSEUM AT TRING (1937)

Founded by Lord Rothschild, the Museum displays British and exotic birds (1,500 species) including

many rarities and extinct species. Galleries open all year except Dec 24-26. Adjacent to the Bird Group of the Natural History Museum - with over a million specimens and an extensive ornithological library, an internationally important centre for bird research.
Contact: The Natural History Museum at Tring, Akeman Street, Tring, Herts HP23 6AP. 020 7942 6171; e-mail: tring-enquiries@nhm.ac.uk
www.nhm.ac.uk/tring

NATURE PHOTOGRAPHERS' PORTFOLIO (1944; 71)

A society for photographers of wildlife, especially birds. Circulates postal portfolios of prints and transparencies, and an on-line folio.
Contact: A Winspear-Cundall, Hon Secretary, Nature Photographers' Portfolio, 8 Gig Bridge Lane, Pershore, Worcs WR10 1NH. 01386 552 103;
e-mail: arthurcundall@hotmail.co.uk
www.nature-photographers-portfolio.co.uk

NORTHERN IRELAND BIRDWATCHERS' ASSOCIATION (1991; 120)

The NIBA Records Committee, established in 1997, has full responsibility for the assessment of records in N Ireland. NIBA also publishes the Northern Ireland Bird Report and is responsible for Flightline, a local rate telephone hotline for rare bird sightings.
Contact: The Membership Secretary, Northern Ireland Birdwatchers' Assoc, 9 Ballymacash Rd, Lisburn, Co. Antrim, N Ireland BT28 3DX . 01247 467 408;
http://nibirds.blogspot.com

NORTHERN IRELAND ORNITHOLOGISTS' CLUB (1965; 150)

Formed to focus the interests of active birdwatchers in Northern Ireland, it operates Tree Sparrow and Barn Owl nestbox schemes and a winter feeding programme for Yellowhammers. Has a regular programme of lectures and field trips for members and organises a high quality annual photographic competition. Publishes *The Harrier* quarterly.
Contact: The Honorary Secretary, C Gillespie, Northern Ireland Ornithologists Club, 4 Demesne Gate, Saintfield, Co. Down, BT24 7BE. 02897 519 371; e-mail: carolgillespie@btinternet.com; www.nioc.co.uk

NORTH SEA BIRD CLUB (1979; 200)

The Club aims to: provide a recreational pursuit for people employed offshore; obtain, collate and analyse observations of all birds seen offshore; produce reports of observations, including an annual report; promote the collection of data on other wildlife offshore. Currently it holds in excess of 100,000 records of birds, cetaceans and insects reported since 1979.
Contact: The North Sea Bird Club, Ocean Laboratory and Culterty Field Station, University of Aberdeen, Newburgh, Aberdeenshire AB41 6AA. 01224 274 428; e-mail: nsbc@abdn.ac.uk www.abdn.ac.uk/nsbc

PEOPLE'S DISPENSARY FOR SICK ANIMALS (1917)

Provides free veterinary treatment for sick and injured animals whose owners qualify for this charitable service.
Contact: PDSA, Whitechapel Way, Priorslee, Telford, Shropshire TF2 9PQ. 01952 290 999; e-mail: pr@pdsa.org.uk www.pdsa.org.uk

POND CONSERVATION

Pond Conservation is dedicated to creating and protecting ponds and the wildlife they support. It carries out research, surveys and practical conservation,

Pond Conservation
For Life in Fresh Waters

working in partnership with others. It also works to protect the wildlife of other freshwaters. Key projects include: the Million Ponds Project; Garden ponds survey; Pond Habitat Action Plan, in conjunction with the Environment Agency.
Contact: Pond Conservation, 01865 483 249; e-mail: info@pondconservation.org.uk www.pondconservation.org.uk

RAPTOR FOUNDATION (1989)

Involved in the care of wild, disabled birds of prey, as well as raptors rescued from breeders. The foundation researches raptor ailments and assists veterinary schools. A full 24 hour rescue service is available for injured raptors and owls and the centre assists in breed-and-release schemes to rebuild populations across Europe. Centre is open to the public (200 birds of 40 different species on display)

10am to 5pm each day apart from Jan 1 and Dec 25/26.
Contact: The Raptor Foundation, The Heath, St Ives Road, Woodhurst, Cambs PE28 3BT. 01487 741 140; e-mail: info@raptorfoundation.org.uk www.raptorfoundation.org.uk

RAPTOR RESCUE (1978)

Since inauguration, Raptor Rescue has evolved into one of the UK's foremost organisations dedicated to ensuring all sick and injured birds of prey are cared for by suitably qualified people, and wherever possible, released back into the wild. Facilities include secluded aviaries, rehabilitation aviaries/ flights, and foster birds for rearing young to avoid imprinting.
Contact: Raptor Rescue, Bird of Prey Rehabilitation, 0870 241 0609; www.raptorrescue.org.uk e-mail: secretary@raptorrescue.org.uk

RARE BREEDING BIRDS PANEL (1973; 7)

An independent body funded by the JNCC and RSPB, it collects all information on rare breeding birds in the United Kingdom, so that changes in status can be monitored as an aid to conservation and stored for posterity. Special forms are used (obtainable from the website) and records should be submitted via the county and regional recorders. Since 1996 the Panel also monitors breeding by scarcer non-native species and seeks records of these in the same way. Annual report is published in *British Birds*. For details of species covered by the Panel see Log Charts and the websites.
Contact: The Secretary, Rare Breeding Birds Panel, The Old Orchard, Grange Road, North Berwick, East Lothian EH39 4QT. 01620 894 037; e-mail: secretary@rbbp.org.uk www.rbbp.org.uk

ROYAL AIR FORCE ORNITHOLOGICAL SOCIETY (1965; 250)

RAFOS organises regular field meetings for members, carries out ornithological census work on MoD properties and mounts major expeditions annually to various UK and overseas locations. Publishes a Newsletter twice a year, a Journal annually, and reports on its expeditions and surveys.
Contact: General Secretary by e-mail: rafos_secretary@hotmail.com www.rafos.org.uk

ROYAL NAVAL BIRDWATCHING SOCIETY (1946; 250)

Covering all main ocean routes, the Society reports the positions and identity of seabirds and landbirds at sea by means of standard sea report forms. Maintains an extensive worldwide seabird database. Members are encouraged to photograph birds and a library of images is maintained. Publishes a Bulletin and an annual report entitled *The Sea Swallow*. The Simpson Scholarship provides assistance to embryonic ornithologists for studies regarding seabirds and landbirds at sea.
Contact: General Secretary, CPO Steve Copsey (temporary position) www.rnbws.org.uk

NATIONAL ORGANISATIONS

ROYAL PIGEON RACING ASSOCIATION (1897; 39,000)

Exists to promote the sport of pigeon racing and controls pigeon racing within the Association. Organises liberation sites, issues rings, calculates distances between liberation sites and home lofts, and assists in the return of strays. May be able to assist in identifying owners of ringed birds caught or found.

Contact: Royal Pigeon Racing Association, The Reddings, Cheltenham, GL51 6RN. 01452 713 529; e-mail: gm@rpra.org www.rpra.org

ROYAL SOCIETY FOR THE PREVENTION OF CRUELTY TO ANIMALS (1824; 43,690)

In addition to its animal centres, the Society also runs a woodland study centre and nature reserve at Mallydams Wood in East Sussex, and specialist wildlife rehabilitation centres at West Hatch, Taunton, Somerset TA3 5RT (0870 0101 847), at Station Road, East Winch, King's Lynn, Norfolk PE32 1NR (0870 9061 420), and London Road, Stapeley, Nantwich, Cheshire CW5 7JW (not open to the public). Inspectors are contacted through their National Communication Centre, which can be reached via the Society's 24-hour national cruelty and advice line: 08705 555 999.

Contact: RSPCA Headquarters, Willberforce Way, Horsham, West Sussex RH13 9RS. 0300 1234 555; (Fax) 0303 123 0284. 24-hour cruelty and advice line: 0300 1234 999. www.rspca.org.uk

ROYAL SOCIETY FOR THE PROTECTION OF BIRDS (1899 1,000,000+)

UK Partner of BirdLife International, and Europe's largest voluntary wildlife conservation body.
The RSPB, a registered charity, is governed by an elected body (see also RSPB Phoenix and RSPB Wildlife Explorers). Its work in the conservation of wild birds and habitats covers the acquisition and management of nature reserves; research and surveys; monitoring and responding to development proposals, land use practices and pollution which threaten wild birds and biodiversity; and the provision of an advisory service on wildlife law enforcement.

The RSPB currently manages 200 nature reserves in the UK, covering almost 130,00 hectares and home to 80% of Britain's rarest or most threatened bird species. The aim is to conserve a countrywide network of reserves with all examples of the main bird communities and with due regard to the conservation of plants and other animals. Current national projects include extensive work on agriculture, and conservation and campaigning for the conservation of the marine environment and to halt the illegal persecution of birds of prey. Increasingly, there is involvement with broader environmental concerns such as climate change and transport.

The RSPB's International Dept works closely with Birdlife International and its partners in other countries and is involved with numerous projects overseas, especially in Europe and Asia.

Contact: RSPB, The Lodge, Sandy, Beds SG19 2DL. Membership enquiries: 01767 693 680. Wildlife enquiries: 01767 693 690; www.rspb.org.uk e-mail: (firstname.name)@rspb.org.uk

Regional Offices:

ENGLAND

Eastern England, Stalham House, 65 Thorpe Road, Norwich NR1 1UD. 01603 661 662.
Covers: Beds, Cambs, Essex, Herts, Lincs, Norfolk, Suffolk.

London Office, RSPB London Office, 2nd Floor, 65 Petty France, London, SW1H 9EU. 0207 808 1240.

Midlands, 46 The Green, South Bar, Banbury, Oxfordshire, OX16 9AB. 01295 253 330.
Covers: Bucks, Derbys, Herefordshire, Leicestershire, Northants, Notts, Oxon, Rutland, Shropshire, Staffs, Warwickshire, West Midlands, Worcestershire.

Northern England, Denby Dale Office, Westleigh Mews, Wakefield Road, Denby Dale, Huddersfield, HD8 8QD. 01484 861 148.
Covers: Cheshire, Cleveland, Cumbria, East Riding of Yorkshire, Greater Manchester, Lancashire, Merseyside, Middlesbrough, North, South and West Yorkshire, North East and North Lincolnshire, Northumberland, Tyne and Wear.

South East, 2nd Floor, 42 Frederick Place, Brighton, East Sussex, BN1 4EA. 01273 775 333.
Covers: East Sussex, Hampshire, Isle of Wight, Kent, Surrey, West Berkshire, West Sussex.

South West, Keble House, Southernhay Gardens, Exeter EX1 1NT. 01392 432 691.
Covers: Bristol, Cornwall, Devon, Dorset, Somerset, Gloucs, Wiltshire.

SCOTLAND

Scotland Headquarters, Dunedin House, 25 Ravelston Terrace, Edinburgh, EH4 3TP. 0131 311 6500.
e-mail: rspb.scotland@rspb.org.uk

East Scotland, 10 Albyn Terrace, Aberdeen, Aberdeenshire, AB10 1YP. 01224 624 824.
Covers: Aberdeen, Aberdeenshire, Angus, Moray, Perth and Kinross.

North Scotland, Etive House, Beechwood Park, Inverness, IV2 3BW. 01463 715 000;
e-mail: nsro@rspb.org.uk
Covers: Eilean Siar, Highland.

South and West Scotland, 10 Park Quadrant, Glasgow, G3 6BS. 0141 331 0993;
e-mail: glasgow@rspb.org.uk
Covers: Argyll and Bute, Clackmannanshire, Dumfries and Galloway, East Ayrshire, East Lothian, East Dunbartonshire, East Renfrewshire, Midlothian, North Ayrshire, North Lanarkshire, Renfrewshire, Scottish

NATIONAL ORGANISATIONS

borders, South Ayrshire, South Lanarkshire, Stirling, West Dunbartonshire, West Lothian.

WALES
RSPB Wales, Sutherland House, Castlebridge, Cowbridge Road East, Cardiff CF11 9AB. 029 2035 3000.

NORTHERN IRELAND
Northern Ireland Headquarters, Belvoir Park Forest, Belfast, BT8 7QT. 028 9049 1547.
Covers: County Antrim, County Armagh, County Down, County Fermanagh, County Londonderry, County Tyrone.

RSPB WILDLIFE EXPLORERS and RSPB PHOENIX (formerly YOC) (1965; 168,000)
Junior section of the RSPB. There are more than 100 groups run by 300 volunteers. Activities include projects, holidays, roadshows, competitions, and local events for children, families and teenagers. Phoenix members (13 years and over) receive *BirdLife* magazine every two months, plus *Wingbeat* — the only environmental magazine written by teenagers for teenagers — four times a year.
Contact: The Youth Manager, RSPB Youth and Education Dept, The Lodge, Sandy, Beds SG19 2DL. 01767 680 551; e-mail: explorers@rspb.org.uk and phoenix@rspb.org.uk www.rspb.org.uk/youth

SCOTTISH BIRDS RECORDS COMMITTEE (1984; 7 members, plus secretary)
Set up by the Scottish Ornithologists' Club to ensure that records of species not deemed rare enough to be considered by the British Birds Rarities Committee, but which are rare in Scotland, are fully assessed; also maintains the official list of Scottish birds.
Contact: Angus Hogg, Secretary, Scottish Birds Records Committee, 11 Kirkmichael Road, Crosshill, Maybole, Ayrshire KA19 7RJ. www.the-soc.org.uk e-mail: dcgos@globalnet.co.uk

SCOTTISH ORNITHOLOGISTS' CLUB (1936; 2,250)
The Club has 14 branches (see County Directory), each with a programme of winter meetings and field trips throughout the year. The SOC organises an annual weekend conference in the autumn and a joint SOC/BTO one-day birdwatchers' conference in spring. *Scottish Birds* is published quarterly and incorporates the *Scottish Bird News* and the scarce sightings journal *Birding Scotland*. The SOC is based in a large resource centre which offers panoramic views of Aberlady Bay and houses the George Waterston Library.
Contact: The Scottish Birdwatching Resource Centre, The SOC, Waterston House, Aberlady, East Lothian EH32 0PY. 01875 871 330; (Fax) 01875 871 035; e-mail: mail@the-soc.org.uk www.the-soc.org.uk

SCOTTISH NATURAL HERITAGE (1991)
SNH is the Scottish Executive's statutory advisor in respect to the conservation, enhancement,

enjoyment, understanding and sustainable use of the natural heritage.
Contact: Scottish Natural Heritage, Great Glen House, Leachkin Road, Inverness IV3 8NW. 01463 725 000; e-mail: enquiries@snh.gov.uk www.snh.org.uk

SCOTTISH SOCIETY FOR THE PREVENTION OF CRUELTY TO ANIMALS (1839; 45,000 supporters)
Represents animal welfare interests to Government, local authorities and others. Educates young people to realise their responsibilities. Maintains an inspectorate to patrol and investigate and to advise owners about the welfare of animals and birds in their care. Maintains welfare centres, two of which include oiled bird cleaning centres. Bird species, including birds of prey, are rehabilitated and where possible released back into the wild.
Contact: Scottish SPCA, Braehead Mains, 603 Queensferry Road, Edinburgh EH4 6EA. 03000 999 999; (Fax) 0131 339 4777; www.scottishspca.org e-mail: enquiries@scottishspca.org

SCOTTISH WILDLIFE TRUST (1964; 35,000)
The Trust aims to re-establish: 'a network of healthy and resilient ecosystems supporting expanding communities of native species across large areas of Scotland's land, water and seas.' Its main activities focus on managing 123 wildlife reserves and undertaking practical conservation tasks; influencing and campaigning for better wildlife-related policy and action; inspiring people to enjoy and find out more about wildlife. Member of The Wildlife Trusts partnership and organises Scottish Wildlife Week. Publishes *Scottish Wildlife* three times a year.
Contact: Scottish Wildlife Trust, Harbourside House, 110 Commercial Street, Edinburgh EH6 6NF. 0131 312 7765; (Fax) 0131 312 8705; e-mail: enquiries@swt.org.uk www.swt.org.uk

SEABIRD GROUP (1966; 350)
Concerned with conservation issues affecting seabirds. Assists with co-ordination of census and monitoring work on breeding seabirds; has established and maintains the Seabird Colony Register in collaboration with the JNCC; organises regular conferences on seabird biology and conservation topics. Small grants available to assist with research and survey work on seabirds. Publishes the *Seabird Group Newsletter* every four months and the journal *Seabird* annually.
Contact: Linda Wilson, JNCC, Inverdee House, Baxter Street, Aberdeen, AB11 9QA. www.seabirdgroup.org.uk e-mail: linda.wilson@jncc.gov.uk

SOCIETY FOR CONSERVATION IN AVICULTURE (1993)
The Society aims to promote and develop all species and varieties of birds kept by aviculturists, with special regard to threatened and endangered species both in the wild and in captivity. Officers play an active role in promoting responsible care and ownership of all birds. Members do not have to be bird keepers.
Contact: SCA, PO Box 208, Wirral CH29 9DD. Helpline: 0845 634 2193. www.thesca.org.uk

NATIONAL ORGANISATIONS

SOCIETY OF WILDLIFE ARTISTS (1964; 62 Members, 68 Associates)

Registered charity that seeks to generate an appreciation of the natural world through all forms of fine art. Annual exhibition held in Oct/Nov at the Mall Galleries, London. Through bursary schemes, the Society has been able to help young artists with awards of up to £1,000 towards travel, education or the cost of materials. **Contact:** The Secretary, Society of Wildlife Artists, Federation of British Artists, 17 Carlton House Terrace, London SW1Y 5BD. 020 7930 6844; e-mail: info@mallgalleries.com www.swla.co.uk

SWAN SANCTUARY (2005)

Founded by Dorothy Beeson BEM, this registered charity operates nationally. Has a fully equipped swan hospital. New site has several nursing ponds and a four acre rehabilitation lake where around 4,000 swans and the same number of other forms of wildlife are treated. 24-hour service operated, with volunteer rescuers on hand to recover victims of oil spills, vandalism etc. **Contact:** The Swan Sanctuary, Felix Lane, Shepperton, Middlesex TW17 8NN. Emergency number: 01932 240 790; www.swanuk.org.uk e-mail: swans@swanuk.org.uk

SWIFT CONSERVATION (2009)

An advice service which aims to reverse the decline in the UK's Swifts. Swift Conservation runs a website providing extensive information on Swifts, and on how to both preserve and set up Swift nest sites. Swift Conservation also runs a lecture and training service, providing guidance for the general public, Planners and Architects. It supplies local advice and help via a network of volunteer helpers, and has links to similar assistance across Europe. Together with the RSPB it conducts an annual cumulative survey of known Swift nest places, from information supplied by the general public and its volunteers. It campaigns for better protection of Swifts and other birds that rely on nest places in or on buildings. **Contact:** Swift Conservation, 28 Yale Court, Honeybourne Road, London NW6 1JG, 020 7794 2098; e-mail@swift-conservation.org www.swift-conservation.org

UK400 CLUB (1981)

Serves to monitor the nation's leading twitchers and their life lists, and to keep under review contentious species occurrences. Publishes a bi-monthly magazine *Rare Birds*. Membership open to all. **Contact:** LGR Evans, UK400 Club, 8 Sandycroft Road, Little Chalfont, Amersham, Bucks HP6 6QL. 01494 763 010; e-mail: LGREUK400@aol.com www.uk400clubonline.co.uk

WADER STUDY GROUP (1970; 600)

An association of wader enthusiasts, both amateur and professional, from all parts of the world, the Group aims to maintain contact between them, help organise co-operative studies, and provide a vehicle for the exchange of information. Publishes the *Wader*

Study Group Bulletin three times a year and holds annual meetings throughout Europe. **Contact:** The General Secretary, International Wader Study Group, The British Trust for Ornithology, The Nunnery, Thetford, Norfolk IP24 2PU. www.waderstudygroup.org

WELSH KITE TRUST (1996; 1,200)

A registered charity that undertakes the conservation and annual monitoring of Red Kites in Wales. It attempts to locate all the breeding birds, to compile data on population growth, productivity, range expansion etc. The Trust liaises with landowners, acts as consultant on planning issues and with regard to filming and photography, and represents Welsh interests on the UK Kite Steering Group. Provides a limited rescue service for injured kites and eggs or chicks at risk of desertion or starvation. Publishes a newsletter *Boda Wennol* twice a year, sent free to subscribing Friends of the Welsh Kite and to all landowners with nesting kites. **Contact:** Tony Cross, Project Officer, Welsh Kite Trust, Samaria, Nantmel, Llandrindod Wells, Powys LD1 6EN. 01597 825 981; www.welshkitetrust.org; e-mail: info@welshkitetrust.org

WELSH ORNITHOLOGICAL SOCIETY (1988; 250)

Promotes the study, conservation and enjoyment of birds throughout Wales. Runs the Welsh Records Panel which adjudicates records of scarce species in Wales. Publishes the journal *Birds In Wales* and organises an annual conference. **Contact:** Membership details from Welsh Ornithological Society, Alan Williams, Treasurer/Membership Secretary; e-mail: treasurer@birdsinwales.org.uk www.birdsinwales.org.uk

WETLAND TRUST

Set up to encourage conservation of wetlands and develop study of migratory birds, and to foster international relations in these fields. Destinations for recent expeditions inc. Brazil, Senegal, The Gambia, Guinea-Bissau, Nigeria, Kuwait, Thailand, Greece and Jordan. Large numbers of birds are ringed each year in Sussex and applications are invited from individuals to train in bird ringing or extend their experience. **Contact:** Phil Jones, Wetland Trust, Elms Farm, Pett Lane, Icklesham, Winchelsea, E Sussex TN36 4AH. 01797 226374; e-mail: phil@wetlandtrust.org

WILDFOWL & WETLANDS TRUST (1946; 130,000 members)

Founded by Sir Peter Scott to conserve wetlands and their biodiversity, WWT has nine centres (see below). The centres are nationally, or internationally, important for wintering wildfowl. Programmes of walks and talks are available for visitors, and resources and programmes are provided for

NATIONAL ORGANISATIONS

school groups. Centres, except Caerlaverock and Welney, have wildfowl from around the world, inc. endangered species.
Research Department works on population dynamics, species management plans and wetland ecology. The Wetland Advisory Service (WAS) undertakes contracts, and Wetland Link International promotes the role of wetland centres for education and public awareness.
Contact: Wildfowl and Wetlands Trust, Slimbridge, Glos, GL2 7BT. 01453 891 900; (Fax) 01453 890 827; e-mail: enquiries@wwt.org.uk www.wwt.org.uk

CENTRES:
WWT Arundel Wetland Centre, Mill Road, Arundel, Sussex BN18 9PB. 01903 883 355; (Fax) 01903 884834; e-mail: info.arundel@wwt.org.uk

WWT Caerlaverock Wetland Centre, Eastpark Farm, Caerlaverock, Dumfriesshire, Scotland DG1 4RS. 01387 770 200 (Fax) 01387 770 539; e-mail: info.caerlaverock@wwt.org.uk

WWT Castle Espie Wetland Centre, 78 Ballydrain Road, Comber, Co Down, N Ireland BT23 6EA. 028 9187 4146 (Fax) 028 9187 3857; e-mail: info.castleespie@wwt.org.uk

WWT London Wetland Centre, Queen Elizabeth's Walk, Barnes, London SW13 9WT. 020 8409 4400 (Fax) 020 8409 4401; e-mail: info.london@wwt.org.uk

WWT Martin Mere Wetland Centre, Fish Lane, Burscough, Lancashire L40 0TA. 01704 895 181 (Fax) 01704 892 343; e-mail: info.martinmere@wwt.org.uk

WWT National Wetland Centre Wales, Llwynhendy, Llanelli, Carmarthenshire SA14 9SH. 01554 741 087; (Fax) 01554 744 101; e-mail: info.llanelli@wwt.org.uk

WWT Slimbridge Wetland Centre, Slimbridge, Gloucestershire GL2 7BT. 01453 891 900; (Fax) 01453 890 827; e-mail: info.slimbridge@wwt.org.uk

WWT Washington Wetland Centre, Pattinson, Washington, Tyne and Wear NE38 8LE. 0191 416 5454; e-mail: info.washington@wwt.org.uk

WWT Welney Wetland Centre, Hundred Foot Bank, Welney, Nr. Wisbech, PE14 7TN. 01353 860 711; (Fax) 01353 863 524; e-mail: info.welney@wwt.org.uk

WILDLIFE SOUND RECORDING SOCIETY (1968; 327)
Works closely with the Wildlife Section of the National Sound Archive. Members carry out recording work for scientific purposes as well as for pleasure. A field weekend is held each spring, and members organise meetings locally. Four CD sound magazines of members' recordings are produced for members each year, and a journal, *Wildlife Sound*, is published twice a year.
Contact: Hon Membership Secretary, WSRS, Wildlife Sound Recording Society; www.wildlife-sound.org/ e-mail: enquiries@wildlife-sound.org

WILDLIFE TRUSTS (1995; 800,000)
Founded in 1912 and now the largest UK charity exclusively dedicated to conserving all habitats and species, with a membership of more than 800,000 people including 108,000 junior members

in 47 individual county trusts. Collectively, they manage more than 2,200 nature reserves spanning over 80,000 hectares. The Wildlife Trusts also lobby for better protection of the UK's natural heritage and are dedicated to protecting wildlife for the future.
Members receive *Natural World* magazine three times a year.
Contact: The Wildlife Trusts, The Kiln, Waterside, Mather Road, Newark NG24 1WT. 01636 677 711; (Fax) 01636 670 001; e-mail: enquiry@wildlifetrusts.org www.wildlifetrusts.org

WILDLIFE WATCH (1977; 108.000)
The junior branch of The Wildlife Trusts. It supports 1,500 registered volunteer leaders running Watch groups across the UK. Publishes *Watchword* and *Wildlife Extra* for children, and activity books for adults working with young people.
Contact: Wildlife Watch, The Wildlife Trusts, The Kiln, Waterside, Mather Road, Newark NG24 1WT. 01636 677 711; (Fax) 01636 670 001; e-mail: watch@wildlifetrusts.org www.wildlifewatch.org.uk

WWF-UK (1961)
WWF is the world's largest independent conservation organisation, comprising 27 national organisations. It works to conserve and species, protect endangered spaces, and address global threats to nature by seeking long-term solutions with people in government and industry, education and civil society.
Publishes *WWF News* (quarterly magazine)
Contact: WWF-UK (World Wide Fund for Nature), Panda House, Weyside Park, Catteshall Lane, Godalming, Surrey GU7 1XR. 01483 426 444; (Fax) 01483 426 409; www.wwf.org.uk

ZOOLOGICAL PHOTOGRAPHIC CLUB (1899)
Circulates black and white and colour prints of zoological interest via a series of postal portfolios.
Contact: Martin B Withers, Hon Secretary, Zoological Photographic Club, 93 Cross Lane, Mountsorrel, Loughborough, Leics LE12 7BX. 0116 229 6080.

ZOOLOGICAL SOCIETY OF LONDON (1826)
Carries out research, organises symposia and holds scientific meetings. Manages the Zoological Gardens in Regent's Park (first opened in 1828) and Whipsnade Wild Animal Park near Dunstable, Beds, each with extensive collections of birds. The Society's library has a large collection of ornithological books and journals. Publications include the *Journal of Zoology, Animal Conservation, Conservation Biology* book series, *The Symposia* and *The International Zoo Yearbook*.
Contact: Zoological Society of London, Regent's Park, London, NW1 4RY. 020 7722 3333; www.zsl.org

NATIONAL PROJECTS

National ornithological projects depend for their success on the active participation of amateur birdwatchers. In return they provide birdwatchers with an excellent opportunity to contribute in a positive and worthwhile way to the scientific study of birds and their habitats, which is the vital basis of all conservation programmes. The following entries provide a description of each particular project and a note of whom to contact for further information (full address details of project organisers are in the previous section).

BIRD ATLAS 2007-11
BTO, in partnership with BirdWatch Ireland and Scottish Ornithologists' Club
Atlases have provided a periodic stock-take of the birds of Britain and Ireland. This latest Atlas will do just that, this time in both the breeding season and in winter. It will generate range and abundance maps for all species, while giving the opportunity to contrast past and present distributions and assess changes, for better or worse.
Fieldwork was completed at the end of the 2011 breeding season, though around 20 counties undertaking local atlases will continue for another year or more. Look online to see if your county is continuing fieldwork and please submit you records. National results and statistics continue to be updated daily.
Contact: e-mail: birdatlas@bto.org and www.birdatlas.net

BirdTrack
Organised by BTO on behalf of BTO, RSPB, BirdWatch Ireland and WOS
BirdTrack is a free, online bird recording system for birdwatchers to store and manage bird records from anywhere in Britain and Ireland. The idea is simple. Make a note of the birds seen or heard at each site visited, and then enter your observations on an easy-to-use web page (www.birdtrack.net).
Exciting real-time outputs are generated by BirdTrack, including species reporting-rate graphs and animated maps of sightings, all freely-available online. The data collected are used by researchers to investigate migration movements and the distribution of scarce birds, and to support species conservation at local, national and international scales.
Contact: Nick Moran, BTO.
E-mail: birdtrack@bto.org

BREEDING BIRD SURVEY
Supported by BTO, JNCC and RSPB
Started in 1994, the BBS is designed to keep track of the changes in populations of our common breeding birds. It is dependent on volunteer birdwatchers throughout the country who make two visits, about five hours in total, to survey the breeding birds in a 1x1km square. Survey squares are picked at random by computer to ensure that all habitats and regions are covered.
Since its inception it has been a tremendous success, with more than 3,000 squares covered and more than 200 species recorded each year.
Contact: Kate Risely, e-mail: bbs@bto.org, or your local BTO Regional Representative (see County Directory).

CONSTANT EFFORT SITES (CES) SCHEME
Funded by a partnership between BTO, JNCC, The National Parks & Wildlife Service (Ireland) and ringers themselves
The CES scheme, run since 1983, coordinates standardised summer ringing at over 120 sites across Britain and Ireland. This allows the BTO to monitor trends in the numbers of 25 scrub and woodland species, while simultaneously providing annual estimates of breeding success and survival rates of adult birds.
Information from CES complements demographic information collected by other BTO surveys and feeds into the BTO's Integrated Population Monitoring, highlighting the causes of changes in bird populations. Results are updated annually and published on-line as part of the BirdTrends Report (www.bto.org/BirdTrends).
Contact: Allison Kew, BTO ces@bto.org and www.bto.org/ces

GARDEN BIRD FEEDING SURVEY
A BTO project
The Garden Bird Feeding Survey is the longest-running study of garden birds in Britain. Each year, approximately 250 householders record the numbers and variety of birds using food supplements and water that they have provided in their garden. Observations are made on a weekly basis from October to March inclusive. Gardens are selected by region and type; from city flats to suburban semis, rural houses to outlying farms.
Contact: Tim Harrison, BTO.
E-mail: tim.harrison@bto.org

NATIONAL PROJECTS

BTO GARDEN BIRDWATCH
A BTO project
Started in January 1995, this project is a year-round survey that monitors the use that birds and other types of wildlife make of gardens. Approximately 15,000 participants from all over the UK and Ireland keep a weekly log of species using their gardens. The data collected are used to monitor regional, seasonal and year-to-year changes in the garden populations of our commoner birds, mammals, butterflies, reptiles and amphibians.
To cover running costs there is an annual subscription of £15. Participants receive a quarterly colour magazine *The Bird Table* and all new joiners receive a full-colour, garden bird handbook. Results and more information are available online: www.bto.org/gbw
Contact: Garden Ecology Team, BTO.
E-mail: gbw@bto.org

GOOSE AND SWAN MONITORING
A WWT project
Geese and swans are a cornerstone of the Wildfowl and Wetland Trust's conservation work. During winter, geese and swans from Canada to central Russia undertake arduous migrations to reach their wintering grounds in the UK. In order to safeguard them WWT tracks how many individuals are in each population, where they are found, and the overall trend of the population (whether it is increasing, decreasing, or remaining stable). Other demographic measures — most importantly, productivity (how many young are born each year) and survival (or mortality) rates — help to understand the reasons behind any increase or decrease. To get information like this WWT use a number of techniques and tools, including counts and capture and marking. A large amount of this work is carried out by volunteer birdwatchers who give their time to assist with data collection.
Contact: e-mail:enquiries@wwt.org.uk
http://monitoring.wwt.org.uk

HERONRIES CENSUS
A BTO project
This survey, started in 1928, has been carried out under the auspices of the BTO since 1934 and represents the longest continuous series of population data for any European breeding bird (Grey Heron). Counts of apparently occupied nests are made at as many UK heronries as possible each year, to provide an index of current population levels.

Data from Scotland and Northern Ireland are scant, and more contributions from these countries would be especially welcomed. Herons may be hit hard during periods of severe weather and are vulnerable to pesticides and pollution. Currently, however, population levels are relatively high. Little Egret and other incoming species of colonial waterbird such as Cattle Egret are now fully included, whether nesting with Grey Herons, or on their own. Counts of Cormorant nests at heronries are also encouraged.
Contact: John Marchant, BTO.
E-mail: john.marchant@bto.org

IRISH WETLAND BIRD SURVEY
(I-WeBS)
A joint project of BirdWatch Ireland, the National Parks & Wildlife Service of the Dept of Arts, Culture & the Gaeltacht, and WWT, and supported by the Heritage Council and WWF-UK.
The Irish Wetland Bird Survey (I-WeBS) is the scheme that monitors wintering waterbirds in Ireland. The survey runs from September to March each winter. Wetlands of all types and sizes are monitored, including estuaries, coastlines, bays, rivers, turloughs, lakes, streams and flooded fields. Each winter, more than 350 people take part. These counters go out and count waterbirds at over 800 wetlands throughout the country. The counts are done once-monthly by skilled volunteers, as well  as by professional staff of the National Parks and Wildlife Service and BirdWatch Ireland.
Contact: Helen, I-WeBS Office, BirdWatch Ireland, 353 (0)1 281 9878; www.birdwatchireland.ie
e-mail: hboland@birdwatchireland.ie

NEST BOX CHALLENGE
A BTO project
NBC is an on-line survey which aims to monitor the breeding success of birds in Britain's green spaces. Participants are asked to register one or more nests, or nest boxes, in their garden or local green space, monitoring their progress via regular nest inspections and recording the number of eggs and/or chicks present at each visit. Records of unused boxes are also valuable as they can be used to determine next box occupancy rates.

NATIONAL PROJECTS

Anyone who has a nest box or nest in their garden or local park can take part.
Contact: Carl Barimore, BTO. E-mail: nbc@bto.org and www.bto.org/nbc

NEST RECORD SCHEME
A BTO Project carried out under contract with the JNCC.
The scheme monitors changes in the nesting success and the timing of breeding of Britain's bird species by gathering information on nests found anywhere in the country, from a Blackbird in a garden to an Oystercatcher on a Scottish loch. Participants locate nests and monitor their progress over several visits, making counts of the number of eggs and/or chicks on each occasion and recording whether they are successful. Information from NRS complements demographic information collected by other BTO surveys and feeds into the BTO's Integrated Population Monitoring, highlighting the causes of changes in bird populations.
More than 30,000 nest records are submitted to the BTO each year by volunteer surveyors and the results are updated annually and published on-line as part of the BirdTrends Report (www.bto.org/BirdTrends). Guidance on how to become a BTO nest recorder, including best practice guidelines on minimising disturbance while visiting nests, is available online. A free starter pack is available on request.
Contact: Carl Barimore, BTO E-mail: nrs@bto.org and www.bto.org/nrs

RAPTOR AND OWL RESEARCH REGISTER
A BTO project
The Register has helped considerably over the past 30 years in encouraging and guiding research, and in the co-ordination of projects. There are currently almost 500 on-going projects. Barn Owls and Tawny Owls are currently receiving most attention. As to raptors, the most popular subjects are Kestrels, Buzzards, Sparrowhawks, Hobbies and Peregrines, with researchers showing increasing interest in Red Kites, and fewer large in-depth studies of Goshawks, Ospreys and harriers.
Contributing is a simple process and involves all raptor enthusiasts, whether it is to describe an amateur activity or professional study. The nature of research on record varies widely, and includes local pellet analyses, captive breeding and rehabilitation programmes, and national surveys of Peregrines, Buzzards and Golden Eagles. Birdwatchers, both in Britain and abroad, are encouraged to write for photocopies of cards relevant to the species or nature of their work.

The effectiveness of the Register depends upon those running projects (however big or small) ensuring that their work is included.
Contact: David Glue, BTO.

RETRAPPING ADULTS FOR SURVIVAL (RAS) SCHEME
Funded by a partnership between BTO, JNCC, The National Parks & Wildlife Service (Ireland) and ringers themselves
The RAS scheme, started in 1998, gathers information on recaptures or re-sightings of adult birds. Ringers choose a target species, typically one that is poorly monitored by CES or general ringing, and aim to catch or re-sight as many of the breeding adults within their study area as possible on an annual basis. These data allow the BTO to monitor survival rates in adult birds, which helps us to understand the causes underlying changes in population sizes as part of the BTO's Integrated Population Monitoring framework. Results are updated annually and published on-line as part of the BirdTrends Report (www.bto.org/BirdTrends).
Contact: Allison Kew, BTO. E-mail: ras@bto.org and www.bto.org/ras

RINGING SCHEME
Funded by a partnership between BTO, JNCC (on behalf of the Country Agencies), The National Parks & Wildlife Service (Ireland) and ringers themselves
Marking birds with individually numbered metal rings allows us to study survival, productivity and movements of British and Irish birds.
More than 2,700 trained and licensed ringers operate in Britain and Ireland, marking around one million birds annually. Training takes at least a year, but more often two or more years, depending on the aptitude of the trainee and the amount of ringing they do. A restricted permit can usually be obtained more quickly.
Anyone can contribute to the scheme by reporting any ringed or colour-marked birds they see or find. Reports can be submitted online at www.ring.ac or direct to BTO HQ. Anyone finding a ringed bird should note the ring number, species, when and where found and, if possible, what happened to it. If the bird is dead, it may also be possible to remove the ring, which should be kept in case there is a query. Anyone reporting a ringed bird will be sent details of where and when the bird was originally ringed. More info: www.bto.org/ringing
The 'Demog Blog' for up to date news and stories is at: http://btoringing.blogspot.com
Contact: Jacquie Clark, BTO. E-mail: Jacquie.clark@bto.org

NATIONAL PROJECTS

TOOTH & CLAW

An independent project aimed at improving knowledge about Britain's predators and promoting discussion on the issues that surround them.

tooth&claw

Tooth & Claw explores some of the complex issues surrounding our relationship with wild predators and questions how we really feel and why.

Through the web site, Tooth & Claw provides a meeting place between anecdotal input and scientific research and encourages constructive and imaginative dialogue on predator issues. A series of case studies led by powerful imagery will provide insightful interviews and personal accounts of our lives alongside the likes of eagles and foxes with a glimpse into the future and the return of creatures we have not known for centuries.

Contact: Peter Cairns, Northshots, Ballintean, Glenfeshie, Kingussie, Scotland, PH21 1NX. (44) (0)1540 651 352;

e-mail: peter@wildmedia.org

www.wildmedia.org/our_projects_tooth_and_claw.asp

WATERWAYS BREEDING BIRD SURVEY

A BTO project, supported by the Environment Agency

WBBS uses transect methods like those of the Breeding Bird Survey to record bird populations along randomly chosen stretches of rivers and canals throughout the UK. Just two survey visits are needed during April-June. WBBS began in 1998 and has now taken over from the Waterways Bird Survey as the main monitoring scheme for birds in this habitat.

Contact: BTO Regional Representative (see County Directory) to enquire if any local stretches require coverage, otherwise John Marchant at BTO HQ. E-mail: John.marchant@bto.org

WETLAND BIRD SURVEY (WeBS)

A joint scheme of BTO, WWT, RSPB & JNCC

The Wetland Bird Survey (WeBS) is the monitoring scheme for non-breeding waterbirds in the UK. The principal aims are:
1. To determine the population sizes of waterbirds.
2. To determine trends in numbers and distribution.
3. To identify important sites for waterbirds. WeBS data are used to designate important waterbird sites and protect them against adverse development, for research into the causes of declines, for establishing conservation priorities and strategies and to formulate management plans for wetland sites and waterbirds. Monthly, synchronised Core Counts are made at as many wetland sites as possible. Low Tide Counts are made on about 20 estuaries each winter to identify important feeding areas. Counts are relatively straightforward and can take from a few minutes up to a few hours, depending on the size of the site. The 3,000 participants receive an annual newsletter and a comprehensive annual report. New counters are always welcome.

Contact: General Webs Enquiries - Heidi Mellan - WeBS Office, BTO.
E-mail webs@bto.org   www.bto.org/webs

INTERNATIONAL DIRECTORY

David Cromack

Great Grey Owls are commonly found in coniferous forest areas
across Canada, northern USA and northern Eurasia.

INTERNATIONAL DIRECTORY

305

BirdLife™
INTERNATIONAL

The BirdLife Partnership
BirdLife is a Partnership of non-governmental organisations (NGOs) with a special focus on conservation and birds. Each NGO Partner represents a unique geographic territory/country.

The BirdLife Network explained
Partners: Membership-based NGOs who represent BirdLife in their own territory. Vote holders and key implementing bodies for BirdLife's Strategy and Regional Programmes in their own territories.

Partners Designate: Membership-based NGOs who represent BirdLife in their own territory, in a transition stage to becoming full Partners. Non-vote holders.

Affiliates: Usually NGOs, but also individuals, foundations or governmental institutions when appropriate. Act as a BirdLife contact with the aim of developing into, or recruiting, a BirdLife Partner in their territory.

Secretariat: The co-ordinating and servicing body of BirdLife International.

SECRETARIAT ADDRESSES

BirdLife Global Office
BirdLife International
Wellbrook Court, Girton Road
Cambridge CB3 0NA
United Kingdom
Tel. +44 1 223 277 318
Fax +44 1 223 277 200
E-mail: birdlife@birdlife.org.uk
www.birdlife.org

Birdlife Africa Regional Office
c/o ICIPE Campus
Kasarani Road, off Thika Road
Nairobi, Kenya
Postal Address
PO Box 3502
00100 GPO
Nairobi, Kenya
Tel: +254 020 806 8314
Fax: +254 020 806 8315
E-mail: birdlife-africa@birdlife.org
www.birdlife.org

BirdLife Americas Regional Office
Birdlife International
Juan de Dios Martinez N35-76 y
Av Portugal
Quito Ecuador

Postal address
BirdLife International
Casilla 17-17-717
Quito, Equador
Tel. +593 (2) 2464 768
Fax +593 (2) 2469 838
E-mail: americas @birdlife.org
www.birdlife.org/regional/americas/
partnership

BirdLife Asia Regional Office
TM Suidobashi Building
4F, Misaki-cho 2-14-6
Chiyoda-ku
Tokyo 101-0061, Japan
Tel.+81 (3) 5213 0461
Fax.+81 (3) 5213 0422
E-mail: info@birdlife-asia.org
www.birdlife.org/regional/asia/
partnership

BirdLife Europe
Avenue de la Toison d'Or 67
(2nd floor), B-1060 Brussels
Belgium
Tel. +32 2280 08 30
Fax +32 2230 38 02
E-mail: europe@birdlife.org
www.birdlife.org/regional/europe/
partnership

BirdLife Middle East Regional Office
BirdLife International Middle East Division
P. O. Box 2295
Amman 11953
Jordan
Postal address
Amman
Khalda
Salameh El-Ma'aaytah Street
Building No 6. Jordan
Tel: +962 (6) 564-8173
Fax: +962 (6) 564-8172
E-mail: me@birdlife.org
www.birdlife.org/regional/
middle_east/partnership

BirdLife Pacific Regional Office
10 MacGregor Road
Suva, Fuji
Postal address
GPO Box 18332
Suva, Fuji
Tel: +679 331 3492
Fax: +679 331 9658
E-mail: don@birdlifepacific.org.fj

PARTNERS

Burkina Faso
La Fondation NATURAMA 01 B.P. 6133, Ouagadougou 01, Burkina Faso; e-mail: info@naturama.bf
www.naturama.bf

Ethiopia
Ethiopian Wildlife and Natural History Society, PO Box 13303, Addis Ababa, Pub: *Agazen; Ethiopian Wildl. and Nat. Hist. News. (& Annual Report); Ethiopian Wildl.*

and *Nat. Hist. Soc. Quarterly News (WATCH); Walia (WATCH) (Ethiopia);* www.ewnhs.org.ete-mail: ewnhs.ble@ethionet.et

Ghana
Ghana Wildlife Society, PO Box 13252, Accra, Pub: *Bongo News; NKO (The Parrots);*
e-mail: ghanawild@4u.co.gh
www.ghanawildlifesociety.org

Kenya
Nature Kenya, PO Box 44486, 00100 GPO. Nairobi. Pub: *Bulletin of the EANHS; Journal of East African Natural; Kenya Birds;* e-mail: office@naturekenya.org
www.naturekenya.org

Seychelles
Nature Seychelles, Roche Caiman, Box 1310, Victoria, Mahe, Seychelles. Pub: *Zwazo - a BirdLife Seychelles Newsletter;* e-mail: nature@seychelles.net www.natureseychelles.org.

Sierra Leone
Conservation Society of Sierra Leone, PO Box 1292, Freetown. Pub: *Rockfowl Link, The.*
e-mail: cssl_03@yahoo.com http://conservationsl.org

South Africa
BirdLife South Africa, PO Box 515, Randburg, Johannesburg 2125, South Africa, Pub: *Newsletter of BirdLife South Africa; Ostrich;*
e-mail: secretary@birdlife.org.za www.birdlife.org.za

Tanzania
Wildlife Conservation Society of Tanzania, PO Box 70919, Dar es Salaam, Pub: *Miombo.*
e-mail: wcst@africaonline.co.tz
www.wcst@arusha.org

Tunisia
Association Les Amis des Oiseaux, Bureau des Projets, Ariana Centre – Bureau C 208/209, 2080 Ariana, Tunis. Pub: *Feuille de Liaison de l'AAO; Houbara, l'.*
e-mail: aao@topnet.tn www.aao.org.tn

Uganda
Nature Uganda, The EANHS, PO Box 27034, Kampala. Pub: *Naturalist - A Newsletter of the East Africa Nat. His. Soc;* e-mail: nature@natureuganda.org
www.natureuganda.org/

Zimbabwe
BirdLife Zimbabwe, P O Box RV 100, Runiville, Harare, Zimbabwe. Pub: *Babbler (WATCH) (Zimbabwe); Honeyguide;* e-mail: birds@zol.co.zw
www.birdlifezimbabwe.co.zw/

PARTNERS DESIGNATE

Botswana
Birdlife Botswana, PO Box 26691, Game City, Gaborone, Botswana; www.birdlifebotswana.org.bw
e-mail: blb@birdlifebotswana.org.bw

Burundi
Association Burundaise pour la Protection des Oiseaux, P O Box 7069, Bujumbura, Burundi;
e-mail: info@aboconservation.org
http://www.aboconservation.org/

Nigeria
Nigerian Conservation Foundation, PO Box 74638, Victoria Island, Lagos. Pub: *NCF Matters/News/ Newsletter; Nigerian Conservation Foundation Annual Report;* e-mail: info@ncf-nigeria

AFFILIATES

Cameroon
Cameroon Biodiversity Conservation Society (CBCS), PO Box 3055, Messa, Yaoundé; e-mail: cbcs_cam@yahoo.fr

Djibouti Nature
Djibouti (DN)
Djibouti Nature is the BirdLife Affiliate in Djibouti.
P. O. Box 3088-Djibouti
Djibouti; e-mail: naturedjibouti@gmail.com

Egypt
Nature Conservation Egypt, 10 Managem wa Mahager str, Mohandeseen, Giza.
e-mail: halabarakat2002@yahoo.com
https://sites.google.com/site/natconegy/
E-mail: Natureegypt@gmail.com

Ivory Coast
Cote d'Ivoire (SOS-FORETS), 22 BP 918 Abidjan 22.
E-mail: sosforets@hotmail.com

Liberia
Society for Conservation of Nature in Liberia, SCNL, Monrovia Zoo, Lakpazee, PO Box 2628, Monrovia.
E-mail: scnlliberia@yahoo.com www.scnlib.net

Madagascar
Asity Madagascar, Lot IIN 184 PH Ter Analamahitsy – 101 Antananarivio, Madagascar BP 1074;
e-mail: zicoma@birdlife-mada.org
http://asitymadagascar.org

Malawi
Wildlife & Environmental Socity of Malawi, Private Bag 578, Limbe. E-mail: wesm-hq@africa-online.net
www.wildlifemalawi.org

Rwanda
Association pour la Conservation de la Nature au Rwanda, P O Box 4290, Kigali, www.acnrwanda.org/
e-mail: conserverwanda@yahoo.fr

Zambia
Zambian Ornithological Society, Box 33944, Lusaka 10101, Pub: *Zambian Ornithological Society Newsletter;* e-mail: zos@zamnet.zm www.wattledcrane.com

AMERICAS

PARTNERS

Argentina
Aves Argentina (AOP), Matheu 1246/8, C1249AAB, Buenos Aires. Pub: *Hornero; Naturaleza & Conservacion; Nuestras Aves; Vuelo de Pajaro;*
e-mail: info@avesargentinas.org.ar
www.avesargentinas.org.ar

Belize
The Belize Audubon Society, PO Box 1001, 12 Fort Street, Belize City. Pub: *Belize Audubon Society Newsletter;* e-mail: base@btl.net
www.belizeaudubon.org

Bolivia
Asociacion Armonia, Avenidad Lomas de Arena 400, Casilla 3566, Santa Cruz. Pub: *Aves en Bolivia;*
e-mail: armonia@armonia-bo.org www.armonia-bo.org

Canada
Bird Studies Canada, PO Box/160, Port Rowan, Ontario N0E 1M0. Pub: *Bird Studies Canada - Annual Report; Birdwatch Canada;* e-mail: generalinfo@bsc-eoc.org
www.bsc-eoc.org

Canada
Nature Canada, 85 Albert Street,Suite 900, Ottawa, Ontario K1P 6A4. Pub: *Grass 'n Roots; IBA News Canada; Nature Canada; Nature Matters; Nature Watch News (CNF);* e-mail: info@naturecanada.ca
www.naturecanada.ca

INTERNATIONAL ORGANISATIONS

Ecuador
Aves & Conservación (Corporación Ornitológica del
Ecuador, Pasaje Joaquin Tinajero E3-05 y Jorge Drom,
Casilla 17-17-906, Quito; www.avesconservaccion.org
e-mail: aves_direccion@avesconservacion.org

Falkland Islands
Falklands Conservation, PO Box 26, Stanley, Falklands or
UK Office, 14 East Hatley, sandy, Bedfordshire SG19 3JA.
UK. Pub: *Falklands Conservation.*
e-mail: info@falklandsconservation.com
www.falklandsconservation.com

Panama
Panama Audubon Society, Apartado 0843-03076, Balboa,
Ancon. Pub: *Toucan;* e-mail: info@panamaaudubon.org
www.panamaaudubon.org

United States
Audubon Society, 225 Varick Street, 7th Floor New York,
NY, 10004. Pub: *American Birds; Audubon (USA);
Audubon Field Notes; Audubon Bird Conservation
Newsletter;* e-mail: international@audubon.org
www.audubon.org

PARTNER DESIGNATE

Paraguay
Guyra Paraguay, Gaetano Martino 215 esq. Tte. Ross,
Asunción. Pub: *Boletin Jara Kuera;*
e-mail: guyra@guyra.org.py www.guyra.org.py/

AFFILIATES

Bahamas
Bahamas National Trust, PO Box 4105, Nassau. Pub:
Bahamas Naturalist; Currents; Grand Bahama Update.
e-mail: bnt@bnt.bs www.bnt.bs

Brazil
SAVE Brasil
Rua Fernão Dias, 219 conj 2 Pinheiros, São Paulo SP,
Brasil 05427-010; http://www.savebrasil.org.br

Chile
Comite Nacional Pro defensa de la Flora y Fauna
(CODEFF), Ernesto Reyes 035, Providencia, Santiago 21.
Pub: *Boletin Chileno de Ornitologia; Boletin Informativo
(WATCH) (Chile).*
e-mail: administra@codeff.cl www.codeff.cl

Cuba
Centro Nacional de Áreas Protegidas (CNAP). Calle 18 a,
No 1441, e/ 41 y 47, Playa, Ciudad Habana, Cuba.
e-mail: cnap@snap.cu www.snap.co.cu/

Dominican Republic
Grupo Jaragua (GJI), Calle El Vergel No 33 Ensanche, El
Vergel, Santo Domingo. E-mail: jaragua@tricom.net
www.grupojaragua.org.do

El Salvador
SalvaNATURA, 33 Avenida Sur #640, Colonia Flor
Blanca, San Salvador. e-mail: info@salvanatura.org
www.salvanatura.org

Mexico
Pronatura, Chiapas, A.C. es: Calle Pedro Moreno # 1
esq. Benito Juárez, Barrio Santa Lucia C.P. 29200, San
Cristobal de las Casas, Chiapas, México
e-mail: pronatura@pronatura.org.mx
www.pronatura.org.mx

Puerto Rico (to USA)
Sociedad Ornitológica Puertorriqueña, Inc. (SOPI), SOPI
PO Box 195166, San Juan, Puerto Rico, 00919-5166
e-mail: directivasopi@yahoo.com
www.avesdepuertorico.org

Suriname
Foundation for Nature Preservation in Suriname, Cornelis
Jongbawstraat 14, PO Box 12252, Paramaribo
e-mail: research@stinasu.sr www.stinasu.sr

Uruguay
Aves Uruguay (GUPECA), Canelones 1164, Montevideo,
Uruguay. Pub: *Achara;* www.avesuruguay.org.uy/
e-mail: info@avesuruguay.org.uy

ASIA

PARTNERS

India
Bombay Natural History Society, Hornbill House,
Shaheed Bhagat Singh Road, Mumbai-400 023. Pub:
*Buceros; Hornbill; Journal of the Bombay Natural History
Society;* e-mail: bnhs@bom4.vsnl.net.in www.bnhs.org

Japan
Wild Bird Society of Japan (WBSJ), Maruw Bldg, 3-9-23,
Nishi-Gotanda, Shinagawa-ku, Tokyo 141-0031, Japan.
Pub: *Strix; Wild Birds; Wing.*
e-mail: hogo@wbsj.org www.wbsj.org

Malaysia
Malaysian Nature Society, PO Box 10750, Kuala Lumpur
50724. Pub: *Enggang; Suara Enggang; Malayan Nature
Journal; Malaysian Naturalist.*
e-mail: mns@mns.org.my www.mns.my

Philippines
Haribon Foundation, 2/F, Santos and Sons Building, 973
Aurora Blvd, Cubao, Quezon CIty 1109. Pub: *Haribon
Foundation Annual Report; Haring Ibon; Philippine
Biodiversity;* e-mail: act@haribon.org.ph
www.haribon.org.ph

Singapore
Nature Society (Singapore), 510 Geylang Road, #02-
05, The Sunflower, 398466. Pub: *Nature News; Nature
Watch (Singapore);* e-mail: nss@nss.org.sg
www.nss.org.sg

Taiwan
Chinese Wild Bird Federation (CWBF), 1F, No. 3, Lane
36 Jing-Long St., 116 Taipei, Taiwan. Pub: *Yuhina Post;*
e-mail: mail@bird.org.tw www.bird.org.tw

Thailand
Bird Conservation Society of Thailand, 221 Moo 2, Soi
Ngamwongwan 2, Tambol Bangkhen, Ampur Meung,
Nontaburi 11000. Pub: *Bird Conservation Society of
Thailand;* e-mail: bcst@bcst.or.th www.bcst.or.th

PARTNERS DESIGNATE

Hong Kong
The Hong Kong Birdwatching Society, 14/F Ruby
Commercial Building, 480 Nathan Road, Kowloon, Hong
Kong, People's Republic of China. Pub: *Hong Kong Bird
Report;* e-mail: hkbws@hkbws.org.uk
www.hkbws.org.hk

INTERNATIONAL ORGANISATIONS

Nepal
Bird Conservation Nepal, P.O.Box 12465, Kathmandu, Nepal. Pub: *Bird Conservation Nepal (Danphe); Ibisbill;* e-mail: bcn@mail.com.np www.birdlifenepal.org

AFFILIATES

Indonesia
Burung Indonesia (Perhimpunan Pelestari Burung dan Habitatnya), Jl. Dadali 32, Bogor 16161, PO. Box 310/ Boo, Bogor 16003, Indonesia; e-mail: birdlife@burung.org www.burung.org

Kazakhstan
Association for the Conservation of Biodiversity of Kazakhstan (ACBK), Office 406, 40 Beibitshilik Str, Astana 010000, Kazakhstan. E-mail: office@acbk.kz www.acbk.kz

Kyrgyzstan
NABS Public Association. www.wildlife.kg

Myanmar (Burma)
Biodiversity and Nature Conservation Association (BANCA), 145(B), Thirimingalar Lane, 8th Mile, Ward (4), Mayangone Township, Yangon, Myanmar +951 667 067; e-mail: banca@yangon.net.mm - www.banca-env.org

Sri Lanka
Field Ornithology Group of Sri Lanka, Dept of Zoology, University of Colombo, Colombo 03. Pub: *Malkoha - Newsletter of the Field Ornithology Group of Sri Lanka.* e-mail: fogsl@slt.lk www.fogsl.net

Uzbekistan
Uzbekistan Society for the Protection of Birds (UzSPB), Off.89, Institte of Zoology of Uzkek Academy of sciences, A. Niyazov str.1, Tashkent 100095. E-mail: roman.kashkarov@iba.uz www.uzspb.uz

UNAFFILIATED COUNTRIES

Cambodia
BirdLife International Cambodia Programme, ±9 Street 29, Tonie Basac, Chamkarmon, Phnom Penh. e-mail: admin@birdlifecambodia.org www.birdlifeindochina.org

Laos
BirdLife International in Indochina, No 4 Lane 209, Doi Can, Ba Dinh, Hanoi, Vietnam; e-mail: birdlife@birdlife.netnam.vn www.birdlifeindochina.org

Vietnam
BirdLife International in Indochina, PO Box 89 – 6 Dinh Le, Hanoi, Vietnam. e-mail: birdlife@birdlife.org.vn - www.birdlifeindochina.org

EUROPE

PARTNERS

Austria
BirdLife Austria, Museumplatz 1/10/8, AT-1070 Wien. Pub: *Egretta; Vogelschutz in Osterreich.* e-mail: office@birdlife.at www.birdlife.at/

Belarus
BirdLife Belarus (APB), PO Box 306, Minsk, 220050

Belarus. Pub: *Subbuteo - The Belarusian Ornithological Bulletin;* e-mail: apb@tut.by www.ptushki.org

Belgium
BirdLife Belgium (Natuurpunt-Natagora), Natuurpunt, Michiel Coxiestraat 11N 2800 Mechelen, Belgium. e-mail: wim.vandenbossche@natuurpunt.be www.natuurreservaten.be (Dutch) and Natagora, rue du Wisconsin 3, 5000 Namur, Belgium; e-mail (Natagora): Philippe.funcken@natagora. be - www.natagora.be (French)

Bulgaria
Bulgarian Society for the Protection of Birds (BSPB), PO Box 50, Yavorov Complex, Block 71, vh.4, ap 1, BG-1111, Sofia, Bulgaria. Pub: *Neophron (& UK);* e-mail: bspb_hq@bspb.org www.bspb.org

Czech Republic
Czech Society for Ornithology (CSO), Na Belidle 252/34, 150 00 Prague 5. Pub: *Ptaci Svet; Sylvia; Zpravy Ceske Spolecnosti Ornitologicke.* e-mail: cso@birdlife.cz www.birdlife.cz

Denmark
Dansk Ornitologisk Forening (DOF), Vesterbrogade 138-140, DK-1620, Copenhagen V, Denmark. Pub: *DAFIF - Dafifs Nyhedsbrev; Dansk Ornitologisk Forenings Tidsskrift; Fugle og Natur;* e-mail: dof@dof.dk www.dof.dk

Estonia
Estonian Ornithological Society (EOU), PO Box 227, Vesti Str. 4, EE-50002 Tartu, Estonia. Pub: *Hirundo Eesti Ornitoogiauhing;* e-mail: eoy@eoy.ee www.eoy.ee

Finland
BirdLife FINLAND, Annankatu 29 A 16, FI 00101, Helsinki. Pub: *Linnuston-Suojelu; Linnut; Tiira;* e-mail: office@birdlife.fi www.birdlife.fi

France
(also covers New Caledonia, Wallis & Futuna Islands) Ligue pour la Protection des Oiseaux (LPO), Fonderies Royale, 8-10 rue de Docteur Pujos, B.P. 90263, 17305 Rochefort Cedex. Pub: *Lettre Internationale; Ligue Francaise Pour La Protection des Oiseaux; Oiseau, L' (LPO); Outarde infos;* e-mail: lpo@lpo.fr www.lpo.fr/

Germany
Naturschutzbund Deutschland (NABU), Charitestr. 3, D-10117, Berlin. Pub: *Naturschutz Heute (NABU) Naturschutzbund Deutschland.* e-mail: nabu@nabu.de www.nabu.de

Gibraltar
Gibraltar Ornithological and Nat. History Society, Gibraltar Natural History Field Centre, Jew's Gate, Upper Rock Nature Reserve, PO Box 843, GI. Pub: *Alectoris; Gibraltar Nature News.* e-mail: gohns@gibnet.gi www.gonhs.org

Greece
Hellenic Ornithological Society (HOS), Themistokleous 80, 10861, Athens, Greece. Pub: *HOS Newsletter.* e-mail: info@ornithologiki.gr www.ornithologiki.gr

Hungary
Hungarian Orn. and Nature Cons. Society (MME), Kolto u. 21, 1121 Budapest. Pub: *Madartani Tajekoztato;*

INTERNATIONAL ORGANISATIONS

Madartavlat; Ornis Hungarica; Tuzok.
e-mail: mme@mme.hu www.mme.hu

Ireland
BirdWatch Ireland, Unit 20, Block D, Bullford Business Campus, Kilcoole, Co Wicklow, Eire. Pub: *Irish Birds; Wings (IWC Birdwatch Ireland);* e-mail**:** info@birdwatchireland.org www.birdwatchireland.ie

Israel
Society for the Protection of Nature in Israel (SPNI), Hanagev 2 St, Tel-Aviv 66186. Pub: *SPNI News.* e-mail**:** ioc@netvision.net.il www.birds.org.il

Italy
Lega Italiana Protezione Uccelli (LIPU), Via Trento 49, 43100, Parma. Pub: *Ali Giovani; Ali Notizie.* e-mail: info@lipu.it www.lipu.it

Latvia
Latvijas Ornitologijas Biedriba (LOB), Kalnciema iela 27-18, Riga LV-1046. Pub: *Putni Daba.* e-mail**:** putni@lob.lv www.lob.lv

Luxembourg
Letzebuerger Natur-a Vulleschutzliga (LNVL), Kraizhaff, 5 Route de Luxembourg, L-1899 Kockelscheuer. Pub: *Regulus (WATCH); Regulus Info (& Annual Report) (WATCH); Regulus Wissenschaftliche Berichte;* e-mail: birgit.jacoby@luxnatur.lu www.lnvl.lu

Malta
BirdLife Malta, 57 /28, Triq Abate Rigord, Ta' Xbiex, XBX 1120, Malta. Pub: *Bird Talk (WATCH) (Malta); Bird's Eye View (WATCH) (Malta); Il-Merill;* e-mail: office@birdlifemalta.org www.birdlifemalta.org

Netherlands
Vogelbescherming Nederland (VBN), Boulevard 12, 3707, BM Zeist. Pub: *Vogelniews; Vogels.* e-mail**:** info@vogelbescherming.nl www.vogelbescherming.nl/

Norway
Norsk Ornitologisk Forening (NOF), Sandgata 30 B, N-7012 Trondheim, Norway. Pub: *Fuglearet; Fuglefauna; Var; Ringmerkaren;* e-mail: nof@birdlife.no www.birdlife.no

Poland
Ogólnopolskie Towarzystwo Ochrony Ptaków (OTOP), ul.Odrowaza 24, 05-270 Marki k. Warsaw, Poland. Pub: *Ptaki; Ptasie Ostoje;* e-mail: office@otop.most.org.pl www.otop.org.pl/

Portugal
Sociedade Portuguesa para o Estuda das, Aves (SPEA), Avenida João Crisóstomo, nº 18 – 4º Dir. | 1000-179 Lisboa | Portugal. Pub: *Pardela;* e-mail: spea@spea.pt www.spea.pt

Romania
Romanian Ornithological Society (SOR), Bd. M Kogalniceanu nr 49, sc. A, ap 8, 0150108 Sector 5, Bucharest. Pub: *Alcedo; Buletin AIA; Buletin de Informare Societatea Ornitologica Romana; Milvus (Romania);* e-mail: office@sor.ro www.sor.ro/

Slovakia
Slovak Ornithological Society (SOS), Mlynske Nivy 41, 821 09 Bratislava, Slovakia. Pub: *Spravodaj SOVS;*

Vtacie Spravy; e-mail: vtaky@vtaky.sk www.birdlife.sk

Slovenia
BirdLife Slovenia (DOPPS), Trzaska 2, PO Box 2990, SI-1000 Ljubljana, Slovenia. Pub: *Acrocephalus; Svet Ptic;* e-mail: dopps@dopps.si www.ptice.si

Spain
Sociedad Espanola de Ornitologia (SEO), Melquiades Biencinto 34, ES-28053, Madrid. Pub: *Ardeola; Areas Importantes para las Aves.* e-mail: seo@seo.org www.seo.org

Sweden
Sveriges Ornitologiska Forening (SOF), Stenhusa Gard, SE-380 62 Morbylanga. Pub: *Fagelvarld; var; Ornis Svecica;* e-mail: info@sofnet.org www.sofnet.org

Switzerland
SVS/BirdLife Switzerland, Wiedingstrasse 78, PO Box, CH-8036, Zurich, Switzerland. Pub: *Oiwvos Ornis; Ornis Junior; Ornithologische Beobachter; Der Ornithos; Steinadler;* e-mail: svs@birdlife.ch www.birdlife.ch

Turkey
Doga Dernegi (DD), PK: 640 06445, Yenisehir, Ankara, Turkey. Pub: *Kelaynak; Kuscu Bulteni.* e-mail: doga@dogadernegi.org www.dogadernegi.org

Ukraine
Ukrainian Union for Bird Conservation (UTOP), PO Box 33, Kiev, 1103, UA. Pub: *Life of Birds.* e-mail: uspb@birdlife.org.ua www.birdlife.org.ua

United Kingdom
Royal Society for the Protection of Birds, The Lodge, Sandy, Bedfordshire, SG19 2DL; e-mail: info@rspb.org.uk www.rspb.org.uk

PARTNERS DESIGNATE

Azerbaijan
Azerbaijan Ornithological Society (AOS), Mukhtarov str. 13, apt 16, AZ1001 Baku. e-mail: info@aos.az http://aos.az/eng/index.php

Georgia
Georgian Centre for the Conservation of Wildlife, Nature House (2nd Floor), Didi Digomi, 0131, Tbilisi, Georgia; e-mail: office@gccw.org http://gccw.bunebaprint.ge/

Iceland
Icelandic Society for the Protection of Birds (ISPB), Fuglaverndarfélag Islands, Skulatuni 6, , 105 Reykjavik, Simi 5620477. www.fuglavernd.is e-mail: fuglavernd@fuglavernd.is

AFFILIATES

Andorra
Associacio per a la Defensa de la Natura (AND), Apartado de Correus Espanyols No 96, Andora La Vella, Principat d'Andorra. Pub: *Aiguerola;* e-mail: adn@andorra.ad www.adn-andorra.org/

Armenia
Armenian Society for the Protection of Birds (ASPB), Garaegin Njdeh 27/2, 10 Yerevan, 0026, Armenia. E-mail: armbirds@yahoo.com www.aspbirds.org

Cyprus
BirdLife Cyprus, PO Box 28076, 2090 Lefkosia, Cyprus.

e-mail: birdlifecyprus@birdlifecyprus.org.cy
www.birdlifecyprus.org

Faroe Islands
Føroya Fuglafrødifelag (Faroese Orginithological Society)
(FOS), Postssmoga 1230, FR-110 Torshavn, Faroe
Islands; e-mail: doreteb@ngs.fo
www.faroenature.net/foroya-fuglafrodifelag/kunning/
blog.html

Liechtenstein
Botanish-Zoologische Gesellschaft (ZG), Im Bretscha 22,
FL-9494 Schaan, Liechtenstein;
e-mail: bzg@bzg.li www.bzg.li

Lithuania
Lietuvos Ornitologu Draugija (LOD), Naugarduko St.
47-3, LT-2006, Vilnius, Lithuania. Pub: *Baltasis Gandras;*
e-mail: lod@birdlife.lt www.birdlife.lt

**Former Yugoslav Republic of Macedonia
(FYROM)**
Macedonia (MES)Macedonian Ecological Society, Blvd
"Kuzman Josifovski - Pitu" 28/3-7, 1000 Skopje
Macedonia; e-mail:contact@mes.org.mk -
www.mes.org.mk

MIDDLE EAST

PARTNERS

Jordan
Royal Society of the Conservation of Nature, PO Box
6354, Jubeiha-Abu-Nusseir Circle, Amman 11183. Pub:
Al Reem; e-mail: adminrscn@rscn.org.jo
www.rscn.org.jo

Lebanon
Society for the Protection of Nature in Lebanon, Awad
Bldg, 6th Floor, Abdel Aziz Street, P.O.Box: 11-5665,
Beirut, Lebanon; e-mail: spnlorg@cyberia.net.lb
www.spnlb.org

Palestinian Authority Territories
Palestine Wildlife Society (PWLS), Beit Sahour, PO Box
89, Palestine. Pub: *Palestine Wildlife Society - Annual
Report.*
e-mail: pwls@wildlife-pal.org www.wildlife-pal.org

AFFILIATES

Bahrain
Dr Saeed A. Mohamed, PO Box 1858, Manama, Bahrain.
e-mail: saeed@alreem.com http://bahrainwildlife.com

Iraq
Nature Iraq, House 25, Street 27, Qtr 104 Ashti,
Sulaimani, Kurdistan, Iraq. e-mail: info@natureiraq.org
www.natureiraq.org

Kuwait
Kuwait Environment Protection Society, PO Box 1896,
Safat 13019, Kuwait; e-mail: rasamhory@hotmail.com
www.keps.org.kw

Qatar
Friends of the Environment Centre, PO Box 1822, Doha,
Qatar. E-mail: cefdoha@qatar.net.qa
http:// my qatar.org

Saudi Arabia
Saudi Wildlife Commission (SWC), PO Box 61681, Riyadh
11575. Pub: *Phoenix; The.*
e-mail: ncwcd@zajil.net www.ncwcd.gov.sa/
Syria
Syrian Society ofr the Conservation of Wildlife (SSCW),
PO Box 9853, Damascus, Syria;
e-mail: sscw.syria@gmail.com www.sscw-syria.org/ar/
Yemen
Yemen Society for the Protection of Wildlife (YSPW), 29
Alger Street, PO Box 19759, Sana'a, Yemen.
e-mail: wildlife.yemen@y.net.ye

PACIFIC

PARTNER

**Australia
(also covers Christmas Island, Cocos Islands,
Norfolk Island, Heard & Mcdonald Islands,
Antarctica)**
Birds Australia, Suite 2-05, 60 Leicester Street, Carlton,
VIC 3053, Australia. Pub: *Australia Garcilla; Birds
Australia Annual Report; Eclectus; Emu; Wingspan*
(WATCH) (Australia); from wingspan@birdsaustralia.
com.au; e-mail: info@birdlife.org.au -
www.birdlife.org.au/

French Polynesia
Société d'Ornithologie de Polynésie 'Manu', B.P. 7023,
98719 Taravao, Tahiti, French Polynesia;
e-mail: sop@manu.pf www.manu.pf

**New Zealand
(also covers Niue and Tokelau)**
Forest & Bird, Level 1, 90 Ghunzee Street, PO Box 631,
Wellington 6140. Pub: *Forest & Bird; Forest & Bird
Annual Report; Forest & Bird Conservation News.*
e-mail: office@forestandbird.org.nz
www.forestandbird.org.nz/

Palau
Palau Conservation Society, PO Box 1811, Koror,
PW96940, Republic of Palau. Pub: *Ngerel a Biib;*
e-mail: pcs@palaunet.com www.palauconservation.org

AFFILIATES

Cook Islands
Te Ipukarea Society (TIS), PO Box 649, Rarotonga, Cook
Islands; e-mail: 2tis@oyster.net.ck

New Caledonia (to France)
Société Calédonienne d'Ornithologie (SCO)
BP 13641, 98 803 Nouméa Cedex, New Caledonia
e-mail: president@sco.asso.nc - www.sco.asso.nc

Samoa
O le Si'osi'omaga Society Incorporated (OLSSI), P O Box
2282, Apia, Western Samoa;
e-mail: ngo_siosiomaga@samoa.ws

INTERNATIONAL DIRECTORY

SPECIAL INTEREST ORGANISATIONS

AFRICAN BIRD CLUB.

c/o Birdlife International as below.
e-mail (general): contact@african-
birdclub.org
e-mail: (membership and sales):
membership@africanbirdclub.org
www.africanbirdclub.org
Pub: *Bulletin of the African Bird Club*.

BIRDLIFE INTERNATIONAL.
Wellbrook Court, Girton Road, Cambridge, CB3
ONA, +44 (0)1223 277 318; (Fax) +44 (0)1223 277
200; www.birdlife.org
e-mail: birdlife@birdlife.org
Pub:*World Birdwatch*.

**EAST AFRICA NATURAL HISTORY SOCIETY see Kenya in
preceding list.**

EURING (European Union for Bird Ringing).
Euring Data Bank, c/o BTO, The Nunnery, Thetford, Norfolk IP24 2PU. 01842 750 050.
www.euring.org

FAUNA AND FLORA INTERNATIONAL.
Jupiter House, 4th Floor, Station Road,
Cambridge, CB1 2JD. Call on +44 (0)1223 571 000;
(Fax) +44 (0)1223 461 481. www.fauna-flora.org
e-mail: info@fauna-flora.org
Pub: *Fauna & Flora News*; *Oryx*.

LIPU-UK
**(the Italian League for the
Protection of Birds).**
David Lingard, Fernwood,
Doddington Road, Whisby,
Lincs, LN6 9BX, +44
(0)1522 689 030,
e-mail: david@lipu-uk.org
www.lipu-uk.org
Pub:*The Hoopoe*, annually, *Ali Notizie*, quarterly.

NEOTROPICAL BIRD CLUB.
(Central and South America
and the Caribbean)
c/o The Lodge, Sandy,
Bedfordshire, SG19 2DL.
Pub:*Cotinga*.
e-mail: secretary@neotropicalbirdclub.org
www.neotropicalbirdclub.org

ORIENTAL BIRD CLUB.
P.O.Box 324, Bedford, MK42 0WG
Pub:*The Forktail*; *BirdingASIA*.
email: mail@orientalbirdclub.org
www.orientalbirdclub.org

ORNITHOLOGICAL SOCIETY OF THE MIDDLE EAST (OSME).
c/o The Lodge, Sandy, Beds, SG19 2DL.
Pub: *Sandgrouse*. e-mail: secretary@osme.org
www.osme.org

**TRAFFIC International (formerly Wildlife Trade
Monitoring Unit).**
219a Huntingdon Road, Cambridge, CB3 ODL.
+44 (0)1223 277 427; (Fax) +44 (0)1223 277 237.
Pub:*TRAFFIC Bulletin*.
e-mail: traffic@traffic.org
www.traffic.org

WEST AFRICAN ORNITHOLOGICAL SOCIETY.
R E Sharland, 1 Fisher's Heron, East Mills, Hants,
SP6 2JR. Pub: *Malimbus*.
http://malimbus.free.fr

WETLANDS INTERNATIONAL.
PO Box 471, 6700 AL Wageningen, Netherlands,
+31 317 485 774; (Fax) +31 317 486 770,
Pub:*Wetlands*.
e-mail: post@wetlands.org
www.wetlands.org

WORLD OWL TRUST.
The World Owl Centre, Muncaster Castle, Raven-
glass, Cumbria, CA18 1RQ, +44 (0)1229 717393;
www.owls.org

WORLD PHEASANT ASSOCIATION.
7-9 Shaftesbury St, Fordingbridge, Hants SP6 1JF.
01425 657 129; (Fax) 01425 658 053. Pub:*WPA
News*. e-mail: office@pheasant.org.uk
www.pheasant.org.uk

WORLD WIDE FUND FOR NATURE.
Panda House, Weyside Park,
Godalming
United Kingdom. +44 1483 426
444;
(Fax) +44 1483 426 409,
e-mail: supporterrelations@wwf.org.uk
www.panda.org

QUICK REFERENCE SECTION

David Cromack

While it is perfectly OK to photograph Ruff on passage or feeding in winter, a Schedule 1 licence is needed to take images at or near the nest. For a complete list of protected species see page 323.

TIDE TABLES: USEFUL INFORMATION

BRITISH SUMMER TIME

In 2013 BST applies from 01:00 on March 31 to 01:00 on October 27.
Note that all the times in the following tables are GMT.

During British Summer Time one hour should be added.

Shetland 42, 43
Orkney 44, 45

Predictions are given for the times of high water at Dover throughout the year.

The times of tides at the locations shown here may be obtained by adding or subtracting their 'tidal difference' as shown opposite (subtractions are indicated by a minus sign).

Tidal predictions for Dover have been computed by the Proudman Oceanographic Laboratory. Copyright reserved.

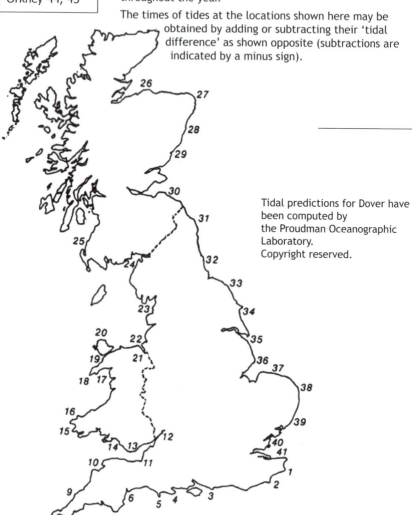

Map showing locations for which tidal differences are given on facing page.

TIDE TABLES 2013

Example 1
To calculate the time of first high water at Girvan on February 9
1. Look up the time at Dover (10 12)*
   = 10:12 am
2. Add the tidal difference for Girvan
   = 0.54
3. Therefore the time of high water at Girvan = 11:06 am

Example 2
To calculate the time of second high water at Blakeney on June 22
1. Look up the time at Dover (21 54)
   = 21:54 pm
2. Add 1 hour for British Summer Time
   = 22:54 pm
3. Subtract the tidal difference for Blakeney = - 4.07
4. Therefore the time of second high water at Blakeney = 18:47 pm

*All Dover times are shown on the 24-hour clock.
Following the time of each high water the height of the tide is given, in metres.

(Tables beyond April 2014 are not available at the time of going to press.)

TIDAL DIFFERENCES

1	Dover	See pp 338-341		23	Morecambe	0	20
2	Dungeness	-0	12	24	Silloth	0	51
3	Selsey Bill	0	09	25	Girvan	0	54
4	Swanage (lst H.W.Springs)	-2	36	26	Lossiemouth	0	48
5	Portland	-4	23	27	Fraserburgh	1	20
6	Exmouth (Approaches)	-4	48	28	Aberdeen	2	30
7	Salcombe	-5	23	29	Montrose	3	30
8	Newlyn (Penzance)	5	59	30	Dunbar	3	42
9	Padstow	-5	47	31	Holy Island	3	58
10	Bideford	-5	17	32	Sunderland	4	38
11	Bridgwater	-4	23	33	Whitby	5	12
12	Sharpness Dock	-3	19	34	Bridlington	5	53
13	Cardiff (Penarth)	-4	16	35	Grimsby	-5	20
14	Swansea	-4	52	36	Skegness	-5	00
15	Skomer Island	-5	00	37	Blakeney	-4	07
16	Fishguard	-3	48	38	Gorleston	-2	08
17	Barmouth	-2	45	39	Aldeburgh	-0	13
18	Bardsey Island	-3	07	40	Bradwell Waterside	1	11
19	Caernarvon	-1	07	41	Herne Bay	1	28
20	Amlwch	-0	22	42	Sullom Voe	-1	34
21	Connahs Quay	0	20	43	Lerwick	0	01
22	Hilbre Island			44	Kirkwall	-0	26
	(Hoylake/West Kirby)	-0	05	45	Widewall Bay	-1	30

NB. Care should be taken when making calculations at the beginning and end of British Summer Time. See worked examples above.

TIDE TABLES 2013

Time Zone: GMT
Units: METRES

Tidal Predictions : HIGH WATERS 2013
Datum of Predictions = Chart Datum : 3.67 metres below Ordnance Datum (Newlyn)
British Summer Time Dates for 2013 : 31st March to 27th October (data not adjusted)

DOVER — January

Date	Morning time	m	Afternoon time	m
1 Tu	00:59	6.5	13:07	6.3
2 W	01:33	6.4	13:42	6.2
3 Th	02:07	6.4	14:21	6.1
4 F	02:48	6.2	15:09	6.0
5 Sa	03:39	6.1	16:09	5.8
6 Su	04:42	6.0	17:18	5.7
7 M	05:52	5.9	18:30	5.7
8 Tu	07:05	6.0	19:45	5.9
9 W	08:15	6.2	20:53	6.2
10 Th	09:18	6.4	21:52	6.5
11 F	10:15	6.6	22:45	6.7
12 Sa	11:07	6.8	23:33	6.9
13 Su	11:56	6.8	##	#
14 M	00:18	6.8	12:42	6.8
15 Tu	01:00	6.9	13:24	6.6
16 W	01:40	6.8	14:05	6.4
17 Th	02:21	6.6	14:48	6.2
18 F	03:05	6.4	15:35	6.0
19 Sa	03:54	6.1	16:30	5.6
20 Su	04:54	5.6	17:39	5.3
21 M	06:08	5.4	18:57	5.2
22 Tu	07:26	5.5	20:08	5.4
23 W	08:32	5.6	21:04	5.6
24 Th	09:24	5.7	21:49	5.9
25 F	10:05	6.0	22:26	6.2
26 Sa	10:39	6.1	22:59	6.4
27 Su	11:09	6.3	23:31	6.5
28 M	11:41	6.4	##	#
29 Tu	00:04	6.6	12:14	6.5
30 W	00:38	6.7	12:48	6.5
31 Th	01:11	6.7	13:22	6.5

DOVER — February

Date	Morning time	m	Afternoon time	m
1 F	01:44	6.6	13:59	6.4
2 Sa	02:21	6.5	14:43	6.2
3 Su	03:09	6.3	15:38	6.0
4 M	04:09	6.1	16:45	5.8
5 Tu	05:22	5.8	18:05	5.6
6 W	06:46	5.7	19:33	5.7
7 Th	08:10	5.9	20:50	6.0
8 F	09:18	6.2	21:48	6.3
9 Sa	10:12	6.5	22:36	6.6
10 Su	11:00	6.7	23:19	6.8
11 M	11:43	6.8	##	#
12 Tu	00:00	7.0	12:23	6.7
13 W	00:38	7.0	13:00	7.0
14 Th	01:15	6.9	13:36	6.9
15 F	01:51	6.7	14:14	6.7
16 Sa	02:29	6.4	14:54	6.4
17 Su	03:11	6.0	15:41	6.0
18 M	04:02	5.6	16:42	5.6
19 Tu	05:14	5.2	18:04	5.3
20 W	06:44	5.2	19:28	5.1
21 Th	08:01	5.5	20:33	5.4
22 F	08:58	5.8	21:21	5.5
23 Sa	09:39	6.1	21:59	5.8
24 Su	10:12	6.3	22:31	6.1
25 M	10:42	6.5	23:03	6.3
26 Tu	11:14	6.6	23:36	6.5
27 W	11:48	6.8	##	#
28 Th	00:11	6.8	12:24	6.7

DOVER — March

Date	Morning time	m	Afternoon time	m
1 F	00:45	6.8	13:00	6.6
2 Sa	01:21	6.7	13:39	6.5
3 Su	02:00	6.6	14:24	6.3
4 M	02:48	6.3	15:19	6.0
5 Tu	03:51	6.0	16:28	5.7
6 W	05:09	5.7	17:53	5.5
7 Th	06:43	5.8	19:28	5.6
8 F	08:11	6.0	20:42	5.9
9 Sa	09:15	6.1	21:36	6.1
10 Su	10:05	6.4	22:21	6.4
11 M	10:46	6.6	23:00	6.6
12 Tu	11:24	6.7	23:37	6.7
13 W	##	#	12:00	6.7
14 Th	00:14	6.9	12:35	6.9
15 F	00:48	6.8	13:09	6.8
16 Sa	01:22	6.6	13:42	6.6
17 Su	01:55	6.3	14:18	6.1
18 M	02:30	6.0	14:57	5.8
19 Tu	03:14	5.6	15:49	5.6
20 W	04:18	5.2	17:05	5.2
21 Th	05:51	4.9	18:36	5.0
22 F	07:17	5.0	19:48	5.3
23 Sa	08:18	5.4	20:42	5.6
24 Su	09:02	5.7	21:22	6.0
25 M	09:36	6.0	21:57	6.3
26 Tu	10:09	6.3	22:30	6.5
27 W	10:44	6.6	23:05	6.8
28 Th	11:21	6.7	23:42	6.9
29 F	##	#	12:00	6.8
30 Sa	00:21	6.9	12:42	6.6
31 Su	01:02	6.8	13:26	6.8

DOVER — April

Date	Morning time	m	Afternoon time	m
1 M	01:47	6.6	14:15	6.4
2 Tu	02:41	6.3	15:13	6.1
3 W	03:47	5.9	16:21	5.8
4 Th	05:05	5.6	17:44	5.6
5 F	06:40	5.8	19:14	5.7
6 Sa	08:01	5.8	20:24	5.9
7 Su	09:00	6.0	21:15	6.2
8 M	09:47	6.3	21:57	6.5
9 Tu	10:25	6.4	22:36	6.6
10 W	11:00	6.5	23:13	6.7
11 Th	11:36	6.6	23:49	6.7
12 F	##	#	12:11	6.5
13 Sa	00:24	6.6	12:45	6.5
14 Su	00:57	6.5	13:18	6.3
15 M	01:27	6.2	13:50	6.1
16 Tu	01:59	6.0	14:26	5.9
17 W	02:39	5.6	15:12	5.6
18 Th	03:35	5.3	16:15	5.3
19 F	04:54	5.1	17:35	5.2
20 Sa	06:18	5.1	18:51	5.3
21 Su	07:24	5.3	19:51	5.6
22 M	08:15	5.7	20:37	5.9
23 Tu	08:56	6.0	21:17	6.3
24 W	09:34	6.3	21:55	6.6
25 Th	10:14	6.6	22:35	6.8
26 F	10:56	6.8	23:17	6.8
27 Sa	11:40	6.8	##	#
28 Su	00:03	6.9	12:29	6.8
29 M	00:51	6.8	13:20	6.7
30 Tu	01:45	6.6	14:13	6.5

National Oceanography Centre (www.noc.ac.uk)

TIDE TABLES 2013

Time Zone: GMT

Units: METRES

Tidal Predictions : HIGH WATERS 2013
Datum of Predictions = Chart Datum : 3.67 metres below Ordnance Datum (Newlyn)
British Summer Time Dates for 2013 : 31st March to 27th October (data not adjusted)

DOVER — May

Day	Morning time	m	Afternoon time	m
1 W	02:42	6.3	15:09	6.2
2 Th	03:44	6.0	16:11	6.0
3 F	04:57	5.7	17:24	5.8
4 Sa	06:21	5.7	18:45	5.8
5 Su	07:35	5.8	19:51	5.9
6 M	08:33	5.9	20:45	6.1
7 Tu	09:19	6.1	21:30	6.3
8 W	09:59	6.3	22:10	6.4
9 Th	10:36	6.3	22:49	6.5
10 F	11:13	6.4	23:27	6.5
11 Sa	11:50	6.4	##:##	##
12 Su	00:03	6.4	12:25	6.4
13 M	00:36	6.3	12:58	6.3
14 Tu	01:07	6.2	13:31	6.2
15 W	01:39	6.0	14:06	6.0
16 Th	02:16	5.8	14:46	5.8
17 F	03:03	5.5	15:38	5.6
18 Sa	04:06	5.3	16:42	5.5
19 Su	05:17	5.3	17:50	5.5
20 M	06:25	5.4	18:54	5.7
21 Tu	07:24	5.7	19:49	6.0
22 W	08:15	6.0	20:38	6.3
23 Th	09:02	6.3	21:24	6.5
24 F	09:48	6.6	22:10	6.7
25 Sa	10:36	6.7	22:59	6.9
26 Su	11:27	6.8	23:51	6.9
27 M	##:##	##	12:21	6.8
28 Tu	00:45	6.8	13:15	6.8
29 W	01:42	6.6	14:06	6.6
30 Th	02:36	6.4	14:56	6.4
31 F	03:31	6.1	15:50	6.2

DOVER — June

Day	Morning time	m	Afternoon time	m
1 Sa	04:33	5.9	16:52	6.0
2 Su	05:35	5.7	18:03	5.9
3 M	06:53	5.7	19:10	5.9
4 Tu	07:54	5.8	20:09	5.9
5 W	08:47	5.9	21:01	6.0
6 Th	09:33	6.0	21:47	6.2
7 F	10:14	6.2	22:28	6.2
8 Sa	10:53	6.3	23:07	6.3
9 Su	11:30	6.4	23:44	6.3
10 M	##:##	##	12:06	6.4
11 Tu	00:18	6.2	12:40	6.4
12 W	00:51	6.1	13:13	6.3
13 Th	01:22	6.1	13:47	6.2
14 F	01:57	5.9	14:22	6.1
15 Sa	02:36	5.8	15:04	5.9
16 Su	03:25	5.7	15:55	5.8
17 M	04:24	5.6	16:56	5.8
18 Tu	05:30	5.6	18:01	5.8
19 W	06:35	5.7	19:05	6.0
20 Th	07:37	6.0	20:05	6.2
21 F	08:36	6.2	20:58	6.4
22 Sa	09:31	6.5	21:54	6.6
23 Su	10:25	6.7	22:48	6.8
24 M	11:19	6.8	23:42	6.9
25 Tu	##:##	##	12:12	6.9
26 W	00:37	6.8	13:02	6.9
27 Th	01:30	6.7	13:48	6.8
28 F	02:19	6.5	14:34	6.6
29 Sa	03:06	6.3	15:22	6.4
30 Su	03:58	6.0	16:15	6.2

DOVER — July

Day	Morning time	m	Afternoon time	m
1 M	04:57	5.8	17:17	5.9
2 Tu	06:04	5.6	18:27	5.7
3 W	07:12	5.5	19:34	5.7
4 Th	08:15	5.7	20:35	5.7
5 F	09:09	5.8	21:26	5.9
6 Sa	09:54	6.0	22:10	6.1
7 Su	10:33	6.2	22:48	6.2
8 M	11:09	6.3	23:24	6.3
9 Tu	11:45	6.4	23:57	6.3
10 W	##:##	##	12:18	6.5
11 Th	00:29	6.3	12:51	6.4
12 F	01:00	6.2	13:24	6.4
13 Sa	01:33	6.2	13:55	6.3
14 Su	02:07	6.1	14:30	6.2
15 M	02:48	6.0	15:14	6.1
16 Tu	03:41	5.9	16:10	6.0
17 W	04:45	5.8	17:18	5.9
18 Th	05:55	5.7	18:30	5.9
19 F	07:10	5.8	19:42	6.0
20 Sa	08:21	6.1	20:48	6.3
21 Su	09:24	6.4	21:48	6.5
22 M	10:19	6.7	22:42	6.7
23 Tu	11:09	6.9	23:33	6.8
24 W	11:57	7.0	##:##	##
25 Th	00:23	6.8	12:42	7.0
26 F	01:09	6.8	13:25	6.9
27 Sa	01:52	6.6	14:06	6.8
28 Su	02:33	6.4	14:48	6.5
29 M	03:19	6.1	15:36	6.2
30 Tu	04:11	5.8	16:33	5.8
31 W	05:15	5.5	17:42	5.5

DOVER — August

Day	Morning time	m	Afternoon time	m
1 Th	06:30	5.3	19:00	5.4
2 F	07:44	5.4	20:11	5.5
3 Sa	08:45	5.7	21:07	5.7
4 Su	09:33	5.9	21:51	5.9
5 M	10:12	6.2	22:28	6.1
6 Tu	10:47	6.4	23:00	6.3
7 W	11:19	6.5	23:30	6.4
8 Th	11:51	6.6	##:##	##
9 F	00:02	6.4	12:24	6.6
10 Sa	00:33	6.5	12:55	6.6
11 Su	01:06	6.4	13:25	6.6
12 M	01:39	6.3	13:58	6.5
13 Tu	02:18	6.2	14:40	6.3
14 W	03:07	6.0	15:35	6.1
15 Th	04:12	5.8	16:46	5.9
16 F	05:28	5.7	18:09	5.7
17 Sa	06:56	5.7	19:35	5.9
18 Su	08:17	6.0	20:47	6.2
19 M	09:19	6.3	21:45	6.5
20 Tu	10:10	6.7	22:33	6.7
21 W	10:55	6.9	23:18	6.8
22 Th	11:37	7.0	##:##	##
23 F	00:02	6.9	12:18	7.1
24 Sa	00:42	6.8	12:57	7.0
25 Su	01:21	6.6	13:35	6.8
26 M	01:59	6.4	14:13	6.5
27 Tu	02:39	6.1	14:56	6.2
28 W	03:27	5.8	15:48	5.8
29 Th	04:25	5.5	16:56	5.4
30 F	05:43	5.2	18:24	5.2
31 Sa	07:09	5.2	19:45	5.3

National Oceanography Centre (www.noc.ac.uk)

TIDE TABLES 2013

Time Zone: GMT

Tidal Predictions : HIGH WATERS 2013
Datum of Predictions = Chart Datum : 3.67 metres below Ordnance Datum (Newlyn)
British Summer Time Dates for 2013 : 31st March to 27th October (data not adjusted)

Units: METRES

DOVER — September

Day	Morning time	m	Afternoon time	m
1 Su	08:16	5.5	20:45	5.6
2 M	09:06	5.9	21:29	5.9
3 Tu	09:46	6.2	22:03	6.1
4 W	10:19	6.4	22:31	6.3
5 Th	10:50	6.6	23:00	6.6
6 F	11:21	6.7	23:31	6.6
7 Sa	11:52	6.8	##:##	#.#
8 Su	00:04	6.7	12:24	6.8
9 M	00:39	6.6	12:57	6.7
10 Tu	01:15	6.5	13:33	6.6
11 W	01:55	6.4	14:16	6.4
12 Th	02:45	6.1	15:14	6.1
13 F	03:52	5.8	16:30	5.8
14 Sa	05:15	5.6	18:03	5.6
15 Su	06:51	5.6	19:37	5.8
16 M	08:11	6.0	20:45	6.1
17 Tu	09:09	6.4	21:38	6.5
18 W	09:55	6.7	22:21	6.7
19 Th	10:36	6.9	23:00	6.8
20 F	11:15	7.0	23:38	6.8
21 Sa	11:52	7.0	##:##	#.#
22 Su	00:15	6.8	12:29	6.9
23 M	00:51	6.7	13:04	6.7
24 Tu	01:26	6.5	13:39	6.5
25 W	02:03	6.2	14:18	6.1
26 Th	02:45	5.9	15:03	5.7
27 F	03:38	5.5	16:06	5.3
28 Sa	04:50	5.2	17:36	5.0
29 Su	06:19	5.2	19:06	5.1
30 M	07:35	5.4	20:10	5.4

DOVER — October

Day	Morning time	m	Afternoon time	m
1 Tu	08:30	5.7	20:55	5.8
2 W	09:11	6.1	21:29	6.1
3 Th	09:45	6.4	21:58	6.4
4 F	10:15	6.6	22:28	6.6
5 Sa	10:48	6.8	23:01	6.7
6 Su	11:21	6.9	23:38	6.8
7 M	11:57	6.9	##:##	#.#
8 Tu	00:16	6.8	12:35	6.8
9 W	00:57	6.7	13:16	6.7
10 Th	01:43	6.5	14:05	6.4
11 F	02:38	6.2	15:08	6.1
12 Sa	03:45	5.9	16:27	5.7
13 Su	05:04	5.7	18:00	5.6
14 M	06:36	5.7	19:29	5.8
15 Tu	07:53	6.0	20:33	6.1
16 W	08:49	6.3	21:22	6.4
17 Th	09:33	6.6	22:03	6.6
18 F	10:13	6.8	22:39	6.6
19 Sa	10:51	6.9	23:14	6.7
20 Su	11:27	6.9	23:51	6.7
21 M	##:##	#.#	12:03	6.8
22 Tu	00:26	6.6	12:39	6.6
23 W	01:00	6.5	13:12	6.4
24 Th	01:36	6.3	13:47	6.1
25 F	02:13	6.0	14:27	5.8
26 Sa	02:59	5.7	15:20	5.4
27 Su	03:58	5.4	16:36	5.1
28 M	05:15	5.2	18:03	5.1
29 Tu	06:35	5.3	19:15	5.3
30 W	07:37	5.6	20:06	5.6
31 Th	08:24	5.9	20:45	6.0

DOVER — November

Day	Morning time	m	Afternoon time	m
1 F	09:03	6.3	21:21	6.3
2 Sa	09:39	6.5	21:57	6.6
3 Su	10:15	6.8	22:35	6.8
4 M	10:54	6.9	23:16	6.8
5 Tu	11:36	7.0	##:##	#.#
6 W	00:00	6.9	12:21	6.9
7 Th	00:48	6.8	13:09	6.7
8 F	01:40	6.6	14:05	6.4
9 Sa	02:36	6.4	15:08	6.1
10 Su	03:36	6.1	16:18	5.9
11 M	04:45	5.9	17:40	5.7
12 Tu	06:05	5.9	19:02	5.8
13 W	07:20	6.0	20:06	6.0
14 Th	08:19	6.2	20:57	6.2
15 F	09:07	6.4	21:39	6.3
16 Sa	09:50	6.5	22:18	6.5
17 Su	10:29	6.6	22:54	6.6
18 M	11:07	6.6	23:31	6.6
19 Tu	11:45	6.6	##:##	#.#
20 W	00:07	6.5	12:19	6.5
21 Th	00:42	6.5	12:53	6.3
22 F	01:16	6.4	13:26	6.1
23 Sa	01:51	6.2	14:02	5.9
24 Su	02:30	6.0	14:45	5.6
25 M	03:16	5.7	15:40	5.4
26 Tu	04:15	5.5	16:49	5.3
27 W	05:23	5.4	18:01	5.3
28 Th	06:31	5.6	19:04	5.5
29 F	07:30	5.8	19:57	5.9
30 Sa	08:19	6.1	20:44	6.2

DOVER — December

Day	Morning time	m	Afternoon time	m
1 Su	09:05	6.4	21:29	6.5
2 M	09:49	6.7	22:15	6.7
3 Tu	10:35	6.9	23:02	6.9
4 W	11:22	6.9	23:51	7.0
5 Th	##:##	#.#	12:13	6.9
6 F	00:43	6.8	13:06	6.8
7 Sa	01:34	6.8	14:01	6.6
8 Su	02:25	6.6	14:56	6.3
9 M	03:18	6.4	15:55	6.0
10 Tu	04:16	6.2	17:01	5.8
11 W	05:23	6.0	18:15	5.7
12 Th	06:36	5.9	19:25	5.7
13 F	07:42	5.9	20:25	5.9
14 Sa	08:39	6.1	21:15	6.1
15 Su	09:28	6.2	21:58	6.2
16 M	10:12	6.3	22:37	6.4
17 Tu	10:51	6.4	23:15	6.5
18 W	11:28	6.4	23:51	6.5
19 Th	##:##	#.#	12:03	6.4
20 F	00:25	6.5	12:36	6.3
21 Sa	00:58	6.5	13:08	6.2
22 Su	01:31	6.4	13:40	6.1
23 M	02:03	6.2	14:15	5.9
24 Tu	02:39	6.1	14:56	5.7
25 W	03:24	5.9	15:49	5.6
26 Th	04:20	5.7	16:53	5.5
27 F	05:26	5.7	18:02	5.5
28 Sa	06:34	5.7	19:09	5.7
29 Su	07:39	6.0	20:12	6.0
30 M	08:36	6.3	21:08	6.3
31 Tu	09:30	6.5	22:01	6.6

National Oceanography Centre (www.noc.ac.uk)

QUICK REFERENCE

TIDE TABLES 2014

Time Zone: **GMT**

Tidal Predictions : HIGH WATERS 2014

Units: **METRES**

Datum of Predictions = Chart Datum : 3.67 metres below Ordnance Datum (Newlyn)

British Summer Time Dates for 2014 : 30th March to 26th October (data not adjusted)

DOVER — January

Day	Morning time	m	Afternoon time	m
1 W	10:22	6.8	22:52	6.8
2 Th	11:14	6.9	23:43	7.0
3 F	##:##	#.#	12:06	6.9
4 Sa	00:33	7.0	12:57	6.9
5 Su	01:21	7.0	13:47	6.7
6 M	02:06	6.9	14:35	6.5
7 Tu	02:53	6.6	15:24	6.2
8 W	03:43	6.4	16:19	5.9
9 Th	04:41	6.0	17:24	5.6
10 F	05:49	5.8	18:38	5.5
11 Sa	07:04	5.6	19:50	5.6
12 Su	08:12	5.7	20:51	5.8
13 M	09:10	5.9	21:39	6.0
14 Tu	09:57	6.0	22:21	6.2
15 W	10:36	6.2	22:57	6.4
16 Th	11:12	6.3	23:32	6.5
17 F	11:45	6.4	##:##	#.#
18 Sa	00:06	6.6	12:17	6.4
19 Su	00:38	6.6	12:47	6.5
20 M	01:08	6.5	13:16	6.3
21 Tu	01:36	6.4	13:46	6.2
22 W	02:06	6.3	14:21	6.1
23 Th	02:42	6.2	15:04	5.9
24 F	03:30	6.0	16:02	5.7
25 Sa	04:35	5.8	17:12	5.6
26 Su	05:49	5.7	18:30	5.6
27 M	07:07	5.8	19:48	5.8
28 Tu	08:19	6.1	20:56	6.1
29 W	09:20	6.4	21:52	6.5
30 Th	10:14	6.7	22:43	6.8
31 F	11:05	6.9	23:31	7.0

DOVER — February

Day	Morning time	m	Afternoon time	m
1 Sa	11:54	7.0	##:##	#.#
2 Su	00:18	7.1	12:42	6.9
3 M	01:01	7.1	13:26	6.8
4 Tu	01:43	7.0	14:09	6.6
5 W	02:25	6.8	14:51	6.3
6 Th	03:10	6.5	15:40	6.0
7 F	04:02	6.0	16:39	5.6
8 Sa	05:06	5.6	17:51	5.3
9 Su	06:27	5.4	19:14	5.3
10 M	07:46	5.4	20:24	5.5
11 Tu	08:51	5.8	21:18	5.8
12 W	09:41	6.1	22:01	6.1
13 Th	10:20	6.3	22:37	6.3
14 F	10:53	6.2	23:10	6.4
15 Sa	11:23	6.3	23:42	6.6
16 Su	11:52	6.4	##:##	#.#
17 M	00:12	6.6	12:21	6.4
18 Tu	00:41	6.6	12:49	6.4
19 W	01:08	6.6	13:19	6.4
20 Th	01:36	6.5	13:52	6.3
21 F	02:11	6.4	14:33	6.1
22 Sa	02:57	6.2	15:28	5.9
23 Su	04:00	5.9	16:39	5.6
24 M	05:20	5.6	18:06	5.5
25 Tu	06:50	5.6	19:35	5.7
26 W	08:10	5.9	20:46	6.1
27 Th	09:13	6.3	21:42	6.5
28 F	10:06	6.6	22:30	6.8

DOVER — March

Day	Morning time	m	Afternoon time	m
1 Sa	10:53	6.8	23:14	7.0
2 Su	11:38	6.9	23:57	7.1
3 M	##:##	#.#	12:21	6.9
4 Tu	00:39	7.1	13:02	6.8
5 W	01:18	7.0	13:41	6.6
6 Th	01:56	6.7	14:21	6.4
7 F	02:38	6.4	15:05	6.0
8 Sa	03:26	6.0	15:58	5.6
9 Su	04:27	5.5	17:07	5.3
10 M	05:48	5.2	18:33	5.1
11 Tu	07:16	5.2	19:51	5.3
12 W	08:25	5.4	20:49	5.6
13 Th	09:17	5.7	21:34	5.9
14 F	09:56	5.9	22:10	6.2
15 Sa	10:26	6.2	22:42	6.4
16 Su	10:54	6.3	23:12	6.5
17 M	11:22	6.4	23:42	6.6
18 Tu	11:52	6.5	##:##	#.#
19 W	00:11	6.6	##:##	#.#
20 Th	00:40	6.6	12:23	6.6
21 F	01:12	6.6	12:56	6.5
22 Sa	01:50	6.4	13:32	6.4
23 Su	02:38	6.2	14:15	6.2
24 M	03:44	5.9	15:12	6.0
25 Tu	05:09	5.6	16:25	5.7
26 W	06:43	5.6	17:53	5.5
27 Th	08:03	5.9	19:23	5.7
28 F	09:03	6.2	20:32	6.1
29 Sa	09:52	6.5	21:25	6.4
30 Su	10:36	6.7	22:53	6.9
31 M	11:18	6.8	23:34	7.0

DOVER — April

Day	Morning time	m	Afternoon time	m
1 Tu	11:59	6.8	##:##	#.#
2 W	00:15	7.0	12:38	6.7
3 Th	00:52	6.8	13:15	6.6
4 F	01:30	6.6	13:53	6.4
5 Sa	02:09	6.3	14:35	6.1
6 Su	02:54	5.9	15:24	5.7
7 M	03:50	5.4	16:25	5.4
8 Tu	05:05	5.1	17:45	5.1
9 W	06:33	5.3	19:06	5.2
10 Th	07:46	5.3	20:09	5.5
11 F	08:39	5.8	20:56	5.5
12 Sa	09:19	5.8	21:34	6.1
13 Su	09:50	6.1	22:06	6.3
14 M	10:19	6.3	22:37	6.5
15 Tu	10:50	6.5	23:09	6.6
16 W	11:24	6.6	23:42	6.6
17 Th	##:##	#.#	12:00	6.6
18 F	00:18	6.7	12:39	6.6
19 Sa	00:57	6.6	13:21	6.5
20 Su	01:42	6.4	14:11	6.3
21 M	02:36	6.2	15:11	6.1
22 Tu	03:45	5.9	16:21	5.8
23 W	05:06	5.7	17:41	5.7
24 Th	06:33	5.7	19:03	5.8
25 F	07:47	5.9	20:09	6.1
26 Sa	08:45	6.2	21:03	6.4
27 Su	09:33	6.4	21:48	6.6
28 M	10:16	6.5	22:30	6.7
29 Tu	10:57	6.6	23:12	6.8
30 W	11:37	6.7	23:52	6.7

National Oceanography Centre (www.noc.ac.uk)

SUNRISE AND SUNSET TIMES
FOR 2013

Predictions are given for the times of sunrise and sunset on every Saturday throughout the year. For places on the same latitude as the following, add 4 minutes for each degree of longitude west (subtract if east).

These times are in GMT, except between 01:00 on Mar 31 and 01:00 on Oct 27, when the times are in BST (1 hour in advance of GMT).

		London Rise	London Set	Manchester Rise	Manchester Set	Edinburgh Rise	Edinburgh Set
January	1	08 06	16 02	08 25	16 00	08 44	15 49
	8	08 05	16 10	08 23	16 08	08 41	15 58
	15	08 00	16 20	08 18	16 19	08 34	16 10
	22	07 53	16 31	08 10	16 31	08 25	16 24
	29	07 44	16 44	08 00	16 45	08 14	16 38
February	5	07 34	16 56	07 48	16 58	08 01	16 54
	12	07 21	17 09	07 35	17 12	07 46	17 09
	19	07 08	17 22	07 21	17 26	07 30	17 24
	26	06 54	17 35	07 05	17 40	07 13	17 39
March	4	06 39	17 47	06 49	17 53	06 56	17 54
	11	06 23	17 59	06 32	18 06	06 38	18 09
	18	06 07	18 11	06 16	18 19	06 19	18 23
	25	06 51	19 23	06 59	19 32	07 01	19 38
April	1	06 35	19 35	06 42	19 45	06 43	19 52
	8	06 20	19 46	06 25	19 58	06 24	20 06
	15	06 04	19 58	06 09	20 11	06 07	20 20
	22	05 50	20 10	05 53	20 23	05 49	20 35
	29	05 36	20 21	05 38	20 36	05 33	20 49
May	6	05 23	20 33	05 24	20 48	05 18	21 03
	13	05 11	20 44	05 11	21 00	05 03	21 16
	20	05 01	20 54	05 00	21 12	04 51	21 29
	27	04 53	21 03	04 51	21 22	04 41	21 40
June	3	04 48	21 11	04 45	21 30	04 33	21 50
	10	04 44	21 17	04 41	21 37	04 28	21 57
	17	04 43	21 21	04 39	21 41	04 26	22 02
	24	04 44	21 22	04 41	21 42	04 27	22 03

SUNRISE AND SUNSET TIMES

		London Rise	London Set	Manchester Rise	Manchester Set	Edinburgh Rise	Edinburgh Set
July	1	04 48	21 21	04 45	21 41	04 32	22 01
	8	04 54	21 17	04 51	21 37	04 39	21 56
	15	05 02	21 11	04 59	21 30	04 49	21 48
	22	05 10	21 03	05 09	21 21	05 00	21 38
	29	05 20	20 53	05 20	21 10	05 12	21 25
August	5	05 31	20 41	05 32	20 57	05 25	21 11
	12	05 42	20 28	05 44	20 43	05 39	20 56
	19	05 53	20 14	05 56	20 28	05 52	20 39
	26	06 04	19 59	06 08	20 12	06 06	20 22
September	2	06 15	19 44	06 20	19 56	06 20	20 04
	9	06 26	19 28	06 33	19 39	06 33	19 45
	16	06 38	19 12	06 45	19 22	06 47	19 27
	23	06 49	18 56	06 57	19 04	07 01	19 08
	30	07 00	18 40	07 09	18 47	07 14	18 50
October	7	07 12	18 24	07 22	18 30	07 28	18 32
	14	07 23	18 09	07 35	18 14	07 43	18 14
	21	07 36	17 54	07 48	17 58	07 57	17 57
	28	06 48	16 40	07 01	16 44	07 12	16 41
November	4	07 00	16 28	07 15	16 30	07 27	16 25
	11	07 12	16 17	07 28	16 18	07 42	16 12
	18	07 24	16 07	07 41	16 07	07 56	16 00
	25	07 36	16 00	07 53	15 59	08 10	15 50
December	2	07 46	15 54	08 04	15 53	08 22	15 43
	9	07 54	15 52	08 13	15 50	08 32	15 39
	16	08 01	15 52	08 20	15 50	08 39	15 38
	23	08 05	15 55	08 24	15 53	08 43	15 41
	30	08 06	16 01	08 25	15 58	08 44	15 47

SEA AREAS

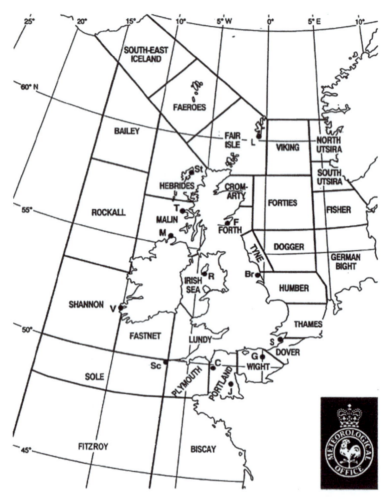

STATIONS WHOSE LATEST REPORTS ARE BROADCAST IN THE
5-MINUTE FORECASTS

Br Bridlington; C Channel Light-Vessel Automatic; F Fife Ness; G Greenwich Light-Vessel Automatic;
J Jersey; L Lerwick; M Malin Head; R Ronaldsway; S Sandettie Light-Vessel Automatic; Sc Scilly
Automatic; St Stornoway; T Tiree; V Valentia.

From information kindly supplied by the Meteorological Office

REVISION OF SEA AREAS

On 4 February 2002, the southern boundary of areas Plymouth and Sole, and the northern
boundary of areas Biscay and Finisterre were realigned along the Metarea I/II boundary at 48°27′
North. At the same time, sea area Finisterre was renamed FitzRoy.

Did you know that the FitzRoy shipping area is named after the founder of the Met Office?

SCHEDULE 1 SPECIES

Under the provisions of the Wildlife and Countryside Act 1981 the following bird species (listed in Schedule 1 - Part I of the Act) are protected by special penalties at all times.

Avocet	Falcon, Gyr	Owl, Barn	Shrike, Red-backed
Bee-eater	Fieldfare	Owl, Snowy	Spoonbill
Bittem	Firecrest	Peregrine	Stilt, Black-winged
Bittern, Little	Garganey	Petrel, Leach's	Stint, Temminck's
Bluethroat	Godwit, Black-tailed	Phalarope, Red-necked	Swan, Bewick's
Brambling	Goshawk	Plover, Kentish	Swan, Whooper
Bunting, Cirl	Grebe, Black-necked	Plover, Little Ringed	Tern, Black
Bunting, Lapland	Grebe, Slavonian	Quail, Common	Tern, Little
Bunting, Snow	Greenshank	Redstart, Black	Tern, Roseate
Buzzard, Honey	Gull, Little	Redwing	Tit, Bearded
Chough	Gull, Mediterranean	Rosefinch, Scarlet	Tit, Crested
Corncrake	Harriers (all species)	Ruff	Treecreeper, Short-toed
Crake, Spotted	Heron, Purple	Sandpiper, Green	Warbler, Cetti's
Crossbills (all species)	Hobby	Sandpiper, Purple	Warbler, Dartford
Stone-curlew	Hoopoe	Sandpiper, Wood	Warbler, Marsh
Divers (all species)	Kingfisher	Scaup	Warbler, Savi's
Dotterel	Kite, Red	Scoter, Common	Whimbrel
Duck, Long-tailed	Merlin	Scoter, Velvet	Woodlark
Eagle, Golden	Oriole, Golden	Serin	Wryneck
Eagle, White-tailed	Osprey	Shorelark	

The following birds and their eggs (listed in Schedule 1 - Part II of the Act) are protected by special penalties during the close season, which is Feb 1 to Aug 31 (Feb 21 to Aug 31 below high water mark), but may be killed outside this period - Goldeneye, Greylag Goose (in Outer Hebrides, Caithness, Sutherland, and Wester Ross only), Pintail.

BIRDWATCHERS AND TWITCHERS TAKE NOTE!

Be tick-aware while enjoying the great outdoors

IF YOU'RE a keen birdwatcher, the following situations may be familiar: wandering through bracken to spot nesting locations, walking through long grass to view wetland birds, and waiting in scrubland, watching migratory birds fly overhead. What you might not be so familiar with, however, is checking yourself for ticks afterwards.

Wherever you choose to enjoy birdwatching – be it forest, wetland or coast, UK or abroad – spending prolonged periods outside and in among the bushes increases the chance of being bitten by a tick which, if infected, can lead to the potential problem of Lyme disease.

Says Stella Huyshe-Shires, Chair of the charity Lyme Disease Action: "As a high-risk group, birdwatchers need to be particularly tick-aware. The number of cases of Lyme disease in the UK has risen over the last few years. It's important that awareness of potential problems associated with tick bites increases too."

Ticks, which can be tiny (the size of a full stop on an A4 page) blood-sucking parasites, peak

BIRDWATCHERS AND TWITCHERS TAKE NOTE!

in population from April to October, and are found throughout the UK, North America and across Europe.

Lyme disease causes a range of unpleasant symptoms which may include a circular red rash, headaches, a stiff neck, extreme fatigue, muscle and joint pain, and disturbances of sight, hearing, digestive system and sleep. If left untreated it can progress to the joints, the heart and the nervous system.

To reduce the risk of being bitten by an infected tick, the charity Lyme Disease Action advises birdwatchers to take the following precautions:

- Wear long sleeves and trousers.
- Wear light-coloured clothing so ticks are easier to spot.
- Use an insect repellent effective against ticks (look for those containing the chemical DEET).
- Keep to pathways and try to avoid areas of overgrown vegetation.
- Check for ticks regularly during the day.
- Remove any ticks found attached as soon as possible.
- Pack a tick remover if birdwatching away from home.

Tick removal

Ticks should be removed immediately with a tick removal tool or fine pointed tweezers. Gently pull the tick's body away from your skin directly outwards, without jerking. Do not try to pull the tick out with your fingers, burn the tick or cover it with creams or chemicals. If you don't have a tick removal tool, use a thread of cotton wound round close to the skin and pull upwards or, alternatively, cut a slit in a plastic card and slide that under the tick's body.

Treatment

If you have been bitten by a tick and notice any of the above symptoms, seek medical help straight away. Diagnosed and treated early, Lyme disease can be treated successfully with antibiotics.

DOES AND DON'TS OF REMOVING A TICK

Your main aims are to remove all parts of the tick's body and to prevent it releasing additional saliva or regurgitating its stomach contents into your bite wound.

DO use a proprietary tick removal tool (available from www.lymediseaseaction.org.uk or many vets and pet shops), and follow the instructions provided, or a pair of tweezers.

If no tools are available, rather than delay use a cotton thread. Tie a single loop of cotton around the tick's mouthparts, as close to the skin as possible, then pull gently upwards and outwards.

DO commence by cleansing the tweezers with antiseptic. After tick removal, cleanse the bite site and the tweezers with antiseptic.

DO wash hands thoroughly afterwards.

DO save the tick in a container in case you develop symptoms later (label with date and location). The Health Protection Agency are currently running a scheme to investigate ticks, details available at www.lymediseaseaction.org.uk/information/tick.htm or from the HPA at www.hpa.org.uk.

DO NOT squeeze or twist the body of the tick, as this may cause the head and body to separate, leaving the head embedded in your skin.

DO NOT use your fingernails to remove a tick. Infection can enter via any breaks in your skin, e.g. Close to the fingernail.

DO NOT crush the tick's body, as this may cause it to regurgitate its infected stomach contents into the bite wound.

DO NOT try to burn the tick off, apply petroleum jelly, nail polish or any other chemical. Any of these methods can cause discomfort to the tick, resulting in regurgitation, or saliva release.

A detailed leaflet (free to download) is available from www.lymediseaseaction.org.uk

Leaflets are also available from:
Lyme Disease Action,
PO Box 235, Penryn. TR10 8WZ. UK
Including a donation/sae will help them in their work for people affected by Lyme disease.

Lyme Disease Action (www.lymediseaseaction.org.uk) is a charity striving for greater awareness of Lyme disease and associated tick-borne diseases.

THE COUNTRYSIDE CODE

Launched on 12 July 2004, this Code for England has been produced through a partnership between the Countryside Agency and Countryside Council for Wales.

The Countryside Code has been revised and re-launched to reflect the introduction of new open access rights (Countryside & Rights of Way Act 2000) and changes in society over the last 20 years.

● **Be safe – plan ahead**
Follow any signs, even when going out locally, it's best to get the latest information about where and when you can go; for example, your rights to go onto some areas of open land may be restricted while work is carried out, for safety reasons or during breeding seasons. Follow advice and local signs, and be prepared for the unexpected.

● **Leave gates and property as you find them**
Please respect the working life of the countryside, as our actions can affect people's livelihoods, our heritage, and the safety and welfare of animals and ourselves.

● **Protect plants and animals, and take your litter home**
We have a responsibility to protect our countryside now and for future generations,

so make sure you don't harm animals, birds, plants, or trees.

● **Keep dogs under close control**
The countryside is a great place to exercise dogs, but it's every owner's duty to make sure their dog is not a danger or nuisance to farm animals, wildlife or other people.

● **Consider other people**
Showing consideration and respect for other people makes the countryside a pleasant Environment for everyone – at home, at work and at leisure.

BIRDLINE NUMBERS - National and Regional

Birdline name	To obtain information	To report sightings (hotlines)
National		
Bird Information Service	09068 700 222	
www.birdingworld.co.uk		
Flightline (Northern Ireland)	028 9146 7408	
Regional		
Northern Ireland	028 9146 7408	
Scotland	09068 700 234	01292 611 994
Wales	09068 700 248	01492 544 588
East Anglia	09068 700 245	07941 333 970
Midlands	09068 700 247	01905 754 154
North East	09068 700 246	07974 358 988
North West	09068 700 249	01492 544 588
South East	09068 700 240	01845 570 444
www.southeastbirdnews.co.uk		or 08000 377 240
South West	09068 700 241	0845 4567 938

Charges
At the time of compilation, calls to premium line numbers cost 60p per minute.

INDEX TO RESERVES

INDEX TO RESERVES